ECONOMIC COMMISSION FOR EUR
INLAND TRANSPORT COMMITTEE

European Agreement

concerning the international carriage
of dangerous goods by road (ADR)
and protocol of signature

done at Geneva on 30 September 1957

Volume II

(Annex B with amendments thereto up to 1 January 1997)

Distributed in the United Kingdom by The Stationery Office Ltd

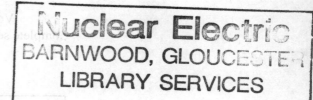

The Stationery Office

Books

UNITED NATIONS
New York and Geneva, 1996

NOTE

The designations employed and the presentation of the material in this publication do not imply the expression of any opinion whatsoever on the part of the Secretariat of the United Nations concerning the legal status of any country, territory, city or area, or of its authorities, or concerning the delimitation of its frontiers or boundaries.

ECE/TRANS/115(Vol.II)

Bibliographic data for The Stationery Office

Volume II: ISBN 0-11-941520-8
Complete set of two volumes: ISBN 0-11-941518-6

UNITED NATIONS PUBLICATION
Sales No. E.96.VIII.2
ISBN 92-1-139054-0 (Vol. II)
Complete set of two volumes: ISBN 92-1-139055-9

Volumes I and II not to be sold separately

CORRIGENDUM

Ref. Sales No.: E.96-VIII.2
(ECE/TRANS/115)

October 1996
New York and Geneva

**EUROPEAN AGREEMENT
CONCERNING THE INTERNATIONAL CARRIAGE
OF DANGEROUS GOODS BY ROAD (ADR)**

(as amended on 1 January 1997)

<u>Corrigendum</u>

<u>Volume 1</u>

Page	Marginal		
146	2314		**Add** the superscript "<u>7</u>/" **after** "nomenclature approved by ISO". In footnote <u>6</u>/, **delete** "In the case of pesticides, the name to be entered should be that given in ISO Standard 1750 if listed." **Add** a new footnote: "<u>7</u>/ See ISO 1750:1981, as amended, and addenda."
211	2500	(4)	**For** "section 34" **read** "section 34.4".
241/242	2551	15°(b)	**Add** the superscript "<u>26</u>/" **after** the concentration figure in column "Diluent type A or B" for the following entries: Cumyl peroxyneoheptanoate; Di-(2-Neodecanoylperoxyisopropyl)benzene; and tert-Butyl peroxyneoheptanoate.
243		17°(b)	**Add** the superscript "<u>*</u>/" **after** the concentration figure in column "Diluent type A or B" for the following entry: 1,1-Dimethyl-3-hydroxybutylperoxyneoheptanoate **Add** a new footnote: "<u>*</u>/ Only diluent type A shall be used."
249	2555 (2)		**Insert** "3120" **before** the entry "ORGANIC PEROXIDE, TYPE F, SOLID, TEMPERATURE CONTROLLED".

(pto)

Page	Marginal		

271   2601   59°   **For** identification number 1549, **insert** "inorganic, " **after** "compound, ".

281   2601a   (2)(a)   **For** "2 litres" **read** "2 kg".

289   2614   In footnote <u>4</u>/ **delete** "In the case of pesticides, the name to be entered should be that given in ISO Standard 1750 if listed."

290   **Add** the superscript "<u>5</u>/" **after** "nomenclature approved by ISO".
      Add a new footnote: "<u>5</u>/   See ISO 1750:1981, as amended, and addenda."

399   2901   5°, NOTE 3 (a), (b)   **For** "section 38" **read** "section 38.3".

400   8°, NOTE 1   **For** "Part I of the Manual of Tests and Criteria" **read** "the Manual of Tests and Criteria, Part I, Chapter 16".

403   36°, NOTE   In the second sentence, **insert** "Class 5.1, 5°, ", "Class 6.2, " and "Class 8, 6° and 14°".

405   2901a   (5) (i)   **For** "section 38 of the Manual of Tests and Criteria" **read** "the Manual of Tests and Criteria, Part III, section 38.3".

418   3170   NOTE 1   **For** "the Manual of Tests and Criteria mentioned in marginal 3101 (1)" **read** "the Manual of Tests and Criteria, Part I"

445   3300   (1) (e) **Add** ":1983" **after** "3679" and "3680".

                 (2) (d) **For** "DIN 53213, Part 1: 1978" **read** "DIN 53213: 1978, Part 1".

447   In the page header, for "3204 (cont'd)" **read** "3304 (cont'd)".

450   3310   (a)   **For** "(see Figure 1)" **read** "(see Figure 3)".

581   3900   (1)   **For** "[see also marginal 2224 (4)]" **read** "[see also marginal 2224 (3)]".

<u>Volume 2</u>

72   62 385 (1)(a)   **For** "in the cases provided for in marginal 10 385 (1)(d)" **read** "in case of breakage or deterioration of packagings or of the dangerous substances carried, particularly where such dangerous substances have spilled over the road, ".

84   91 385 (3)(a)   **For** "in the case of damage to or leakage from a package containing substances of 13°," **read** "in case of breakage or deterioration of packagings or of the dangerous substances carried, particularly where such dangerous substances have spilled over the road, ".

284   250 000   Table 1: **Insert** the following entry: "Petroleum gases, liquefied; 1075; 23; 3; 2, 2°F"
310   Table 3: **Insert** the following entry: "1075; Petroleum gases, liquefied; 23; 3; 2, 2°F"

----------/-----------------------

CORRIGENDUM

Ref. Sales No.: E.96-VIII.2
(ECE/TRANS/115)

November 1996
New York and Geneva

**EUROPEAN AGREEMENT
CONCERNING THE INTERNATIONAL CARRIAGE
OF DANGEROUS GOODS BY ROAD (ADR)
(as amended on 1 January 1997)**

<u>Corrigendum</u>

Page   Marginal

Volume I

260	2601	1°	Identification numbers 1051 and 1614, **for** "containing not more than 3% water" **read** "containing less than 3% water".
		9°(a)	The name of the first substance should **read**: "<u>1239 methyl chloromethyl ether</u>" (These corrections apply to the English text only.)
281	2601a (2)(a)		**For** "2 litres" **read** "4 kg". (This correction applies to the English text only.)

Volume II

IMPORTANT NOTE: The following modifications have been adopted by the Working Party on the Transport of Dangerous Goods at its 61st session held from 4 to 8 November 1996. Their entry into force is subject to the amendment procedure of Article 14 of ADR, and is expected before 1 July 1997. The national competent authority should be consulted as regards their application.

9	10 014 (1)	**Delete** the definition of "Auxiliary heating devices".
14	10 221(1)	**Delete** in the first sentence: "as well as motor vehicles authorized to tow such trailers,".
29	10 605	**Add**: "These transport units shall be subject, until that date, to the provisions of marginal 10 283 which were in force until 31 December 1996".
	10 606	**Add** the following new marginal:

"10 606   The provisions of marginals 10 260 and 10 385 which were in force until 31 December 1996 may continue to be applied until 31 December 1998 instead of those which entered into force on 1 January 1997."

(PTO)

ECE/TRANS/115/Corr.3
ENGLISH AND FRENCH
(Corrigendum 1 applies to the French version only)
(Corrigendum 2 applies to the English version only)

GE.96-24886

232   220 500   In the table, **delete** the crosses at the intersection of the line "220 536 Auxiliary heating devices" and columns FL and OX.

**238/
239   220 536**   **Replace** the text with that in force before 1 January 1997 as follows:

"Auxiliary heating for the cab shall be sufficiently secure from the standpoint of fire prevention and shall be placed forward of the protective wall (rear wall of the cab). The heating appliance shall be placed as far forward and as high as possible (at least 80 cm above ground level) and shall be fitted with devices preventing any object from being brought into contact with the hot surfaces of the appliance or its exhaust pipe.   Only appliances with a means of rapidly restarting the combustion air ventilator (max. 20 s) may be used."

_____

TABLE OF CONTENTS OF ANNEX B

(VOLUME II)

PROVISIONS CONCERNING TRANSPORT EQUIPMENT AND TRANSPORT OPERATIONS

Part I. GENERAL PROVISIONS APPLICABLE TO THE CARRIAGE OF DANGEROUS SUBSTANCES OF ALL CLASSES

Table of contents

Part II. SPECIAL PROVISIONS APPLICABLE TO THE CARRIAGE OF DANGEROUS SUBSTANCES OF CLASSES 1 TO 9

Table of contents

Part III. APPENDICES TO ANNEX B

EUROPEAN AGREEMENT CONCERNING THE INTERNATIONAL CARRIAGE OF DANGEROUS GOODS BY ROAD (ADR)

ANNEX B

PROVISIONS CONCERNING TRANSPORT EQUIPMENT AND TRANSPORT OPERATIONS

PROVISIONS CONCERNING TRANSPORT EQUIPMENT AND TRANSPORT OPERATIONS

Plan of the Annex

10 000 (1)   This Annex comprises:

(a)   General provisions applicable to the carriage of dangerous substances of all classes (Part I);

(b)   Special provisions applicable to the carriage of dangerous substances of Classes 1 to 9 (Part II);

(c)   Appendices as follows:

- Appendix B.1a concerning fixed tanks (tank-vehicles), demountable tanks and battery-vehicles;

- Appendix B.1b concerning tank-containers;

- Appendix B.1c concerning fixed tanks and demountable tanks made of reinforced plastics;

- Appendix B.1d relating to requirements concerning the materials and construction of fixed welded tanks, of demountable welded tanks, and of welded shells of tank-containers, intended for the carriage of deeply-refrigerated liquefied gases of Class 2 or for which a test pressure of not less than 1 Mpa (10 bar) is required;

- Appendix B.2 containing uniform provisions concerning the construction of vehicles intended for the carriage of dangerous goods including provisions for their type approval where appropriate;

- Appendix B.3 containing a model certificate of approval for vehicles;

- Appendix B.4 containing provisions concerning the training of drivers of vehicles carrying dangerous goods;

- Appendix B.5 containing the list of substances covered by marginal 10 500 (2);

- Appendix B.6 containing a model driver's training certificate;

- Appendix B.7 for the mark for elevated temperature substances.

(2)   The general provisions of Part I and the special provisions of Part II are divided into sections with the following headings:

General   This section describes the scope of this Annex and includes the provisions concerning permitted exemptions and definitions;

Section 1   Mode of carriage of goods (this section contains the provisions concerning method of dispatch, restrictions on forwarding, full loads and the possibility of carriage of goods in bulk, in containers or in tanks);

- 1 -

10 000 (contd)	Section 2	Special requirements to be fulfilled by the means of transport and its equipment;
	Section 3	General Service provisions;
	Section 4	Special provisions concerning loading, unloading and handling (this section contains also the prohibitions on mixed loading);
	Section 5	Special provisions concerning the operation of vehicles;
	Section 6	Transitional provisions, derogations and provisions peculiar to certain countries.

Applicability of other regulations, national or international

10 001   (1)   If the vehicle carrying out a transport operation subject to the provisions of ADR is conveyed over a section of the journey otherwise than by road haulage, any national or international regulations which govern the carriage of dangerous goods on that section by the mode of transport used for conveying the road vehicle shall alone be applicable to that section of the journey.

(2)   In cases where a transport operation subject to the provisions of ADR is likewise subject over the whole or a part of the road journey to the provisions of an international convention which regulates the carriage of dangerous goods by a mode of transport other than road carriage by virtue of clauses extending the applicability of that convention to certain motor-vehicle services, then the provisions of that international convention shall apply over the journey in question, concurrently with those of ADR which are not incompatible with them; the other clauses of ADR shall not apply over the journey in question.

(3)   In article 1 (c) of ADR the word "vehicles" need not refer to one and the same vehicle. An international transport operation may be performed by several different vehicles provided that the operation takes place on the territory of at least two Contracting Parties to ADR between the consignor and the consignee indicated in the transport document.

Applicability of the provisions of Part I of this Annex

10 002   Where provisions of Part II or of the Appendices to this Annex conflict with provisions of Part I, those provisions of Part I shall not apply.

Nevertheless

(a)   the provisions of marginals 10 010 to 10 013 shall take precedence over those of Part II;

(b)   the provisions of marginal 10 403 shall take precedence over the prohibitions on mixed loading prescribed in the sections 4 of Part II.

10 003-
10 009

PART I

GENERAL PROVISIONS APPLICABLE TO THE CARRIAGE
OF DANGEROUS SUBSTANCES OF ALL CLASSES

(See, however, marginal 10 002)

General

Scope of this Annex

10 010   Annex A exempts from the provisions of this Annex, other than the provisions of marginal 10 381 (1) (a) where applicable, carriage performed under the conditions (of packaging, mass, etc.) laid down in marginals 2201a, 2301a, 2401a, 2471a, 2501a, 2551a, 2601a, 2801a and 2901a.

10 011   Table specifying the limited quantities of dangerous substances in packages which may be carried in one transport unit without application of the provisions of this Annex relating to:

-          special requirements to be fulfilled by the means of transport and its equipment (all sections 2 of Parts I and II), subject, however, to compliance with the provisions of marginals 10 240 (1) (a) and 21 212;

-          vehicle crews (marginals XX 311 of Parts I and II);

-          special training of drivers (marginal 10 315):

-          carriage of passengers (marginal 10 325);

-          instructions in writing (marginals XX 385 of Parts I and II);

-          places of loading and unloading (marginals XX 407 of Part II); and

-          special provisions concerning the operation of vehicles (all sections 5 of Parts I and II).

Classes	SUBSTANCES — Multipliers for calculating total quantities exempted for a load which includes several substances each of which is affected by different mass limits (see note 1 below)	Maximum total quantity per transport unit (gross mass)							
		A 200 5 kg	**B** 50 20 kg	**C** 20 50 kg	**D** 10 100 kg	**E** 3 333 kg	**F** 2 500 kg	**G** 1 1000 kg	unlimited
1,2 (Only gases classified under A,O,F) 3, 4.1, 4.2, 4.3, 5.1, 5.2, 6.1, 6.2 (only substances of 2° and substances classified under (b)), 8 and 9	Empty packagings (including receptacles, excluding tanks)								X
1	1°, 3°, 4° (UN Numbers 0081, 0082 and 0241), 5° - 7°, 9°, 10°, 12°, 13°, 15°, 17° - 19°, 21° - 23°, 25°, 27°, 30° - 32°, 34°, 48° (UN Nos. 0331 and 0332)			X					
	2°, 4° (UN Numbers other than 0081, 0082 and 0241), 8°, 11°, 24°	X							
	26°, 29°, 33°		X						
	35° to 43°						X		
	46°, 47°								X
	48° (UN No. 0482)	X							
2	Gases and articles of 1°, 2°, 4°, 5°, 6° and 7° under A and O							X	
	Gases of 3° under A and O						X		
	Gases of 1°F						X		
	Gases and articles of 2°, 3°, 4°, 5°, 6°, 7° under F					X			
	Cyanogen chloride of 2°TC	X							
	Phosgene of 2°TC, Fluorine of 1°TOC			X					
	Other gases and articles of 1°, 2°, 4°, 5°, 6°, 7° under T, TC, TO, TF, TOC, TFC					X			
	Empty packagings of 8° under T, TC, TO, TF, TOC, TFC, or other empty receptacles having contained gases classified under T, TC, TO, TF TOC or TFC					X			
3	6°, 12°, 13° and substances of "(a)" of 11°, 14° to 28° and 41°, 57°	X							
	Substances of (b) of 11° and 14° to 28° and 41° to 57°				X				
	1° (a), 2° (a) and 3° (b), 4° (a) and (b), 5° (a), and 7° (b)					X			
	31° (c) and 34° (c)							X	
	Other substances						X		
4.1	1° (b) and 2° (c)								X
	6° (c) and 11° (c)					X			
	21° to 26°	X [1/]							
	35°, 36°, 45°, 46°		X [1/]						
	37° to 40° and 47° to 50°			X [1/]					
	Other substances			X					

[1/] *Excluding the mass of the refrigerating appliance if any.*

Classes	SUBSTANCES Multipliers for calculating total quantities exempted for a load which includes several substances each of which is affected by different mass limits (see note 1 below)	Maximum total quantity per transport unit (gross mass)							
		A 200 5 kg	**B** 50 20 kg	**C** 20 50 kg	**D** 10 100 kg	**E** 3 333 kg	**F** 2 500 kg	**G** 1 1000 kg	unlimited
	1° c)								X
4.2	Substances classified under (b)					X			
	Substances classified under (c)							X	
4.3	11° (a), 13° (a), 14° (a), and 16° (a) to 18° (a)	X							
	11° (b) to 17° (b)					X			
	11° (c) to 15° (c)							X	
5.1	Substances classified under (a)			X					
	Substances classified under (b)				X				
	Substances classified under (c)						X		
	5°		X						
5.2	5°, 6°, 15°, 16°		X $^{1/}$						
	7° to 10°, 17° to 20°			X $^{1/}$					
6.1	Substances classified under (c)				X				
	Substances classified under (b)			X					
	Other substances (except 1° and 2°)	X							
6.2	2°		X						
	Substances of (b)				X				
7	Material of marginal 2704, schedules 1° to 4°								X
8	6°, 14° and substances and articles classified under (a)		X						
	Substances and articles classified under (b)				X				
	Substances and articles classified under (c)						X		
9	Substances or articles classified under 1° (b), 4° (c) or 5°			X					
	Articles of 8° (c)								X
	11° (c), 12° (c), 31° (c), 32° (c), 33° (c) & 35° (b)							X	
	13° (b) & 34° (c)				X				
	20° (c) and 21° (c)						X		

NOTE 1: *The maximum quantities shown in the above table represent a degree of danger which may, from a highly simplified standpoint, be considered as equivalent for each of the substances listed. This danger level shall not be exceeded even where a load not affected by any prohibition on mixed loading includes more than one dangerous substance.*

$^{1/}$ *Excluding the mass of the refrigerating appliance if any.*

10 011
(contd) *Where the same exemption limit applies to the substances concerned, their respective masses are added and the total must not exceed that limit. Where, however, different exemption limits apply to the substances, the maximum quantities allowed for each shall be calculated as follows:*

(a) *The total actual mass of each substance referred to in any one column of the table shall be multiplied by the factor shown at the head of the column;*

(b) *The products so obtained are added together and their total shall not exceed 1,000.*

Up to that figure, the difference divided by the factor corresponding to some other substance gives the exemption limit still not taken up.

Example of these calculations

Cl.	Substance	Maximum quantity						
		5 kg	20 kg	50 kg	100 kg	333 kg	500 kg	1000 kg
2	2° A							100
3	33° (c)						50	
4.1	4° (c)			2				
6.1	16° (b)			3				
6.1	16° (c)				25			
Total of quantities carried				5	25		50	100
Multiplier factor		200	50	20	10	3	2	1
Product (factor x quantity)				100	250		100	100
Total of products			100 + 250 + 100 + 100 = 550					

Since the total of the products is less than 1,000, the case set out above leaves available within the exemption limit 1,000 - 550 = 450, which could be used to make up the load with, for example, gas cylinders of Class 2, 5°F (limit 333 kg) up to a value of 450 : 3 = 150 kg.

NOTE 2: *For the purposes of this marginal and its table, the masses of liquids or gases contained in the ordinary fixed tanks of means of transport for their propulsion or for the operation of their specialized equipment (refrigerating appliances, for example) or for ensuring their safety shall not be taken into account.*

NOTE 3: *For the application of this marginal and its table to samples of Class 1, the provisions applicable to the item number of the substance or article corresponding to the classification code of the samples should be followed.*

NOTE 4: *In the case of carriage by private individuals, intervention services or by enterprises when such carriage is ancillary to their main activity, see also marginal 10 603.*

General provisions

10 011 (contd) These multiplications or divisions can be avoided by using the mass tables below.

Maximum mass of each of two different substances shown in columns A to G of the above table which may be loaded together on a transport unit without exceeding the exemption limits (in kg):

- Columns A et seq.

A	A
1	4
2	3
3	2
4	1
5	0

A	and B
1	16
2	12
3	8
4	4
5	0

A	and C
1	40
2	30
3	20
4	10
5	0

A	and D
1	80
2	60
3	40
4	20
5	0

A	and E
1	266
2	200
3	133
4	66
5	0

A	and F
1	400
2	300
3	200
4	100
5	0

A	and G
1	800
2	600
3	400
4	200
5	0

- Columns B et seq.

B	B
2	18
4	16
6	14
8	12
10	10
12	8
14	6
16	4
18	2
20	0

B	and C
2	45
4	40
6	35
8	30
10	25
12	20
14	15
16	10
18	5
20	0

B	and D
2	90
4	80
6	70
8	60
10	50
12	40
14	30
16	20
18	10
20	0

B	and E
2	300
4	266
6	233
8	200
10	166
12	133
14	100
16	66
18	33
20	0

B	and F
2	450
4	400
6	350
8	300
10	250
12	200
14	150
16	100
18	50
20	0

B	and G
2	900
4	800
6	700
8	600
10	500
12	400
14	300
16	200
18	100
20	0

- Columns C et seq.

C	C
5	45
10	40
15	35
20	30
25	25
30	20
35	15
40	10
45	5
50	0

C	and D
5	90
10	80
15	70
20	60
25	50
30	40
35	30
40	20
45	10
50	0

C	and E
5	300
10	266
15	233
20	200
25	166
30	133
35	100
40	66
45	33
50	0

C	and F
5	450
10	400
15	350
20	300
25	250
30	200
35	150
40	100
45	50
50	0

C	and G
5	900
10	800
15	700
20	600
25	500
30	400
35	300
40	200
45	100
50	0

- Columns D et seq.

D	D
10	90
20	80
30	70
40	60
50	50
60	40
70	30
80	20
90	10
100	0

D	and E
10	300
20	266
30	233
40	200
50	166
60	133
70	100
80	66
90	33
100	0

D	and F
10	450
20	400
30	350
40	300
50	250
60	200
70	150
80	100
90	50
100	0

D	and G
10	900
20	800
30	700
40	600
50	500
60	400
70	300
80	200
90	100
100	0

- Columns E et seq.

E	E
25	308
50	283
75	258
100	233
125	208
150	183
175	158
200	133
225	108
250	83
275	58
300	33
325	8
333	0

E	and F
25	462
50	425
75	387
100	350
125	312
150	271
175	237
200	200
225	162
250	125
275	87
300	50
325	12
333	0

E	and G
25	925
50	850
75	775
100	700
125	625
150	550
175	475
200	400
225	325
250	250
275	175
300	100
325	25
333	0

- Columns F and G

F	F
50	450
100	400
150	350
200	300
250	250
300	200
350	150
400	100
450	50
500	0

F	and G
50	900
100	800
150	700
200	600
250	500
300	400
350	300
400	200
450	100
500	0

If, on taking into account the mass of the first substance to be loaded (as shown in one of the columns of a quick reference table), the maximum quantity for the second substance is not reached (in the other column of the same table) the mass remaining available may be used for a third substance. To ascertain the permissible mass of that substance, reference should be made to the quick-reference table which is headed by the column letters corresponding to the second and third substances. If the maximum quantity for the third substance is not used up either, the same procedure may be followed in regard to loading one or more other substances.

In the left-hand column of each table, an intermediate higher value for a quantity actually loaded (e.g. in the B and D table, 9 between 8 and 10) may be rounded down to the lower value shown (in this case 8). In the right-hand column, on the other hand, an intermediate value for a quantity actually loaded (e.g. in the same table, 55 instead of 60) must be rounded up to the higher value shown (in this case 60).

10 012 (1) In the case of exemptions provided for in marginal 10 011, the transport document prescribed by marginal 2002 (3) shall bear the following inscription after the particulars specified in chapter B of the special requirements for each class of Annex A:

"Load not exceeding the exemption limits prescribed in marginal 10 011."

(2) Where consignments from more than one consignor are carried in the same transport unit, the transport documents accompanying these consignments need not bear the inscription mentioned in paragraph (1).

10 013

Definitions

10 014 (1) For the purposes of this Annex:

- the term "*competent authority*" means the authority designated as such in each country and in each specific case by the Government;

- the term "*gas*" means a gas or vapour;

- the term "*dangerous substances*", when used alone, means the substances and articles designated as being substances and articles of ADR;

- the term "*RID*" signifies Regulations concerning the international carriage of dangerous goods by rail, which are Annex I of COTIF - Convention concerning international carriage by rail, Appendix B - Uniform rules concerning the contract for international carriage of goods by rail (CIM);

- the term "*carriage in bulk*" means the carriage of a solid substance without packaging;

- the term "*container*" means an article of transport equipment (lift van or other similar structure):

  - of a permanent character and accordingly strong enough to be suitable for repeated use;

  - specially designed to facilitate the carriage of goods, by one or more means of transport, without breakage of load;

  - fitted with devices permitting its ready handling, particularly when being transloaded from one means of transport to another;

  - so designed as to be easy to fill and empty, and having an internal volume of not less than 1 m^3.

  The term "*container*" does not cover conventional packagings or IBCs, or vehicles, or tank-containers; for Class 7 only, the term "container" is defined in marginal 2700 (2).

  - The term "*large container*" means a container having an internal volume of more than 3 m^3;

10 014
(contd)

- the term "*small container*" means a container having an internal volume of not less than 1 m³ and not more than 3 m³;

- the term "*tank-container*" means an article of transport equipment (including tank swap-bodies) conforming to the definition of the term "container" given above and built to contain liquid, powdery or granular substances but having a capacity of more than 0.45 m³. Tank-containers for substances of Class 2 have a capacity of more than 1000 l;

- the term "*demountable tank*" means a tank, other than a fixed tank, a tank-container or an element of a battery-vehicle, which has a capacity of over 1,000 litres, is not designed for the carriage of goods without breakage of load, and normally can only be handled when it is empty;

- the term "*fixed tank*" means a tank which is structurally attached to a vehicle (which then becomes a tank-vehicle) or is an integral part of the frame of such vehicle;

- the term "*tank*" when used alone, means a tank-container or a tank of a capacity exceeding 1 m³ which may be a fixed tank, a demountable tank or an element of a battery-vehicle. (See, however, a limitation of the meaning of the word "tank" in the provisions common to the B.1 Appendices, marginal 200 000 (2));

- the term "*transport unit*" means a motor vehicle without an attached trailer, or a combination consisting of a motor vehicle and an attached trailer;

- the term "*closed vehicle*" means a vehicle having a body capable of being closed;

- the term "*open vehicle*" means a vehicle the platform of which has no superstructure or is merely provided with side boards and a tailboard;

- the term "*sheeted vehicle*" means an open vehicle provided with a sheet to protect the load;

- the term "*tank-vehicle*" means a vehicle built to carry liquids, gases, or powdery or granular substances and comprising one or more fixed tanks;

- the term "*battery-vehicle*" means a vehicle with an assembly of:

  - several cylinders as defined in marginal 2211 (1); or
  - several tubes as defined in marginal 2211 (2); or
  - several pressure drums as defined in marginal 2211 (3); or
  - several bundles of cylinders as defined in marginal 2211 (5); or
  - several tanks as defined in this Annex;

  interconnected by a manifold, permanently mounted in a frame and permanently fixed to the transport unit;

- the term "*base vehicle*" means any incomplete motor vehicle or its trailer corresponding to a type approved in accordance with Appendix B.2.

- "*Auxiliary heating devices*" are appliances exclusively intended for raising the temperature in the driver's cab, the load compartment or other vehicle assemblies. They shall not be operated by the waste heat of the vehicle engine.

10 014
(contd)
(2)   For the purposes of this Annex, tanks [see definition in (1) above] are not placed on the same footing as receptacles, the term "receptacle" being used in a restrictive sense. Provisions concerning receptacles apply to fixed tanks, elements of battery-vehicles, demountable tanks and tank-containers only if this is expressly stipulated.

(3)   The term "full load" means any load originating from one sender, for which the use of a vehicle or a large container is exclusively reserved and all operations for loading and unloading are carried out in conformity with the instructions of the sender or consignee (see marginal 10 108).

(4)   "Wastes" are substances, solutions, mixtures or articles for which no direct use is envisaged but which are transported for reprocessing, dumping, elimination by incineration or other methods of disposal.

10 015
(1)   Unless expressly stated otherwise, the sign "%" in this Annex represents:

      (a)   In the case of mixtures of solids or of liquids, and also in the case of solutions and of solids wetted by a liquid: a percentage by mass based on the total mass of the mixture, the solution or the wetted solid;

      (b)   in the case of mixtures of compressed gases: when filled by pressure, the proportion of the volume indicated as a percentage of the total volume of the gaseous mixture, or, when filled by mass, the proportion of the mass indicated as a percentage of the total mass of the mixture;

      in the case of mixtures of liquefied gases and gases dissolved under pressure: the proportion of the mass indicated as a percentage of the total mass of the mixture.

(2)   Whenever the mass of a package is mentioned in this Annex, the gross mass is meant unless otherwise stated. The mass of containers or tanks used for the carriage of goods is not included in the gross mass.

(3)   Pressures of all kinds relating to tanks (such as test pressure, working pressure, safety-valve opening pressure) are always indicated in gauge pressure (pressure in excess of atmospheric pressure); however, the vapour pressure of substances is always expressed in absolute pressure.

(4)   Where this Annex specifies a degree of filling for tanks, the degree of filling is always given for a temperature of the substances of 15 °C unless some other temperature is indicated.

10 016-
10 099

    SECTION 1.   **Mode of carriage of goods**

10 100-
10 104

    Method of dispatch, restrictions on forwarding

10 105   The carriage of certain dangerous goods is subject to the mandatory uses of a particular type of transport or equipment. These special conditions are set out in this Annex, Part II, marginals XX 105.

10 106-
10 107

General provisions

Full load

10 108   Where the provisions relating to carriage as a "full load" are applied, the competent authorities may require the vehicle or large container used for such carriage to be loaded at only one point and unloaded at only one point.

**10 109-
10 110**

Carriage in bulk

10 111   (1)   Solid dangerous substances may not be carried in bulk unless this mode of carriage is expressly authorized for such substances by the provisions of Part II of this Annex, and then only under the conditions stipulated by those provisions. Nevertheless, empty packagings, uncleaned, may be carried in bulk if this mode of carriage is not explicitly prohibited by the requirements of Annex A, Part II.

(2)   For carriage in bulk in containers, see marginal 10 118 (2).

NOTE: See marginal 10 500 for marking and labelling of bulk vehicles.

**10 112-
10 117**

Carriage in containers

NOTE: The provisions concerning carriage in tank-containers are set out in the marginals headed "Carriage in tanks".

10 118   (1)   The carriage of packages in containers is authorized.

(2)   Substances and articles may not be carried in bulk in containers unless their carriage in bulk is expressly authorized (see marginal 10 111); small containers shall be of the closed type and have complete walls.

(3)   Large containers shall meet the requirements concerning the body of the vehicle laid down in this Annex for the load in question; the body of the vehicle need not then satisfy those provisions.

However, large containers transported on vehicles whose platforms have insulation and heat-resistant qualities which satisfy those requirements need not then satisfy the said requirements.

(4)   Subject to the provisions of the last phrase in (3) above, the fact that dangerous substances are contained in one or more containers shall not affect the conditions to be met by the vehicle by reason of the nature and quantities of the dangerous substances carried.

(5)   Large containers and tank-containers which meet the definition of "container" given in the 1972 International Convention for Safe Containers (CSC, 1972) [2], as amended or in UIC leaflets [3] 590 (updated 1.1.89) and 592-1 to 592-4 (updated 1.1.94) may not be used to carry

---

[2]   *Published by the International Maritime Organization, 4 Albert Embankment, London SE1 7SR.*

[3]   *UIC leaflets are published by the "Union Internationale des chemins de fer, Service Publications - 16, rue Jean Rey - F - 75015 Paris".*

**10 118
(contd)** dangerous goods unless the large container or the frame of the tank-container satisfies the provisions of the CSC or of UIC leaflets 590 and 592-1 to 592-4.

(6)   A large container may be presented for transport only if it is structurally serviceable.

"*Structurally serviceable*" means that the container is free from major defects in its structural components, e.g. top and bottom side rails, door sill and header, floor cross members, corner posts, and (in a container) corner fittings. "*Major defects*" are dents or bends in structural members greater than 19 mm in depth, regardless of length; cracks or breaks in structural members; more than one splice or an improper splice (eg. a lapped splice) in top or bottom end rails or door headers or more than two splices in any one top or bottom side rail or any splice in a door sill or corner post; door hinges and hardware that are seized, twisted, broken, missing or otherwise inoperative; non-closing gaskets and seals; any distortion of the overall configuration sufficient to prevent proper alignment of handling equipment, mounting and securing on a chassis or vehicle.

In addition, deterioration in any component of the container, such as rusted metal in sidewalls or disintegrated fibreglass is unacceptable, regardless of the material of construction. Normal wear, including oxidization (rust), slight dents and scratches and other damage that do not affect serviceability or weather-tightness are, however, acceptable.

Prior to loading the container shall also be checked to ensure that it is free from any residue of a previous load and that the interior floor and walls are free from protrusions.

NOTE: See marginal 10 500 for the marking and labelling of containers.

**10 119-
10 120**

Carriage in tanks

10 121 (1)   Dangerous substances may be carried in tanks only if this mode of carriage is expressly authorized for those substances by the provisions on the use of fixed tanks, demountable tanks and battery-vehicles set out in each section 1 of Appendix B.1a, Part II, and those on the use of tank-containers set out in each section 1 of Appendix B.1b, Part II.

(2)   Reinforced-plastics tanks may be used only if their use is expressly authorized in Appendix B.1c, marginal 213 010 (Use). The temperature of the substance carried shall not exceed 50 °C at the time of filling.

NOTE: See marginal 10 500 for the marking and labelling of vehicles with fixed or demountable tanks.

**10 122-
10 199**

SECTION 2.   **Special requirements to be fulfilled by the means of transport and its equipment**

**10 200-
10 203**

General provisions

Types of vehicle

10 204   (1)   A transport unit loaded with dangerous substances may in no case include more than one trailer or semi-trailer.

(2)   Special provisions concerning the types of vehicle to be used for the carriage of certain dangerous substances will, where appropriate, be found in Part II of this Annex (see also the marginals dealing with carriage in containers, the carriage of solid substances in bulk, carriage in tanks, and tanks).

(3)   Packages comprising packagings made of materials sensitive to moisture shall be loaded on to closed or on to sheeted vehicles.

10 205-
10 219

Tank-vehicles (fixed tanks), battery-vehicles and vehicles used for the carriage of dangerous goods in demountable tanks or in tank-containers of a capacity greater than 3000 litres

NOTES: *(a)   The provisions concerning the design, inspection, filling and use of fixed tanks, demountable tanks and battery-vehicles, and various provisions concerning tank-vehicles and their use, will be found in Appendix B.1a and, so far as the design of fixed tanks, demountable tanks and battery-vehicles intended for the carriage of deeply refrigerated liquefied gases of Class 2 or requiring a test pressure of not less than 1 MPa (10 bar) is concerned, in Appendix B.1d (for the approval of tank-vehicles, see marginal 10 282).*

(b)   The provisions concerning the construction, items of equipment, type approval, tests, marking, etc. of tank-containers are to be found in Appendix B.1b and, so far as the construction of tank-containers intended for the carriage of deeply refrigerated liquefied gases of Class 2 or requiring a test pressure of not less than 1 MPa (10 bar) is concerned, in Appendix B.1d.

(c)   The provisions concerning the construction of fixed tanks and demountable tanks of reinforced plastics are to be found in Appendix B.1c.

(d)   The provisions common to the B.1 Appendices are to be found in marginal 200 000.

(e)   For receptacles, see Annex A.

10 220   (1)   Rear protection of vehicles: A bumper sufficiently resistant to rear impact shall be fitted over the full width of the tank at the rear of the vehicle. There shall be a clearance of at least 100 mm between the rear wall of the tank and the rear of the bumper (this clearance being measured from the rearmost point of the tank wall or from projecting fittings or accessories in contact with the substance being carried). Vehicles with a tilting tank for the carriage of powdery or granular substances with rear discharge do not require a bumper if the rear fittings of the tank are provided with a means of protection which protects the tank in the same way as a bumper.

NOTE 1: This provision does not apply to vehicles used for the carriage of dangerous goods in tank-containers.

NOTE 2: For the protection of tanks against damage by lateral impact or overturning, see marginal 211 127 (4) and (5) and marginal 212 127 (4) and (5).

10 220
(contd) (2)   Vehicles carrying liquids having a flash-point of 61°C or below or flammable substances of Class 2 as defined in marginal 2200 (5) and (7) shall, in addition, comply with the requirements of marginals 220 532, 220 533 and 220 534 of Appendix B.2.

Braking

10 221 (1)   Motor vehicles (tractors and rigid vehicles) having a maximum mass exceeding 16 tonnes and trailers (i.e. full trailers, semi-trailers and centre-axle trailers) with a maximum mass exceeding 10 tonnes, as well as motor vehicles authorized to tow such trailers, making up the following types of transport unit:

-    tank vehicles,

-    battery-vehicles with a capacity of more than 1000 litres

-    vehicles carrying demountable tanks,

-    vehicles carrying tank-containers with a capacity of more than 3 000 litres, and

-    type III transport units [see marginal 11 204 (3)],

first registered after 30 June 1993, shall be fitted with an anti-lock braking system, the performance of which shall meet the provisions of marginals 220 520 and 220 521 of Appendix B.2.

This provision is applicable also to motor vehicles authorized to tow trailers with a maximum mass exceeding 10 tonnes as above, which have been first registered after 30 June 1995.

(2)   Each transport unit of a type specified in paragraph (1) above, which includes a motor vehicle with or without an attached trailer of a type specified in (1) above, shall be fitted with an endurance braking system meeting the requirements of marginals 220 522 and 220 535 of Appendix B.2.

When the transport unit comprises a motor vehicle and a trailer, the requirement applies when the motor vehicle is registered after 30 June 1993.

(3)   Each transport unit of a type specified in paragraph (1) above in service after 31 December 1999 shall be equipped with the devices referred to in paragraphs (1) and (2).

(4)   Each vehicle (motor vehicle or trailer) which forms part of a transport unit of a type not specified in paragraph (1) above, and is first registered after 30 June 1997, shall meet all the relevant technical requirements of ECE Regulation No. 13 [4/] in their latest amended form applicable at the time of the vehicle approval.

[4/]   *ECE Regulation No. 13 (Uniform provisions concerning the approval of vehicles of categories M, N and O with regard to braking), (in its latest amended form) annexed to the Agreement concerning the adoption of uniform technical prescriptions for wheeled vehicles, equipment and parts which can be fitted and/or used on wheeled vehicles and the conditions for reciprocal recognition of approvals granted on the basis of these prescriptions (1958 Agreement, as amended). As an alternative, the corresponding provisions of Directive 71/320/EEC (originally published in the Official Journal of the European Communities No. L 202 of 6.9.1971) may apply, provided that they have been amended in accordance with the latest amended form of Regulation No.13 applicable at the time of the vehicle approval.*

10 221
(contd) (5)   A declaration of conformity of the endurance braking system with marginal 220 522 shall be issued by the vehicle manufacturer. This declaration shall be presented at the first technical inspection mentioned under marginal 10 282 (1).

10 222-
10 239

Fire-fighting appliances

10 240 (1)   Every transport unit carrying dangerous goods shall be equipped with:

  (a)   at least one portable fire extinguisher of minimum capacity 2 kg dry powder (or equivalent rating for suitable extinguishants) suitable for fighting a fire in the engine or cab of the transport unit, and such that, if it is used to fight a fire involving the load, it does not aggravate the fire and, if possible, controls it; however, if the vehicle is equipped with a fixed fire extinguisher, automatic or easily brought into action for fighting a fire in the engine, the portable extinguisher need not be suitable for fighting a fire in the engine;

  (b)   in addition to the equipment prescribed under (a) above, at least one portable fire extinguisher of minimum capacity 6 kg dry powder (or equivalent rating for suitable extinguishants) suitable for fighting a tyre/brake fire or one involving the load, and such that, if it is used to fight a fire in the engine or cab of the transport unit, it does not aggravate the fire. Motor vehicles with a permissible maximum laden weight of less than 3.5 tons may be equipped with a portable fire extinguisher of a minimum capacity of 2 kg of powder.

(2)   The extinguishing agents contained in the fire extinguishers with which a transport unit is equipped shall be such that they are not liable to release toxic gases into the driver's cab or under the influence of the heat of the fire.

(3)   The portable fire extinguishers conforming to the provisions of paragraph (1) above shall be fitted with a seal verifying that they have not been used. In addition, they shall bear a mark of compliance with a standard recognized by a competent authority and an inscription indicating the date when they should next be inspected.

10 241-
10 250

Electrical equipment

10 251 The requirements concerning the electrical equipment set out in marginal 220 511 of Appendix B.2 shall apply to every transport unit carrying dangerous substances for which an approval according to marginals 10 282 is required (except transport units of type II according to marginal 11 204). The requirements in marginal 220 512 to 220 516 of Appendix B.2 shall apply only to the following vehicles:

  (a)   Transport units carrying fixed tanks or demountable tanks or tank-containers exceeding 3000 litres capacity or comprising battery-vehicles with a capacity of more than 1000 litres transporting either liquids having a flash-point of 61 °C or below, or flammable substances of Class 2 as defined in marginal 2200 (5) and (7). Transport units carrying tanks (fixed or demountable) transporting diesel fuel, gas-oil or heating oil light, with the identification number 1202, registered before 1 July 1995 and not conforming to this marginal, may, however, be used;

10 251   (b)   Transport units intended for the carriage of explosives and having to comply with the
(contd)   requirements set out in marginal 11 204 (3) for transport units of type III.

          NOTE: For transitional provisions see also marginal 10 605.

10 252-
10 259

Miscellaneous equipment

10 260   Every transport unit carrying dangerous goods shall be equipped with:

        (a)   a tool kit for emergency repairs to the vehicle;

        (b)   for each vehicle, at least one scotch of a size suited to the weight of the vehicle and
               to the diameter of the wheels;

        (c)   two amber lights. These lights shall be independent of the electrical equipment of the
               vehicle and be so designed that their use cannot cause the goods being carried to
               ignite; they shall be steady or flashing;

        (d)   the necessary equipment to take the first safety measures referred to in the safety
               instructions set out in marginal 10 385, in particular:

               i)   **for the protection of the driver:**

- a warning vest;
- suitable eye protection;
- appropriate respiratory protection when toxic substances are transported;
- suitable gloves;
- suitable foot protection (e.g. boots);
- basic body protection (e.g. apron);
- one handlamp (see also marginal 10 353);
- eye wash bottle with water;

             ii)   **for the protection of the public:**

- four reflective self-standing warning signs (e.g. cones, triangles);

             iii)   **for the protection of the environment:**

- cover for sewers and drains resistant to the transported substance;
- a suitable shovel;
- a broom;
- a suitable absorbent;
- a suitable collecting container (only for small amounts).

10 261   (1)   Motor vehicles (tractors and rigid vehicles) with a maximum mass exceeding 12 tons,
registered for the first time after 1 July 1995, shall be equipped with a speed limitation device in
accordance with marginal 220 540 of Appendix B.2.

        (2)   The requirements of paragraph (1) above are also applicable to vehicles with the same
characteristics registered between 1 January 1988 and 1 July 1995, as from 1 July 1996.

General provisions

10 262-
10 280

Approval of vehicles

10 281 At the request of the manufacturer or his duly accredited representative, base vehicles of new motor vehicles and their trailers which are subject to approval according to marginals 10 282, may be type approved by a competent authority in accordance with Appendix B.2. This type-approval shall be accepted as ensuring the conformity of the base vehicle when the approval of the complete vehicle is obtained, provided that no modification of the base vehicle alters its validity.

10 282 (1) Tank-vehicles, vehicles carrying demountable tanks, battery-vehicles with a capacity of more than 1000 litres, vehicles intended for the carriage of tank-containers exceeding 3000 litres capacity, and, where so required under the provisions of Part II of this Annex, other vehicles shall be subject to annual technical inspections in their country of registration to make sure that they conform to the relevant provisions of this Annex, including those of its appendices, and to the general safety regulations (concerning brakes, lighting, etc.) in force in their country of registration; if these vehicles are trailers or semi-trailers coupled behind a drawing vehicle, the drawing vehicle shall be subject to technical inspection for the same purposes.

NOTE: For transitional provisions see also marginal 10 605.

(2) A certificate of approval shall be issued by the competent authority of the country of registration for each vehicle whose inspection yields satisfactory results. It shall be drawn up in the language or one of the languages of the country issuing it, and also, if that language is not English, French, or German, in English, French or German, unless agreements concluded between the countries concerned in the transport operation provide otherwise. It shall conform to the model shown in Appendix B.3.

(3) A certificate of approval issued by the competent authorities of one Contracting Party for a vehicle registered in the territory of that Contracting Party shall be accepted, so long as its validity continues, by the competent authorities of the other Contracting Parties.

(4) The validity of a certificate of approval shall expire not later than one year after the date of the technical inspection of the vehicle preceding the issue of the certificate. The next approval term shall however be related to the last nominal expiry date, if the technical inspection is performed within one month before or after that date. However, in the case of tanks subject to compulsory periodic inspection this provision shall not mean that tightness (leakproofness) tests, hydraulic pressure tests or internal inspections of tanks have to be carried out at intervals shorter than those laid down in Appendices B.1a and B.1c.

10 283-
10 299

SECTION 3.   General service provisions

10 300-
10 310

Vehicle crews

10 311 Where the relevant provisions of Part II of this Annex require the presence in the vehicle of an assistant, the assistant must be able to take over from the driver.

10 312-
10 314

Special training of drivers

10 315   (1)   Drivers of vehicles carrying dangerous goods in fixed or demountable tanks, drivers of battery-vehicles with a total capacity exceeding 1000 litres and drivers of vehicles carrying dangerous goods in tank-containers with an individual capacity exceeding 3000 litres on a transport unit, shall hold a certificate issued by the competent authority or by any organization recognized by that authority stating that they have participated in a training course and passed an examination on the particular requirements that have to be met during carriage of dangerous goods in tanks.

(2)   Drivers of vehicles with a permissible maximum weight exceeding 3500 kg carrying dangerous goods, other than those referred to in paragraph (1) and, where so required under the provisions of Part II of this Annex, drivers of other vehicles shall hold a certificate issued by the competent authority or by any organization recognized by that authority stating that they have participated in a training course and passed an examination on the particular requirements that have to be met during carriage of dangerous goods other than in tanks.

(3)   By means of appropriate endorsements on his certificate made every five years by the competent authority or by any organization recognized by that authority, a vehicle driver shall be able to show that he has in the year before the date of expiry of his certificate completed a refresher training course and has passed corresponding examinations. The new period of validity shall begin with the date of expiry of the certificate.

(4)   Drivers of vehicles specified in paragraphs (1) and (2) shall attend a basic training course. Training shall be given in the form of courses approved by the competent authority. Its main objectives are to make drivers aware of hazards arising in the carriage of dangerous goods and to give them basic information indispensable for minimizing the likelihood of an incident taking place and, if it does, to enable them to take measures which may prove necessary for their own safety and that of the public and the environment, for limiting the effects of an incident. This training, which shall include individual practical exercises, shall act as the basis of training for all categories of drivers covering at least the subjects defined in marginal 240 102 of Appendix B.4.

(5)   Drivers of vehicles specified in paragraph (1) shall attend a specialization training course for transport in tanks covering at least the subjects defined in marginal 240 103 of Appendix B.4.

(6)   Drivers of vehicles carrying dangerous goods of Class 1 or Class 7 shall attend specialization training courses covering specific requirements for these classes (see marginals 11 315 and 71 315).

(7)   Initial or refresher basic training courses and initial or refresher specialization training courses may be given in the form of comprehensive courses, performed in an integrated way, on the same occasion and by the same training organisation.

(8)   Initial training courses, refresher courses, practical exercises, examinations and the role of competent authorities shall comply with the provisions of Appendix B.4.

(9)   All training certificates conforming to the requirements of this marginal and issued in accordance with the model shown in Appendix B.6 by the competent authority of a Contracting Party or by any organization recognized by that authority shall be accepted during their period of validity by the competent authorities of other Contracting Parties.

**10 315
(contd)**   (10)   The certificate shall be prepared in the language or one of the languages of the country of the competent authority which issued the certificate or recognized the issuing organization and, if this language is not English, French or German, also in English, French or German, except where otherwise provided by agreements concluded between the countries concerned with the transport operation.

**10 316-
10 320**

Supervision of vehicles

10 321   Vehicles carrying dangerous goods in the quantities shown in the relevant marginals of Part II shall be supervised or alternatively may be parked, unsupervised, in a secure depot or secure factory premises. If such facilities are not available, the vehicle, after having been properly secured, may be parked in an isolated position meeting the requirements of paragraphs (i), (ii) or (iii) below. The parking facilities permitted in paragraph (ii) shall be used only if those described in paragraph (i) are not available, and those described in paragraph (iii) may be used only if facilities described in paragraphs (i) and (ii) are not available.

(i)   A vehicle park supervised by an attendant who has been notified of the nature of the load and the whereabouts of the driver;

(ii)   A public or private vehicle park where the vehicle is not likely to suffer damage from other vehicles; or

(iii)   A suitable open space separated from the public highway and from dwellings, where the public does not normally pass or assemble.

**10 322-
10 324**

Carriage of passengers

10 325   Apart from members of the vehicle's crew, no passengers may be carried in transport units carrying dangerous substances.

**10 326-
10 339**

Use of fire-fighting appliances

10 340   The crew of the vehicle must know how to use the fire-fighting appliances.

**10 341-
10 352**

Portable lighting apparatus

10 353   (1)   A vehicle may not be entered by persons carrying lighting apparatus comprising a flame. In addition, the lighting apparatus used shall not exhibit any metal surface liable to produce sparks.

(2)   Closed vehicles carrying liquids having a flash-point of 61°C or below or flammable substances or articles of Class 2, as defined in marginal 2200 (5) and (7), shall not be entered by persons carrying lighting apparatus other than portable lamps so designed and constructed that they cannot ignite any flammable vapours or gases which may have penetrated into the interior of the vehicle.

**10 354-
10 377**

General provisions

Empty tanks

10 378 (1) For fixed tanks (tank vehicles), demountable tanks and battery-vehicles, see marginal 211 177.

(2) For tank-containers, see marginal 212 177.

**10 379-
10 380**

Documents to be carried on the transport unit

10 381 (1) In addition to the documents required under other regulations, the following documents shall be carried on the transport unit:

(a) the transport documents prescribed in Annex A, marginal 2002 (3), (4) and (9), covering all the dangerous substances carried and, when appropriate, the container packing certificate prescribed in marginal 2008;

(b) a copy of the main text of the special agreement(s) concluded in accordance with marginals 2010 and 10 602 if transport is carried out on the basis of such agreement(s).

(2) Where the provisions of this Annex require the following documents to be drawn up, they shall likewise be carried on the transport unit:

(a) The certificate of approval referred to in marginal 10 282 for each transport unit or element thereof;

(b) The driver's training certificate prescribed in marginal 10 315 and reproduced in Appendix B.6;

(c) The instructions prescribed in marginal 10 385, relating to all the dangerous substances carried and;

(d) The permit authorizing the transport operation.

**10 382-
10 384**

Instructions in writing for the driver

10 385 (1) As a precaution against any accident or emergency that may occur or arise during carriage, the driver shall be given instructions in writing, specifying concisely for each dangerous substance or article carried or for each group of dangerous goods presenting the same dangers to which the substance(s) or article(s) carried belong(s) :

(a) the name of the substance or article or group of goods, the Class and the identification number or for a group of goods the identification numbers of the goods for which these instructions are intended or are applicable;

(b) the nature of the danger inherent in these goods as well the measures and personal protection to be applied by the driver;

(c) the immediate actions to be taken by the driver in the event of an accident.

- 20 -

General provisions

**10 385
(contd)**
(2)   These instructions shall be provided by the consignor who shall be responsible for their content, in a language the driver(s) taking over the dangerous goods is (are) able to read and to understand, as far as this language is an official language of one of the ADR contracting parties.

(3)   These instructions shall be kept in the driver's cab.

(4)   Instructions in writing according to this marginal which are not applicable to the goods which are on board of the vehicle, shall be kept separate from pertinent documents in such a way as to prevent confusion.

(5)   The carrier shall ensure that the drivers concerned understand and are capable of carrying out these instructions properly.

(6)   In case of mixed loads of packaged goods including dangerous goods which belong to different groups of goods presenting the same dangers, the instructions in writing may be restricted to one instruction per Class of dangerous goods carried on board of the vehicle. In such case no name of goods, nor identification number has to be mentioned in the instructions.

(7)   These instructions shall be drafted according to the following format:

LOAD   -   Mention of the proper shipping name of the substance or article, or the name of the group of goods presenting the same dangers, the Class and the identification number or for a group of goods the identification numbers of the goods for which these instructions are intended or are applicable.

-    Description shall be restricted to e.g. the physical state with indication coloured or not, and mention of a possible odour, to aid identification of leakages or spillages.

NATURE OF DANGER   Short enumeration of dangers :

-    Main danger

-    Additional dangers inclusive possible delayed effects and dangers for the environment

-    Behaviour under fire or heating (decomposition, explosion, development of toxic fumes, ...).

BASIC PERSONAL PROTECTION

Mention of the basic personal protection intended for the driver in accordance with the requirements of marginals 10 260, 11 260, 21 260, 43 260 and 71 260 according to the class(es) of the goods carried.

IMMEDIATE ACTION BY DRIVER

-    Notify police and fire brigade
-    Stop the engine
-    No naked lights, No smoking
-    Mark roads and warn other road users
-    Keep public away from danger area
-    Keep upwind

- 21 -

**10 385
(contd)**

SPILLAGE

It is considered that drivers of vehicles should be instructed and trained to deal with minor leakages or spillages to prevent their escalation, provided that this can be achieved without personal risk.

Appropriate instructions shall be reminded here as well as the list of equipment in accordance with the requirements of marginals 10 260, 11 260, 21 260, 43 260 and 71 260 according to the class(es) of the goods being carried (e.g. bucket, shovel, ...) which has to be on board of the vehicle to deal with minor leakages or spillages.

FIRE

Drivers should be instructed during training to deal with minor vehicle fires. They shall not attempt to deal with any fire involving the load.

When applicable, it shall be mentioned here that the goods carried react dangerously with water.

FIRST AID

Information for the driver in case he would have been in contact with the transported good(s).

ADDITIONAL INFORMATION

**10 386-
10 399**

SECTION 4. **Special provisions concerning loading, unloading and handling**

10 400

(1) The vehicle and its driver, upon arrival at the loading and unloading sites, shall comply with the regulatory provisions (especially those concerning safety, cleanliness and satisfactory operation of the vehicle equipment used in loading and unloading)

(2) The loading shall not be carried out if an examination of the documents and a visual inspection of the vehicle and its equipment show that the vehicle or the driver do not comply with the regulatory provisions

(3) The unloading shall not be carried out, if the above-mentioned inspections reveal deficiencies that might affect the safety of the unloading.

Limitation of the quantities carried

10 401

The fact that dangerous substances are contained in one or more containers shall not affect the weight limitations laid down by this Annex regarding carriage in a single vehicle or in a single transport unit.

10 402

Prohibition of mixed loading on one vehicle

10 403

Unless the contrary is explicitly prescribed by the provisions of the sections 4 of Part II of this Annex, the prohibitions of mixed loading on one vehicle shall not apply to consignments of goods packed together in the manner permitted by the provisions on mixed packing contained in Annex A. Compliance with the prohibitions on mixed loading shall be based on the danger labels of Appendix A.9, which shall be affixed to packages in accordance with the requirements laid down for the various classes in Annex A.

NOTE: As prescribed in marginal 2002 (4), separate transport documents shall be prepared for consignments which may not be loaded together on the same vehicle.

General provisions

Prohibition of mixed loading in one container

10 404   The prohibitions of mixed loading on one vehicle shall also be observed within each container.

Prohibition of mixed loading with goods contained in a container

10 405   For the purpose of the application of the prohibitions of mixed loading on one vehicle, no account shall be taken of substances contained in closed containers with complete sides.

10 406-
10 409

Precautions with respect to foodstuffs, other articles of consumption and animal feeds

10 410   Packages, including intermediate bulk containers (IBCs), as well as uncleaned empty packagings, including uncleaned empty intermediate bulk containers (IBCs), bearing labels conforming to models Nos. 6.1 or 6.2 and those bearing labels of Class 9, containing substances of 1°, 2°(b), 3° or 13°(b) of Class 9, shall not be stacked on or loaded in immediate proximity to packages known to contain foodstuffs, other articles of consumption or animal feeds in vehicles and at places of loading, unloading or transhipment.

When these packages, bearing the said labels, are loaded in immediate proximity of packages known to contain foodstuffs, other articles of consumption or animal feeds, they shall be kept apart from the latter:

    (a)   by complete partitions which should be as high as the packages bearing the said labels, or

    (b)   by packages not bearing labels conforming to models Nos. 6.1, 6.2 or 9 or packages bearing labels of Class 9 but not containing substances or articles of 1°, 2°, 3° or 13° of that class, or

    (c)   by a space of at least 0.8 m,

unless the packages bearing the said labels are provided with an additional packaging or are completely covered (e.g. by a sheeting, a fibreboard cover or other measures).

10 411-
10 412

Cleaning before loading

10 413   All the provisions in this Annex which relate to the cleaning of vehicles before loading shall also apply to the cleaning of containers.

Handling and stowage

10 414   (1)   The various components of a load comprising dangerous substances shall be properly stowed on the vehicle and secured by appropriate means to prevent them from being significantly displaced in relation to each other and to the walls of the vehicle. The load may be protected, for example, by the use of side wall fastening straps, sliding slatboards and adjustable brackets, air bags and anti-slide locking devices. The load is also sufficiently protected within the meaning of the first sentence if each layer of the whole loading space is completely filled with packages.

10 414
(contd)   (2)   All the provisions in this Annex which relate to the loading and unloading of vehicles and to the stowage and handling of substances shall also apply to the loading, stowage and unloading of containers on to and from vehicles.

(3)   A driver or a driver's assistant may not open a package containing dangerous substances.

Cleaning after unloading

10 415   (1)   If, when a vehicle which has been loaded with packaged dangerous substances is unloaded, some of the contents are found to have escaped, the vehicle shall be cleaned as soon as possible and in any case before reloading.

(2)   Vehicles which have been loaded with dangerous substances in bulk shall be properly cleaned before reloading unless the new load consists of the same dangerous substance as the preceding load.

(3)   All the provisions of this Annex which relate to the cleaning or decontamination of vehicles shall also apply to the cleaning or decontamination of containers.

Prohibition of smoking

10 416   Smoking shall be prohibited during handling operations in the vicinity of vehicles and inside the vehicles.

Precautions against electrostatic charges

10 417   In the case of substances with a flash-point of 61 °C or below, a good electrical connection from the vehicle chassis to earth shall be established before tanks are filled or emptied. In addition, the rate of filling shall be limited.

10 418

Loading and unloading of dangerous substances in containers

10 419   The provisions of this Annex which relate to the loading and unloading of vehicles and the stowage and handling of dangerous substances shall also apply to the loading and unloading of dangerous substances in containers.

10 420-
10 430

Running the engine during loading or unloading

10 431   Except where the engine has to be used to drive the pumps or other appliances for loading or unloading the vehicle and the laws of the country in which the vehicle is operating permit such use, the engine shall be shut off during loading and unloading operations.

10 432-
10 499

General provisions

10 500   *NOTE: For marking and labelling of containers and tank-containers for carriage prior to or following maritime transport, see also marginal 2007.*

(1)   Transport units carrying dangerous goods shall display two rectangular reflectorized orange-coloured plates of 40 cm base and not less than 30 cm high, set in a vertical plane. The plates shall have a black border not more than 15 mm wide. They shall be affixed one at the front and the other at the rear of the transport unit, both perpendicular to the longitudinal axis of the transport unit. They shall be clearly visible. If the size and construction of the vehicle are such that the available surface area is insufficient to affix these orange-coloured plates, their dimensions may be reduced to 300 mm for the base, 120 mm for the height and 10 mm for the black border.

NOTE: The colour of the orange plates in conditions of normal use should have chromaticity co-ordinates lying within the area on the chromaticity diagram formed by joining the following co-ordinates:

Chromaticity co-ordinates of points at the corners of the area on the chromaticity diagram			
X	*0.52*	*0.52*	*0.578*	*0.618*
Y	*0.38*	*0.40*	*0.422*	*0.38*

Luminance factor of reflectorized colour: ß > 0.12.

Reference centre E, standard illuminant C, normal incidence 45°, viewed at 0°.

Co-efficient of reflex luminous intensity at an angle of illumination of 5°, viewed at 0.2°: not less than 20 candelas per lux per m².

(2)   Tank-vehicles or transport units having one or more tanks carrying dangerous goods covered by Appendix B.5, shall in addition display on the sides or each tank or tank compartment, clearly visible and parallel to the longitudinal axis of the vehicle, orange-coloured plates identical with those prescribed in paragraph (1). These orange-coloured plates shall bear the identification numbers prescribed in Appendix B.5 for each of the substances carried in the tank or in a compartment of the tank.

(3)   Transport units and containers carrying dangerous solid substances in bulk covered by Appendix B.5 shall in addition display on the sides of each transport unit or container, clearly visible and parallel to the longitudinal axis of the vehicle, orange-coloured plates identical with those prescribed in paragraph (1). These orange-coloured plates shall bear the identification numbers prescribed for each of the substances carried in bulk in the transport unit or in the container.

(4)   For containers carrying dangerous solid substances in bulk and for tanks-containers, the plates prescribed in paragraphs (2) and (3) may be replaced by a self-adhesive sheet, by paint or by any other equivalent process, provided the material used for this purpose is weather-resistant and ensures durable marking. In this case, the provisions of the last sentence of paragraph (6), concerning resistance to fire, shall not apply.

**10 500
(contd)** (5) For transport units carrying only one of the substances listed in Appendix B.5, the orange-coloured plates prescribed in paragraphs (2) and (3) shall not be necessary provided that those displayed at the front and rear in accordance with paragraph (1) bear the identification numbers prescribed in Appendix B.5.

(6) The identification numbers shall consist of black digits 100 mm high and of 15 mm stroke thickness. The hazard-identification number shall be inscribed in the upper part of the plate and the substance-identification number in the lower part; they shall be separated by a horizontal black line, 15 mm in stroke width, extending from side to side of the plate at mid-height (see Appendix B.5). The identification numbers shall be indelible and shall remain legible after 15 minutes' engulfment in fire.

(7) The above requirements are also applicable to empty fixed or demountable tanks, tank-containers and battery-vehicles of receptacles, uncleaned and not degassed and empty bulk vehicles and empty bulk containers, uncleaned.

(8) Orange-coloured plates which do not relate to dangerous goods carried, or residues thereof, shall be removed or covered. If plates are covered, the covering shall be total and remain effective after 15 minutes' engulfment in fire.

Labelling

(9) If the dangerous goods carried in a container are such that, under Annex A, one or more danger labels have to be affixed to the packages containing them, the same label or labels shall be affixed to both sides and at each end of the container containing those goods in packages or in bulk. However, label No. 11 need not be affixed.

(10) Bulk containers, tank-containers and battery-vehicles shall bear on both sides the labels prescribed in the XX 500 marginals of each class. If these labels are not visible from outside the carrying vehicles, the same labels shall also be affixed on both sides and at the rear of the vehicle.

(11) Bulk vehicles and vehicles with fixed or demountable tanks shall bear on both sides and at the rear the labels prescribed in marginal XX 500 of each class.

(12) The requirements of marginal 10 500 (10) and (11) are also applicable to empty fixed or demountable tanks, tank-containers and battery-vehicles, uncleaned and not degassed and empty bulk vehicles and empty bulk containers, uncleaned.

(13) Labels which do not relate to dangerous goods being carried, or residues thereof, shall be removed or covered.

**10 501-
10 502**

Parking in general

10 503 No transport unit carrying dangerous substances may be parked without the parking brakes being applied.

10 504

Parking at night or in poor visibility

10 505   (1)   If a vehicle is parked at night or in poor visibility and its lights are not working, the amber lights referred to in marginal 10 260 (c) shall be placed on the road,

-   one about 10 m ahead of the vehicle; and
-   the other about 10 m to the rear of the vehicle.

(2)   The provisions of this marginal shall not apply in the territory of the United Kingdom.

10 506

Parking of a vehicle constituting a special danger

10 507   Without prejudice to the measures prescribed in marginal 10 505 above, if the nature of the dangerous substances carried in the parked vehicle constitutes a source of special danger to road-users (e.g. in the event of substances dangerous to pedestrians, animals or vehicles spilling over the road) and the crew of the vehicle is unable to eliminate the danger quickly, the driver shall alert the nearest competent authorities, or cause them to be alerted, immediately. He shall also, where necessary, take the measures prescribed in the instructions provided for in marginal 10 385.

10 508-
10 598

Other provisions

10 599   (1)   Subject to the provisions of paragraph (2) below, a Contracting Party may apply to vehicles engaged in the international carriage of dangerous goods by road on its territory certain additional provisions not included in this Part or in Part II of this Annex, provided that those provisions do not conflict with Article 2, paragraph 2 of the Agreement, and are contained in its domestic legislation applying equally to vehicles engaged in the domestic carriage of dangerous goods by road on the territory of that Contracting Party.

(2)   Additional provisions falling within the scope of paragraph (1) above are as follows:

(a)   additional safety requirements or restrictions concerning vehicles using certain structures such as bridges or tunnels, vehicles using combined transport modes such as ferries or trains, or vehicles entering or leaving ports or other transport terminals;

(b)   requirements for vehicles to follow prescribed routes to avoid commercial or residential areas, environmentally sensitive areas, industrial zones containing hazardous installations or roads presenting severe physical hazards;

(c)   emergency requirements regarding routing or parking of vehicles carrying dangerous goods resulting from extreme weather conditions, earthquake, accident, industrial action, civil disorder or military hostilities;

(d)   restrictions on movement of dangerous goods traffic on certain days of the week or year.

**10 599
(contd)** (3)   The competent authority of the Contracting Party applying on its territory any additional provisions within the scope of paragraph 2 (a) and (d) above shall notify the competent service of the United Nations Secretariat of the additional provisions, which service shall bring them to the attention of the Contracting Parties.

SECTION 6.   **Transitional provisions, derogations, and provisions peculiar to certain countries**

**10 600-
10 601**

Rapid procedure for authorizing derogations for the purpose of trials

10 602   For the purpose of carrying out the trials necessary with a view to amending the provisions of this Annex in order to adapt them to technological and industrial developments, the competent authorities of the Contracting Parties may agree directly among themselves to authorize certain transport operations in their territories by temporary derogation from the provisions of this Annex. The period of validity of the temporary derogation shall be not more than five years from the date of its entry into force. Temporary derogations agreed before 1 January 1995 shall not be valid after 31 December 1998 unless renewed. The temporary derogation shall automatically come to an end from the date of the entry into force of a corresponding amendment to this annex. The authority which has taken the initiative with respect to the temporary derogation so granted shall notify the competent service of the United Nations Secretariat of the derogation, which service shall bring it to the attention of the Contracting Parties.

Derogations

10 603   The provisions laid down in this Annex do not apply:

(a)   to the carriage of dangerous goods by private individuals where the goods in question are packaged for retail sale and are intended for their personal or domestic use or for their leisure or sporting activities;

(b)   to the carriage of machinery or equipment not specified in Annex A and which happen to contain dangerous goods in their internal or operational equipment;

(c)   to carriage undertaken by enterprises which is ancillary to their main activity, such as deliveries to building or civil engineering sites, or in relation to surveying, repairs and maintenance, in quantities of not more than 450 litres per packaging and within the maximum quantities specified in marginal 10 011.

However, carriage undertaken by such enterprises for their supply or external or internal distribution does not fall within the scope of this exemption.

(d)   to carriage undertaken by, or under the supervision of, the intervention services, in particular by breakdown vehicles carrying vehicles which have been involved in accidents or have broken down and contain dangerous goods.

(e)   to emergency transport intended to save human lives or protect the environment provided that all measures are taken to ensure that such transport is carried out in complete safety.

Transitional Provisions

10 604   The substances and articles of ADR may be carried until 30 June 1997 in accordance with the requirements of this annex applicable until 31 December 1996. The transport document shall in such cases, bear the inscription **"Carriage in accordance with ADR in force before 1 January 1997"**.

10 605   Transport units intended for the carriage of tank-containers exceeding 3000 litres capacity first registered before 1 July 1997 which do not comply with the requirements of marginal 10 251 and 10 282 may continue to be used until 31 December 2004.

**10 606-
10 999**

PART II

SPECIAL PROVISIONS APPLICABLE TO THE CARRIAGE OF DANGEROUS SUBSTANCES OF CLASSES 1 TO 9 SUPPLEMENTING OR AMENDING THE REQUIREMENTS OF PART I

CLASS 1. EXPLOSIVE SUBSTANCES AND ARTICLES

General

(Only the general provisions of Part I apply)

11 000-
11 099

SECTION 1.   Mode of carriage

11 100-
11 107

Full loads

11 108   (1)   Substances and articles of Compatibility Group L shall only be carried as a full load.

(2)   When substances and articles of divisions 1.1, 1.2 or 1.5 are carried in large containers, such consignments may be carried only as a full load.

11 109-
11 117

Carriage in containers

11 118   Provided that small containers satisfy the requirements prescribed in respect of the body of the vehicle for the transport operation concerned, the body of the vehicle need not satisfy those requirements. However, small containers carried on vehicles whose platforms have insulation and heat-resistant qualities which satisfy those requirements need not satisfy the said requirements.

11 119-
11 199

SECTION 2.   Special requirements to be fulfilled by the means of transport and its equipment

11 200-
11 203

Types of vehicles

11 204   For the purpose of this Annex, transport units authorized to carry substances and articles of Class 1 are classified as follows:

(1)   "Type I" transport units:

These vehicles shall be either closed or sheeted. The sheet of a sheeted vehicle shall be of impermeable material not readily inflammable. It shall be tautened so as to cover the vehicle on all sides, with an overlap of not less than 20 cm down the sides of the vehicle, and be kept in position by a lockable device.

11 204   (2)   "Type II" transport units: whose engines shall use a liquid fuel with a flash point of 55 °C
(contd)   or above.

(a)   <u>General</u>

These vehicles shall be either closed or sheeted. The body shall be solidly constructed in such a manner that it adequately protects the goods carried. The loading surface, including the front wall, shall be continuous. If the vehicle is sheeted, the provisions relating to the sheeting on "Type I" transport units shall be met.

If the transport unit includes a trailer, this trailer shall have a coupling device which is quickly detachable and robust; and it shall be fitted with an effective braking device which acts on all the wheels, is actuated by the drawing vehicle's service-brake control and automatically stops the trailer in the event of breakage of the coupling.

(b)   <u>Engine and exhaust system</u>

The engine and the exhaust system shall comply with the requirements of marginals 220 533 and 220 534 of Appendix B.2.

(c)   <u>Fuel tank</u>

The fuel tank shall comply with the requirements of marginal 220 532 of Appendix B.2.

(d)   <u>Driver's Cab</u>

The material used in the construction of the driver's cab shall comply with the requirements of marginal 220 531 (1) of Appendix B.2.

Auxiliary heating appliances shall comply with the requirements of marginal 220 536 of Appendix B.2.

(3)   "Type III" transport units:

which possess all the characteristics of closed vehicles of "Type II" with bodies which also meet the following provisions:

(a)   The body shall be closed and have a continuous surface. It shall be solidly constructed of materials which are not readily inflammable, in such a manner that it adequately protects the goods carried. The materials used for the lining shall be incapable of producing sparks. The insulating and heat resisting properties of the body shall be at least equivalent to those of a partition consisting of a metal outer wall lined with a layer of fire-proofed wood of 10 mm thickness; or the body shall be of a construction which ensures that no flame penetration of the wall or hot spots of more than 120 °C on the inner wall surface will occur within 15 minutes from the start of a fire likely to occur from the operation of the vehicle.

(b)   All the doors shall be capable of being locked. They shall be so placed and constructed as to overlap the joints.

Class 1

Special requirements for the use of vehicles of certain types

11 205   (1)   Trailers, except semi-trailers, loaded with substances and articles of Class 1, and meeting the specifications required for transport units of Types II and III, may be drawn by motor vehicles which do not meet these specifications.

(2)   For carriage in containers the provisions of marginals 10 118 (3) and 11 118 shall apply. For free-flowing powdery substances of 2°, 4°, 8°, 26° and 29°, and for fireworks of 9°, 21° and 30°, the floor of a container shall have a non-metallic surface or covering.

(3)   Where substances or articles of Class 1 in quantities requiring a type III transport unit are being carried in containers to or from harbour areas, rail terminals or airports of arrival or departure as part of a multimodal journey, a type II transport unit may be used instead, provided that the containers being carried comply with the appropriate requirements of the IMDG Code, the RID or the ICAO Technical Instructions.

11 206-
11 209

Materials to be used in the construction of vehicle bodies

11 210   No materials likely to form dangerous compounds with the substances carried shall be used in the construction of the body [see also marginal 11 204 (3)].

11 211-
11 250

Electrical equipment

11 251   (1)   The rated voltage of the electric lighting system shall not exceed 24V.

(2)   Transport units of Types II and III shall meet the following requirements:

         (a)   Batteries shall be adequately secured and protected from damage due to collision and shall have their terminals protected by an electrically insulating cover.

         (b)   The installation of interior lighting in the load-carrying compartment shall be dust-tight (at least IP54 or equivalent) or, in the case of Compatibility Group J, flame-proof Ex d (at least IP65 or equivalent). The switch shall be located on the outside.

11 252-
11 259

Other equipment

11 260   (1)   The equipment mentioned in marginal 10 260 (d) iii) is not necessary.

(2)   The equipment mentioned in marginal 10 260 (d) i) is not necessary except:

        -     two warning vests
        -     two handlamps

11 261-
11 281

Class 1

Approval of vehicles

11 282   The requirements of marginal 10 282 are applicable to Type II and Type III transport units.

11 283-
11 299

SECTION 3.   General service provisions

11 300-
11 310

Vehicle crews

11 311   (1)   A driver's assistant shall be carried on every transport unit. If the national regulations so provide, the competent authority of a country party to ADR may require an approved official to be carried in the vehicle at the carrier's expense.

(2)   The first sentence of paragraph (1) does not apply to convoys of more than two vehicles if the drivers of the first and last vehicles of the convoy are accompanied by an assistant.

(3)   The presence of a driver's assistant on board shall not be required in the case of articles of 43°, identification No. 0336, carried in a type I transport unit.

11 312-
11 314

Special training of drivers

11 315   (1)   Irrespective of the permissible maximum weight of the vehicle, the requirements of marginal 10 315 apply to drivers of vehicles carrying substances or articles of Class 1.

(2)   Drivers of vehicles carrying substances or articles of Class 1 shall attend a specialization training course covering at least the subjects defined in marginal 240 104 of Appendix B.4.

(3)   If according to other regulations applicable in the country of a Contracting Party a driver has followed approved equivalent training under a different regime or for a different purpose, covering the subjects referred to in paragraph (2), the specialization course may be, partially or totally, dispensed with.

11 316-
11 320

Supervision of vehicles

11 321   The requirements of marginal 10 321 shall be applicable only when substances and articles of Class 1 having a total mass of explosive substance of more than 50 kg are carried in a vehicle. In addition, these substances and articles shall be supervised at all times in order to prevent any malicious act and to alert the driver and the competent authorities in the event of loss or fire. Empty packagings of 51° are exempted.

11 322-
11 353

Class 1

Prohibition of fire and naked flame

11 354 The use of fire or naked flame shall be prohibited on vehicles carrying substances and articles of Class 1, in their vicinity and during the loading and unloading of these substances and articles.

11 355-
11 399

SECTION 4. **Special provisions concerning loading, unloading and handling**

11 400

Limitation of the quantities carried

11 401 The total net mass in kg of explosive substance (or in the case of explosive articles, the total net mass of explosive substance contained in all the articles combined) which may be carried on one transport unit shall be limited as indicated in the table below (see also marginal 11 403 as regards the prohibition of mixed loading):

Maximum permissible net mass in kg of explosive in Class 1 goods per transport unit

Division Item	1.1		1.2	1.3	1.4		1.5 and 1.6	
Transport Unit	01°	1°-12°	13°-25°	26°-34°	35°-45°	46°, 47°	48°, 49°, 50°	51°
Type I	1.25	50	50	50	300*/	Unlimited	50	Unlimited
Type II	6.25	1 000	3 000	5 000	15 000	Unlimited	5 000	Unlimited
Type III	18.75	15 000	15 000	15 000	15 000	Unlimited	15 000	Unlimited

*/ *Identification Number 0336: 3 000 kg (4 000 kg for a transport unit with a trailer).*

11 402 Where substances and articles of different divisions of Class 1 are loaded on one transport unit in conformity with the prohibitions of mixed loading contained in 11 403, the load as a whole shall be treated as if it belonged to the most dangerous division (in the order 1.1, 1.5, 1.2, 1.3, 1.6, 1.4).

Where substances of 48° are carried in one transport unit together with substances or articles of division 1.2, the entire load shall be treated for carriage as if it belonged to division 1.1.

Prohibitions on mixed loading

11 403 (1) Packages bearing a label conforming to models Nos. 1, 1.4, 1.5 or 1.6 but which are assigned to different compatibility groups shall not be loaded together on one vehicle, unless mixed loading of the corresponding compatibility groups is authorized in the following table:

Compatibility group	A	B	C	D	E	F	G	H	J	L	N	S
A	X											
B		X		1/								X
C		X	X	X	X		X				2/, 3/	X
D		1/	X	X	X		X				2/, 3/	X
E			X	X	X		X				2/, 3/	X
F						X						X
G			X	X	X		X					X
H								X				X
J									X			X
L										4/		
N			2/, 3/	2/, 3/	2/, 3/						2/	X
S		X	X	X	X	X	X	X			X	X

X = mixed loading authorized

(2) Packages bearing a label conforming to models Nos. 1, 1.4 (except for compatibility group S), 1.5 or 1.6 shall not be loaded together in one vehicle with packages bearing a label conforming to models Nos. 2, 3, 4.1, 4.2, 4.3, 5.1, 5.2, 6.1, 6.2, 7A, 7B, 7C, 8 or 9.

11 404

Prohibition of mixed loading with goods contained in a container

11 405   (1)   The prohibitions of mixed loading of goods laid down in marginal 11 403 shall apply within each container.

1/   Packages containing articles of compatibility group B and substances and articles of compatibility group D may be loaded together on one vehicle provided they are carried in separate containers/ compartments of a design approved by the competent authority or a body designated by it, such that there is no danger of transmission of detonation from the articles of compatibility group B to the substances or articles of compatibility group D.

2/   Different types of 1.6N articles may be transported together as 1.6N articles only when it is proven by testing or analogy that there is no additional risk of sympathetic detonation between the articles. Otherwise they should be treated as hazard division 1.1.

3/   When articles of compatibility group N are carried with substances or articles of compatibility groups C, D or E, the articles of compatibility group N should be considered as having the characteristics of compatibility group D.

4/   Packages containing substances and articles of Compatibility Group L may be loaded together on one vehicle with packages containing the same type of substances and articles of that compatibility group.

11 405
(contd) (2)   The provisions of marginal 11 403 shall apply as between the dangerous goods contained in a container and the other dangerous goods loaded on the same vehicle, whether or not the latter goods are enclosed in one or more other containers.

11 406

Places of loading and unloading

11 407 (1)   The following operations are prohibited:

    (a)   Loading or unloading substances and articles of Class 1 in a public place in a built-up area without special permission from the competent authorities;

    (b)   Loading or unloading substances and articles of Class 1 in a public place elsewhere than in a built-up area without prior notice thereof having been given to the competent authorities, unless these operations are urgently necessary for reasons of safety.

    (2)   If, for any reason, handling operations have to be carried out in a public place, then substances and articles of different kinds shall be separated according to the labels.

11 408-
11 412

Cleaning before loading

11 413   Before substances and articles of Class 1 are loaded, the loading surface of the vehicle shall be thoroughly cleaned.

11 414-
11 499

SECTION 5.   **Special provisions concerning the operation of vehicles and containers**

Marking and labelling

Labelling

11 500 (1)   In addition to the provisions of marginal 10 500, transport units carrying packages or articles bearing labels conforming to models Nos. 1, 1.4, 1.5 or 1.6 shall bear a similar label on both sides and at the rear. Compatibility groups shall not be indicated on labels if the transport unit is carrying substances and articles belonging to several compatibility groups.

    (2)   A transport unit carrying substances or articles of different divisions shall bear only labels conforming to the model of the most dangerous division, in the order:

    1.1 (most dangerous), 1.5, 1.2, 1.3, 1.6, 1.4 (least dangerous). When substances of 48° are carried with substances or articles of division 1.2, the transport unit shall be labelled as division 1.1.

11 500
(contd)

(3)   Transport units carrying substances or articles of the following items and identification numbers shall in addition bear labels conforming to model No. 6.1:

01° No. 0224
4° Nos. 0076 and 0143
21° No. 0018
26° No. 0077
30° No. 0019
43° No. 0301.

(4)   Transport units carrying articles of the following items and identification numbers shall in addition bear labels conforming to model No. 8:

21° Nos. 0015 and 0018
30° Nos. 0016 and 0019
43° No. 0301 and 0303.

(5)   The provisions of paragraphs (1) to (4) shall not apply to transport units carrying containers providing the containers are labelled in accordance with the requirements of marginal 10 500 (9).

(6)   If the size and construction of the vehicle are such that the available surface area is insufficient to affix the labels prescribed in paragraphs (1) to (4), their dimensions may be reduced to 100 mm on each side.

11 501-
11 508

Halts for operational requirements

11 509   When vehicles carrying substances and articles of Class 1 are obliged to stop for loading or unloading operations in a public place, a distance of at least 50 m shall be maintained between the stationary vehicles.

11 510-
11 519

Convoys

11 520   (1)   When vehicles carrying substances and articles of Class 1 travel in convoy, a distance of not less than 50 m shall be maintained between each transport unit and the next.

(2)   The competent authority may lay down rules for the order or composition of convoys.

11 521-
11 599

SECTION 6.   **Transitional provisions, derogations and provisions peculiar to certain countries**

(Only the general provisions of Part I apply)

11 600-
20 999

CLASS 2. GASES

General

(Only the general provisions of Part I apply)

21 000-
21 099

SECTION 1.   **Mode of carriage**

21 100-
21 117

Carriage in containers

21 118   The carriage in small containers of packages containing gases of 3° is prohibited.

21 119-
21 199

SECTION 2.   **Special requirements to be fulfilled by the means of transport and its equipment**

21 200-
21 211

Ventilation

21 212   If packages containing gases of 1°, 2°, 3° or 1001 acetylene dissolved of 4°F are carried in a closed vehicle, the vehicle shall be provided with adequate ventilation.

21 213-
21 259

Special equipment

21 260   (1)   When gases or articles designated with letters T, TO, TF, TC, TFC, TOC are being carried, the crew of the vehicle shall be provided with gas-masks enabling them to escape without being affected by dangerous emanations in case of emergency.

(2)   The equipment mentioned in marginal 10 260 (d) iii) is not necessary.

21 261-
21 299

SECTION 3.   **General service provisions**

21 300-
21 320

Supervision of vehicles

21 321   The provisions of marginal 10 321 apply to the dangerous goods listed below in quantities exceeding those specified:

Substances of 1° other than 1°A, 1°O and 1°F; substances of 2° other than 2°A, 2°O and 2°F; and substances of 3°F: 1000 kg;

Substances of 2°F, 3°A and 3°O: 10 000 kg.

21 322-
21 399

SECTION 4.   **Special provisions concerning loading, unloading and handling**

21 400-
21 402

Prohibition of mixed loading on one vehicle

21 403   Packages bearing a label conforming to models Nos. 2, 3 or 6.1 shall not be loaded together on the same vehicle with packages bearing a label conforming to models Nos. 1, 1.4 (except for compatibility group S), 1.5, 1.6 or 01.

21 404-
21 413

Handling and stowage

21 414   (1)   Packages shall not be thrown or subjected to impact.

(2)   Receptacles shall be so stowed in the vehicle that they cannot overturn or fall and that the following requirements are met:

         (a)   The cylinders referred to in marginal 2211 (1) shall be laid parallel to or at right angles to the longitudinal axis of the vehicle; however, those situated near the forward transverse wall shall be laid at right angles to the said axis.

             Short cylinders of large diameter (about 30 cm and over) may be stowed longitudinally with their valve-protecting devices directed towards the middle of the vehicle.

             Cylinders which are sufficiently stable or are carried in suitable devices effectively preventing them from overturning may be placed upright.

             Cylinders which are laid flat shall be securely and appropriately wedged, attached or secured so that they cannot shift.

21 414
(contd)

(b) Receptacles containing gases of 3° shall always be placed in the position for which they were designed and be protected against any possibility of being damaged by other packages.

21 415-
21 499

SECTION 5. Special provisions concerning the operation of (tank-)vehicles and (tank-)containers

Marking and labelling of vehicles

Labelling

21 500 Vehicles with fixed or demountable tanks, tank-containers and battery-vehicles containing or having contained (empty, uncleaned) substances of Class 2 shall bear the label(s) indicated below:

Substances of the various items which have been classified under the following groups	Label model nos.
A	2
O	2 + 05
F	3
T	6.1
TF	6.1 + 3
TC	6.1 + 8
TO	6.1 + 05
TFC	6.1 + 3 + 8
TOC	6.1 + 05 + 8

21 501-
21 599

SECTION 6. Transitional provisions, derogations and provisions peculiar to certain countries

(Only the general provisions of Part I apply)

21 600-
30 999

CLASS 3. FLAMMABLE LIQUIDS

General

(Only the general provisions of Part I apply)

**31 000-
31 099**

SECTION 1.   **Mode of carriage**

(Only the general provisions of Part I apply).

**31 100-
31 199**

SECTION 2.   **Special requirements to be fulfilled by the means of transport and its equipment**

(Only the general provisions of Part I apply)

**31 200-
31 299**

SECTION 3.   **General service provisions**

**31 300-
31 320**

Supervision of vehicles

31 321   The provisions of marginal 10 321 shall apply to the dangerous goods listed below in quantities exceeding those specified:

Substances of 1° to 5° (a) and (b), 7° (b), 21° to 26° and slightly toxic substances of 41°: 10 000 kg

Substances of 6° and 11° to 19°, 27°, 28°, and toxic or very toxic substances of 41°: 5 000 kg.

**31 322-
31 399**

SECTION 4.   **Special provisions concerning loading, unloading and handling**

**31 400-
31 402**

Prohibition of mixed loading on one vehicle

31 403   Packages bearing a label conforming to model No. 3 shall not be loaded together on the same vehicle with packages bearing a label conforming to models Nos. 1, 1.4 (except for compatibility group S), 1.5, 1.6 or 01.

**31 404-
31 414**

Cleaning after unloading

31 415 If any substances of 6° and 11° to 19°, 27°, 28°, 32° and the toxic or very toxic substances of 41° have leaked and been spilled in a vehicle, it may not be re-used until after it has been thoroughly cleaned and, if necessary, decontaminated. Any other goods and articles carried in the same vehicle shall be examined for possible contamination.

31 416-
31 499

SECTION 5. Special provisions concerning the operation of (tank-)vehicles and (tank-)containers

Marking and labelling

Labelling

31 500 (1) Vehicles with fixed or demountable tanks and tank-containers containing or having contained (empty, uncleaned) substances of this Class shall bear labels conforming to model No. 3.

Those containing or having contained the substances of this Class listed in marginal 2312 (3) to (5) shall also bear labels in accordance with that marginal.

(2) It is unnecessary to affix the orange-coloured plates prescribed in marginal 10 500 (2) to multi-compartment tank vehicles carrying two or more substances with identification numbers 1202, 1203 or 1223, but no other dangerous substance, if the plates affixed at the front and rear, in accordance with marginal 10 500 (1) bear the identification numbers prescribed in Appendix B.5 for the most hazardous substance carried, i.e., the substance with the lowest flashpoint.

31 501-
31 599

SECTION 6. Transitional provisions, derogations, and provisions peculiar to certain countries

(Only the general provisions of Part I apply)

31 600-
40 999

CLASS 4.1. FLAMMABLE SOLIDS

General

(Only the general provisions of Part I apply)

41 000-
41 099

SECTION 1.   Mode of carriage

41 100-
41 104

Method of dispatch and restrictions on forwarding

41 105   (1)   Substances of 5° and 15° may be carried only in tank-vehicles, demountable tanks and tank-containers.

(2)   Substances of 26° shall be shielded from direct sunlight and heat during carriage.

(3)   Substances of 41° to 50° shall be forwarded so that the control temperatures indicated in marginal 2400 (20), given for listed substances in marginal 2401 and for non-listed substances in the approved conditions of carriage [see marginal 2400 (16)], are not exceeded.

(4)   Maintenance of the prescribed temperature is essential for the safe carriage of many self-reactive substances. In general, there shall be:

-   thorough inspection of the transport unit prior to loading;

-   instructions to the carrier about the operation of the refrigeration system, including a list of the suppliers of coolant available en route;

-   procedures to be followed in the event of loss of control;

-   regular monitoring of operating temperatures; and

-   provision of a back-up refrigeration system or spare parts.

(5)   Any control and temperature sensing devices in the refrigeration system shall be readily accessible and all electrical connections weather-proof. The temperature of the air space within the transport unit shall be measured by two independent sensors and the output shall be so recorded that temperature changes are readily detectable. The temperature shall be checked every four to six hours and logged. When substances having a control temperature of less than +25° C are carried, the transport unit shall be equipped with visible and audible alarms, powered independently of the refrigeration system, set to operate at or below the control temperature.

(6)   If the control temperature is exceeded during carriage, an alert procedure shall be initiated involving any necessary repairs to the refrigeration equipment or an increase in the cooling capacity (e.g. by adding liquid or solid coolant). There shall also be frequent checking of the temperature and preparations for implementation of the emergency procedures. If the emergency temperature (see also marginals 2400 (20) and 2401) is reached, the emergency procedures shall be set in operation.

41 105 (contd) (7) The suitability of a particular means of temperature control for carriage depends on a number of factors. Amongst those to be considered are:

- the control temperature(s) of the substance(s) to be carried;

- the difference between the control temperature and the anticipated ambient temperature conditions;

- the effectiveness of the thermal insulation;

- the duration of carriage; and

- allowance of a safety margin for delays.

(8) Suitable methods for preventing the control temperature being exceeded are, in order of increasing capability:

(a) thermal insulation; provided that the initial temperature of the self-reactive substance(s) is sufficiently below the control temperature;

(b) thermal insulation and coolant system; provided that:

- an adequate quantity of non-flammable coolant (e.g. liquid nitrogen or solid carbon dioxide), allowing a reasonable margin for delay, is carried or the possibility of replenishment is assured;

- liquid oxygen or air is not used as coolant;

- there is a uniform cooling effect even when most of the coolant has been consumed; and

- the need to ventilate the transport unit before entering is clearly indicated by a warning on the door(s);

(c) thermal insulation and single mechanical refrigeration; provided that flameproof electrical fittings are used within the coolant compartment to prevent ignition of flammable vapours from the self-reactive substances.

(d) thermal insulation and combined mechanical refrigeration system and coolant system; provided that:

- the two systems are independent of one another; and

- the requirements (b) and (c) are met;

(e) thermal insulation and dual mechanical refrigeration system provided that:

- apart from the integral power supply unit, the two systems are independent of one another;

- each system alone is capable of maintaining adequate temperature control; and

- flameproof electrical fittings are used within the coolant compartment to prevent ignition of flammable vapours from the self-reactive substances.

41 105
(contd)
(9)   For substances of 41° and 42°, one of the following methods of temperature control described in paragraph (8) shall be used:

-   method (c) when the maximum ambient temperature to be expected during carriage does not exceed the control temperature by more than 10 °C; or

-   method (d) or (e).

For substances of 43° to 50°, one of the following methods shall be used:

-   method (a) when the maximum ambient temperature to be expected during carriage is at least 10 °C below the control temperature;

-   method (b) when the maximum ambient temperature to be expected during carriage does not exceed the control temperature by more than 30 °C; or

-   method (c), (d) or (e).

41 106-
41 110

Carriage in bulk

41 111
(1)   Solid substances and mixtures (such as preparations and wastes) of 6° (c), with the exception of naphthalene, 11° (c), 12° (c), 13° (c) and 14° (c) may be carried in bulk in closed or sheeted vehicles.

Naphthalene of 6° (c) may be carried in bulk in closed vehicles with a metal body or in vehicles covered with a non-combustible sheet and having a metal body or having floor and walls protected from the load.

(2)   Waste of 4° (c) may be carried in bulk in open but sheeted vehicles with adequate ventilation. Suitable measures shall be taken to ensure that none of the contents, particularly liquid components, can escape.

41 112-
41 117

Carriage in containers

41 118
Small containers used for the carriage in bulk of substances mentioned in marginal 41 111 shall meet the requirements for vehicles in that marginal.

41 119-
41 199

SECTION 2.   **Special requirements to be fulfilled by the means of transport and its equipment**

41 200-
41 203

Types of vehicle

41 204
Substances of 31° to 40° shall be loaded in closed or sheeted vehicles. Where, under the provisions of 41 105, substances are required to be carried in insulated, refrigerated or mechanically-refrigerated vehicles, those vehicles shall satisfy the provisions of 41 248.

41 204
(contd) Substances of 41° to 50° contained in protective packagings filled with a coolant shall be loaded in closed or sheeted vehicles. If the vehicles used are closed they shall be adequately ventilated. Sheeted vehicles shall be fitted with side boards and a tail-board. The sheets of these vehicles shall be of an impermeable and non-combustible material.

41 205-
41 247

Insulated, refrigerated and mechanically-refrigerated vehicles

41 248 Insulated, refrigerated and mechanically-refrigerated vehicles used in accordance with the provisions of 41 105 shall conform to the following conditions:

    (a)   the vehicle shall be such and so equipped as regards its insulation and means of refrigeration (see marginal 41 105) that the maximum temperature prescribed in 41 105 is not exceeded. The overall heat transfer coefficient shall be not more than 0.4 W/m^2 K;

    (b)   the vehicle shall be so equipped that vapours from the substances or the coolant carried cannot penetrate into the driver's cab;

    (c)   a suitable device shall be provided enabling the temperature prevailing in the loading space to be determined at any time from the cab;

    (d)   the loading space shall be provided with vents or ventilating valves if there is any risk of a dangerous excess pressure arising therein. Care shall be taken where necessary to ensure that refrigeration is not impaired by the vents or ventilating valves;

    (e)   the refrigerant shall not be flammable; and

    (f)   the refrigerating appliance of a mechanically- refrigerated vehicle shall be capable of operating independently of the engine used to propel the vehicle.

41 249-
41 299

SECTION 3.   **General service provisions**

41 300-
41 320

Supervision of vehicles

41 321 The provisions of 10 321 shall apply to the dangerous goods listed below in quantities exceeding those specified:

-	substances of 21° to 25°:	1 000 kg
-	substances of 26°:	100 kg
-	substances of 31°, 32°, 43° and 44°:	1 000 kg
-	substances of 33°, 34°, 45° and 46°:	2 000 kg
-	substances of 35°, 36°, 47° and 48°:	5 000 kg
-	substances of 41° and 42°:	500 kg.

In addition, vehicles carrying more than 500 kg of substances of 41° and 42° shall be subject at all times to supervision to prevent any malicious act and to alert the driver and competent authorities in the event of loss or fire.

41 322-
41 399

Class 4.1

SECTION 4. **Special provisions concerning loading, unloading and handling**

41 400

Limitation of the quantity carried

41 401 (1) A transport unit shall carry not more than:

- 5 000 kg of substances of 31° and 32° if its loading space is ventilated at the top and the transport unit is insulated with heat-resistant material [see marginal 11 204 (3) (a)] or 1 000 kg of substances of 31° and 32° if the transport unit does not meet these requirements;

- 10 000 kg of substances of 33° and 34°;

- 20 000 kg of substances of 35°, 36°, 37°, 38°, 39° and 40°;

- 1 000 kg of substances of 41° and 42° or 5 000 kg if insulated with heat-resistant material;

- 5 000 kg of substances of 43° and 44° or 10 000 kg if insulated with heat-resistant material; and

- 20 000 kg of substances of 45°, 46°, 47°, 48°, 49° and 50°.

(2) When substances of this Class are carried together in one transport unit, the limits given in paragraph (1) shall not be exceeded and the total contents shall not exceed 20 000 kg.

41 402 The provisions of marginals 10 500 and 41 204 shall not apply to the carriage of substances listed in or covered by 31° to 34° and 41° to 44° provided that the substance is packaged in accordance with packing method OP1 or OP2, as required, and the quantity per transport unit is limited to 10 kg.

Prohibition on mixed loading on one vehicle

41 403 (1) Packages bearing a label conforming to model No. 4.1 shall not be loaded together on one vehicle with packages bearing a label conforming to models Nos. 1, 1.4 (except for compatibility group S), 1.5, 1.6 or 01.

(2) Packages bearing labels conforming to models Nos. 4.1 and 01 shall not be loaded together in the same vehicle with packages bearing a label conforming to models Nos. 1, 1.4, 1.5, 1.6, 2, 3, 4.2, 4.3, 5.1, 5.2, 6.1, 7A, 7B, 7C, 8 or 9.

41 404-
41 413

Handling and stowage

41 414 (1) Packages containing substances of 26° shall be stored only in cool, well-ventilated places away from heat sources.

(2) Packages containing substances of 41° to 50° shall not be placed on top of other goods; in addition, they shall be so stowed as to be readily accessible.

**41 414
(contd)**   (3)   For packages containing substances of 41° to 50°, the specified control temperature shall be maintained during the whole transport operation, including loading and unloading, as well as any intermediate stops [see marginal 41 105 (2)].

(4)   Packages shall be loaded so that a free circulation of air within the loading space provides a uniform temperature of the load. If the contents of one vehicle or large container exceed 5 000 kg of flammable solids, the load shall be divided into stacks of not more than 5 000 kg separated by air spaces of at least 0.05 m.

**41 415-
41 499**

SECTION 5.   **Special provisions concerning the operation of (tank-)vehicles and (tank-)containers**

Marking and labelling

Labelling

41 500   Vehicles with fixed or demountable tanks and tank-containers, as well as vehicles and containers for the carriage of dangerous solid substances in bulk, containing or having contained (empty, uncleaned) substances of this Class shall bear labels conforming to model No. 4.1.

Those containing or having contained the substances of this Class listed in marginal 2412 (3) shall also bear labels in accordance with that marginal.

**41 501-
41 508**

Halts of limited duration for service requirements

41 509   During the carriage of substances of 31°, 32°, 41° and 42°, stops for service requirements shall as far as possible not be made near inhabited places or frequented places. A longer stop near such places is permissible only with the consent of the competent authorities. The same rule shall apply if a transport unit is loaded with more than 2 000 kg of substances of 33°, 34°, 43° and 44°.

**41 510-
41 599**

SECTION 6.   **Transitional provisions, derogations and provisions peculiar to certain countries**

(Only the general provisions of Part I apply)

**41 600-
41 999**

CLASS 4.2. SUBSTANCES LIABLE TO SPONTANEOUS COMBUSTION

General

(Only the general provisions of Part I apply)

42 000-
42 099

SECTION 1. Mode of carriage

42 100
42 104

Method of dispatch and restrictions on forwarding

42 105 Phosphorus of 22° may be carried only in tank-vehicles, demountable tanks and tank-containers.

42 106-
42 110

Carriage in bulk

42 111 Substances of 1° (c), 2° (c), 3°, borings, shavings, turnings and cuttings of ferrous metals of 12° (c), spent iron oxide and spent iron sponge of 16° (c) and solid wastes classified under (c) of the above-mentioned items, may be carried in bulk.

These substances shall, however, be carried in closed or sheeted vehicles with a metal body.

42 112-
42 117

Carriage in containers

42 118 Small containers used for the carriage in bulk of substances mentioned in marginal 42 111 shall meet the requirements for vehicles in that marginal.

42 119-
42 199

SECTION 2. Special requirements to be fulfilled by the means of transport and its equipment

42 200-
42 203

Types of vehicle

42 204 Packages containing substances of Class 4.2 shall be carried in closed or sheeted vehicles.

42 205-
42 299

SECTION 3. General service provisions

42 300-
42 320

Supervision of vehicles

42 321 The provisions of marginal 10 321 shall apply to the dangerous goods listed below when their quantity exceeds the mass indicated:

Substances classified under (a) of the various items and substances of 22°: 10 000 kg.

- 51 -

42 322-
42 377

       Empty tanks

42 378   For tanks which have contained phosphorus of 11° (a) and 22°, see also marginals 211 470 (2) and 212 470 (2).

42 379-
42 399

       SECTION 4.   **Special provisions concerning loading, unloading and handling**

42 400-
42 402

       Prohibition of mixed loading on one vehicle

42 403   Packages bearing a label conforming to model No. 4.2 shall not be loaded together on one vehicle with packages bearing a label conforming to models Nos. 1, 1.4 (except for compatibility group S), 1.5, 1.6 or 01.

42 404-
42 999

       SECTION 5.   **Special provisions concerning the operation of tank-vehicles and tank-containers**

       Marking and labelling

       Labelling

42 500   Vehicles with fixed or demountable tanks and tank-containers, as well as vehicles and containers for the carriage of dangerous solid substances in bulk, containing or having contained (empty, uncleaned) substances of this Class shall bear labels conforming to model No. 4.2.

       Those containing or having contained the substances of this Class listed in marginal 2442 (3) to (5) shall also bear labels in accordance with that marginal.

42 501-
42 599

       SECTION 6.   **Transitional provisions, derogations and provisions peculiar to certain countries**

       (Only the general provisions of Part I apply)

42 600-
42 999

CLASS 4.3. SUBSTANCES WHICH, IN CONTACT WITH WATER, EMIT FLAMMABLE GASES

General

(Only the general provisions of Part I apply)

43 000-
43 099

SECTION 1. Mode of carriage

43 100-
43 110

Carriage in bulk

43 111 (1) Solid substances and mixtures (such as preparations and wastes) of 11° (c), 12° (c), 13° (c), 14° (c), 17° (b) and 20° (c) may be carried in bulk in specially equipped vehicles. The openings used for loading and unloading shall be capable of being closed hermetically.

(2) Aluminium smelting by-products or aluminium remelting by-products of 13° (b) may be carried in bulk in well-ventilated sheeted vehicles.

(3) Aluminium smelting by-products or aluminium remelting by-products of 13° (c), ferrosilicon of 15° (c), calcium silicide in pieces of 12° (b) and substances of 12° (c) in pieces may also be carried in bulk in sheeted or closed vehicles.

43 112-
43 117

Carriage in containers

43 118 Small containers used for the carriage in bulk of substances mentioned in marginal 43 111 shall meet the requirements for vehicles in that marginal.

43 119-
43 199

SECTION 2. Special requirements to be fulfilled by the means of transport and its equipment

43 200-
43 203

Types of vehicle

43 204 Packages containing substances or articles of Class 4.3 shall be loaded in closed or sheeted vehicles.

43 205-
43 259

Other equipment

43 260 In addition to the equipment mentioned in marginal 10 260 a plastic sheet of at least 2 × 3 m shall be carried on board the transport unit.

43 261-
43 299

SECTION 3.   **General service provisions**

43 300-
43 320

Supervision of vehicles

43 321   The provisions of marginal 10 321 shall apply to the dangerous goods listed below when their quantity exceeds the mass indicated:

Substances classified under (a) of the various items: 10 000 kg.

43 322-
43 399

SECTION 4.   **Special provisions concerning loading, unloading and handling**

43 400-
43 402

Prohibition of mixed loading on one vehicle

43 403   Packages bearing a label conforming to model No. 4.3 shall not be loaded together on one vehicle with packages bearing a label conforming to models Nos. 1, 1.4 (except for compatibility group S), 1.5, 1.6 or 01.

43 404-
43 413

Handling and stowage

43 414   While packages are being handled, special measures shall be taken to prevent them from coming into contact with water.

43 415-
43 499

SECTION 5.   **Special provisions concerning the operation of (tank-)vehicles and (tank-)containers**

Marking and labelling

Labelling

43 500   Vehicles with fixed or demountable tanks and tank-containers, as well as vehicles and containers for the carriage of dangerous solid substances in bulk, containing or having contained (empty, uncleaned) substances of this Class shall bear labels conforming to model No. 4.3.

Those containing or having contained the substances of this Class listed in marginal 2482 (3) to (7) shall also bear labels in accordance with that marginal.

43 501-
43 599

SECTION 6.   **Transitional provisions, derogations, and provisions peculiar to certain countries**

(Only the general provisions of Part I apply)

43 600-
50 999

CLASS 5.1. OXIDIZING SUBSTANCES

General

(Only the general provisions of Part I apply)

**51 000-
51 099**

SECTION 1.   Mode of carriage

**51 100-
51 104**

Method of dispatch and restrictions on forwarding

51 105   Ammonium nitrate of 20° may be carried only in tank-vehicles, demountable tanks and tank-containers.

**51 106-
51 110**

Carriage in bulk

51 111   (1)   Substances of 11° to 13°, 16°, 18°, 21°, 22° (c) and solid wastes, classified under the above-mentioned items may be carried in bulk as a full load.

(2)   Substances of 11° to 13°, 16°, 18°, 21°, 22° (c) and solid wastes classified under the above-mentioned items shall be carried in closed vehicles or sheeted vehicles covered with an impermeable non-combustible sheet. Vehicles shall be so constructed either that the substance cannot come into contact with wood or any other combustible material or that the entire surface of the floor and walls, if combustible, has been provided with an impermeable and incombustible surfacing or treated with substances rendering the wood difficult to ignite.

**51 112-
51 117**

Carriage in containers

51 118   (1)   With the exception packages containing hydrogen peroxide or solutions of hydrogen peroxide of 1° (a) or tetranitromethane of 2°, packages containing substances listed in this Class may be carried in small containers.

(2)   Containers intended for the carriage in bulk of substances of 11° to 13°, 16° and 18° shall be made of metal, be leakproof, be covered with a lid or an impermeable sheet resistant to combustion, and be so constructed that the substances in the containers cannot come into contact with wood or any other combustible material.

(3)   Containers intended for the carriage in bulk of substances of 21° and 22° (c) shall be covered with a lid or an impermeable non-combustible sheet and be so constructed either that the substance in the containers cannot come into contact with wood or any other combustible material or that the entire surface of the floor and walls, if made of wood, has been provided with an impermeable surfacing resistant to combustion or has been coated with sodium silicate or a similar substance.

**51 119-
51 199**

SECTION 2.   Special requirements to be fulfilled by the means of transport and its equipment

**51 200-
51 203**

Types of vehicle

51 204   Flexible IBCs containing substances of 11° to 13° and 16° (b) shall be carried in closed or sheeted vehicles. The sheet shall be of an impermeable and non-combustible material. Steps shall be taken to ensure that, if a leakage occurs, the substances contained in the vehicle cannot come into contact with wood or any other combustible material.

**51 205-
51 219**

Vehicles used for the carriage of dangerous goods in fixed or demountable tanks, or tank-containers of a capacity greater than 3000 litres

51 220   For carriage of liquids of 1° (a):

(1)   The provisions of marginals 220 531 (2), 220 532 and 220 533 of Appendix B.2 shall apply;

(2)   No wood, unless covered with metal or with a suitable synthetic material, shall be used in the construction of any part of the vehicle situated to the rear of the shield prescribed in marginal 220 531 (2).

**51 221-
51 259**

51 260   For the carriage of liquids of 1° (a), the vehicles shall be fitted with a tank placed as securely as possible and having a capacity of about 30 litres of water. An anti-freeze preparation which does not attack the skin or the mucous membranes and does not react chemically with the load shall be added to the water. Where the liquids are carried on a tank-vehicle trailer that may become separated from the motor vehicle, the water tank shall be placed on the trailer.

**51 261-
51 299**

SECTION 3.   General service provisions

**51 300-
51 320**

Supervision of vehicles

51 321   The provisions of marginal 10 321 shall apply to the dangerous goods listed below when their quantity exceeds the mass indicated:

Substances of 5° and substances classified under (a) of all other items: 10 000 kg.

**51 322-
51 399**

Class 5.1

SECTION 4.   Special provisions concerning loading, unloading and handling

51 400-
51 402

Prohibition of mixed loading on one vehicle

51 403   Packages bearing a label conforming to model No. 5.1 shall not be loaded together on one vehicle with packages bearing a label conforming to models Nos. 1, 1.4 (except for compatibility group S), 1.5, 1.6 or 01.

51 404-
51 413

Handling and stowage

51 414   The use of readily flammable materials for stowing packages in vehicles is prohibited.

51 415-
51 499

SECTION 5.   Special provisions concerning the operation of (tank-)vehicles and (tank-)containers

Marking and labelling

Labelling

51 500   Vehicles with fixed or demountable tanks and tank-containers, as well as vehicles and containers for the carriage of dangerous solid substances in bulk, containing or having contained (empty, uncleaned) substances of this Class shall bear labels conforming to model No. 5.1. Those containing or having contained the substances of this Class listed in marginal 2512 (3) shall also bear labels in accordance with that marginal.

51 501-
51 599

SECTION 6.   Transitional provisions, derogations, and provisions peculiar to certain countries

(Only the general provisions of Part I apply)

51 600-
51 999

CLASS 5.2. ORGANIC PEROXIDES

General

(Only the general provisions of Part I apply)

52 000-
52 099

SECTION 1.　　Mode of carriage

52 100-
52 104

Method of dispatch and restrictions on forwarding

52 105　(1)　Substances of 11° to 20° shall be forwarded in such manner that the control temperatures indicated in marginal 2550 (16) to (19), given for substances listed in marginal 2551 and for non-listed substances in the approved conditions of carriage [see marginal 2550 (8)], are never exceeded.

(2)　Maintenance of the prescribed temperature is essential for the safe carriage of many organic peroxides.　In general, there shall be:

-　thorough inspection of the transport unit prior to loading;

-　instructions to the carrier about the operation of the refrigeration system including a list of the suppliers of coolant available en route;

-　procedures to be followed in the event of loss of control;

-　regular monitoring of operating temperatures;　and

-　provision of a back-up refrigeration system or spare parts.

(3)　Any control and temperature sensing devices in the refrigeration system shall be readily accessible and all electrical connections shall be weather-proof.　The temperature of the air inside the transport unit shall be measured by two independent sensors and the output shall be recorded so that any change in temperature is readily detectable.　The temperature shall be checked every four to six hours and logged.　When substances having a control temperature of less than +25 °C are carried, the transport unit shall be equipped with visible and audible alarms, powered independently of the refrigeration system and set to operate at or below the control temperature.

(4)　If the control temperature is exceeded during carriage, an alert procedure shall be initiated involving any necessary repairs to the refrigeration equipment or an increase in the cooling capacity (e.g. by adding liquid or solid coolant).　There shall also be frequent checking of the temperature and preparations for implementation of the emergency procedures.　If the emergency temperature [see also marginals 2550 (17) and 2551] is reached, the emergency procedures shall be set in operation.

(5)　The means of temperature control chosen for the transport operation depends on a number of factors.　Amongst those to be considered are:

-　the control temperature(s) of the substance(s) to be carried;
-　the difference between the control temperature and the expected ambient temperature;
-　the effectiveness of the thermal insulation;
-　the duration of the transport operation;　and
-　the safety margin to be allowed for delays en route.

- 59 -

52 105 (6)   Suitable methods to prevent the control temperature from being exceeded are listed below,
(contd)   in ascending order of effectiveness:

(a)   thermal insulation; provided that the initial temperature of the organic peroxide(s) is sufficiently below the control temperature;

(b)   thermal insulation and coolant system; provided that:

-    an adequate quantity of non-flammable coolant (e.g. liquid nitrogen or solid carbon dioxide), allowing a reasonable margin for possible delay, is carried or a means of replenishment is assured;

-    liquid oxygen or air is not used as coolant;

-    there is a uniform cooling effect even when most of the coolant has been consumed; and

-    the need to ventilate the transport unit before entering is clearly indicated by a warning on the door(s);

(c)   thermal insulation and single mechanical refrigeration; provided that flameproof electrical fittings are used within the coolant compartment to prevent ignition of flammable vapours from the organic peroxides;

(d)   thermal insulation and combined mechanical refrigeration system and coolant system; provided that:

-    the two systems are independent of one another; and

-    the requirements in (b) and (c) are met;

(e)   thermal insulation and dual mechanical refrigeration system; provided that:

-    apart from the integral power supply unit, the two systems are independent of one another;

-    each system alone is capable of maintaining adequate temperature control; and

-    flameproof electrical fittings are used within the coolant compartment to prevent ignition of flammable vapours from the organic peroxides.

(7)   For substances of 11° and 12°, one of the following methods of temperature control described in paragraph (6) shall be used:

-    method (c) when the maximum ambient temperature to be expected during carriage does not exceed the control temperature by more than 10 °C; otherwise

-    (d) or (e).

52 105
(contd)

For substances of 13° to 20°, one of the following methods shall be used:

- method (a) when the maximum ambient temperature to be expected during carriage is at least 10 °C below the control temperature;

- method (b) when the maximum ambient temperature to be expected during carriage does not exceed the control temperature by more than 30 °C; otherwise

- method (c), (d) or (e).

52 106-
52 117

Carriage in containers

52 118   Packages containing substances of 1° or 2°, shall not be carried in small containers.

52 119-
52 199

SECTION 2.   **Special requirements to be fulfilled by the means of transport and its equipment**

52 200-
52 203

Types of vehicle

52 204   Substances of 1° to 10° shall be loaded in closed or sheeted vehicles. Where, under the provisions of 52 105, substances are required to be carried in insulated, refrigerated or mechanically-refrigerated vehicles, those vehicles shall satisfy the provisions of 52 248. Substances of 11° to 20° contained in protective packagings filled with a coolant shall be loaded in closed or sheeted vehicles. If the vehicles used are closed they shall be adequately ventilated. Sheeted vehicles shall be fitted with side boards and a tail-board. The sheets of these vehicles shall be of an impermeable and non-combustible material.

52 205-
52 247

Insulated, refrigerated and mechanically-refrigerated vehicles

52 248   Insulated, refrigerated and mechanically-refrigerated vehicles used in accordance with the provisions of 52 105 shall conform to the following conditions:

(a)   the vehicle shall be such and so equipped as regards its insulation and means of refrigeration (see marginal 52 105) that the maximum temperature prescribed in 52 105 is not exceeded. The overall heat transfer coefficient shall be not more than 0.4 W/m² K;

(b)   the vehicle shall be so equipped that vapours from the substances or the coolant carried cannot penetrate into the driver's cab;

(c)   a suitable device shall be provided enabling the temperature prevailing in the loading space to be determined at any time from the cab;

52 248
(contd)

(d)   the loading space shall be provided with vents or ventilating valves if there is any risk of a dangerous excess pressure arising therein. Care shall be taken where necessary to ensure that refrigeration is not impaired by the vents or ventilating valves;

(e)   the refrigerant shall not be flammable; and

(f)   the refrigerating appliance of a mechanically refrigerated vehicle shall be capable of operating independently of the engine used to propel the vehicle.

52 249-
52 299

SECTION 3.   General service provisions

52 300-
52 320

Supervision of vehicles

52 321   The provisions of 10 321 shall apply to the dangerous goods listed below when their quantity exceeds the mass indicated:

-     substances of 1°, 2°, 13° and 14°:   1 000 kg
-     substances of 3°, 4°, 15° and 16°:   2 000 kg
-     substances of 5°, 6°, 17° and 18°:   5 000 kg
-     substances of 11° and 12°:   500 kg

In addition, vehicles carrying more than 500 kg of substances of 11° and 12° shall be subject at all times to supervision to prevent any malicious act and to alert the driver and competent authorities in the event of loss or fire.

52 322-
52 399

SECTION 4.   Special provisions concerning loading, unloading and handling

52 400

Limitation of the quantities carried

52 401   (1)   A transport unit shall not carry more than:

-     5 000 kg of substances of 1° and 2° if its loading space is ventilated at the top and the transport unit is insulated with heat-resistant material [see marginal 11 204 (3)(a)], or 1 000 kg of substances of 1° and 2° if the transport unit does not meet these requirements;
-     10 000 kg of substances of 3° and 4°;
-     20 000 kg of substances of 5°, 6°, 7°, 8°, 9° and 10°;
-     1 000 kg of substances of 11° and 12°, or 5 000 kg if insulated with heat-resistant material;
-     5 000 kg of substances of 13° and 14°, or 10 000 kg if insulated with heat-resistant material; and
-     20 000 kg of substances of 15°, 16°, 17°, 18°, 19° and 20°.

Class 5.2

52 401
(contd)

(2)   When substances of this Class are loaded together in one transport unit, the limits given in paragraph (1) shall not be exceeded and the total contents shall not exceed 20 000 kg.

52 402   The provisions of marginals 10 500 and 52 204 shall not apply to the carriage of substances listed in or covered by 1° to 4° and 11° to 14° provided that the substance is packaged in accordance with packing method OP1 or OP2, as required, and the quantity per transport unit is limited to 10 kg.

Prohibition of mixed loading on one vehicle

52 403   (1)   Packages bearing a label conforming to model No. 5.2 shall not be loaded together in the same vehicle with packages bearing a label conforming to models Nos. 1, 1.4 (except for compatibility group S), 1.5, 1.6 or 01.

(2)   Packages bearing labels conforming to models Nos. 5.2 and 01 shall not be loaded together in the same vehicle with packages bearing a label conforming to models Nos. 1, 1.4, 1.5, 1.6, 2, 3, 4.1, 4.2, 4.3, 5.1, 6.1, 7A, 7B, 7C, 8 or 9.

52 404-
52 412

Cleaning before loading

52 413   Vehicles intended for the carriage of packages containing substances of Class 5.2 shall be carefully cleaned.

Handling and stowage

52 414   (1)   The use of readily flammable materials for stowing packages in vehicles is prohibited.

(2)   Packages containing substances of 11° to 20° shall be so stowed as to be readily accessible.

(3)   For packages containing substances of 11° to 20°, the control temperature shall be maintained during the whole transport operation, including loading and unloading, as well as any intermediate stops [see marginal 52 105 (1)].

(4)   Packages shall be loaded so that a free circulation of air within the loading space provides a uniform temperature of the load. If the contents of a vehicle or large container exceed 5 000 kg of organic peroxide, the load shall be divided into stacks of not more than 5 000 kg separated by air spaces of at least 0.05 m.

52 415-
52 499

SECTION 5.   **Special provisions concerning the operation of (tank-)vehicles and (tank-)containers**

Marking and labelling

Labelling

52 500   Vehicles with fixed or demountable tanks and tank-containers, containing or having contained (empty, uncleaned) substances of this Class shall bear labels conforming to model No. 5.2.

Those containing or having contained the substances of this Class listed in marginal 2559 (3) to (4) shall also bear labels in accordance with that marginal.

Class 5.2

52 501-
52 508

Halts of limited duration for service requirements

52 509   During the carriage of substances of 1°, 2°, 11° and 12° halts for service requirements shall so far as possible not be made in residential or urban areas. A halt near such a place may not be prolonged except with the agreement of the competent authorities. The same rule shall apply if a transport unit is loaded with more than 2 000 kg of substances of 3°, 4°, 13° and 14°.

52 510-
52 599

SECTION 6.   **Transitional provisions, derogations, and provisions peculiar to certain countries**

(Only the general provisions of Part I apply)

52 600-
59 999

- 64 -

CLASS 6.1. TOXIC SUBSTANCES

General

(Only the general provisions of Part I apply)

61 000-
61 099

SECTION 1.   Mode of carriage

61 100-
61 110

Carriage in bulk

61 111   (1)   Substances of 60° (c) and 3243 solids containing toxic liquid of 65° (b) may be carried in bulk as a full load.

(2)   Substances of 60° (c) and 3243 solids containing toxic liquid of 65° (b) shall in such case be carried in sheeted, open vehicles. Vehicles containing 3243 solids containing toxic liquid of 65° (b) in bulk shall be leakproof or rendered leakproof, for example by means of a suitable and sufficiently stout inner lining.

(3)   Solid mixtures (such as preparations and wastes) containing substances of 60° (c) may be carried under the same conditions as the substances themselves. Other solid substances, including mixtures (such as preparations and wastes) classified under the letter (c) of the various items may be carried in bulk only in containers under the conditions of marginal 61 118.

61 112-
61 117

Carriage in containers

61 118   Containers intended for the carriage in bulk of solid substances including mixtures (such as preparations and wastes) classified under (c) of the various items and 3243 solids containing toxic liquid of 65° (b) shall have complete walls and be sheeted or have a cover.

Containers containing 3243 solids containing toxic liquid of 65° (b) in bulk shall be leakproof or rendered leakproof, for example by means of a suitable and sufficiently stout inner lining.

61 119-
61 199

SECTION 2.   Special requirements to be fulfilled by the means of transport and its equipment

61 200-
61 259

Special equipment

61 260   Whenever motor fuel anti-knock mixtures of 31° (a) or receptacles having contained them are carried, the driver shall, when he is given the transport document, at the same time be given a portable equipment box fitted with a handle and containing:

-        three copies of the written instructions specifying the action to be taken in the event of an accident or incident occurring during carriage (see marginal 61 385);

61 260
(contd)

- two pairs of gloves and two pairs of boots made of rubber or some suitable plastics material;

- two respirators with an activated-charcoal cartridge of 500 cm³ capacity;

- a bottle (made of bakelite, for example) containing 2 kg of potassium permanganate and bearing the inscription "dissolve in water before use";

- six fibreboard notices bearing the inscription "DANGER - volatile poison spilled. Do not approach without respirator" in the language or languages of each of the countries in whose territory carriage takes place.

- this equipment box shall be kept in the driver's cab in a place where it can easily be found by the decontamination team.

61 261-
61 299

SECTION 3.   **General service provisions**

61 300-
61 301

Action to be taken in the event of accident

61 302   (See marginal 61 385)

61 303-
61 320

Supervision of vehicles

61 321   The provisions of marginal 10 321 shall apply to the dangerous goods listed below in quantities exceeding those specified:

- substances of 1° to 5° and substances classified under (a) of all items: 1 000 kg
- substances classified under (b) of all items: 5 000 kg.

61 322-
61 384

Instructions in writing

61 385   Where motor fuel anti-knock mixtures of 31° (a), or receptacles which have contained them, are carried, the text of the written instructions shall specify, <u>inter alia</u>, the following:

(A)   Precautions to be observed

The substance being carried is highly toxic. In the event of leakage from one of the receptacles the following precautions should be taken:

1.   Avoid:

(a)   contact with the skin;

(b)   inhalation of vapours;

(c)   introduction of the liquid into the mouth.

**61 385
(contd)**

2.   When drums which are torn open or damaged or wetted with liquid are being handled, the use of the following is compulsory:

(a)   respirators;

(b)   gloves made of rubber or some suitable plastics material;

(c)   boots made of rubber or some suitable plastics material.

In the event of a serious accident involving obstruction of the public highway, it is essential that persons arriving to clear the site should be warned of the danger incurred.

(B)   Action to be taken

All practicable steps, including the use of the notices referred to in marginal 61 260, shall be taken to keep persons at a distance of not less than 15 metres from the site of the accident; the notices contained in the equipment box shall be set up round the enclosure and onlookers shall be kept away.

The respirators, gloves and boots will enable one person to approach the load and verify its condition.

Should any of the drums be torn open, the following should be done:

(a)   additional respirators, gloves and boots with which to equip the workmen should be procured urgently;

(b)   drums still intact should be set aside;

(c)   the liquid spilled on the vehicle or on the ground should be neutralized by copious swilling with an aqueous solution of potassium permanganate (a neutralizing agent a bottle of which is kept in the equipment box); the solution is easily prepared by stirring 0.5 kg of permanganate with 15 litres of water in a bucket; swilling should be carried out several times, because it takes 2 kg of potassium permanganate to neutralize completely 1 kg of the substance being carried.

Where practicable, the best way to decontaminate the area is to pour petrol over the spilled fluid and ignite it.

(C)   Important notice

In case of accident, one of the first steps which must be taken is to notify by telegram or telephone ... (insert here the address and telephone numbers of the establishments to be notified in each of the countries in whose territory carriage is to take place).

A vehicle which has been contaminated with the substance carried shall not be put back into service until it has been decontaminated under the supervision of a competent person. Any wooden parts of the vehicle which have been attacked by the substance carried shall be removed and burnt.

**61 386-
61 399**

- 67 -

Class 6.1

SECTION 4.   Special provisions concerning loading, unloading and handling

61 400-
61 402

Prohibition of mixed loading on one vehicle

61 403 Packages bearing a label conforming to model No. 6.1 shall not be loaded together on one vehicle with packages bearing a label conforming to models Nos. 1, 1.4 (except for compatibility group S), 1.5, 1.6 or 01.

61 404-
61 406

Places of loading and unloading

61 407 (1) The following operations are prohibited:

(a) loading or unloading substances of 1° to 5° and any substance classified under (a) of other items in a public place in a built-up area without special permission from the competent authorities;

(b) loading or unloading the said substances in a public place elsewhere than in a built-up area without prior notice having been given to the competent authorities, unless the said operations are justified for serious reasons of safety.

(2) If, for any reason, handling operations have to be carried out in a public place, then substances and articles of different kinds shall be separated according to the labels.

61 408-
61 414

Cleaning after unloading

61 415 (1) A vehicle which has been contaminated with substances of 31° (a) or with a mixture thereof shall not be put back into service until it has been decontaminated under the supervision of a competent person. Any wooden parts of the vehicle which have been attacked by substances of 31° (a) shall be removed and burnt.

(2) If substances in this Class have leaked and been spilled in a vehicle, it may not be reused until after it has been thoroughly cleaned and, if necessary, decontaminated. All other goods and articles carried in the same vehicle shall be examined for possible contamination.

61 416-
61 499

SECTION 5.   Special provisions concerning the operation of (tank-)vehicles and (tank-)containers

Marking and labelling

Marking

61 500 (1) Whenever substances of 31° (a) are carried, the vehicle shall display on each side a warning notice to the effect that, if any liquid escapes, the greatest caution must be exercised and that the vehicle must not be approached without respirator, gloves and boots of rubber or some suitable plastics material.

61 500
(contd)

Labelling

(2)   Vehicles with fixed or demountable tanks and tank-containers, as well as vehicles and containers for the carriage of dangerous solid substances in bulk, containing or having contained (empty, uncleaned) substances of this Class shall bear labels conforming to model No. 6.1.

Those containing or having contained (empty, uncleaned) the substances of this Class listed in marginal 2612 (3) to (10) shall also bear labels in accordance with that marginal.

61 501-
61 508

Halts of limited duration for service requirements

61 509

Halts for service requirements shall so far as possible not be made in residential or urban areas. A halt near such a place may not be prolonged except with the agreement of the competent authorities.

61 510-
61 514

Protection against the action of the sun

61 515

During the period April to October inclusive, when a vehicle carrying hydrogen cyanide of 1° is stationary, the packages shall, if the legislation of the country in which the vehicle is halted so requires, be effectively protected against the action of the sun, e.g. by means of sheets placed not less than 20 cm above the load.

61 516-
61 599

SECTION 6.   **Transitional provisions, derogations, and provisions peculiar to certain countries**

(Only the general provisions of Part I apply)

61 600-
61 999

CLASS 6.2. INFECTIOUS SUBSTANCES

General

(Only the general provisions of Part I apply)

62 000-
62 099

SECTION 1.   **Mode of carriage**

62 100-
62 104

62 105   Packages containing substances of this Class shall be carried in closed or covered vehicles.

62 106-
62 117

Carriage in containers

62 118   (1)   Packages containing substances of this Class may be carried in small containers.

(2)   The mixed loading prohibitions of marginal 62 403 shall also apply to the contents of small containers.

62 119-
62 199

SECTION 2.   **Special requirements to be fulfilled by the means of transport and its equipment**

62 200-
62 239

Fire-fighting appliances

62 240   The provisions of marginal 10 240 (1) (b) and (3), shall not apply.

62 241-
62 299

SECTION 3.   **General service provisions**

62 300-
62 301

Action to be taken in the event of accident

62 302   (See marginal 62 385)

62 303-
62 320

Supervision of vehicles

62 321   The provisions of marginal 10 321 shall apply to all substances of 1°, whatever their mass. They shall also apply to substances of 2° whose quantity exceeds a mass of 100 kg. However, the provisions of marginal 10 321 need not be applied where the loaded compartment is locked and the packages carried are otherwise protected against any illicit unloading.

62 322-
62 352

62 353 The provisions of marginal 10 353 shall not apply.

**62 354-
62 384**

Instructions in writing

62 385 (1) The instructions in writing shall also include:

(a) the provision that, in the cases provided for marginal 10 385 (1) (d) the local health or veterinary authorities shall be informed;

(b) information as to how the substance(s) are to be absorbed and contained, and how the dangers of the substance(s) of Class 6.2 are to be eliminated on the spot, e.g. suitable disinfectants;

(c) information on suitable protective equipment for the driver.

**62 386-
62 399**

SECTION 4. **Special provisions concerning loading, unloading and handling**

**62 400-
62 402**

Prohibition of mixed loading on one vehicle

62 403 Packages bearing a label conforming to model No. 6.2 shall not be loaded together in the same vehicle with packages bearing a label conforming to models Nos. 1, 1.4 (except for compatibility group S), 1.5, 1.6 or 01.

**62 404-
62 411**

62 412 Substances of item 4° shall be carried in tanks or in specially equipped vehicles in a manner which avoids risks to humans, animals and the environment, e.g. by loading in bags or by airtight connections.

62 413

Handling and storage

62 414 (1) Packages containing substances of this Class shall be so stowed that they are readily accessible.

(2) When packages of this Class are to be carried at ambient temperature of not more than 15 °C or refrigerated, the temperature shall be maintained when unloading or during storage.

(3) Packages of this Class shall be stored only in cool places away from sources of heat.

Cleaning after unloading

62 415 If substances of this Class have leaked and been spilled in a vehicle, it may not be reused until after it has been thoroughly cleaned and, if necessary, disinfected. All goods and articles carried in such a vehicle shall be checked for possible contamination. The wooden parts of the vehicle which have come into contact with the substances of items 1° and 2° shall be removed and burnt.

**62 416-
62 499**

SECTION 5.   **Special provisions concerning the operation of (tank-)vehicles and (tank-)containers**

Marking and labelling

Labelling

62 500   Vehicles with fixed tanks or demountable tanks, specially equipped vehicles and tank-containers containing or having contained (empty, uncleaned) substances of 4°, shall bear labels conforming to model No. 6.2.

62 501-
62 508

Halts of limited duration for service requirements

62 509   Halts of vehicles carrying substances of 1° and 2° for service, requirements shall so far as possible not be made in residential or urban areas. A halt near such a place may not be prolonged except with the agreement of the competent authorities.

62 510-
62 599

SECTION 6.   **Transitional provisions, derogations and provisions peculiar to certain countries**

(Only the general provisions of Part I apply)

62 600-
70 999

CLASS 7. RADIOACTIVE MATERIAL

General

Carriage

71 000   For details see the relevant schedule in marginal 2704.

71 001-
71 099

SECTION 1.   Mode of carriage

Provisions

71 100   For details see the relevant schedule in marginal 2704.

71 101-
71 199

SECTION 2.   Special requirements to be fulfilled by the means of transport and its equipment

Provisions

71 200   For details see the relevant schedule in marginal 2704.

71 201-
71 259

Other equipment

71 260   The equipment mentioned in marginal 10 260 (d) iii) is not necessary.

71 261-
71 299

SECTION 3.   General service provisions

Provisions

71 300   For details see the relevant schedule in marginal 2704.

71 301-
71 314

Special training of drivers

71 315   (1)   Irrespective of the permissible maximum weight of the vehicle, the requirements of marginal 10 315 with regard to approved training and the issue of an approved training certificate shall apply to:

   (a)   drivers of vehicles carrying radioactive material covered by one of Schedules 5 to 8 or 10 to 13;

   (b)   drivers of vehicles carrying non-fissile radioactive material covered by Schedule 9, if the total number of packages containing radioactive material carried on the vehicle exceeds 10, or where the sum of the transport indices of the packages carried exceeds 3.

- 75 -

71 315   (2)   Drivers of vehicles mentioned under (1) above shall attend a specialization training course
(contd)   covering at least the subjects defined in marginal 240 105 of Appendix B.4.

(3)   Drivers of vehicles carrying radioactive material covered by Schedule 9, if the total number of packages containing radioactive material carried does not exceed 10, and the sum of the transport indices does not exceed 3, shall receive appropriate training, commensurate with and appropriate to their duties, which provides them with an awareness of the radiation hazards involved in the carriage of radioactive material. Such awareness training shall be confirmed by a certificate provided by their employer.

(4)   If, according to other regulations applicable in the country of a Contracting Party, a driver has followed approved equivalent training under a different regime or for a different purpose covering the subjects referred to paragraph (2), the specialization course may be totally or partially dispensed with.

71 316-
71 320

Supervision of vehicles

71 321   The provisions of marginal 10 321 shall apply to all material, in whatever mass. In addition, these goods shall be subject at all times to supervision to prevent any malicious act and to alert the driver and the competent authorities in the event of loss or fire. However, the provisions of marginal 10 321 need not be applied where:

(a)   The loaded compartment is locked and the packages carried are otherwise protected against illicit unloading; and

(b)   The dose rate does not exceed 5 µSv/h (0.5 mrem/h) at any accessible point on the outer surface of the vehicle.

In addition, these goods shall be subject at all times to supervision to prevent any malicious act and to alert the driver and the competent authorities in the event of loss or fire.

71 322-
71 324

Carriage of passengers

71 325   The provisions of marginal 10 325 shall not apply to transport units carrying only radioactive material of schedules 1 to 4.

71 326-
71 352

Portable lighting apparatus

71 353   The provisions of marginal 10 353 shall not apply provided there is no subsidiary risk.

71 354-
71 384

Instructions in writing

71 385   The provisions of marginal 10 385 shall not apply to transport units carrying only radioactive material of schedules 1 to 4.

71 386-
71 399

SECTION 4.   Special provisions concerning loading, unloading and handling

Provisions

71 400   For details see the relevant schedule in marginal 2704.

71 401-
71 402

Prohibition of mixed loading on one vehicle

71 403   Packages bearing a label conforming to models Nos. 7A, 7B or 7C shall not be loaded together on the same vehicle with packages bearing a label conforming to models Nos. 1, 1.4 (except for compatibility group S), 1.5, 1.6 or 01.

71 404-
71 414

Cleaning after unloading

71 415   For decontamination requirements, see marginal 3712.

71 416-
71 499

SECTION 5.   Special provisions concerning the operation of (tank-) vehicles and (tank-) containers

Marking and labelling

Labelling

71 500   (1)   In addition to the requirements of marginal 10 500, every vehicle carrying radioactive material shall bear on the outside of each side wall and of the rear wall a label conforming to model No. 7D.

However, these requirements shall not apply to vehicles carrying only the radioactive material referred to in schedules 1 to 4 of marginal 2704.

If the size and construction of the vehicle are such that the available surface area is insufficient to affix the label of model No. 7 D, its dimensions may be reduced to 100 mm on each side.

(2)   The labels prescribed in marginal 10 500 (9) shall be affixed to all four sides of the container.

71 500
(contd)

(3)   The labels and the orange-coloured plates as prescribed in Class 7 shall be affixed to all four sides of the tank container. If these labels or plates are not visible from outside the vehicle, the same labels and plates shall be affixed to the sides and the rear of the vehicle.

71 501-
71 506

Parking of a vehicle constituting a special danger

71 507

In addition to marginal 10 507, see Appendix A.7 marginal 3712. These requirements shall, however, not apply to vehicles carrying only radioactive material of schedules 1 to 4 of marginal 2704.

71 508-
71 599

SECTION 6.   **Transitional provisions, derogations and provisions peculiar to certain countries**

(Only the general provisions of Part I apply)

71 600-
80 999

CLASS 8. CORROSIVE SUBSTANCES

General

(Only the general provisions of Part I apply)

81 000-
81 099

SECTION 1.   Mode of carriage

81 100-
81 110

Carriage in bulk

81 111   (1)   Lead sulphate of 1° (b), substances of 13° (b) and 3244 solids with corrosive liquid of 65° (b) may be carried in bulk as a full load. The body of the vehicle shall be equipped with a suitable and sufficiently stout inner lining. If the vehicle is sheeted the sheet shall be so placed that it cannot touch the load.   Vehicles containing substances of 65° (b) (identification number 3244) shall be leakproof or rendered leakproof, for example by the means of a suitable and sufficiently stout inner lining.

(2)   Solid mixtures (such as preparations and wastes) containing substances of 13° may be carried under the same conditions as the substances themselves. Other solid substances, including mixtures (such as preparations and wastes) classified under the letter (c) of the various items may be carried in bulk only in containers under the conditions of marginal 81 118.

81 112   (1)   Used batteries of 81° (c) may be carried in bulk in specially equipped vehicles.

(2)   The load compartments of vehicles shall be of steel resistant to the corrosive substances contained in the batteries. Less resistant steels may be used when there is a sufficiently great wall thickness or a plastic lining/layer resistant to the corrosive substances.

The design of the load compartments of vehicles shall take account of any residual currents and impact from the batteries.

NOTE: Steel exhibiting a maximum rate of progressive reduction of 0.1 mm per year under the effects of the corrosive substances may be considered as resistant.

(3)   It shall be ensured by means of constructional measures that there will be no leakage of corrosive substances from the load compartments of vehicles during carriage.   Open load compartments shall be covered. The cover shall be resistant to the corrosive substances.

(4)   Before loading the load compartments of vehicles including their equipment shall be inspected for damage. Vehicles with damaged load compartments shall not be loaded.

The load compartments of vehicles shall not be loaded above the top of their walls.

(5)   No batteries containing different substances and no other goods liable to react dangerously with each other shall be present in the load compartments of vehicles [see marginal 2811 (6)].

During transport no dangerous residue of the corrosive substances contained in the batteries shall adhere to the outer surface of the load compartments of vehicles.

81 113-
81 117

Carriage in containers

81 118 (1) Containers intended for the carriage in bulk of lead sulphate of 1° (b), substances of 13° (b), 3244 solids containing corrosive liquid of 65° (b) or solid substances or wastes classified under (c) of the various items shall have complete walls and a suitable lining and be sheeted or have a cover.

Containers containing 3244 solids containing corrosive liquid of 65° (b) in bulk shall be leakproof or rendered leakproof, for example by the means of a suitable and sufficiently stout inner lining.

(2) Used batteries of 81° (c) may also be carried in bulk in containers under the conditions in marginal 81 112 (2)-(5). Large containers made of plastics material are not permitted. Small containers made of plastics material shall be able to withstand a drop test from 0.8 m fully loaded, flat on the bottom on to a hard surface at -18°C without breakage.

81 119-
81 199

SECTION 2. **Special requirements to be fulfilled by the means of transport and its equipment**

(Only the general provisions of Part I apply).

81 200-
81 299

SECTION 3. **General service provisions**

81 300-
81 320

Supervision of vehicles

81 321 The provisions of marginal 10 321 shall apply to the substances listed below in quantities exceeding those specified:

      Substances classified under (a) of all items: 10 000 kg
      Bromine of 14°:   1 000 kg

81 322-
81 399

SECTION 4. **Special provisions concerning loading, unloading and handling**

81 400-
81 402

Prohibition of mixed loading on one vehicle

81 403 Packages bearing a label conforming to model No. 8 shall not be loaded together on the same vehicle with packages bearing a label conforming to models Nos. 1, 1.4 (except for compatibility group S), 1.5, 1.6 or 01.

81 404-
81 412

Cleaning before loading

81 413 Vehicles intended to carry packages containing substances of 2° (a) 2., 3° (a), 4°, 73° or 74° shall be carefully cleaned and in particular be free of all combustible waste (straw, hay, paper, etc.).

Cleaning after unloading

81 415 If substances from packages bearing labels conforming to model No. 6.1 have leaked and been spilled in a vehicle, it may not be reused until after it has been thoroughly cleaned and, if necessary, decontaminated. All other goods and articles carried in the same vehicle shall be examined for possible contamination.

81 416-
81 499

SECTION 5. **Special provisions concerning the operation of (tank-)vehicles and (tank-) containers)**

Marking and labelling

Labelling

81 500 Vehicles with fixed or demountable tanks or tank-containers, as well as vehicles and containers for the carriage of dangerous solid substances in bulk, containing or having contained (empty, uncleaned) substances of this Class shall bear labels conforming to model No. 8.

Those containing or having contained (empty, uncleaned) the substances of this Class listed in marginal 2812 (3) to (10) shall also bear labels in accordance with that marginal.

81 501-
81 599

SECTION 6. **Transitional provisions, derogations and provisions peculiar to certain countries**

(Only the general provisions of Part I apply)

81 600-
90 999

CLASS 9. MISCELLANEOUS DANGEROUS SUBSTANCES AND ARTICLES

General

(Only the general provisions of Part I apply)

91 000-
91 099

SECTION 1.   **Mode of carriage**

91 100-
91 104

Method of dispatch and restrictions on forwarding

91 105   Packages containing substances of this Class shall be carried in closed or covered vehicles.

NOTE: 3268 Airbag inflators or 3268 airbag modules or 3268 seat-belt pretensioners may be transported unpackaged in dedicated handling devices, vehicles or large containers when transported from where they are manufactured to an assembly plant.

91 106-
91 110

Carriage in bulk

91 111   (1)   2211 polymeric beads, expandable of 4° (c) and solid substances and mixtures (such as preparations and wastes) of 12° (c) may be carried in bulk in open but sheeted vehicles with adequate ventilation.

(2)   Substances of 20° (c) for which carriage in tank-vehicles in accordance with Appendix B.1a or tank-containers in accordance with Appendix B.1b is unsuitable because of the high temperature and density of the substance may be carried in special vehicles.

Substances of 21° (c) may be carried in bulk in specially equipped vehicles.

These special vehicles for substances of 20° (c) and specially equipped vehicles for substances of 21° (c) shall be in accordance with standards specified by the competent authority of the country of origin.

If the country of origin is not party to ADR, the conditions laid down shall be recognized by the competent authority of the first ADR country reached by the consignment.

91 112-
91 117

Carriage in containers

91 118   2211 polymeric beads, expandable of 4° (c) and 12° (c) may also be packed may also be packed without inner packaging in small containers of the closed type with complete walls.

91 119-
91 199

SECTION 2.   Special requirements to be fulfilled by the means of transport and its equipment

(Only the general provisions of Part I apply).

91 200-
91 299

SECTION 3.   General service provisions

91 300-
91 320

Supervision of vehicles

91 321   The provisions of 10 321 apply to the dangerous goods listed below, except those of 35° (b), in quantities exceeding those specified:

- substances classified under (b) of all items: 5 000 kg
- substances classified under 13° (b): 1 000 kg

91 322-
91 384

91 385   (1)   For the carriage of substances of 2° (b) or apparatus of 3°, the text of the written instructions must give the indication that highly toxic dioxins may form in the event of fire.

(2)   For substances of 11° and 12°, the instructions in writing shall also include, the measures to be taken to avoid or minimize damage in the event of spillage of these substances which are considered to be pollutant to the aquatic environment.

(3)   For substances of 13°, the instructions in writing shall also include:

(a)   the provision that, in the case of damage to or leakage from a package containing substances of 13°, the local health or veterinary authorities shall be informed;

(b)   information as to how the substance(s) is/are to be absorbed and contained, and how the dangers of the substance(s) of 13° are to be eliminated on the spot, e.g. suitable disinfectants;

(c)   information on suitable protective equipment for the driver.

91 386-
91 399

SECTION 4.   Special provisions concerning loading, unloading and handling

91 400-
91 402

Prohibition of mixed loading on one vehicle

91 403   Packages bearing a label conforming to model No. 9 shall not be loaded together on the same vehicle with packages bearing a label conforming to models Nos. 1, 1.4 (except for compatibility group S), 1.5, 1.6 or 01.

**91 404-
91 406**

Places of loading and unloading

91 407   (1)   The following operations are prohibited:

(a)   loading or unloading substances classified under (b) of the various items, except 35° (b) in a public place in a built-up area without special permission from the competent authorities;

(b)   loading or unloading substances classified under (b) of the various items, except 35° (b) in a public place elsewhere than in a built up area without prior notice having been given to the competent authorities, unless these operations are urgently necessary for reasons of safety.

(2)   If for any reason handling operations have to be carried out in a public place, then substances and articles of different kinds shall be separated according to the labels.

**91 408-
91 413**

Handling and storage

91 414   (1)   Packages containing substances of 13° shall be so stowed that they are readily accessible.

(2)   When packages containing substances of 13° are to be carried refrigerated, the functioning of the cooling chain shall be ensured when unloading or during storage.

(3)   Packages containing substances of 13° shall only be stored in cool places away from sources of heat.

Cleaning after unloading

91 415   (1)   If substances or articles of 1°, 2° (b), 3°, 11° (c), 12° (c) or 13° (b) have leaked and been spilled in a vehicle, it may not be re-used until after it has been thoroughly cleaned and, if necessary, decontaminated. All other goods carried in the same vehicle shall be examined for possible contamination.

(2)   If a substance of 13° has escaped and has contaminated a vehicle, this vehicle may be reused only after it has been thoroughly cleaned and, if necessary, disinfected. All goods and articles carried in such a vehicle shall be checked for possible contamination. The wooden parts of the vehicle which have come into contact with the substances of 13° shall be removed and burnt.

**91 416-
91 499**

SECTION 5.   Special provisions concerning the operation of (tank-) vehicles and (tank-) containers

Marking and labelling

Marking

91 500   (1)   Small containers containing expandable polymers of 4° (c) shall bear the marking: "**Keep away from any source of ignition**". This marking shall be in the official language of the country of departure, and also, if that language is not English, French or German, in English, French or German, unless any agreements concluded between the countries concerned in the transport operation provide otherwise.

Labelling

(2)   Vehicles with fixed or demountable tanks and tank-containers, as well as vehicles and containers for the carriage of dangerous solid substances in bulk containing or having contained (tanks, containers for bulk and vehicles for bulk empty, uncleaned) substances of this Class, with the exception of substances of 4° (c), shall bear labels conforming to model No. 9.

Those containing or having contained substances of this Class listed in marginal 2912 (4) to (6) shall also bear labels in accordance with that marginal.

(3)   Special vehicles carrying substances of 20° (c) and specially equipped vehicles carrying substances of 21° (c) shall also bear on two sides and at the rear the mark referred to in Appendix B.7, marginal 270 000.

91 501-
91 599

SECTION 6.   Transitional provisions, derogations, and provisions peculiar to certain countries

(Only the general provisions of Part I apply)

91 600-
199 999

PART III

APPENDICES TO ANNEX B

APPENDICES B.1: Provisions concerning tanks

PROVISIONS COMMON TO THE B.1 APPENDICES

200 000 (1) The scope of application of the various B.1 Appendices is as follows:

(a) **Appendix B.1a** applies to tanks other than tank-containers;

(b) **Appendix B.1b** applies to tank-containers;

(c) **Appendix B.1c** applies to tanks, other than elements of battery-vehicles and tank-containers, made of reinforced plastics;

(d) **Appendix B.1d** is concerned with the materials and construction of fixed welded tanks, of demountable welded tanks, and of welded shells of tank-containers, intended for the carriage of deeply-refrigerated liquefied gases of Class 2, or for which a test pressure of not less than 1 MPa (10 bar) is required.

NOTE: For receptacles, see the relevant requirements of Annex A (Packages).

(2) By derogation from the definition given in marginal 10 014, the term "tank" when used alone in Appendix B.1a and Appendix B.1c does not cover tank-containers. However, some of the requirements of Appendix B.1a may be made applicable to tank-containers by the provisions of Annex B and Appendix B.1b.

(3) It is recalled that marginal 10 121 (1) prohibits the carriage of dangerous substances in tanks except where such carriage is expressly authorized under each Section 1 of Part II in Appendices B.1a or B.1b and Section 1 of Appendix B.1c.

**200 001-
210 999**

Appendix B.1a

PROVISIONS CONCERNING FIXED TANKS (TANK-VEHICLES), DEMOUNTABLE TANKS AND BATTERY-VEHICLES

NOTE: Part I sets out the requirements applicable to fixed tanks (tank-vehicles), demountable tanks and battery-vehicles intended for the carriage of substances of any class. Part II contains special requirements supplementing or modifying the requirements of Part I.

PART I. REQUIREMENTS APPLICABLE TO ALL CLASSES

211 000-
211 099

SECTION 1.   General; scope (use of tanks); definitions

NOTE: In accordance with the provisions of marginal 10 121 (1), the carriage of dangerous substances in fixed or demountable tanks or battery-vehicles is permitted only where this mode of carriage is expressly authorized for such substances in each Section 1 of Part II of this Appendix.

211 100 These requirements shall apply to fixed tanks (tank-vehicles), demountable tanks and battery-vehicles used for the carriage of liquid, gaseous, powdery or granular substances.

NOTE: For the purposes of the requirements of this Appendix, the following shall be considered to be substances carried in a liquid state:

- *substances which are liquid at normal temperatures and pressures*
- *solids offered for carriage at elevated temperatures or hot, in the molten state.*

211 101 (1)   In addition to the vehicle proper, or the units of running gear used in its stead, a tank-vehicle comprises one or more shells, their items of equipment and the fittings for attaching them to the vehicle or to the running-gear units.

(2)   When attached to the carrier vehicle, the demountable tank shall meet the requirements prescribed for tank-vehicles.

211 102 In the following requirements:

(1)   (a)   "*shell*" means the sheathing containing the substance (including the openings and their closures);

(b)   "*service equipment of the shell*" means the filling, discharge, venting, safety, heating and heat-insulating devices and the measuring instruments;

(c)   "*structural equipment*" means the internal or external reinforcing, fastening, protective or stabilizing members external to the shell.

(2)   (a)   "*calculation pressure*" means a theoretical pressure at least equal to the test pressure which, according to the degree of danger exhibited by the substance being carried, may to a greater or lesser degree exceed the working pressure. It is used solely to determine the thickness of the walls of the shell, independently of any external or internal reinforcing device;

(b)   "*test pressure*" means the highest effective pressure which arises in the shell during the pressure test;

**211 102
(contd)**

(c) "*filling pressure*" means the maximum pressure actually built up in the shell when it is being filled under pressure;

(d) "*discharge pressure*" means the maximum pressure actually built up in the shell when it is being discharged under pressure;

(e) "*maximum working pressure (gauge pressure)*" means the highest of the following three pressures:

(i) the highest effective pressure allowed in the shell during filling ("maximum filling pressure allowed");

(ii) the highest effective pressure allowed in the shell during discharge ("maximum discharge pressure allowed"); and

(iii) the effective gauge pressure to which the shell is subjected by its contents (including such extraneous gases as it may contain) at the maximum working temperature.

Unless the special requirements for each class provide otherwise, the numerical value of this working pressure (gauge pressure) shall not be lower than the vapour pressure (absolute pressure) of the filling substance at 50 °C.

For shells equipped with safety valves (with or without bursting disc), the maximum working pressure (gauge pressure) shall however be equal to the prescribed opening pressure of such safety valves.

(3) "*Leakproofness test*" means the test which consists in subjecting the shell to an effective internal pressure equal to the maximum working pressure, but not less than 20 kPa (0.2 bar) (gauge pressure), by a procedure approved by the competent authority.

For shells equipped with venting systems and a safety device to prevent the contents spilling out if the shell overturns, the pressure for the leakproofness test shall be equal to the static pressure of the filling substance.

**211 103-
211 119**

SECTION 2.   Construction

211 120 Shells shall be designed and constructed in accordance with the provisions of a technical code recognized by the competent authority, in which the material is chosen and the wall thickness determined taking into account maximum and minimum filling and working temperatures, but the following minimum requirements shall be met:

(1) Shells shall be made of suitable metallic materials which unless other temperature ranges are prescribed in the various classes, shall be resistant to brittle fracture and to stress corrosion cracking between -20 °C and +50 °C. However, suitable non-metallic materials may be used to manufacture equipment and accessories.

(2) For welded shells only materials of faultless weldability and whose adequate impact strength at an ambient temperature of -20 °C can be guaranteed, particularly in the weld seams and the zones adjacent thereto, shall be used.

211 120
(contd)
(3)   Welds shall be skilfully made and shall afford the fullest safety. For the execution and checking of weld beads, see also marginal 211 127 (8). Shells whose minimum wall thicknesses have been determined in accordance with 211 127 (2) to (6) shall be checked by the methods described in the definition of the weld coefficient 0.8.

(4)   The materials of shells, or of their protective linings in contact with the contents, shall not contain substances liable to react dangerously with the contents, to form dangerous compounds, or substantially to weaken the material.

(5)   The protective lining shall be so designed that its leakproofness remains intact whatever the deformation liable to occur in normal conditions of carriage [211 127 (1)].

(6)   If contact between the substance carried and the material used for the construction of the shell entails a progressive decrease in the thickness of the walls, this thickness shall be increased at manufacture by an appropriate amount. This additional thickness to allow for corrosion shall not be taken into consideration in calculating the thickness of the shell walls.

211 121   (1)   Shells, their attachments and their service and structural equipment shall be designed to withstand without loss of contents (other than quantities of gas escaping through any degassing vents):

-        static and dynamic stresses in normal conditions of carriage;
-        prescribed minimum stresses as defined in marginals 211 125 and 211 127.

(2)   In the case of vehicles in which the shell constitutes a stressed self-supporting member, the shell shall be designed to withstand the stresses thus imposed in addition to stresses from other sources.

211 122   The pressure on which the wall thickness of the shell is based shall not be less than the calculation pressure, but the stresses referred to in marginal 211 121 shall also be taken into account.

211 123   Unless specially prescribed otherwise in the various classes, the following particulars shall be taken into account in the design of shells:

(1)   Gravity-discharge shells intended for the carriage of substances having a vapour pressure not exceeding 110 kPa (1.1 bar) (absolute pressure) at 50 °C shall be designed for a calculation pressure of twice the static pressure of the substance to be carried but not less than twice the static pressure of water.

(2)   Pressure-filled or pressure-discharge shells intended for the carriage of substances having a vapour pressure not exceeding 110 kPa (1.1 bar) (absolute pressure) at 50 °C shall be designed for a calculation pressure equal to 1.3 times the filling or discharge pressure.

(3)   Shells intended for the carriage of substances having a vapour pressure of more than 110 kPa (1.1 bar) but not more than 175 kPa (1.75 bar) (absolute pressure) at 50 °C shall, whatever their filling or discharge system, be designed for a calculation pressure of not less than 150 kPa (1.5 bar) gauge pressure or 1.3 times the filling or discharge pressure, whichever is the higher.

(4)   Shells intended for the carriage of substances having a vapour pressure of more than 175 kPa (1.75 bar) (absolute pressure) at 50 °C shall, whatever their filling or discharge system, be designed for a calculation pressure equal to 1.3 times the filling or discharge pressure but not less than 400 kPa (4 bar) gauge pressure.

Appendix B.1a

211 124   Tanks intended to contain certain dangerous substances shall be provided with special protection. This may take the form of additional thickness of the shell (such additional thickness being determined in the light of the dangers inherent in the substance concerned: see the relevant classes) or of a protective device.

211 125   At the test pressure, the stress σ (sigma) at the most severely stressed point of the shell shall not exceed the material-dependent limits prescribed below. Allowance shall be made for any weakening due to the welds.

(1)   For all metals and alloys, the stress σ at the test pressure shall be lower than the smaller of the values given by the following formulae:

$$\sigma \leq 0.75 \, Re \quad \text{or} \quad \sigma \leq 0.5 \, Rm$$

where

Re	=	apparent yield stress, or 0.2% or, in the case of austenitic steels, 1%
Rm	=	minimum tensile strength.

Ratios of Re/Rm exceeding 0.85 are not allowed for steels used in the construction of welded tanks.

The values of Re and Rm to be used shall be specified minimum values according to material standards. If no material standard exists for the metal or alloy in question, the values of Re and Rm used shall be approved by the competent authority or by a body designated by that authority.

When austenitic steels are used, the specified minimum values according to the material standards may be exceeded by up to 15% if these higher values are attested in the inspection certificate.

The values specified in the certificate shall be taken as a basis in determining the Re/Rm ratio in each case.

(2)   For steel, the elongation at fracture in % shall be not less than

$$\frac{10\,000}{\text{determined tensile strength in N/mm}^2}$$

but in any case it shall be not less than 16% for fine-grained steels and not less than 20% for other steels. For aluminium alloys the elongation at fracture shall be not less than 12% [1].

---

[1]   *In the case of sheet metal the axis of the tensile test piece shall be at right angles to the direction of rolling. The permanent elongation at fracture (l = 5d) shall be measured on a test piece of circular cross section in which the gauge length 1 is equal to five times the diameter d; if test pieces of rectangular section are used, the gauge length shall be calculated by the formula*

$$l = 5{,}65 \sqrt{F_o,}$$

where F_o is the initial cross-sectional area of the test piece.

Appendix B.1a

211 126 Shells intended for the carriage of liquids having a flash-point of 61 °C or below or for the carriage of flammable gases, shall be linked to the chassis by means of at least one good electrical connection. Any metal contact capable of causing electrochemical corrosion shall be avoided. Shells shall be provided with at least one earth fitting clearly marked with the symbol ⊥, capable of being electrically connected.

211 127 Shells and their fastenings shall withstand the stresses specified in paragraph (1) below, and the wall thicknesses of shells shall be at least as determined in accordance with paragraphs (2) to (6).

(1)   The shells and their fastenings shall be capable of absorbing, under the maximum permissible load, the forces exerted by:

-      in the direction of travel: twice the total mass;

-      at right angles to the direction of travel: the total mass;

-      vertically upwards: the total mass;

-      vertically downwards: twice the total mass.

Under the stresses defined above, the stress at the most severely stressed point of the shell and its fastenings shall not exceed the value σ defined in marginal 211 125.

(2)   The thickness of the cylindrical wall of the shell and of the ends and cover plates shall not be less than the greater of the values determined by the following formulae:

$$e = \frac{P_{ep}\, D}{2\sigma\lambda} \quad (mm)$$

$$e = \frac{P_{cal}\, D}{2\sigma} \quad (mm)$$

where:

P_{ep}	=	test pressure in MPa
P_{cal}	=	calculation pressure in MPa as specified in marginal 211 123
D	=	internal diameter of shell in mm
σ	=	permissible stress, as defined in marginal 211 125 (1) in N/mm²
λ	=	a coefficient not exceeding or equal to 1, allowing for any weakening due to welds.

The thickness shall in no case be less than that defined in paragraphs (3) to (6) below.

- 93 -

Appendix B.1a

211 127 **(3)** The walls, ends and cover plates of shells of circular cross-section not more than 1.80 m
(contd) in diameter [2/], other than those referred to in paragraph (5), shall not be less than 5 mm thick if
of mild steel [3/], or of equivalent thickness if of another metal. Where the diameter is more than
1.80 m [2/], this thickness shall be increased to 6 mm except in the case of shells intended for the
carriage of powdery or granular substances, if the shell is of mild steel [3/], or to an equivalent
thickness if the shell is of another metal. "Equivalent thickness" means the thickness obtained by
the following formula:

$$e_1 = \frac{21.4 \times e_o}{\sqrt[3]{Rm_1 \times A_1}} \qquad [4/]$$

(4) Where protection of the shell against damage through lateral impact or overturning is
provided, the competent authority may allow the aforesaid minimum thicknesses to be reduced in
proportion to the protection provided; however, the said thicknesses shall not be less than 3 mm
in the case of mild steel [3/], or than an equivalent thickness in the case of other materials, for shells
not more than 1.80 m in diameter [2/]. For shells with a diameter exceeding 1.80 m [2/] the aforesaid
minimum thickness shall be increased to 4 mm in the case of mild steel [3/] and to an equivalent
thickness in the case of other metal. "Equivalent thickness" means the thickness obtained by the
following formula:

$$e_1 = \frac{21.4 \times e_o}{\sqrt[3]{Rm_1 \times A_1}} \qquad [4/]$$

(5) For tanks built after 1 January 1990, there is protection against damage as referred to in
paragraph (4) when the following measures or equivalent measures are adopted:

    (a) For shells intended for the carriage of powdery or granular substances, the protection
against damage shall satisfy the competent authority.

[2/]   *For shells not of circular cross-section, for example box-shaped or elliptical shells, the indicated
diameters shall correspond to those calculated on the basis of a circular cross-section of the same area. For
such shapes of cross-section the radius of convexity of the shell wall shall not exceed 2 000 mm at the sides
or 3 000 mm at the top and bottom.*

[3/]   *"Mild steel" means a steel having a minimum breaking strength between 360 and 410 N/mm².*

[4/]   *This formula is derived from the general formula:*

$$e_1 = e_o \sqrt[3]{\frac{Rm_o \times A_o}{Rm_1 \times A_1}}$$

where

Rm_o =   *360*
A_o =   *27 for the mild steel of reference;*
Rm_1 =   *minimum tensile strength of the metal chosen, in N/mm²; and*
A_1 =   *minimum elongation of the metal chosen on fracture under tensile stress, in %.*

211 127
(contd)

(b)   For shells intended for the carriage of other substances, there is protection against damage when:

1.   for shells with a circular or elliptical cross-section having a maximum radius of curvature of 2 m, the shell is equipped with strengthening members comprising partitions, surge plates or external or internal rings, so placed that at least one of the following conditions is met:

-    Distance between two adjacent strengthening elements ≤ 1.75 m.
-    Volume contained between two partitions or surge plates ≤ 7500 1.

The vertical cross-section of a ring, with the associated coupling, shall have a section modulus of at least 10 cm^3.

External rings shall not have projecting edges with a radius of less than 2.5 mm.

Partitions and surge plates shall conform to the requirements of paragraph (7).

The thickness of the partitions and surge plates shall in no case be less than that of the shell.

2.   For shells made with double walls, the space between being evacuated of air, the aggregate thickness of the outer metal wall and the shell wall corresponds to the wall thickness prescribed in paragraph (3), and the thickness of the wall of the shell itself is not less than the minimum thickness prescribed in paragraph (4).

3.   For shells made with double walls having an intermediate layer of solid materials at least 50 mm thick, the outer wall has a thickness of at least 0.5 mm of mild steel [5] or at least 2 mm of a plastic material reinforced with glass fibre. Solid foam (with an impact absorption capacity like that, for example, of polyurethane foam) may be used as the intermediate layer of solid material.

4.   Shells of forms other than in 1., especially box-shaped tanks, are provided, all round the mid-point of their vertical height and over at least 30% of their height with an additional protection designed in such a way as to offer specific resilience at least equal to that of a shell constructed in mild steel of a thickness of 5 mm (for a shell diameter not exceeding 1.80 m) or 6 mm (for a shell diameter exceeding 1.80 m). The additional protection shall be applied in a durable manner to the outside of the shell. This requirement shall be considered to have been met without further proof of the specific resilience when the additional protection involves the welding of a plate of the same material as the shell to the area to be strengthened, so that the minimum wall thickness is in accordance with paragraph (3).

This protection is dependent upon the possible stresses exerted on mild steel shells in the event of an accident, where the ends and walls have a thickness of at least 5 mm for a diameter not exceeding 1.80 m or at least 6 mm for a diameter exceeding 1.80 m. If another metal is used, the equivalent thickness shall be obtained in accordance with the formula in paragraph (3).

For demountable tanks this protection is not required when they are protected on all sides by the drop sides of the carrier vehicles.

---

[5]   *See footnote 3/.*

211 127 (6) The thickness of tank shells designed in accordance with marginal 211 123 (1) which either
(contd) are of not more than 5 000 litres capacity or are divided into leak-proof compartments of not more
than 5 000 litres unit capacity may be adjusted to a level which, unless prescribed otherwise in the
various classes, shall however not be less than the appropriate value shown in the following table:

Maximum radius of curvature of shell (m)	Capacity of shell or shell compartment (m³)	Minimum thickness (mm)
		Mild steel
≤ 2	≤ 5.0	3
2 - 3	≤ 3.5	3
	> 3.5 but ≤ 5.0	4

Where a metal other than mild steel is used, the thickness shall be determined by the equivalence
formula given in paragraph (3). The thickness of the partitions and surge-plates shall in no case
be less than that of the shell.

(7) Surge-plates and partitions shall be dished, with a depth of dish of not less than 10 cm, or
shall be corrugated, profiled or otherwise reinforced to give equivalent strength. The area of the
surge-plate shall be at least 70% of the cross-sectional area of the tank in which the surge-plate
is fitted.

(8) The manufacturer's qualification for performing welding operations shall be one recognized
by the competent authority. Welding shall be performed by skilled welders using a welding
process whose effectiveness (including any heat treatments required) has been demonstrated by test.
Non-destructive tests shall be carried out by radiography or by ultrasound and must confirm that
the quality of the welding is appropriate to the stresses.

In determining the thickness of the shell walls in accordance with paragraph (2), the following
values of the coefficient λ (lambda) should be adopted for the welds:

0.8: where the weld beads are so far as possible inspected visually on both faces and are
  subjected to a non-destructive spot check with particular attention to connexions;

0.9: where all longitudinal beads throughout their length, all connexions, 25 % of circular
  beads, and welds for the assembly of large-diameter items of equipment are subjected
  to non-destructive checks. Beads shall be checked visually on both sides as far as
  possible;

1.0: where all beads are subjected to non-destructive checks and are so far as possible
  inspected visually on both sides. A weld test-piece shall be taken.

Where the competent authority has doubts regarding the quality of weld beads, it may require
additional checks.

(9) Measures shall be taken to protect shells against the risk of deformation as a result of a
negative internal pressure.

Unless otherwise prescribed in the special provisions for the individual classes, these shells may
have valves to avoid an unacceptable negative internal pressure, without intervening bursting discs.

(10) The thermal insulation shall be so designed as not to hinder access to, or the operation of,
filling and discharge devices and safety valves.

Appendix B.1a

Stability

211 128 The overall width of the ground-level bearing surface (distance between the outer points of contact with the ground of the right-hand tyre and the left-hand tyre of the same axle) shall be at least equal to 90% of the height of the centre of gravity of the laden tank-vehicle. In an articulated vehicle the mass on the axles of the load-carrying unit of the laden semi-trailer shall not exceed 60% of the nominal total laden mass of the complete articulated vehicle.

Protection of upper fittings

211 129 The fittings and accessories mounted on the upper part of the shell shall be protected against damage caused by overturning. This protection may take the form of strengthening rings, protective canopies or transverse or longitudinal members so shaped that effective protection is given.

SECTION 3.   Items of equipment

211 130 The items of equipment shall be so arranged as to be protected against the risk of being wrenched off or damaged during carriage or handling. They shall exhibit a suitable degree of safety comparable to that of the shells themselves, and shall in particular:

- be compatible with the substances carried; and
- meet the requirements of marginal 211 121.

As many operating parts as possible shall be served by the smallest possible number of apertures in the shell wall.

The leakproofness of the service equipment shall be ensured even in the event of over-turning of the tank-vehicles, demountable tanks and battery-vehicles. The gaskets shall be made of a material compatible with the substance carried and shall be replaced as soon as their effectiveness is impaired, for example as a result of ageing. Gaskets ensuring the leakproofness of fittings requiring manipulation during normal use of tank-vehicles, demountable tanks and batteries of receptacles, shall be so designed and arranged that manipulation of the fittings incorporating them does not damage them.

211 131 Every bottom-discharge shell, and in the case of compartmented bottom-discharge shells every compartment, shall be equipped with two mutually independent shut-off devices, the first being an internal stop-valve [6] fixed directly to the shell and the second being a sluice-valve or other equivalent device, mounted in series, one at each end of the discharge pipe-socket. The bottom discharge of shells intended for the carriage of powdery or granular substances may be constituted by external piping with a stop-valve if it is made of a malleable metallic material. In addition, the openings of the shells shall be capable of being closed by means of screw-threaded plugs, blank flanges or other equally effective devices. The internal stop-valve shall be operable from above or from below. If possible, the setting - open or closed - of the internal stop-valve shall be capable of being verified from the ground in both cases. The controls of the internal stop-valve shall be so designed as to prevent any inadvertent opening through impact or unconsidered action. The internal shut-off device must continue to be effective in the event of damage to the external control.

---

[6]   *However, in the case of shells intended for the carriage of certain cristallizable or highly viscous substances, deeply refrigerated liquefied gases and shells fitted with an ebonite or thermoplastic coating, the internal stop valve may be replaced by an external stop valve provided with additional protection.*

211 131
(contd)
The position and/or direction of closure of the sluice-valves must be clearly apparent.

In order to avoid any loss of contents in the event of damage to the external filling and discharge fittings (pipes, lateral shut-off devices), the internal stop-valve and its seating shall be protected against the danger of being wrenched off by external stresses or shall be so designed as to withstand them. The filling and discharge devices (including flanges or threaded plugs) and protective caps (if any) shall be capable of being secured against any inadvertent opening.

The shell or each of its compartments shall be provided with an opening large enough to permit inspection.

211 132
Shells intended for the carriage of substances for which all the openings are required to be above the surface level of the liquid may be equipped, in the lower part of the body, with a cleaning aperture (fist-hole). This aperture must be capable of being sealed by a flange so closed as to be leakproof and whose design must be approved by the competent authority or by a body designated by that authority.

211 133
Shells intended for the carriage of liquids having a vapour pressure of not more than 110 kPa (1.1 bar) (absolute) at 50 °C shall have a venting system and a safety device to prevent the contents from spilling out if the shell overturns; otherwise they must conform to the requirements of marginal 211 134 or 211 135.

211 134
Shells intended for the carriage of liquids having a vapour pressure of more than 110 kPa (1.1 bar) but not exceeding 175 kPa (1.75 bar) (absolute) at 50 °C shall have a safety valve set at not less than 150 kPa (1.5 bar) (gauge pressure) and which must be fully open at a pressure not exceeding the test pressure; otherwise they must conform to the requirements of marginal 211 135.

211 135
Shells intended for the carriage of liquids having a vapour pressure of more than 175 kPa (1.75 bar) but not exceeding 300 kPa (3 bar) (absolute) at 50 °C shall have a safety valve set at not less than 300 kPa (3 bar) gauge pressure and which must be fully open at a pressure not exceeding the test pressure; otherwise they must be hermetically closed [1].

211 136
No movable parts such as covers, closures, etc., which are liable to come into frictional or percussive contact with aluminium shells intended for the carriage of flammable liquids having a flash-point of or below 61 °C or for the carriage of flammable gases may be made of unprotected corrodible steel.

211 137-
211 139

SECTION 4. Type approval

211 140
The competent authority or a body designated by that authority shall issue in respect of each new type of tank a certificate attesting that the prototype tank, including the shell fastenings which it has surveyed, is suitable for the purpose for which it is intended and meets the construction requirements of section 2, the equipment requirements of section 3 and the conditions peculiar to the classes of substances carried.

---

[1]   *"Hermetically closed shells" means whose openings are hermetically closed and which are not equipped with safety valves, frangible discs or other similar safety devices. Shells having safety valves preceded by a bursting disc shall be deemed to be hermetically closed.*

211 141
(contd) The test results, the substances and/or the groups of substances for the carriage of which the tank is approved and its type approval number shall be entered in a test report. The substances of a group of substances shall be of similar kind and equally compatible with the characteristics of the shell. The substances or groups of substances permitted shall be specified in the test report, with their chemical names or the corresponding collective heading in the list of substances, and their class and item number.

This approval shall be valid for tanks manufactured according to this prototype without modification.

211 141-
211 149

SECTION 5.   Tests

211 150 Shells and their equipment shall either together or separately undergo an initial inspection before being put into service. This inspection shall include a check of conformity to the approved prototype, a check of the design characteristics [8], an external and internal examination, a hydraulic pressure test [9] and a check of satisfactory operation of the equipment.

The hydraulic pressure test shall be carried out on the shell as a whole at the pressure indicated in Part II of this Appendix, and separately on each compartment of compartment shells at a pressure of not less than 1.3 times the maximum working pressure. The leakproofness test shall be carried out separately on each compartment of compartmented shells.

The hydraulic pressure test shall be carried out before the installation of such thermal equipment as may be necessary. If the shells and their equipment are tested separately, they shall be jointly subjected to a leakproofness test after assembly.

211 151 Shells and their equipment shall undergo periodic inspections at fixed intervals. The periodic inspections shall include: an external and internal examination and, as a general rule, a hydraulic pressure test [9]. Sheathing for thermal or other insulation shall be removed only to the extent required for reliable appraisal of the characteristics of the shell.

The hydraulic pressure test shall be carried out on the shell as a whole at the pressure indicated in Part II of this Appendix, and separately on each compartment of compartmented shells at a pressure of not less than 1.3 times the maximum working pressure.

In the case of shells intended for the carriage of powdery or granular substances, and with the agreement of the expert approved by the competent authority, the periodic hydraulic pressure tests may be omitted and replaced by leakproofness tests in accordance with marginal 211 102 (3).

The maximum intervals for inspections shall be six years.

Tank-vehicles, demountable tanks and battery-vehicles empty, uncleaned, may be moved after expiration of the period for undergoing the test.

---

[8]   *The check of the design characteristics shall also include, for shells requiring a test pressure of 1 MPa (10 bar) or higher, the taking of weld test pieces (work samples) in accordance with the tests prescribed in Appendix B.1d.*

[9]   *In special cases and with the agreement of the expert approved by the competent authority, the hydraulic pressure test may be replaced by a pressure test using another liquid or gas, where such an operation does not present any danger.*

211 152 In addition, a leakproofness test of the shell with its equipment and a check of the satisfactory operation of all the equipment shall be carried out at least every three years. The leakproofness test shall be carried out separately on each compartment of compartmented shells. Empty, uncleaned fixed tanks (tank-vehicles), demountable tanks and battery-vehicles may be moved after expiration of this period, for undergoing inspection.

211 153 When the safety of the shell or of its equipment may have been impaired as a result of repairs, alterations or accident, an exceptional check shall be carried out.

211 154 The tests, inspections and checks in accordance with marginal 211 150 to 211 153 shall be carried out by the expert approved by the competent authority. Certificates shall be issued showing the results of these operations. These certificates shall refer to the list of the substances permitted for carriage in this shell in accordance with 211 140.

211 155-
211 159

SECTION 6. Marking

211 160 Every shell shall be fitted with a corrosion-resistant metal plate permanently attached to the shell in a place readily accessible for inspection. The following particulars at least shall be marked on the plate by stamping or by any other similar method. These particulars may be engraved directly on the walls of the shell itself, if the walls are so reinforced that the strength of the shell is not impaired:

- approval number;

- manufacturer's name or mark;

- manufacturer's serial number;

- year of manufacture;

- test pressure [10/] (gauge pressure);

- capacity [10/] - in the case of multiple-element shells, the capacity of each element;

- design temperature [10/] (only if above +50 °C or below -20 °C);

- date (month and year) of initial test and most recent periodic test in accordance with marginals 211 150 and 211 151;

- stamp of the expert who carried out the tests;

- test pressure on the shell as a whole and test pressure by compartment in MPa or bar (gauge pressure) where the pressure by compartment is less than the pressure on the shell; and

- material of the shell and, where appropriate, the protective lining.

In addition, the maximum working pressure allowed shall be inscribed on pressure-filled or pressure-discharge shells.

[10/] *The units of measurement should be indicated after numerical values.*

Appendix B.1a

211 161 The following particulars shall be inscribed on the tank-vehicle itself or on a plate. These particulars shall not be required in the case of a vehicle carrying demountable tanks:

- name of owner or operator;

- unladen mass; and

- maximum permissible mass.

211 162-
211 169

SECTION 7.   Operation

211 170 The thickness of the walls of the shell shall not, throughout its use, fall below the minimum figure prescribed in marginal 211 127 (2).

211 171 Shells shall not be loaded with any dangerous substances other than those for whose carriage they have been approved and which, in contact with the materials of the shell, gaskets, equipment and protective linings, are not liable to react dangerously with them, to form dangerous products or appreciably to weaken the material. Foodstuffs shall not be carried in these shells unless the necessary steps have been taken to prevent any harm to public health.

211 172 (1)   The following degrees of filling shall not be exceeded in shells intended for the carriage of liquids at ambient temperatures:

    (a)   for flammable substances without additional risks (e.g. toxicity or corrosivity), in shells with a venting system or with safety valves (even where preceded by a bursting disc):

$$degree\ of\ filling = \frac{100}{1 + \alpha\ (50 - t_F)}\ \%\ of\ capacity;$$

    (b)   for toxic or corrosive substances (whether flammable or not) in shells with a venting system or with safety valves (even where preceded by a bursting disc):

$$degree\ of\ filling = \frac{98}{1 + \alpha\ (50 - t_F)}\ \%\ of\ capacity;$$

    (c)   for flammable substances and for slightly toxic or slightly corrosive substances, (whether flammable or not) in hermetically-closed [11] shells without safety device:

$$degree\ of\ filling = \frac{97}{1 + \alpha\ (50 - t_F)}\ \%\ of\ capacity;$$

    (d)   for highly toxic, toxic, highly corrosive or corrosive substances (whether flammable or not) in hermetically closed [11] shells without safety device:

$$degree\ of\ filling = \frac{95}{1 + \alpha\ (50 - t_F)}\ \%\ of\ capacity.$$

---

[11]   See footnote [7] to marginal 211 135.

211 172   (2)   In these formulae, represents the mean coefficient of cubic expansion of the liquid between
(contd)   15 °C and 50 °C, i.e. for a maximum variation in temperature of 35 °C.

$$\alpha \text{ is calculated by the formula : } \alpha = \frac{d_{15} - d_{50}}{35 \times d_{50}}$$

where d_{15} and d_{50} are the relative densities of the liquid at 15 °C and 50 °C respectively and t_F is
the mean temperature of the liquid at the time of filling.

(3)   The provisions of paragraph (1) above shall not apply to shells whose contents are, by
means of a heating device, maintained at a temperature above 50 °C during carriage. In such a
case the degree of filling at the outset shall be such, and the temperature so regulated, that the shell
is not full to more than 95% of its capacity at any time during carriage, and that the filling
temperature is not exceeded.

(4)   Where hot substances are loaded, the temperature of the outer surface of the shell or of the
thermal insulation shall not exceed 70 °C during carriage.

211 173   Where shells intended for the carriage of liquids [12] are not divided by partitions or surge-plates
into sections of not more than 7 500 litres capacity, they shall be filled to not less than 80% of
their capacity unless they are nominally empty.

211 174   During loading and unloading of tanks, appropriate measures shall be taken to prevent the release
of dangerous quantities of gases and vapours.

Shells shall be closed in such a way that the contents cannot run out uncontrolled. The openings
of bottom-discharge shells shall be closed by means of screw-threaded plugs, blank flanges or other
equally effective devices. The leakproofness of the shell closures, particularly in the upper part of
the dip-tube, shall be verified by the consignor after the shell has been filled.

211 175   Where several closure systems are fitted in series, that nearest to the substance being carried shall
be closed first.

211 176   No dangerous residue of the substance carried shall adhere to the outside of shells during carriage,
whether they are laden or empty.

211 177   To be accepted for carriage, empty shells, uncleaned, must be closed in the same manner and
leakproof in the same degree as though they were full.

211 178   The connecting pipes between independent but interconnected shells of a transport unit shall be
empty during carriage.

Flexible filling and discharge pipes which are not permanently connected to the shell shall be
empty during carriage.

---

[12]   *Under this provision, substances whose kinematic viscosity at 20 °C is below 2 680 mm²/s shall
be deemed to be liquids.*

211 179 Substances which may react dangerously with each other shall not be carried in adjoining compartments of tanks.

The following are considered dangerous reactions:

(a) combustion and/or giving off considerable heat
(b) emission of flammable and/or toxic gases
(c) formation of corrosive liquids
(d) formation of unstable substances
(e) dangerous rise in pressure.

Substances which may react dangerously with each other may be carried in adjoining compartments of tanks, when these compartments are separated by a partition with a wall-thickness equal to or greater than that of the tank itself. They may also be carried in compartments of the same tank separated by an empty space or an empty compartment between loaded compartments.

SECTION 8.   Transitional measures

211 180 Fixed tanks (tank-vehicles), demountable tanks and battery-vehicles built before 1 October 1978 and not conforming to the requirements of this Appendix may, if they were built in conformity with the requirements of ADR, be used until 30 September 1984. Fixed tanks (tank-vehicles), demountable tanks and battery-vehicles intended for the carriage of gases of Class 2 may however be used until 30 September 1990 if the periodic-test requirement is complied with.

211 181 On the expiry of this period the aforesaid units may be kept in service if the equipment of the shell meets the present requirements. The thickness of the shell wall, except in the case of shells intended for the carriage of gases of Class 2, 3°, shall be appropriate to a calculation pressure of not less than 400 kPa (4 bar) (gauge pressure) in the case of mild steel and of not less than 200 kPa (2 bar) (gauge pressure) in the case of aluminium and aluminium alloys. For other than circular cross-sections of tanks, the diameter to be used as a basis for calculation shall be that of a circle whose area is equal to that of the actual cross-section of the tank.

211 182 The periodic tests for fixed tanks (tank-vehicles), demountable tanks and battery-vehicles kept in service under these transitional provisions shall be conducted in accordance with the provisions of Section 5 and with the pertinent special provisions for the various Classes. Unless the earlier provisions prescribed a higher test pressure, a test pressure of 200 kPa (2 bar) (gauge pressure) shall suffice for aluminium shells and aluminium-alloy shells.

211 183 Fixed tanks (tank-vehicles), demountable tanks and battery-vehicles which meet these transitional provisions may be used until 30 September 1993 for the carriage of the dangerous goods for which they have been approved. This transitional period shall not apply to fixed tanks (tank-vehicles), demountable tanks and battery-vehicles intended for the carriage of substances of Class 2, or to fixed tanks (tank-vehicles), demountable tanks and battery-vehicles whose wall thickness and items of equipment meet the requirements of this Appendix.

211 184 Fixed tanks (tank-vehicles), demountable tanks and battery-vehicles constructed before 1 May 1985 in accordance with the requirements of ADR in force between 1 October 1978 and 30 April 1985 but not conforming to the provisions applicable from 1 May 1985 may continue to be used after that date.

Appendix B.1a

211 185 Fixed tanks (tank-vehicles), demountable tanks and battery-vehicles, constructed between 1 May 1985 and the entry into force of the provisions applicable from 1 January 1988 which do not conform to those provisions but were constructed according to the requirements of ADR in force until that date, may still be used.

211 186 Fixed tanks (tank-vehicles), demountable tanks and battery-vehicles, constructed before the entry into force of the provisions applicable from 1 January 1993 which do not conform to those provisions but were constructed according to the requirements of ADR in force until that date may still be used.

211 187 Fixed tanks (tank-vehicles), demountable tanks and battery-vehicles constructed before 1 January 1990 shall, if used after 31 December 2004, conform to the provisions of marginal 211 127 (5), applicable as from 1 January 1990, concerning wall thickness and protection against damage.

**211 188-
211 199**

PART II. SPECIAL REQUIREMENTS SUPPLEMENTING OR MODIFYING THE REQUIREMENTS OF PART I

CLASS 2. GASES

211 200-
211 209

SECTION 1.   General; scope (use of tanks); definitions

Use

211 210 The gases of marginal 2201 listed in the tables in marginal 211 251 may be carried in fixed tanks, in demountable tanks, and in battery-vehicles.

211 211-
211 219

SECTION 2.   Construction

211 220 (1)   Shells intended for the carriage of substances of 1°, 2° or 4° shall be made of steel. In the case of weldless shells, by derogation from marginal 211 125 (3), a minimum elongation at fracture of 14% and also a stress σ (sigma) lower than or equal to limits hereafter given according to the material may be accepted:

    (a)   When the ratio Re/Rm of the minimum guaranteed characteristics after heat treatment is higher than 0.66 without exceeding 0.85:

$$\sigma \le 0.75 \; Re;$$

    (b)   When the ratio Re/Rm of the minimum guaranteed characteristics after heat treatment is higher than 0.85:

$$\sigma \le 0.5 \; Rm.$$

(2)   Receptacles as defined in marginals 2211 (1), (2) and (3) and cylinders as part of bundles of cylinders as defined in marginal 2211 (5) which are elements of a battery-vehicle, shall be constructed according to marginal 2212.

211 221 The requirements of Appendix B.1d apply to the materials and construction of welded shells.

211 222 Shells intended for the carriage of 1017 chlorine or 1076 phosgene of 2° TC shall be designed for a calculation pressure [see marginal 211 127 (2)] of at least 2.2 MPa (22 bar) (gauge pressure).

211 223-
211 229

SECTION 3.   Items of equipment

211 230 The discharge pipes of shells shall be capable of being closed by blank flanges or some other equally reliable device. For shells intended for the carriage of gases of 3°, these blank flanges or other equally reliable devices may be fitted with pressure-release openings of a maximum diameter of 1.5 mm.

Appendix B.1a

211 231 Shells intended for the carriage of liquefied gases may be provided with, in addition to the openings prescribed in marginal 211 131, openings for the fitting of gauges, including pressure gauges, and thermometers and with bleed holes, as required for their operation and safety.

211 232 Safety devices shall meet the following requirements:

(1)   Filling and discharge openings of shells intended for the carriage of liquefied flammable and/or toxic gases shall be equipped with an instant-closing internal safety device which closes automatically in the event of an unintended movement of the shell or of fire. It shall also be possible to operate the closing device by remote control.

(2)   All openings, other than those accommodating safety valves and than closed bleed holes, of shells intended for the carriage of liquefied flammable and/or toxic gases shall, if their nominal diameter is more than 1.5 mm, be equipped with an internal shut-off device.

(3)   By derogation from the provisions of (1) and (2), shells intended for the carriage of deeply-refrigerated flammable and/or toxic liquefied gases may be equipped with external devices in place of internal devices if the external devices afford protection against external damage at least equivalent to that afforded by the wall of the shell.

(4)   If the shells are equipped with gauges, the latter shall not be made of a transparent material in direct contact with the substance carried. If there are thermometers, they shall not project directly into the gas or liquid through the shell wall.

(5)   Shells intended for the carriage of 1053 hydrogen sulphide or 1064 methyl mercaptan of 2° TF or 1017 chlorine, 1076 phosgene or 1079 sulphur dioxide of 2° TC shall not have an opening below the surface level of the liquid. In addition, the cleaning apertures (fist holes) referred to in marginal 211 132 shall not be permitted.

(6)   Filling and discharge openings situated in the upper part of shells shall be equipped with, in addition to what is prescribed in (1), a second, external, closing device. This device shall be capable of being closed by a blank flange or some other equally reliable device.

(7)   By derogation from the provisions in paragraphs (1), (2) and (6), for receptacles as defined in marginals 2211 (1), (2), (3) and (5) which form a battery-vehicle, the required closing devices may be provided for within the manifolding arrangement.

211 233 Safety valves shall meet the following requirements:

(1)   Shells intended for the carriage of gases of 1°, 2° or 4° may be provided with not more than two safety valves whose aggregate clear cross-sectional area of passage at the seating or seatings shall be not less than 20 cm^2 per 30 m^3 or part thereof of the receptacle's capacity.

These valves shall be capable of opening automatically at a pressure of between 0.9 and 1.0 times the test pressure of the shell to which they are fitted. They shall be of such a type as to resist dynamic stresses, including liquid surge. The use of dead-weight or counter-weight valves is prohibited.

Shells intended for the carriage of gases of 1° to 4° indicated by the letter T in marginal 2201, shall not have safety valves unless the safety valves are preceded by a bursting disc. In the latter case the arrangement of the bursting disc and the safety valve shall be satisfactory to the competent authority.

211 233
(contd) Where tank-vehicles are intended for carriage by sea, the provisions of this paragraph shall not prohibit the fitting of safety valves conforming to the regulations governing that mode of transport [13].

(2)   Shells intended for the carriage of gases of 3° shall be equipped with two independent safety valves, each so designed as to allow the gases formed by evaporation during normal operation to escape from the shell in such a way that the pressure does not at any time exceed by more than 10% the working pressure indicated on the shell. One of the two safety valves may be replaced by a bursting disc which shall be such as to burst at the test pressure. In the event of loss of the vacuum in a double-walled shell, or of destruction of 20% of the insulation of a single-walled shell, the safety valve and the bursting disc shall permit an outflow such that the pressure in the shell cannot exceed the test pressure.

(3)   The safety valves of shells intended for the carriage of gases of 3° shall be capable of opening at the working pressure indicated on the shell. They shall be so designed as to function faultlessly even at their lowest working temperature. The reliability of their operation at that temperature shall be established and checked either by testing each valve or by testing a specimen valve of each design-type.

Thermal insulation

211 234   (1)   If shells intended for the carriage of gases of 2° are equipped with thermal insulation, such insulation shall consist of either:

-    a sun shield covering not less than the upper third but not more than the upper half of the shell surface and separated from the shell by an air space at least 4 cm across; or

-    a complete cladding, of adequate thickness, of insulating materials.

(2)   Shells intended for the carriage of gases of 3° shall be thermally insulated. Thermal insulation shall be ensured by means of a continuous sheathing. If the space between the shell and the sheathing is under vacuum (vacuum insulation), the protective sheathing shall be so designed as to withstand without deformation an external pressure of at least 100 kPa (1 bar) (gauge pressure). By derogation from marginal 211 102 (2) (a), external and internal reinforcing devices may be taken into account in the calculations. If the sheathing is so closed as to be gas-tight, a device shall be provided to prevent any dangerous pressure from developing in the insulating layer in the event of inadequate gas-tightness of the shell or of its items of equipment. The device shall prevent the infiltration of moisture into the heat-insulating sheath.

(3)   Shells intended for the carriage of liquefied gases having a boiling point below -182 °C at atmospheric pressure shall not include any combustible material either in the thermal insulation or in the means of attachment to the frame.

The means of attachment for shells of vacuum insulated tanks may, with the approval of the competent authority, contain plastics substances between the shell and the sheathing.

---

[13]   *These requirements are contained in Section 13 of the General Introduction to the International Maritime Dangerous Goods (IMDG) Code published by the International Maritime Organization, London.*

211 235 (1)   A battery-vehicle contains elements which are linked to each other by a manifold and permanently fixed to a transport unit. The following elements are considered to be elements of a battery-vehicle:

- cylinders as defined in marginal 2211 (1);

- tubes as defined in marginal 2211 (2);

- pressure drums as defined in marginal 2211 (3);

- bundles of cylinders (also known as frames) as defined in marginal 2211 (5);

- shells as defined in Annex B.

NOTE: Bundles of cylinders as defined in marginal 2211 (5) which are not elements of a battery-vehicle are subject to the requirements of marginals 2204 to 2224.

(2)   The following conditions shall be complied with for battery-vehicles:

(a)   If one of the elements of a battery-vehicle is equipped with a safety valve and shut-off devices are provided between the elements, every element shall be so equipped.

(b)   The filling and discharge devices may be affixed to a manifold.

(c)   Each element of a battery-vehicle, including each individual cylinder of a bundle, as defined in marginal 2211 (5), intended for the carriage of gases designated by capital letter T in marginal 2201, shall be capable of being isolated by a shut-off valve.

(d)   The elements of a battery-vehicle intended for the carriage of gases designated by capital letter F in marginal 2201, when consisting of receptacles as defined in marginals 2211 (1), (2), (3) and (5), shall be combined to groups of not more than 5,000 litres which are capable of being isolated by a shut-off valve.

Each element of a battery-vehicle intended for the carriage of gases designated by capital letter F in marginal 2201 when consisting of shells as defined in Annex B shall be capable of being isolated by a shut-off valve.

(3)   The following requirements apply to demountable tanks:

(a)   they shall not be interconnected by a manifold; and

(b)   if the demountable tanks can be rolled, the valves shall be provided with protective caps.

211 236   By derogation from the provisions of marginal 211 131, shells intended for the carriage of deeply-refrigerated liquefied gases need not have an inspection aperture.

211 237-
211 239

        SECTION 4.   **Type approval**

211 240-
211 249   (No special requirements)

Appendix B.1a

SECTION 5. **Tests**

211 250 (1) Receptacles as defined in marginal 2211 (1), (2) and (3) and cylinders as part of bundles of cylinders as defined in marginal 2211 (5), which are elements of a battery-vehicle, shall be tested according to marginal 2219.

(2) The materials of every welded shell which do not meet the definition of paragraph (1) shall be tested according to the method described in Appendix B.1d.

211 251 (1) The test pressure for shells intended for the carriage of gases of 1° having a critical temperature below -50 °C shall be at least one and one-half times the filling pressure at 15 °C.

(2) The test pressure for shells intended for the carriage of:

- gases of 1° having a critical temperature of -50 °C or above; and

- gases of 2° having a critical temperature below 70 °C

- gases of 4°

shall be such that, when the shell is filled to the maximum mass of the contents per litre of capacity, the pressure reached in the shell by the substance at 55 °C for shells with thermal insulation or 65 °C for shells without thermal insulation does not exceed the test pressure.

(3) The test pressure for shells intended for the carriage of gases of 2° having a critical temperature of 70 °C or above will be:

(a) If the shell is equipped with thermal insulation, at least equal to the vapour pressure, reduced by 0.1 MPa (1 bar) of the liquid at 60 °C, but not less than 1 MPa (10 bar);

(b) If the shell is not equipped with thermal insulation, at least equal to the vapour pressure, reduced by 0.1 MPa (1 bar), of the liquid at 65 °C, but not less than 1 MPa (10 bar).

The maximum permissible mass of contents per litre of capacity in kg/litre prescribed for the degree of filling is calculated as follows:

maximum permissible mass of contents
per litre of capacity   =   0.95 × density of the liquid phase at 50 °C;

moreover the vapour phase shall not disappear below 60 °C.

If the shells are not more than 1.5 metre in diameter the values of the test pressure and maximum permissible mass of contents per litre of capacity conforming to marginal 2219 (d) shall be applicable.

(4) The test pressure for shells intended for the carriage of gases of 3° shall be not less than 1.3 times the maximum permitted working pressure indicated on the shell, but not less than 300 kPa (3 bar) (gauge pressure); for shells with vacuum insulation the test pressure shall be not less than 1.3 times the maximum permitted working pressure increased by 100 kPa (1 bar).

Appendix B.1a

211 251 **(5)** **Table of gases and gas mixtures which may be carried in fixed tanks, demountable tanks**
(contd) **or battery-vehicles, minimum test pressure of the shells and as far as applicable, maximum mass**
of contents per litre of capacity.

In the case of gases and gas mixtures classified under n.o.s. entries, the values of the test pressure and maximum mass of contents per litre of capacity shall be prescribed by the expert approved by the competent authority.

When shells for gases of 1° or 2° having a critical temperature of -50 °C or above and below 70 °C have been subjected to a test pressure lower than shown in the table, and the shells are fitted with thermal insulation, a lower maximum load may be prescribed by the expert approved by the competent authority, provided that the pressure reached in the shell by the substance at 55 °C does not exceed the test pressure stamped on the shell.

Toxic gases and gas mixtures classified under n.o.s. entries with a $LC_{50} < 200$ ppm shall not be authorized for transport in demountable tanks, fixed tanks or battery-vehicles.

NOTE: 1076 Phosgene of 2°TC, 1067 Dinitrogen tetroxide (nitrogen dioxide) of 2°TOC and 1001 Acetylene, dissolved, of 4° F shall only be authorized for transport in battery-vehicles.

Item No. and group	Identification number	Name of the substance	Minimum test pressure for shells				Max. filling ratio (kg/l)
			With thermal insulation		Without thermal insulation		
			MPa	bar	MPa	bar	
1°A	1002	AIR, COMPRESSED	See marginal 211 251 (1)				
	1006	ARGON, COMPRESSED	See marginal 211 251 (1)				
	1046	HELIUM, COMPRESSED	See marginal 211 251 (1)				
	1056	KRYPTON, COMPRESSED	See marginal 211 251 (1)				
	1065	NEON, COMPRESSED	See marginal 211 251 (1)				
	1066	NITROGEN, COMPRESSED	See marginal 211 251 (1)				
	1979	RARE GASES MIXTURE, COMPRESSED	See marginal 211 251 (1)				
	1980	RARE GASES AND OXYGEN MIXTURE, COMPRESSED	See marginal 211 251 (1)				
	1981	RARE GASES AND NITROGEN MIXTURE, COMPRESSED	See marginal 211 251 (1)				
	1982	TETRAFLUOROMETHANE, COMPRESSED (REFRIGERANT GAS R 14, COMPRESSED)	20 30	200 300	20 30	200 300	0.62 0.94
	2036	XENON, COMPRESSED	12	120	13	130	1.3 1.24
	2193	HEXAFLUOROETHANE COMPRESSED (REFRIGERANT GAS R 116, COMPRESSED)	16 20	160 200	20	200	1.1 1.28 1.34
	1956	COMPRESSED GAS, N.O.S.	See marginal 211 251 (1) or (2)				
1°O	1014	CARBON DIOXIDE AND OXYGEN MIXTURE, COMPRESSED	See marginal 211 251 (1)				
	1072	OXYGEN, COMPRESSED	See marginal 211 251 (1)				
	3156	COMPRESSED GAS, OXIDIZING, N.O.S.	See marginal 211 251 (1) or (2)				
1°F	1049	HYDROGEN, COMPRESSED	See marginal 211 251 (1)				
	1957	DEUTERIUM, COMPRESSED	See marginal 211 251 (1)				
	1962	ETHYLENE, COMPRESSED	12 22.5	120 225	22.5 30	225 300	0.34 0.37 0.25 0.36
	1971 1971	METHANE, COMPRESSED or NATURAL GAS, COMPRESSED with high methane content	See marginal 211 251 (1)				
	2034	HYDROGEN AND METHANE MIXTURE, COMPRESSED	See marginal 211 251 (1)				
	2203	SILANE, COMPRESSED [2]	2.5 25	225 250	22.5 25	225 250	0.32 0.41
	1964	HYDROCARBON GAS MIXTURE, COMPRESSED, N.O.S	See marginal 211 251 (1) or (2)				
	1954	COMPRESSED GAS, FLAMMABLE, N.O.S	See marginal 211 251 (1) or (2)				

[2]   *Considered as pyrophoric.*

Item No. and group	Identification number	Name of the substance	Minimum test pressure for shells				Max. filling ratio (kg/l)
			With thermal insulation		Without thermal insulation		
			MPa	bar	MPa	bar	
1°T	1612	HEXAETHYL TETRAPHOSPHATE AND COMPRESSED GAS MIXTURE	See marginal 211 251 (1)				
	1955	COMPRESSED GAS, TOXIC, N.O.S.	See marginal 211 251 (1) or (2) and [2]				
1°TF	1016	CARBON MONOXIDE, COMPRESSED	See marginal 211 251 (1)				
	1023	COAL GAS, COMPRESSED	See marginal 211 251 (1)				
	1071	OIL GAS, COMPRESSED	See marginal 211 251 (1)				
	1911	DIBORANE, COMPRESSED	Not allowed				
	2600	CARBON MONOXIDE AND HYDROGEN MIXTURE, COMPRESSED	See marginal 211 251 (1)				
	1953	COMPRESSED GAS, TOXIC, FLAMMABLE, N.O.S.	See marginal 211 251 (1) or (2) and [2]				
1°TC	1008	BORON TRIFLUORIDE, COMPRESSED	22.5 30	225 300	22.5 30	225 300	0.715 0.86
	1859	SILICON TETRAFLUORIDE, COMPRESSED	20 30	200 300	20 30	200 300	0.74 1.1
	2198	PHOSPHORUS PENTAFLUORIDE, COMPRESSED	Not allowed				
	2417	CARBONYL FLUORIDE, COMPRESSED	20 30	200 300	20 30	200 300	0.47 0.7
	3304	COMPRESSED GAS, TOXIC, CORROSIVE, N.O.S.	See marginal 211 251 (1) or (2) and [2]				
1°TO	2451	NITROGEN TRIFLUORIDE	20 30	200 300	20 30	200 300	0.5 0.75
	3303	COMPRESSED GAS, TOXIC, OXIDIZING, N.O.S.	See marginal 211 251 (1) or (2) and [2]				
1°TFC	3305	COMPRESSED GAS, TOXIC, FLAMMABLE, CORROSIVE, N.O.S.	See marginal 211 251 (1) or (2) and [2]				
1°TOC	1045	FLUORINE, COMPRESSED	Not allowed				
	1660	NITRIC OXIDE, COMPRESSED	Not allowed				
	2190	OXYGEN DIFLUORIDE	Not allowed				
	3306	COMPRESSED GAS, TOXIC, OXIDIZING, CORROSIVE, N.O.S.	See marginal 211 251 (1) or (2) and [2]				
2°A	1009	BROMOTRIFLUOROMETHANE (REFRIGERANT GAS R 13B1)	12	120	4.2 12 25	42 120 250	1.13 1.44 1.6 1.5
	1013	CARBON DIOXIDE	19 22.5	190 225	19 25	190 250	0.66 0.75 0.73 0.78

[2] *Allowed if LC_{50} equal to or greater than 200 ppm.*

Item No. and group	Identification number	Name of the substance	Minimum test pressure for shells				Max. filling ratio (kg/l)
			With thermal insulation		Without thermal insulation		
			MPa	bar	MPa	bar	
2°A (contd)	1015	CARBON DIOXIDE AND NITROUS OXIDE MIXTURE	See marginal 211 251 (2) or (3)				
	1018	CHLORODIFLUOROMETHANE (REFRIGERANT GAS R 22)	2.4	24	2.6	26	1.03
	1020	CHLOROPENTAFLUOROETHANE (REFRIGERANT GAS R 115)	2	20	2.3	23	1.06
	1021	1-CHLORO-1,2,2,2-TETRAFLUOROETHANE (REFRIGERANT GAS R 124)	1	10	1.1	11	1.2
	1022	CHLOROTRIFLUOROMETHANE (REFRIGERANT GAS R 13)			10	100	0.83
					12	120	0.9
					19	190	1.04
					25	250	1.1
			12	120			0.96
			22.5	225			1.12
	1028	DICHLORODIFLUOROMETHANE (REFRIGERANT GAS R 12)	1.5	15	1.6	16	1.15
	1029	DICHLOROFLUOROMETHANE (REFRIGERANT GAS R 21)	1	10	1	10	1.23
	1058	LIQUEFIED GASES, non-flammable, charged with nitrogen, carbon dioxide or air	1.5 × filling pressure See marginal 211 251 (2) or (3)				
	1080	SULPHUR HEXAFLUORIDE	12	120			1.34
					7	70	1.04
					14	140	1.33
					16	160	1.37
	1858	HEXAFLUOROPROPYLENE (REFRIGERANT GAS R 1216)	1.7	17	1.9	19	1.11
	1952	ETHYLENE OXIDE AND CARBON DIOXIDE MIXTURE with not more than 9% ethylene oxide	19	190	19	190	0.66
			25	250	25	250	0.75
	1958	1,2-DICHLORO-1,1,2,2-TETRAFLUOROETHANE (REFRIGERANT GAS R 114)	1	10	1	10	1.3
	1973	CHLORODIFLUOROMETHANE AND CHLOROPENTAFLUOROETHANE MIXTURE with fixed boiling point, with approximately 49% chlorodifluoromethane (REFRIGERANT GAS R 502)	2.5	25	2.8	28	1.05 0.75
	1974	CHLORODIFLUOROBROMOMETHANE (REFRIGERANT GAS R 12B1)	1	10	1	10	1.61
	1976	OCTAFLUOROCYCLOBUTANE (REFRIGERANT GAS R C318)	1	10	1	10	1.34
	1983	1-CHLORO-2,2,2-TRIFLUOROETHANE (REFRIGERANT GAS R 133a)	1	10	1	10	1.18
	1984	TRIFLUOROMETHANE (REFRIGERANT GAS R 23)	19	190			0.92
			25	250			0.99
					19	190	0.87
					25	250	0.95

Item No. and group	Identification number	Name of the substance	Minimum test pressure for shells				Max. filling ratio (kg/l)
			With thermal insulation		Without thermal insulation		
			MPa	bar	MPa	bar	
2°A (contd)	2422	OCTAFLUOROBUT-2-ENE (REFRIGERANT GAS R 1318)	1.2	12	1.2	12	1.34
	2424	OCTAFLUOROPROPANE (REFRIGERANT GAS R 218)	2.5	25	2.5	25	1.09
	2599	CHLOROTRIFLUOROMETHANE AND TRIFLUOROMETHANE, AZEOTROPIC MIXTURE with approximately 60% chlorotrifluoromethane (REFRIGERANT GAS R 503)	3.1 4.2 10	31 42 100	3.1 4.2 10	31 42 100	0.11 0.21 0.76 0.2 0.66
	2602	DICHLORODIFLUOROMETHANE AND 1,1-DIFLUOROETHANE, AZEOTROPIC MIXTURE with approximately 74% dichlorodifluoromethane (REFRIGERANT GAS R 500)	1.8	18	2	20	1.01
	3070	ETHYLENE OXIDE AND DICHLORODIFLUOROMETHANE MIXTURE with not more than 12.5% ethylene oxide	1.5	15	1.6	16	1.09
	3159	1,1,1,2-TETRAFLUOROETHANE (REFRIGERANT GAS R 134a)	1.6	16	1.8	18	1.04
	3220	PENTAFLUOROETHANE (REFRIGERANT GAS R 125)	4.1	4.1	4.9	4.9	0.95
	3296	HEPTAFLUOROPROPANE (REFRIGERANT GAS R 227)	1.5	15	1.5	15	1.2
	3297	ETHYLENE OXIDE AND CHLOROTETRAFLUORO-ETHANE MIXTURE, with not more than 8.8% ethylene oxide	1	10	1	10	1.16
	3298	ETHYLENE OXIDE AND PENTAFLUOROETHANE MIXTURE, with not more than 7.9% ethylene oxide	2.6	26	2.6	26	1.02
	3299	ETHYLENE OXIDE AND TETRAFLUOROETHANE MIXTURE, with not more than 5.6% ethylene oxide	1.7	17	1.7	17	1.03
	1078	REFRIGERANT GASES, N.O.S. such as					
		MIXTURE F1	1	10	1.1	11	1.23
		MIXTURE F2	1.5	15	1.6	16	1.15
		MIXTURE F3	2.4	24	2.7	27	1.03
		Other mixtures	See marginal 211 251 (2) or (3)				
	1968	INSECTICIDE GAS, N.O.S.	See marginal 211 251 (2) or (3)				
	3163	LIQUEFIED GAS, N.O.S.	See marginal 211 251 (2) or (3)				
2°O	1070	NITROUS OXIDE	22.5	225	18 22.5 25	180 225 250	0.78 0.68 0.74 0.75
	3157	LIQUEFIED GAS, OXIDIZING, N.O.S.	See marginal 211 251 (2) or (3)				

Item No. and group	Identification number	Name of the substance	Minimum test pressure for shells				Max. filling ratio (kg/l)
			With thermal insulation		Without thermal insulation		
			MPa	bar	MPa	bar	
2°F	1010	1.2-BUTADIENE, INHIBITED or	1	10	1	10	0.59
	1010	1.3-BUTADIENE, INHIBITED or	1	10	1	10	0.55
	1010	MIXTURES OF 1,3-BUTADIENE AND HYDROCARBONS, INHIBITED	1	10	1	10	0.5
	1011	BUTANE	1	10	1	10	0.51
	1012	BUTYLENES MIXTURE or	1	10	1	10	0.5
	1012	1-BUTYLENE or	1	10	1	10	0.53
	1012	CIS-2-BUTENE or	1	10	1	10	0.55
	1012	TRANS-2-BUTYLENE	1	10	1	10	0.54
	1027	CYCLOPROPANE	1.6	16	1.8	18	0.53
	1030	1,1-DIFLUOROETHANE (REFRIGERANT GAS R 152a)	1.4	14	1.6	16	0.79
	1032	DIMETHYLAMINE, ANHYDROUS	1	10	1	10	0.59
	1033	DIMETHYL ETHER	1.4	14	1.6	16	0.58
	1035	ETHANE	12	120			0.32
					9.5	95	0.25
					12	120	0.29
					30	300	0.39
	1036	ETHYLAMINE	1	10	1	10	0.61
	1037	ETHYL CHLORIDE	1	10	1	10	0.8
	1039	ETHYL METHYL ETHER	1	10	1	10	0.64
	1041	ETHYLENE OXIDE AND CARBON DIOXIDE MIXTURE, with more than 9% ethylene oxide but not more than 87%	2.4	24	2.6	26	0.73
	1055	ISOBUTYLENE	1	10	1	10	0.52
	1060	METHYLACETYLENE AND PROPADIENE MIXTURE, STABILIZED	See marginal 211 251 (2) or (3)				
		PROPADIENE with 1% to 4% methylacetylene	2.2	22	2.2	22	0.5
		MIXTURE P1	2.5	25	2.8	28	0.49
		MIXTURE P2	2.2	22	2.3	23	0.47
	1061	METHYLAMINE, ANHYDROUS	1	10	1.1	11	0.58
	1063	METHYL CHLORIDE (REFRIGERANT GAS R 40)	1.3	13	1.5	15	0.81
	1077	PROPYLENE	2.5	25	2.7	27	0.43
	1081	TETRAFLUOROETHYLENE, INHIBITED	Not allowed				
	1083	TRIMETHYLAMINE, ANHYDROUS	1	10	1	10	0.56
	1085	VINYL BROMIDE, INHIBITED	1	10	1	10	1.37
	1086	VINYL CHLORIDE, INHIBITED	1	10	1.1	11	0.81
	1087	VINYL METHYL ETHER, INHIBITED	1	10	1	10	0.67
	1860	VINYL FLUORIDE, INHIBITED	12	120			0.58
			22.5	225			0.65
					25	250	0.64

Item No. and group	Identification number	Name of the substance	Minimum test pressure for shells				Max. filling ratio (kg/l)
			With thermal insulation		Without thermal insulation		
			MPa	bar	MPa	bar	
2°F (contd)	1912	METHYLCHLORIDE AND METHYLENE CHLORIDE MIXTURE	1.3	13	1.5	15	0.81
	1959	1,1-DIFLUOROETHYLENE (REFRIGERANT GAS R 1132a)	12 22.5	120 225	25	250	0.66 0.78 0.77
	1969	ISOBUTANE	1	10	1	10	0.49
	1978	PROPANE	2.1	21	2.3	23	0.42
	2035	1,1,1-TRIFLUOROETHANE (REFRIGERANT GAS R 143a)	2.8	28	3.2	32	0.79
	2044	2,2-DIMETHYLPROPANE	1	10	1	10	0.53
	2200	PROPADIENE, INHIBITED	2.2	22	2.2	22	0.5
	2419	BROMOTRIFLUOROETHYLENE	1	10	1	10	1.19
	2452	ETHYLACETYLENE, INHIBITED	1	10	1	10	0.57
	2453	ETHYL FLUORIDE (REFRIGERANT GAS R 161)	3	30	3	30	0.57
	2454	METHYL FLUORIDE (REFRIGERANT GAS R 41)	30	300	30	300	0.36
	2517	1-CHLORO-1,1-DIFLUOROETHANE (REFRIGERANT GAS R 142b)	1	10	1	10	0.99
	2601	CYCLOBUTANE	1	10	1	10	0.63
	3153	PERFLUORO(METHYL VINYL ETHER)	2	20	2	20	0.75
	3154	PERFLUORO(ETHYL VINYL ETHER)	1	10	1	10	0.98
	3252	DIFLUOROMETHANE (REFRIGERANT GAS R 32)	3.9	3.9	4.5	45	0.78
	1965	HYDROCARBON GAS MIXTURE, LIQUEFIED, N.O.S.					
		MIXTURE A	1	10	1	10	0.5
		MIXTURE A0	1.2	12	1.4	14	0.47
		MIXTURE A1	1.6	16	1.8	18	0.46
		MIXTURE B	2	20	2.3	23	0.43
		MIXTURE C	2.5	25	2.7	27	0.42
		Other mixtures	See marginal 211 251 (2) or (3)				
	3161	LIQUEFIED GAS, FLAMMABLE, N.O.S.	See marginal 211 251 (2) or (3)				
2°T	1062	METHYL BROMIDE	1	10	1	10	1.51
	1581	CHLOROPICRIN AND METHYL BROMIDE MIXTURE	Not allowed				
	1582	CHLOROPICRIN AND METHYL CHLORIDE MIXTURE	Not allowed				
	2191	SULPHURYL FLUORIDE	5	50	5	50	1.1
	1967	INSECTICIDE GAS, TOXIC, N.O.S.	See marginal 211 251 (2) or (3) and [2/]				
	3162	LIQUEFIED GAS, TOXIC, N.O.S.	See marginal 211 251 (2) or (3) and [2/]				

___

[2/]   *Allowed if LC_{50} equal to or greater than 200 ppm.*

Item No. and group	Identification number	Name of the substance	Minimum test pressure for shells				Max. filling ratio (kg/l)
			With thermal insulation		Without thermal insulation		
			MPa	bar	MPa	bar	
2°TF	1026	CYANOGEN	10	100	10	100	0.7
	1040	ETHYLENE OXIDE WITH NITROGEN up to a total pressure of 1 MPa (10 bar) at 50 °C	1.5	15	1.5	15	0.78 0.77
	1053	HYDROGEN SULPHIDE	4.5	45	5	50	0.67
	1064	METHYL MERCAPTAN	1	10	1	10	0.78
	1082	TRIFLUOROCHLOROETHYLENE, INHIBITED	1.5	15	1.7	17	1.13
	2188	ARSINE	Not allowed				
	2192	GERMANE [a]	Not allowed				
	2199	PHOSPHINE [a]	Not allowed				
	2202	HYDROGEN SELENIDE, ANHYDROUS	Not allowed				
	2204	CARBONYL SULPHIDE	2.6	26	2.6	26	0.84
	2676	STIBINE	Not allowed				
	3300	ETHYLENE OXIDE AND CARBON DIOXIDE MIXTURE with more than 87% ethylene oxide	2.8	28	2.8	28	0.73 0.77
	3160	LIQUEFIED GAS, TOXIC, FLAMMABLE, N.O.S.	See marginal 211 251 (2) or (3) and [b]				
2°TC	1005	AMMONIA, ANHYDROUS	2.6	26	2.9	29	0.53
	1017	CHLORINE	1.7	17	1.9	19	1.25
	1048	HYDROGEN BROMIDE, ANHYDROUS	5	50	5.5	55	1.54
	1050	HYDROGEN CHLORIDE, ANHYDROUS	12	120			0.69
					10	100	0.3
					12	120	0.56
					15	150	0.67
					20	200	0.74
	1069	NITROSYL CHLORIDE	Not allowed				
	1076	PHOSGENE	Only in battery-vehicles				
	1079	SULPHUR DIOXIDE	1	10	1.2	12	1.23
	1589	CYANOGEN CHLORIDE, INHIBITED	Not allowed				
	1741	BORON TRICHLORIDE	Not allowed				
	2194	SELENIUM HEXAFLUORIDE	Not allowed				
	2195	TELLURIUM HEXAFLUORIDE	Not allowed				
	2196	TUNGSTEN HEXAFLUORIDE	Not allowed				
	2197	HYDROGEN IODIDE, ANHYDROUS	2.3	23	2.3	23	2.25
	2418	SULPHUR TETRAFLUORIDE	Not allowed				
	2420	HEXAFLUOROACETONE	2.2	22	2.2	22	1.08
	3057	TRIFLUOROACETYL CHLORIDE	1.3	13	1.5	15	1.17
	3308	LIQUEFIED GAS, TOXIC, CORROSIVE, N.O.S.	See marginal 211 251 (2) or (3) and [b]				

[a]   *Considered as pyrophoric.*

[b]   *Allowed if LC_{50} equal to or greater than 200 ppm.*

Item No. and group	Identification number	Name of the substance	Minimum test pressure for shells				Max. filling ratio (kg/l)
			With thermal insulation		Without thermal insulation		
			MPa	bar	MPa	bar	
2°TO	3083	PERCHLORYL FLUORIDE	3.3	33	3.3	33	1.21
	3307	LIQUEFIED GAS, TOXIC, OXIDIZING, N.O.S.	See marginal 211 251 (2) or (3) and [2]				
2°TFC	2189	DICHLOROSILANE	1	10	1	10	0.9
	2534	METHYLCHLOROSILANE	Not allowed				
	3309	LIQUEFIED GAS, TOXIC, FLAMMABLE, CORROSIVE, N.O.S.	See marginal 211 251 (2) or (3) and [2]				
2°TOC	1067	DINITROGEN TETROXIDE (NITROGEN DIOXIDE)	Only in battery-vehicles				
	1749	CHLORINE TRIFLUORIDE	3	30	3	30	1.4
	1975	NITRIC OXIDE AND DINITROGEN TETROXIDE MIXTURE (NITRIC OXIDE AND NITROGEN DIOXIDE MIXTURE)	Not allowed				
	2548	CHLORINE PENTAFLUORIDE	Not allowed				
	2901	BROMINE CHLORIDE	1	10	1	10	1.5
	3310	LIQUEFIED GAS, TOXIC, OXIDIZING, CORROSIVE, N.O.S.	See marginal 211 251 (2) or (3) and [2]				
3°A	1913	NEON, REFRIGERATED LIQUID	See marginal 211 251 (4)				
	1951	ARGON, REFRIGERATED LIQUID	See marginal 211 251 (4)				
	1963	HELIUM, REFRIGERATED LIQUID	See marginal 211 251 (4)				
	1970	KRYPTON, REFRIGERATED LIQUID	See marginal 211 251 (4)				
	1977	NITROGEN, REFRIGERATED LIQUID	See marginal 211 251 (4)				
	2187	CARBON DIOXIDE, REFRIGERATED LIQUID	See marginal 211 251 (4)				
	2591	XENON, REFRIGERATED LIQUID	See marginal 211 251 (4)				
	3136	TRIFLUOROMETHANE, REFRIGERATED LIQUID	See marginal 211 251 (4)				
	3158	GAS, REFRIGERATED LIQUID, N.O.S.	See marginal 211 251 (4)				
3°O	1003	AIR, REFRIGERATED LIQUID	See marginal 211 251 (4)				
	1073	OXYGEN, REFRIGERATED LIQUID	See marginal 211 251 (4)				
	2201	NITROUS OXIDE, REFRIGERATED LIQUID	See marginal 211 251 (4)				
	3311	GAS, REFRIGERATED, LIQUEFIED, OXIDIZING, N.O.S.	See marginal 211 251 (4)				
3°F	1038	ETHYLENE, REFRIGERATED LIQUID	See marginal 211 251 (4)				
	1961	ETHANE, REFRIGERATED LIQUID	See marginal 211 251 (4)				
	1966	HYDROGEN, REFRIGERATED LIQUID	See marginal 211 251 (4)				
	1972 1972	METHANE, REFRIGERATED LIQUID or NATURAL GAS, REFRIGERATED LIQUID, with high methane content	See marginal 211 251 (4)				

[2] *Allowed if LC_{50} equal to or greater than 200 ppm.*

| Item No. and group | Identification number | Name of the substance | Minimum test pressure for shells | | | | Max. filling ratio (kg/l) |
| | | | With thermal insulation | | Without thermal insulation | | |
			MPa	bar	MPa	bar	
3°F (contd)	3138	ETHYLENE, ACETYLENE AND PROPYLENE IN MIXTURE, REFRIGERATED LIQUID, containing at least 71.5% ethylene with not more than 22.5% acetylene and not more than 6% propylene	See marginal 211 251 (4)				
	3312	GAS, REFRIGERATED, LIQUEFIED, FLAMMABLE, N.O.S.	See marginal 211 251 (4)				
4°A	2073	AMMONIA SOLUTIONS, relative density less than 0.88 at 15 °C					
		with more than 35% and not more than 40% ammonia	1	10	1	10	0.8
		with more than 40% and not more than 50% ammonia	1.2	12	1.2	12	0.77
4°F	1001	ACETYLENE, DISSOLVED	Only in battery vehicles				
4°TC	3318	AMMONIA SOLUTIONS, relative density less than 0.880 at 15 °C in water, with more than 50% ammonia	See marginal 211 251 (2)				

211 252 The first hydraulic pressure test shall be carried out before the thermal insulation is placed in position.

211 253 The capacity of each shell intended for the carriage of gases of 1° filled by mass, or gases of 2° or 4° shall be determined, under the supervision of an expert approved by the competent authority, by weighing or volumetric measurement of the quantity of water which fills the shell; any error in the measurement of shell capacity shall be of less than 1%. Determination by a calculation based on the dimensions of the shell is not permitted. The maximum filling masses allowed in accordance with marginals 2219 and 211 251 (3) shall be prescribed by an approved expert.

211 254 Checking of the welds shall be carried out in accordance with the lambda-coefficient 1.0 requirements of marginal 211 127 (8).

211 255 By derogation from the requirements of marginal 211 151, the periodic tests shall take place:

(1) Every three years in the case of shells intended for the carriage of 1008 boron trifluoride of 1° TC, 1053 hydrogen sulphide of 2° TF, 1048 hydrogen bromide, anhydrous, 1050 hydrogen chloride, anhydrous, 1017 chlorine, 1076 phosgene or 1079 sulphur dioxide of 2° TC, or 1067 dinitrogen tetroxide (nitrogen dioxide) of 2° TOC;

(2) After 6 years' service and thereafter every 12 years in the case of shells intended for the carriage of gases of 3°. A leakproofness test shall be performed by an approved expert six years after each periodic test.

(3) Receptacles as defined in marginals 2211 (1), (2) and (3) and cylinders as part of bundles of cylinders as defined in marginal 2211 (5), which are elements of a battery-vehicle, shall have periodic inspections according to marginal 2217.

211 256 In the case of vacuum-insulated shells, the hydraulic-pressure test and the check of the internal condition may, with the consent of the approved expert, be replaced by a leakproofness test and measurement of the vacuum.

211 257 If apertures have been made, on the occasion of periodic inspections, in shells intended for the carriage of gases of 3°, the method by which they are hermetically closed before the shells are replaced in service shall be approved by the approved expert and shall ensure the integrity of the shell.

211 258 Leakproofness test of shells intended for the carriage of gases of 1°, 2° or 4° shall be performed at a pressure of not less than 400 kPa (4 bar) and not more than 800 kPa (8 bar) (gauge pressure).

211 259

SECTION 6.   Marking

211 260 The following additional particulars shall be marked by stamping or by any other similar method on the plate prescribed in marginal 211 160, or directly on the walls of the shell itself if the walls are so reinforced that the strength of the shell is not impaired:

  (1)   On shells intended for the carriage of only one substance:

  -    the name of the gas in letters in accordance with marginal 2201 and, in addition for gases classified under an n.o.s. entry, the technical name [14].

This indication shall be supplemented in the case of shells intended for the carriage of compressed gases of 1° filled by volume (pressure), by an indication of the maximum filling pressure at 15 °C permitted for the shell, and in the case of shells intended for the carriage of gases of 1° filled by mass, and of gases of 2°, 3° and 4° by the maximum permissible load mass in kg and of the filling temperature if below -20 °C;

  (2)   On multi-purpose shells:

  -    the name of the gas in letters in accordance with marginal 2201 and, in addition for gases classified under an n.o.s. entry, the technical name [14], of the gases for whose carriage the shell is approved.

These particulars shall be supplemented by an indication of the maximum permissible load mass in kg for each gas;

  (3)   On shells intended for the carriage of gases of 3°:

  -    the maximum working pressure allowed; and

---

[14]   *The technical name shall be a name currently used in scientific and technical handbooks, journals and texts. Trade names shall not be used for this purpose.*
Instead of the technical name the use of one of the following names is permitted:

  -    *For 1078 refrigerant gas, N.O.S., of 2°A: mixture F1, mixture F2, mixture F3;*
  -    *For 1060 methyl acetylene and propadiene mixtures, stabilized, of 2°F: mixture P1, mixture P2;*
  -    *For 1965 hydrocarbon gas mixture, liquefied, N.O.S., of 2°F: mixture A, mixture A0, mixture A1, mixture B, mixture C.*

The names customary in the trade and mentioned in NOTE 1 under the entry 1965 of 2°F of marginal 2201 may be used only as a complement.

211 260   (4)   On shells equipped with thermal insulation:
(contd)

-     the inscription "thermally insulated" or "thermally insulated by vacuum".

211 261 (1)   The frame of a battery-vehicle shall bear near the filling point a plate specifying:

-     the test pressure of the elements [15/];

-     the maximum filling pressure [15/] at 15 °C allowed for elements intended for compressed gases;

-     the number of elements;

-     the total capacity [15/] of the elements;

-     the name of the gas in letters in accordance with marginal 2201 and, in addition for gases classified under an n.o.s. entry, the technical name [16/];

and, in addition, in the case of liquefied gases:

-     the permissible maximum load [15/] per element.

(2)   Receptacles as defined in marginal 2211 (1), (2), (3) and (5), which are elements of a battery-vehicle, shall be marked according to marginal 2223. These receptacles need not be labelled individually with the danger labels as required in marginal 2224.

Battery-vehicles shall be marked and labelled according to marginal 10 500.

211 262 In addition to the particulars prescribed in marginal 211 161, the following shall be inscribed either on the shell itself or on a plate:

(a)   -   the inscription: "minimum filling temperature allowed: ...";

(b)   where the shell is intended for the carriage of one substance only:

-     the name of the gas in letters in accordance with marginal 2201 and, in addition for gases classified under an n.o.s. entry, the technical name [16/];

-     for gases of 1° filled by mass, and for gases of 2°, 3° and 4°, the maximum permissible load mass in kg;

(c)   where the shell is a multi-purpose shell:

-     the name of the gas in letters in accordance with marginal 2201 and, in addition for gases classified under an n.o.s. entry, the technical name [16/] of all the gases to whose carriage the shell is assigned, with an indication of the maximum permissible load mass in kg for each of them;

[15/]   *The units of measurement should be indicated after numerical values.*

[16/]   *See footnote 14/ to marginal 211 260.*

211 262
(contd)   (d)   where the shell is equipped with thermal insulation:

- the inscription "thermally insulated" or "thermally insulated by vacuum", in an official language of the country of registration and also, if that language is not English, French or German, in English, French or German, unless any agreements concluded between the countries concerned in the transport operation provide otherwise.

211 263   These particulars shall not be required in the case of a vehicle carrying demountable tanks.

211 264-
211 269

SECTION 7.   Operation

211 270   When shells are approved for different gases, a change of use shall include emptying, purging and evacuation operations to the extent necessary for safe operation.

211 271-
211 273

211 274   When loaded tanks or empty but uncleaned tanks are handed over for carriage, only the particulars specified in marginal 211 262 applicable to the gas loaded or just discharged shall be visible; all particulars concerning other gases shall be covered up.

211 275   All the elements of a battery-vehicle shall contain only one and the same gas.

211 276

211 277   The degree of filling of shells intended for the carriage of gases of 3° F shall remain below the level at which, if the contents were raised to a temperature at which the vapour pressure equalled the opening pressure of the safety valve, the volume of the liquid would reach 95% of the shell's capacity at that temperature.

Shells intended for the carriage of gases of 3° A or 3° O may be filled to 98% at the loading temperature and the loading pressure.

211 278   In the case of shells intended for the carriage of gases of 3° O, the substances used to ensure leakproofness of the joints or for the maintenance of the closures shall be compatible with the contents.

211 279   The requirement in marginal 211 175 shall not apply to gases of 3°.

SECTION 8.   Transitional measures

211 280   Fixed tanks (tank-vehicles), demountable tanks and battery-vehicles intended for the carriage of substances of Class 2, built before 1 January 1997, may bear a marking conforming to the provisions of this appendix applicable until 31 December 1996 until the next periodic test.

211 281-
211 299

Appendix B.1a

CLASS 3. FLAMMABLE LIQUIDS

211 300-
211 309

SECTION 1.   General; scope (use of tanks); definitions

Use

211 310 The following substances of marginal 2301 may be carried in fixed or demountable tanks:

(a)   propyleneimine, inhibited, of 12°;

(b)   substances classified under (a) of 11°, 14° to 22°, 26° and 27°, 41°;

(c)   substances classified under (b) of 11°, 14° to 27°, 41°, and substances of 32° and 33°;

(d)   substances of 1° to 5°, 31°, 34° and 61° (c), with the exception of isopropyl nitrate, n-propyl nitrate and nitromethane of 3° (b).

211 311-
211 319

SECTION 2.   Construction

211 320 Shells intended for the carriage of inhibited propyleneimine of 12° shall be designed for a calculation pressure [see marginal 211 127 (2)] of not less than 1.5 MPa (15 bar) (gauge pressure).

211 321 Shells intended for the carriage of the substances referred to in marginal 211 310 (b) shall be designed for a calculation pressure [see marginal 211 127 (2)] of not less than 1.0 MPa (10 bar) (gauge pressure).

211 322 Shells intended for the carriage of the substances referred to in marginal 211 310 (c) shall be designed for a calculation pressure [see marginal 211 127 (2)] of not less than 400 kPa (4 bar) (gauge pressure).

211 323 Shells intended for the carriage of the substances referred to in marginal 211 310 (d) shall be designed in accordance with the requirements of Part I of this Appendix.

211 324-
211 329

SECTION 3.   Items of equipment

211 330 All openings of shells intended for the carriage of the substances referred to in marginal 211 310 (a) and (b) shall be above the surface level of the liquid. No pipes or pipe connections shall pass through the walls of the shell below the surface level of the liquid. Shells shall be capable of being hermetically closed [17] and the closures shall be capable of being protected with lockable caps.

---

[17]   *See footnote [7] to marginal 211 135.*

211 331   Shells intended for the carriage of the substances referred to in marginal 211 310 (c) and (d) may also be of the bottom-discharge type. Shells intended for the carriage of the substances referred to in marginal 211 310 (c), except those of 33°, shall be capable of being hermetically closed [18/].

211 332   If shells intended for the carriage of the substances referred to in marginal 211 310 (a) and (b) or (c), except those of 33°, are fitted with safety valves, a bursting disc shall be placed before the valve. The arrangement of the bursting disc and safety valve shall be such as to satisfy the competent authority. If shells intended for the carriage of the substances referred to in marginal 211 310 (d) are equipped with safety valves or a venting system, these shall satisfy the requirements of marginals 211 133 to 211 135.

If shells intended for the carriage of the substances of 33° are fitted with safety valves, these shall satisfy the requirements of marginals 211 134 and 211 135.

Shells intended for the carriage of the substances referred to in marginal 211 310 (d) having a flash-point not exceeding 61 °C and equipped with a venting system which cannot be closed shall have a flame-trap in the venting system or the shells shall be explosion-pressure proof.

211 333   If the shells are fitted with non-metallic protective linings (inner layers), these shall be so designed that no danger of ignition from electrostatic charges can occur.

211 334   The bottom discharge system of shells intended for the carriage of substances of 61° (c) may consist of an external pipe with a stop-valve, if it is constructed in a metallic material liable to deformation.

211 335-
211 339

   SECTION 4.   **Type approval**

211 340-
211 349   (No special requirements)

   SECTION 5.   **Tests**

211 350   Shells intended for the carriage of the substances referred to in marginal 211 310 (a), (b) or (c) shall be subjected to the initial and periodic hydraulic pressure tests at a gauge pressure of not less than 400 kPa (4 bar).

211 351   Shells intended for the carriage of the substances referred to in marginal 211 310 (d) shall be subjected to the initial and periodic hydraulic pressure tests at their calculation pressure as defined in marginal 211 123.

211 352-
211 359

   SECTION 6.   **Marking**

211 360-
211 369   (No special requirements)

[18/]   *See footnote 7/ to marginal 211 135.*

SECTION 7.   Operation

211 370 Shells intended for the carriage of the substances referred to in marginal 211 310 (a), (b) and (c) except those of 33° shall be hermetically closed [18] during carriage. The closures of shells intended for the carriage of the substances referred to in 211 310 (a) and (b) shall be protected by a locked cap.

211 371 Tank-vehicles and demountable tanks approved for the carriage of substances of 11°, 12°, 14° to 19°, 27°, 32° and 41° shall not be used for the carriage of foodstuffs, articles of consumption or animal feeds.

211 372 An aluminium-alloy shell shall not be used for the carriage of acetaldehyde of 1° (a) unless the shell is reserved solely for such carriage and the acetaldehyde is free from acid.

211 373 The petrol (gasoline) referred to in the Note to 3° (b) of marginal 2301 may also be carried in tanks designed according to marginal 211 123 (1) and having equipment conforming to marginal 211 133.

211 374-
211 379

SECTION 8.   Transitional measures

211 380 Fixed tanks (tank-vehicles) and demountable tanks intended for the carriage of substances of 32° and 33° of marginal 2301, built according to the requirements of this Appendix applicable prior to 1 January 1995, but which do not, however, conform to the requirements applicable as from 1 January 1995, may still be used up to 31 December 2000.

211 381 Fixed tanks (tank-vehicles) and demountable tanks which were intended for the carriage of substances of 61° (c) of marginal 2301, built before 1 January 1995 according to requirements applicable until that date but which do not conform with the requirements applicable as from 1 January 1995, may still be used until 31 December 2004.

211 382 Fixed tanks (tank-vehicles) and demountable tanks constructed before 1 January 1997 which do not conform to the provisions of marginals 211 332 and 211 333 but were constructed according to the requirements of ADR in force until that date may still be used.

211 383-
211 399

---

[18]   *See footnote 7/ to marginal 211 135.*

CLASS 4.1. FLAMMABLE SOLIDS

CLASS 4.2. SUBSTANCES LIABLE TO SPONTANEOUS COMBUSTION

CLASS 4.3. SUBSTANCES WHICH, IN CONTACT WITH WATER, EMIT FLAMMABLE GASES

211 400-
211 409

SECTION 1. General scope (use of tanks); definitions

Use

211 410 The following substances of marginals 2401, 2431 and 2471 may be carried in fixed or demountable tanks:

(a)   the substances listed under letter (a) of 6°, 17°, 19° and 31° to 33° of marginal 2431;

(b)   the substances of 11° (a) and 22° of marginal 2431;

(c)   the substances listed under letter (a) of 1°, 2°, 3°, 21°, 23° and 25° of marginal 2471;

(d)   the substances of 11° (a) of marginal 2471;

(e)   the substances listed under letter (b) or (c) of 6°, 8°, 10°, 17°, 19° and 21° of marginal 2431 and of 3°, 21°, 23° and 25° of marginal 2471;

(f)   the substances of 5° and 15° of marginal 2401;

(g)   powdery and granular substances listed under letter (b) or (c) of:

1°, 6°, 7°, 8°, 11°, 12°, 13°, 14°, 16° and 17° of marginal 2401,
1°, 5°, 7°, 9°, 12°, 13°, 14°, 15°, 16°, 18° and 20° of marginal 2431,
11°, 12°, 13°, 14°, 15°, 16°, 17°, 19°, 20°, 22° and 24° of marginal 2471.

NOTE: For the carriage in bulk of substances of:

4° (c), 6° (c), 11° (c), 12° (c), 13° (c) and 14° (c) and solid mixtures (such as preparations and wastes) classified under (c) of these items of marginal 2401,

1° (c), 2° (c), 3° (c), 12° (c) and 16° (c) and solid wastes classified under (c) of these items of marginal 2431,

11° (c), 12° (c), 13° (b) and (c), 14° (c), 15° (c), 17° (b) and 20° (c) and solid mixtures (such as preparations and wastes) classified under (c) of these items of marginal 2471,

see marginals 41 111, 42 111 and 43 111.

211 411-
211 419

SECTION 2. **Construction**

211 420 Shells intended for the carriage of the substances referred to in marginal 211 410 (a) shall be designed for a calculation pressure [see marginal 211 127 (2)] of not less than 2.1 MPa (21 bar) (gauge pressure).

The requirements of Appendix B.1d are applicable to the materials and construction of these shells.

211 421 Shells intended for the carriage of the substances referred to in marginal 211 410 (b), (c) and (d) shall be designed for a calculation pressure [see marginal 211 127 (2)] of not less than 1 MPa (10 bar) (gauge pressure).

211 422 Shells intended for the carriage of the substances referred to in marginal 211 410 (e) shall be designed for a calculation pressure [see marginal 211 127 (2)] of not less than 400 kPa (4 bar) (gauge pressure).

211 423 Shells intended for the carriage of the solids referred to in marginal 211 410 (f) and (g) shall be designed in conformity with the requirements of Part I of this Appendix.

211 424 Shells intended for the carriage of substances of marginal 2431, 1° (b) shall be connected to all parts of the vehicle by equipotential connections and shall be capable of being electrically earthed.

211 425-
211 429

SECTION 3. **Items of equipment**

211 430 All openings of shells intended for the carriage of the substances referred to in marginal 211 410 (a), (b), (c) and (e) shall be above the surface level of the liquid. No pipes or pipe connections shall pass through the walls of the shell below the surface level of the liquid. Shells shall be capable of being hermetically closed [18] and the closure shall be capable of being protected with lockable caps. The cleaning apertures (fist-holes) referred to in marginal 211 132 shall not be permitted.

211 431 With the exception of shells intended for the carriage of caesium and rubidium of marginal 2471, 11° (a), shells intended for the carriage of substances referred to in marginal 211 410 (d), (f) and (g) may also be of the bottom-discharge type. The openings of shells intended for the carriage of caesium and rubidium of marginal 2471, 11° (a) shall be equipped with hermetically [18] closing and lockable caps.

211 432 Shells intended for the carriage of the substances referred to in marginal 211 410 (b) shall in addition meet the following requirements:

(1) The heating device shall not penetrate into, but shall be exterior to, the body of the shell. However, a pipe used for extracting the phosphorus may be equipped with a heating jacket. The device heating the jacket shall be so regulated as to prevent the temperature of the phosphorus from exceeding the filling temperature of the shell. Other piping shall enter the shell in its upper part; openings shall be situated above the highest permissible level of the phosphorus and be capable of being completely enclosed under lockable caps. In addition, the cleaning apertures (fist-holes) referred to in marginal 211 132 shall not be permitted.

---

[18]   *See footnote 7/ to marginal 211 135.*

211 432
(contd)   (2)   The shell shall be equipped with a gauging system for verifying the level of the phosphorus and, if water is used as a protective agent, with a fixed gauge mark showing the highest permissible level of the water.

211 433   If shells intended for the carriage of the substances referred to in marginal 211 410 (a), (c) and (e) are fitted with safety valves, a bursting disc shall be placed before the valve. The arrangement of the bursting disc and safety valve shall be such as to satisfy the competent authority.

211 434   Shells intended for the carriage of the substances referred to in marginal 211 410 (f) shall be equipped with thermal insulation made of materials which are not readily flammable.

211 435   If shells intended for the carriage of substances referred to in marginal 211 410 (d) are equipped with thermal insulation, such insulation shall be made of materials which are not readily flammable.

211 436   Shells intended for the carriage of the substances referred to in marginal 211 410 (f) may be equipped with valves opening automatically inwards or outwards under the effect of a difference of pressure of between 20 kPa and 30 kPa (0.2 bar and 0.3 bar).

211 437-
211 439

SECTION 4.   Type approval

211 440-
211 449   (No special requirements.)

SECTION 5.   Tests

211 450   Shells intended for the carriage of the substances referred to in marginal 211 410 (a) shall be subjected to the initial and periodic hydraulic pressure tests at a gauge pressure of at least 1 MPa (10 bar).   The materials of each of these shells shall be tested by the method described in Appendix B.1d.

211 451   Shells intended for the carriage of the substances referred to in marginal 211 410 (b) to (e) shall be subjected to the initial and periodic hydraulic pressure tests at a gauge pressure of at least 400 kPa (4 bar).

By derogation from the requirements of marginal 211 151, shells intended for the carriage of substances referred to in marginal 211 410 (d) shall undergo periodic inspections at least every eight years which shall include a thickness check using suitable instruments. For such shells, the leakproofness test and check, for which provision is made in marginal 211 152, shall be carried out at least every four years.

211 452   Shells intended for the carriage of the substances referred to in marginal 211 410 (f) and (g) shall be subjected to the initial and periodic hydraulic pressure tests at their calculation pressure as defined in marginal 211 123.

211 453-
211 459

SECTION 6.   **Marking**

211 460   Shells intended for the carriage of the substances referred to in marginal 211 410 (a) shall bear in addition to the particulars prescribed in marginal 211 161, the words: "Do not open during carriage. Liable to spontaneous combustion."

Shells intended for the carriage of the substances of marginal 2471 referred to in 211 410 (c) to (e) shall bear in addition to the particulars prescribed in marginal 211 161, the words:

"Do not open during carriage. Gives off flammable gases on contact with water."

These particulars shall be in an official language of the country of approval, and also, if that language is not English, French or German, in English, French or German, unless any agreements concluded between the countries concerned in the transport operation provide otherwise.

211 461   Shells intended for the carriage of substances of marginal 2471, 1° (a) shall also bear, on the plate prescribed in marginal 211 160, the names of the approved substances and the maximum permissible load of the shell in kg.

**211 462-
211 469**

SECTION 7.   **Operation**

211 470   (1)   Substances of 11° and 22° of marginal 2431 shall, if water is used as a protective agent, be covered with a depth of not less than 12 cm of water at the time of filling; the degree of filling at a temperature of 60 °C shall not exceed 98%. If nitrogen is used as a protective agent, the degree of filling at a temperature of 60 °C shall not exceed 96%. The remaining space shall be filled with nitrogen in such a way that, even after cooling, the pressure at no time falls below atmospheric pressure. The shell shall be hermetically closed [18/] so that no leakage of gas occurs.

(2)   Uncleaned empty shells which have contained substances of 11° and 22° of marginal 2431 shall, when handed over for carriage, either:

-       be filled with nitrogen; or

-       be filled with water to not less than 96% and not more than 98% of their capacity; between 1 October and 31 March, this water shall contain sufficient anti-freeze agent to make it impossible for the water to freeze during carriage; the anti-freeze agent shall be free from corrosive action and not liable to react with phosphorus.

211 471   Shells containing substances of 31° to 33° of marginal 2431 and substances of 2° (a), 3° (a) and 3° (b) of marginal 2471 shall be filled to not more than 90% of their capacity; a space of 5% shall remain empty for safety when the liquid is at an average temperature of 50 °C. During carriage, the substances shall be under a layer of inert gas, the gauge pressure of which shall not be less than 50 kPa (0.5 bar). The shells shall be hermetically closed [18/] and the protective caps conforming to marginal 211 430 shall be locked. Uncleaned empty shells shall, when handed over for carriage, be filled with an inert gas at a gauge pressure of at least 50 kPa (0.5 bar).

[18/]   *See footnote [7/] to marginal 211 135.*

211 472 For ethyldichlorosilane, methyldichlorosilane and trichlorosilane of marginal 2471, 1°, the degree of filling shall not exceed 0.93 or 0.95 or 1.14 kg per litre of capacity respectively, if filling is by mass. If filling is by volume, and for chlorosilanes not mentioned by name (n.o.s.) of marginal 2471, 1°, the rate of filling shall not exceed 85%. The shells shall be hermetically closed [18/] and the protective caps conforming to marginal 211 430 shall be locked.

211 473 Shells containing substances of marginal 2401, 5° and 15°, shall not be filled to more than 98% of their capacity.

211 474 For the carriage of caesium and rubidium of marginal 2471, 11° (a), the substance shall be covered by an inert gas and the caps conforming to marginal 211 431 shall be locked. Shells containing other substances of marginal 2471, 11° (a), shall not be handed over for carriage until the substance has solidified completely and been covered by an inert gas.

Uncleaned empty shells which have contained substances of marginal 2471, 11° (a) shall be filled with an inert gas. The shells shall be hermetically closed.

211 475 (1) When substances of marginal 2431, 1° (b) are being loaded, the temperature of the goods being loaded shall not exceed 60 °C.

(2) A maximum loading temperature of 80 °C is allowed provided that smoulder spots are prevented during loading and the shells are hermetically closed [18/].

After loading, the shells shall be pressurized (e.g. with compressed air) to check tightness. It shall be ensured that no depressurization takes place during carriage.

Before unloading, it shall be checked if pressure is still above atmospheric. If this is not the case, an inert gas shall be introduced into the shells prior to unloading.

211 476-
211 499

[18/] *See footnote 7/ to marginal 211 135.*

Appendix B.1a

CLASS 5.1. OXIDIZING SUBSTANCES

CLASS 5.2. ORGANIC PEROXIDES

211 500-
211 509

      SECTION 1.   **General; scope (use of tanks); definitions**

      Use

211 510   The following substances of marginal 2501 may be carried in fixed or demountable tanks:

        (a)   substances of 5°;

        (b)   substances listed under letter (a) or (b) of 1° to 4°, 11°, 13°, 16°, 17°, 22° and 23°, carried in the liquid state or in the molten state;

        (c)   ammonium nitrate liquid of 20°;

        (d)   substances listed under letter (c) of 1°, 11°, 13°, 16°, 18°, 22° and 23°, carried in the liquid state or in the molten state;

        (e)   substances in powdery or granular form listed under letter (b) or (c) of 11°, 13° to 18°, 21° to 27°, 29° and 31°.

        NOTE: For the carriage in bulk of substances of 11° to 13°, 16°, 19°, 21° and 22° (c), and of solid wastes classified in the aforementioned items of marginal 2501, see marginal 51 111.

211 511   Substances of 9° (b), 10° (b), 19° (b) or 20° (b) of marginal 2551 may be carried in fixed or demountable tanks at the latest from 1 January 1995 under conditions laid down by the competent authority of the country of origin if, on the basis of tests (see marginal 211 541), the competent authority is satisfied that such a transport operation can be carried out safely. If the country of origin is not party to ADR, these conditions shall be recognized by the competent authority of the first ADR country reached by the consignment.

211 512-
211 519

      SECTION 2.   **Construction**

211 520   Shells intended for the carriage of the substances referred to in marginal 211 510 (a) shall be designed for a calculation pressure [see marginal 211 127 (2)] of at least 1 MPa (10 bar) (gauge pressure).

211 521   Shells intended for the carriage of the substances referred to in marginal 211 510 (b) shall be designed for a calculation pressure [see marginal 211 127 (2)] of at least 400 kPa (4 bar) (gauge pressure). Shells, and their items of equipment, intended for the carriage of substances of 1° shall be made of aluminium not less than 99.5% pure or of suitable steel not liable to cause hydrogen peroxide to decompose. Where shells are made of aluminium not less than 99.5% pure, the wall thickness need not be greater than 15 mm, even where calculation in accordance with marginal 211 127 (2) gives a higher value.

211 522 Shells intended for the carriage of the substances referred to in marginal 211 510 (c) shall be designed for a calculation pressure [see marginal 211 127 (2)] of at least 400 kPa (4 bar) (gauge pressure). The shells shall be made of austenitic steel.

211 523 Shells intended for the carriage of the liquids referred to in marginal 211 510 (d) and the powdery or granular substances referred to in marginal 211 510 (e) shall be designed in accordance with the requirements of Part I of this Appendix.

211 524 Shells intended for the carriage of substances referred to in marginal 211 511 shall be designed for a calculation pressure of at least 400 kPa (4 bar) (gauge pressure).

211 525-
211 529

SECTION 3.   **Items of equipment**

211 530 Shells intended for the carriage of substances of 1° (a), 3° (a) and 5° of marginal 2501 shall have their openings above the surface level of the liquid. In addition, the cleaning apertures (fist holes) referred to in marginal 211 132 shall not be permitted.

For solutions containing more than 60% but not more than 70% hydrogen peroxide, openings below the surface level of the liquid shall be permissible. In this case the shell-discharge system shall be equipped with two mutually independent shut-off devices mounted in series, the first taking the form of a quick-closing internal stop-valve of an approved type and the second that of a sluice-valve, one at each end of the discharge pipe. A blank flange, or another device providing the same measure of security, shall also be fitted at the outlet of each external sluice-valve. The internal stop-valve shall be such that if the pipe is wrenched off the stop-valve will remain integral with the shell and in the closed position. The connections to the external pipe-sockets of shells shall be made of materials not liable to cause decomposition of hydrogen peroxide.

211 531

211 532 Shells intended for the carriage of substances of 1° or of liquid ammonium nitrate of 20° of marginal 2501 shall be fitted in their upper part with a shut-off device preventing any build-up of excess pressure inside the shell, any leakage of liquid, and any entry of foreign matter into the shell. The shut-off devices of shells intended for the ammonium nitrate liquid of marginal 2501, 20°, shall be so designed as to preclude obstruction of the devices by solidified ammonium nitrate during carriage.

211 533 Where shells intended for the carriage of ammonium nitrate liquid of marginal 2501, 20°, are sheathed in thermally-insulating material, the material shall be of an inorganic nature and entirely free from combustible matter.

211 534 Shells intended for the carriage of substances referred to in marginal 211 511 shall be equipped with thermal insulation complying with the requirements of marginal 211 234 (1). If the SADT of the organic peroxide in the shell is 55 °C or less, or the shell is constructed of aluminium, the shell shall be completely insulated. The sun shield and any part of the shell not covered by it, or the outer sheathing of a complete lagging, shall be painted white or finished in bright metal. The paint shall be cleaned before each transport journey and renewed in case of yellowing or deterioration. The thermal insulation shall be free from combustible matter.

211 535 Shells intended for the carriage of substances referred to in marginal 211 511 shall be fitted with temperature sensing devices.

211 536 (1) Shells intended for the carriage of substances referred to in marginal 211 511 shall be fitted with safety valves and pressure-relief devices. Vacuum-relief devices may also be used. Pressure-relief devices shall operate at pressures determined according to both the properties of the organic peroxide and the construction characteristics of the tank. Fusible elements shall not be permitted in the body of the shell.

(2) Shells intended for the carriage of substances referred to in marginal 211 511 shall be fitted with spring-loaded safety valves to prevent significant pressure build-up within the shell of the decomposition products and vapours released at a temperature of 50 °C. The capacity and start-to-discharge pressure of the safety-valve(s) shall be based on the results of the tests specified in marginal 211 541. The start-to-discharge pressure shall however in no case be such that liquid could escape from the valve(s) if the shell were overturned.

(3) The pressure-relief devices of shells intended for the carriage of substances referred to in marginal 211 511 may be of the spring-loaded type or bursting disc type, designed to vent all the decomposition products and vapours evolved during a period of not less than one hour of fire engulfment (heat load 110 kW/m^2) or self-accelerating decomposition. The start-to-discharge pressure of the pressure-relief device(s) shall be higher than that specified in paragraph (2) and based on the results of the tests referred to in marginal 211 541. The dimensions of the pressure-relief devices shall be such that the maximum pressure in the shell never exceeds the test pressure of the shell.

(4) For shells with an insulation consisting of a complete cladding intended for the carriage of substances referred to in marginal 211 511, the capacity and setting of the pressure-relief device(s) shall be determined assuming a loss of insulation from 1% of the surface area.

(5) Vacuum-relief devices and spring-loaded safety valves of shells for the carriage of substances referred to in marginal 211 511 shall be provided with flame arresters unless the substances to be carried and their decomposition products are non-combustible. Due attention shall be paid to the reduction of the relief capacity caused by the flame arrester.

**211 537-
211 539**

SECTION 4.   Type approval

211 540 Tanks approved for the carriage of liquid ammonium nitrate of 20° of marginal 2501 shall not be approved for the carriage of organic substances.

211 541 For the type approval of shells intended for the carriage of substances referred to in marginal 211 511, tests shall be undertaken:

- to prove the compatibility of all materials normally in contact with the substance during carriage;

- to provide data to facilitate the design of the pressure-relief devices and safety valves taking into account the design characteristics of the tank; and

- to establish any special requirements necessary for the safe carriage of the substance.

The test results shall be included in the report for the type approval of the tank.

**211 542-
211 549**

Appendix B.1a

SECTION 5.   **Tests**

211 550   Shells intended for the carriage of the substances referred to in marginal 211 510 (a), (b) and (c) shall be subjected to the initial and periodic hydraulic pressure tests at a pressure of not less than 400 kPa (4 bar) (gauge pressure). Shells of pure aluminium intended for the carriage of substances of marginal 2501, 1°, may be subjected to the initial and periodic hydraulic pressure tests at a pressure of only 250 kPa (2.5 bar) (gauge pressure).

Shells intended for the carriage of the substances referred to in marginal 211 510 (d) and (e) shall be subjected to the initial and periodic hydraulic pressure tests at their calculation pressure as defined in marginal 211 123.

211 551   Shells intended for the carriage of substances referred to in marginal 211 511 shall be subjected to the initial and periodic hydraulic pressure tests at the calculation pressure as defined in marginal 211 524.

211 552-
211 559

SECTION 6.   **Marking**

211 560   For shells intended for the carriage of substances referred to in marginal 211 511, the following additional particulars shall be marked by stamping or by any other similar method on the plate prescribed in marginal 211 161 or directly on the walls of the shell itself, if the walls are so reinforced that the strength of the shell is not impaired:

-       the chemical name with the approved concentration of the substance concerned.

211 561-
211 569

SECTION 7.   **Operation**

211 570   The inside of the shell and all parts liable to come into contact with the substances referred to in marginals 211 510 and 211 511 shall be kept clean. No lubricant capable of combining dangerously with the substance carried shall be used for pumps, valves or other devices.

211 571   Shells intended for the carriage of substances of 1° (a), 2° (a) and 3° (a) of marginal 2501 shall be filled to not more than 95% of their capacity at a reference temperature of 15 °C. Shells intended for the carriage of substances of marginal 2501, 20°, shall be filled to not more than 97% of their capacity, and the maximum temperature after filling shall not exceed 140 °C. In the event of a change of use, shells and equipment shall be thoroughly cleansed of all residues before and after the carriage of substances of 20°.

211 572   Shells intended for the carriage of substances referred to in marginal 211 511 shall be filled as set out in the test report for the type approval of the tank but shall be filled to not more than 90% of their capacity. Shells shall be free from impurities at the time of filling.

211 573   Service equipment such as valves and external piping of shells intended for the carriage of substances referred to in marginal 211 511 shall be emptied after filling or discharging of the tank.

211 574-
211 599

CLASS 6.1. TOXIC SUBSTANCES

CLASS 6.2. INFECTIOUS SUBSTANCES

211 600-
211 609

       SECTION 1.   **General; scope (use of tanks); definitions**

       Use

211 610 (1)   The following substances of marginal 2601 may be carried in fixed or demountable tanks:

       (a)   the substances listed by name in 2° to 4°;

       (b)   substances classified under (a) of 6° to 13° - with the exception of isopropyl chloroformate of 10° - , 15° to 17°, 20°, 22°, 23°, 25° to 28°, 31° to 36°, 41°, 44°, 51°, 52°, 55°, 61°, 65° to 68°, 71° to 73° and 90°, carried in the liquid state or in the molten state;

       (c)   substances classified under (b) or (c) of 11°, 12°, 14° to 28°, 32° to 36°, 41°, 44°, 51° to 55°, 57° to 62°, 64° to 68°, 71° to 73° and 90°, carried in the liquid state or in the molten state;

       (d)   substances in powdery or granular form classified under (b) or (c) of 12°, 14°, 17°, 19°, 21°, 23°, 25° to 27°, 32° to 35°, 41°, 44°, 51° to 55°, 57° to 68°, 71° to 73° and 90°.

NOTE: For the carriage in bulk of substances of 60° (c), of solids containing toxic liquids of 65° (b) (identification number 3243) and of solid substances, including mixtures (such as preparations and wastes) classified under (c) of the various items, see marginal 61 111.

       (2)   Substances of marginal 2651, 3° and 4°, may be carried in fixed or demountable tanks.

211 611-
211 619

       SECTION 2.   **Construction**

211 620 Shells intended for the carriage of substances referred to in marginal 211 610 (1) (a) listed by name under 2° to 4° of marginal 2601 shall be designed for a calculation pressure [see marginal 211 127 (2)] of not less than 1.5 MPa (15 bar) (gauge pressure).

211 621 Shells intended for the carriage of the substances referred to in marginal 211 610 (1) (b) shall be designed for a calculation pressure [see marginal 211 127 (2)] of not less than 1.0 MPa (10 bar) (gauge pressure).

211 622 Shells intended for the carriage of the substances referred to in marginal 211 610 (1) (c) and 211 610(2) shall be designed for a calculation pressure [see marginal 211 127 (2)] of not less than 400 kPa (4 bar) (gauge pressure).

Shells intended for the carriage of chloroacetic acid of 24° (b) of marginal 2601 shall be provided with an enamel equivalent protective lining if the material of the shell is attacked by chloroacetic acid.

211 623 Shells intended for the carriage of the powdery or granular substances referred to in marginal 211 610 (1) (d) shall be designed in accordance with the requirements of Part I of this Appendix.

211 624-
211 629

SECTION 3.   Items of equipment

211 630 All openings of shells intended for the carriage of the substances referred to in marginal 211 610 (1) (a) and (b) shall be above the surface level of the liquid. No pipe or pipe connections shall pass through the walls of the shell below the surface level of the liquid. Shells shall be capable of being hermetically closed [18] and the closures shall be capable of being protected with lockable caps. The cleaning openings provided for in marginal 211 132 shall not however be permitted for shells intended for the carriage of solutions of hydrocyanic acid of 2°.

211 631 Shells intended for the carriage of the substances referred to in marginal 211 610 (1) (c) and (d) and (2) may also be of the bottom-discharge type. The shells shall be capable of being hermetically closed [18].

211 632 If shells are fitted with safety valves, a bursting disc shall be placed before the valve. The arrangement of the bursting disc and safety valve shall be such as to satisfy the competent authority.

Protection of equipment

211 633 (1)   Fittings and accessories mounted in the upper part of the shell

Such fittings and accessories shall be either:

- inserted in a recessed housing; or

- equipped with an internal safety valve; or

- shielded by a cap, or by transverse and/or longitudinal members, or by other equally effective devices, so profiled that in the event of overturning the fittings and accessories will not be damaged.

(2)   Fittings and accessories mounted in the lower part of the shell

Pipe-sockets, lateral shut-off devices, and all discharge devices shall either be recessed by at lest 200 mm from the extreme outer edge of the shell or be protected by a rail having a coefficient of inertia of not less than 20 cm^3 transversally to the direction of travel; their ground clearance shall be not less than 300 mm with the shell full.

(3)   Fittings and accessories mounted on the rear face of the shell

All fittings and accessories mounted on the rear face shall be protected by the bumper prescribed in marginal 10 220. Their height above the ground shall be such that they are adequately protected by the bumper.

211 634-
211 639

---

[18]   *See footnote 7/ to marginal 211 135.*

SECTION 4.   **Type approval**

211 640-
211 649 (No special requirements)

SECTION 5.   **Tests**

211 650 Shells intended for the carriage of the substances referred to in marginal 211 610 (1) (a), (b) and (c) and (2) shall be subjected to the initial and periodic hydraulic pressure tests at a gauge pressure of not less than 400 kPa (4 bar).

For shells intended for the carriage of substances of 31° (a) of marginal 2601, the periodic tests shall be carried out at intervals of not more than three years and shall include the hydraulic pressure test.

211 651 Shells intended for the carriage of the substances referred to in marginal 211 610 (1) (d) shall be subjected to the initial and periodic hydraulic pressure tests at their calculation pressure as defined in marginal 211 123.

211 652-
211 659

SECTION 6.   **Marking**

211 660-
211 669 (No special requirements)

SECTION 7.   **Operation**

211 670 Shells intended for the carriage of substances of 3° of marginal 2601 shall not be filled to more than 1 kg per litre of capacity.

211 671 Shells shall be hermetically closed [18] during carriage. The closures of shells intended for the carriage of the substances referred to in marginal 211 610 (1) (a) and (b) shall be protected with locked caps.

211 672 Tank vehicles and demountable tanks approved for the carriage of the substances referred to in marginal 211 610 shall not be used for the carriage of foodstuffs, articles of consumption or animal feedstuffs.

211 673-
211 679

SECTION 8.   **Transitional measures**

211 680 Fixed tanks, tank-vehicles and demountable tanks intended for the carriage of substances of 6°, 8°, 9°, 10°, 13°, 15°, 16°, 18°, 20°, 25° or 27° of marginal 2601, built before 1 January 1995 in accordance with the requirements of this Appendix applicable until that date, but which do not, however, conform to the requirements applicable as from 1 January 1995, may still be used until 31 December 2000.

211 681-
211 699

---

[18]   *See footnote 7/ to marginal 211 135.*

Appendix B.1a

CLASS 7. RADIOACTIVE SUBSTANCES

211 700-
211 709

SECTION 1.   General; scope (use of tanks); definitions

Use

211 710 Materials of marginals 2704, Schedules 1, 5, 6, 9, 10 and 11, except uranium hexafluoride, may be carried in fixed or demountable tanks.   The provisions of the appropriate schedule in marginal 2704 are applicable.

NOTE: There may be additional requirements for tanks which are designed as a Type A or Type B packaging.

211 711-
211 719

SECTION 2.   Construction

211 720 See marginal 3736.

211 721-
211 729

SECTION 3.   Items of Equipment

211 730 The openings of shells for the carriage of liquid radioactive material [18] shall be above the level of the liquid. The shell walls shall not have any piping or pipe connections below the level of the liquid.

211 731-
211 739

SECTION 4.   Type approval

211 740 Tanks which are approved for the carriage of radioactive material shall not be approved for the carriage of other substances.

211 741-
211 749

SECTION 5.   Tests

211 750 The shells shall initially and periodically undergo a hydraulic pressure test at a pressure of at least 265 kPa (2.65 bar). Notwithstanding the provisions of marginal 211 151, the periodic internal inspection may be replaced by a programme approved by the competent authority.

211 751-
211 759

---

[18]   *See footnote 7/ to marginal 211 135.*

SECTION 6.   **Marking**

211 760   In addition, the trefoil symbol, as described in marginal 2705 (5), shall be marked by stamping or by any other equivalent method on the plate described in marginal 211 160. This trefoil marking may be applied directly on the walls of the shell itself, if the walls are so reinforced that the strength of the shell is not impaired.

211 761-
211 769

SECTION 7.   **Operation**

211 770   The degree of filling, according to marginal 211 172, at the reference temperature of 15 °C shall not exceed 93% of the capacity of the shell.

211 771   Tanks in which radioactive material has been carried shall not be used for the carriage of other substances. ·

211 772-
211 799

CLASS 8. CORROSIVE SUBSTANCES

211 800-
211 809

SECTION 1.   General; scope (use of tanks); definitions

Use

211 810 The following substances of marginal 2801 may be carried in fixed or demountable tanks:

(a)   substances listed by name in 6° and 14°;

(b)   substances classified under (a) of 1°, 2°, 3°, 7°, 8°, 12°, 17°, 32°, 33°, 39°, 40°, 46°, 47°, 52° to 56°, 64° to 68° and 70°, 72° to 76°, carried in the liquid state or in the molten state;

(c)   phosphorus oxybromide of 15° and substances classified under (b) or (c) of 1° to 5°, 7°, 8° 10°, 12°, 17°, 31° to 40°, 42° to 47°, 51° to 56°, 61° to 76°, carried in the liquid state or in the molten state;

(d)   powdery or granular substances classified under (b) or (c) of 9°, 11°, 13°, 16°, 31°, 34°, 35°, 39°, 41°, 45°, 46°, 52°, 55°, 62°, 65°, 67°, 69°, 71°, 73° and 75°.

NOTE: For the carriage in bulk of lead sulphate of 1° (b), of substances of 13° (b), solids containing a corrosive liquid of 65° (b) of identification number 3244, and of solid substances, including mixtures (such as preparations and wastes) classified under (c) of the various items, see marginal 81 111.

211 811-
211 819

SECTION 2.   Construction

211 820 Shells intended for the carriage of substances listed by name in 6° and 14° shall be designed for a calculation pressure [see marginal 211 127 (2)] of not less than 2.1 MPa (21 bar) (gauge pressure). Shells intended for the carriage of substances of 14° shall be provided with a lead lining not less than 5 mm thick or an equivalent lining. The requirement of Appendix B.1d shall apply to the materials and construction of welded shells intended for the carriage of substances of 6°.

211 821 Shells intended for the carriage of the substances referred to in marginal 211 810 (b) shall be designed for a calculation pressure [see marginal 211 127 (2)] of not less than 1.0 MPa (10 bar) (gauge pressure).

Where the use of aluminium is necessary for shells intended for the carriage of nitric acid of 2° (a), such shells shall be made of aluminium not less than 99.5% pure, in which case, by derogation from the provisions of the paragraph above, the wall thickness need not exceed 15 mm.

211 822 Shells intended for the carriage of the substances referred to in marginal 211 810 (c) shall be designed for a calculation pressure [see marginal 211 127 (2)] of not less than 400 kPa (4 bar) (gauge pressure).

Notwithstanding the provisions of the paragraph above, the wall thickness need not be greater than 15 mm when the shells are made of pure aluminium.

211 823 Shells intended for the carriage of the powdery or granular substances referred to in marginal 211 810 (d) shall be designed in accordance with the requirements of Part I of this Appendix.

211 824-
211 829

SECTION 3. Items of equipment

211 830 All openings of shells intended for the carriage of substances of 6°, 7° and 14° shall be above the surface level of the liquid. No pipes or pipe connections shall pass through the walls of the shell below the surface level of the liquid. Shells shall be capable of being hermetically closed [18/] and the closures shall be capable of being protected by lockable caps. In addition, the cleaning openings referred to in marginal 211 132 shall not be permitted.

211 831 Shells intended for the carriage of the substances referred to in marginal 211 810 (b), (c) and (d) with the exception of substances of 7° may also be of the bottom-discharge type.

211 832 If shells intended for the carriage of the substances referred to in marginal 211 810 (b) are fitted with safety valves, a bursting disc shall be placed before the valve. The arrangement of the bursting disc and safety valve shall be such as to satisfy the competent authority.

211 833 Shells intended for the carriage of sulphur trioxide of 1° (a) shall be thermally insulated and fitted with a heating device on the outside.

211 834 Shells and their service equipment intended for carriage of hypochlorite solutions of 61° shall be so designed as to prevent the entry of foreign matter, leakage of liquid or any building up of dangerous excess pressure inside the shell.

211 835-
211 839

SECTION 4. Type approval

211 840-
211 849 (No special requirements)

SECTION 5. Tests

211 850 Shells intended for the carriage of substances of 6° shall be subjected to the initial and periodic hydraulic pressure tests at a gauge pressure of at least 1.0 MPa (10 bar) and those intended for the carriage of substances of 7° shall be subjected to initial and periodic hydraulic pressure tests at a gauge pressure of not less than 400 kPa (4 bar).

The materials of every welded shell intended for the carriage of substances of 6° shall be tested by the method described in Appendix B.1d.

211 851 Shells intended for the carriage of substances of 14° or of the substances referred to in marginal 211 810 (b) and (c) shall be subjected to the initial and periodic hydraulic pressure tests at a gauge pressure of not less than 400 kPa (4 bar). The hydraulic pressure test for shells intended for the carriage of sulphur trioxide of 1° (a) shall be repeated every three years.

[18/] *See footnote 7/ to marginal 211 135.*

211 851 Shells made of pure aluminium and intended for the carriage of nitric acid of 2° (a) need be
(contd) subjected to the initial and periodic hydraulic pressure tests at a gauge pressure of only 250 kPa
(2.5 bar).

The condition of the lining of shells intended for the carriage of substances of 14° shall be
inspected every year by an expert approved by the competent authority, who shall inspect the
inside of the shell.

211 852 Shells intended for the carriage of the substances referred to in marginal 211 810 (d) shall be
subjected to the initial and periodic hydraulic pressure tests at their calculation pressure as defined
in marginal 211 123.

211 853-
211 859

SECTION 6. Marking

211 860 Shells intended for the carriage of substances of 6° and 14° shall bear, in addition to the particulars
referred to in marginal 211 160, the date (month, year) of the most recent inspection of the internal
condition of the shell.

211 861 Shells intended for the carriage of inhibited sulphur trioxide of 1° (a) and substances of 6° and 14°
shall bear in addition, on the plate referred to in marginal 211 160, the maximum permissible load
mass in kg of the shell.

211 862-
211 869

SECTION 7. Operation

211 870 Shells intended for the carriage of inhibited or stabilized sulphur trioxide of 1° (a) shall not be
filled to more than 88% of their capacity; those intended for the carriage of substances of 14° shall
be filled to not less than 88% and not more than 92% of their capacity or to 2.86 kg per litre of
capacity. For the transport of 1829 sulphur trioxide, 99.95% pure and above, without inhibitor, the
temperature of the substance shall be maintained at or above 32.5° C.

Shells intended for the carriage of substances of 6° shall not be filled to more than 0.84 kg per litre
of capacity.

211 871 Shells intended for the carriage of substances of 6°, 7° and 14° shall be hermetically closed [18]
[see marginal 211 127 (2)] during carriage and the closures shall be protected with lockable caps.

211 872-
211 879

SECTION 8. Transitional measures

211 880 Fixed tanks, tank-vehicles and demountable tanks intended for the carriage of substances of 3°,
12°, 33°, 40° or 54° of marginal 2801, built before 1 January 1995 in accordances with the
requirements of this Appendix applicable until that date, but which do not, however, conform to
the requirements applicable as from 1 January 1995, may still be used until 31 December 2000.

211 881-
211 899

---

[18] *See footnote 7/ to marginal 211 135.*

Appendix B.1a

CLASS 9. MISCELLANEOUS DANGEROUS SUBSTANCES AND ARTICLES

211 900-
211 909

SECTION 1. General; scope (use of tanks); definitions

Use

211 910 Substances of 1°, 2° (b), 11° (c), 12° (c), 20° (c), 31° (c) to 35° (c) and 2211 polymeric beads, expandable of 4° (c) of marginal 2901 may be carried in fixed or demountable tanks.

NOTE: For the carriage in bulk of substances of 4° and 12° of marginal 2901, see marginal 91 111.

211 911-
211 919

SECTION 2. Construction

211 920 Shells intended for the carriage of substances of 1°, 2° (b), 11° (c), 12° (c), 20° (c), 31° to 35° or 2211 polymeric beads, expandable, of 4° (c) of marginal 2901 shall be designed in accordance with the requirements of Part I of this Appendix. The effective minimum thickness of the walls of shells intended for the carriage of substances of 20° (c) shall not be less than 3 mm.

211 921 Shells intended for the carriage of substances of 2° shall be designed for a calculation pressure [see marginal 211 127 (2)] of not less than 400 kPa (4 bar) (gauge pressure).

211 922-
211 929

SECTION 3. Items of equipment

211 930 Shells intended for the carriage of substances of 1° and 2° shall be capable of being hermetically closed [18]. Shells intended for the carriage of substances of 2211 polymeric beads, expandable of 4° (c) shall be equipped with a safety valve.

211 931 If shells intended for the carriage of substances of 1° and 2° are fitted with safety valves, a bursting disc shall be placed before the valves. The arrangement of the bursting disc and safety valve shall be such as to satisfy the competent authority.

211 932 Shells intended for the carriage of substances of 20° (c) shall be equipped with thermal insulation. They may also be equipped with pressure release devices opening automatically inwards or outwards under the effect of a difference of pressure of between 20 kPa and 30 kPa (0.2 bar and 0.3 bar). The thermal insulation directly in contact with the shell intended for the carriage of substances of 20° (c) shall have an ignition temperature at least 50° C higher than the maximum temperature for which the shell was designed.

211 933 The bottom discharge system of shells intended for the carriage of substances of 20° (c) may consist of an external pipe with a stop-valve if it is constructed in a metallic material liable to deformation.

---

[18] *See footnote 7/ to marginal 211 135.*

- 147 -

211 934   Shells intended for the carriage of substances filled at a temperature higher than 190° C shall be equipped with deflectors placed at right angles to the upper filling openings, so as to avoid a sudden localized increase in wall temperature during filling.

211 935-
211 939

SECTION 4.   **Type approval**

211 940-
211 949   (No special requirements)

SECTION 5.   **Tests**

211 950   Shells intended for the carriage of substances of 2° shall be subjected to the initial and periodic hydraulic pressure tests at a pressure of at 400 kPa (4 bar) (gauge pressure).

211 951   Shells intended for the carriage of substances of 1°, 2° (b), 11° (c), 12° (c), 20° (c), 31° to 35° or 2211 polymeric beads, expandable, of 4° (c) of marginal 2901 shall be subject to the initial and periodic hydraulic pressure tests at the calculation pressure used in their design as defined in marginal 211 123.

211 952-
211 959

SECTION 6.   **Marking**

211 960   Shells intended for the transport of substances of 20° (c) shall bear on both sides, in addition to the markings stipulated in marginal 211 161, the mark reproduced in Appendix B.7.

211 961-
211 969   (No special requirements)

SECTION 7.   **Operation**

211 970   Shells intended for the carriage of substances of 1° and 2° shall be hermetically closed [18] during carriage.

211 971   Tank-vehicles and demountable tanks approved for the carriage of substances of 1° and 2° shall not be used for the carriage of foodstuffs, articles of consumption or animal feedstuffs.

211 972-
211 979

SECTION 8.   **Transitional measures**

211 980   Fixed tanks (tank-vehicles) and demountable tanks intended for the carriage of substances of 20° of marginal 2901, built before 1 January 1997, but which do not conform with the requirements applicable as from 1 January 1995, may still be used until 31 December 2006.

211 981-
211 999

---

[18]   *See footnote 7/ to marginal 211 135.*

- 148 -

Appendix B.1b

PROVISIONS CONCERNING TANK-CONTAINERS

NOTE: Part I sets out the requirements applicable to tank-containers intended for the carriage of substances of all classes. Part II contains particular requirements supplementing or modifying the requirements of Part I.

PART I: Requirements applicable to all classes

212 000-
212 099

SECTION 1. General; scope (use of tank-containers); definitions

NOTE: In accordance with the provisions of marginal 10 121 (1), the carriage of dangerous substances in tank-containers is permitted only where expressly authorized for such substances in each of the Sections 1 of Part II of this Appendix.

212 100 These requirements shall apply to tank-containers of a capacity of more than 0.45 m^3 which are used for the carriage of liquid, powdery or granular substances, and to their fittings and accessories. For substances of Class 2, the requirements shall apply to tank-containers of more than 1000 l.

NOTE: For the purposes of the requirements of this Appendix, the following shall be considered to be substances carried in a liquid state:

- *substances which are liquid at normal temperatures and pressures*
- *solids offered for carriage at elevated temperatures or hot in the molten state.*

212 101 A tank-container comprises a shell and items of equipment, including the equipment to facilitate movement of the tank-container without significant change of attitude.

212 102 In the following requirements:

(1)   (a)   "*shell*" means the sheathing containing the substance (including the openings and their closures);

       (b)   "*service equipment*" of the shell means filling and emptying, venting, safety, heating and heat-insulating devices and measuring instruments; and

       (c)   "*structural equipment*" means the internal or external reinforcing, fastening, protective or stabilizing members of the shell.

(2)   (a)   "*calculation pressure*" means a theoretical pressure at least equal to the test pressure which, according to the degree of danger exhibited by the substance being carried, may to a greater or lesser degree exceed the working pressure. It is used solely to determine the thickness of the walls of the shell, independently of any external or internal reinforcing device;

       (b)   "*test pressure*" means the highest effective pressure which arises in the shell during the pressure test;

       (c)   "*filling pressure*" means the maximum pressure actually built up in the shell when it is being filled under pressure;

**212 102
(contd)**

(d) "*discharge pressure*" means the maximum pressure actually built up in the shell when it is being discharged under pressure;

(e) "*maximum working pressure (gauge pressure)*" means the highest of the following three pressures:

(i) the highest effective pressure allowed in the shell during filling ("maximum filling pressure allowed");

(ii) the highest effective pressure allowed in the shell during discharge ("maximum discharge pressure allowed"); and

(iii) the effective gauge pressure to which the shell is subjected by its contents (including such extraneous gases as it may contain) at the maximum working temperature.

· Unless the special requirements for each class provide otherwise, the numerical value of this working pressure (gauge pressure) shall not be lower than the vapour pressure (absolute pressure) of the filling substance at 50 °C.

For shells equipped with safety valves (with or without bursting disc), the maximum working pressure (gauge pressure) shall however be equal to the prescribed opening pressure of such safety valves.

(3) "*Leakproofness test*" means the test which consists of subjecting the shell to an effective internal pressure equal to the maximum working pressure, but not less than 20 kPa (0.2 bar) (gauge pressure), using a method approved by the competent authority.

For shells equipped with venting systems and a safety device to prevent the contents spilling out if the shell overturns, the pressure for the leakproofness test shall be equal to the static pressure of the filling substance.

**212 103-
212 119**

SECTION 2. Construction

212 120 Shells shall be designed and constructed in accordance with the provisions of a technical code recognized by the competent authority, in which the material is chosen and the wall thickness determined taking into account maximum and minimum filling and working temperatures, but the following minimum requirements shall be met:

(1) Shells shall be made of suitable metallic materials which, unless other temperature ranges are prescribed in the various classes, shall be resistant to brittle fracture and to stress corrosion cracking between -20 °C and +50 °C. However, suitable non-metallic materials may be used to manufacture equipment and accessories.

(2) For welded shells only materials of faultless weldability whose adequate impact strength at an ambient temperature of -20 °C can be guaranteed, particularly in the weld seams and the zones adjacent thereto, shall be used.

212 120 (3)   Welds shall be skilfully made and shall afford the fullest safety. For the execution and checking of weld beads, see also marginal 212 127 (6). Shells whose minimum wall thicknesses have been determined in accordance with marginal 212 127 (3) and (4) shall be checked by the methods described in the definition of the weld coefficient of 0.8.

(4)   The materials of shells or of their protective linings which are in contact with the contents shall not contain substances liable to react dangerously with the contents, to form dangerous compounds, or substantially to weaken the material.

(5)   The protective lining shall be so designed that its leakproofness remains intact, whatever the deformation liable to occur in normal conditions of carriage [marginal 212 127 (1)].

(6)   If contact between the substance carried and the material used for the construction of the shell entails a progressive decrease in the thickness of the walls, this thickness shall be increased at manufacture by an appropriate amount. This additional thickness to allow for corrosion shall not be taken into consideration in calculating the thickness of the shell walls.

212 121   Shells, their attachments and their service and structural equipment shall be designed to withstand without loss of contents (other than quantities of gas escaping through any degassing vents):

-    static and dynamic stresses in normal conditions of carriage;
-    prescribed minimum stresses as defined in marginals 212 125 and 212 127.

212 122   The pressure on which the wall thickness of the shell is based shall not be less than the calculation pressure, but the stresses referred to in marginal 212 121 shall also be taken into account.

212 123   Unless specially prescribed otherwise in the various classes, the following particulars shall be taken into account in the design of shells:

(1)   Gravity-discharge shells intended for the carriage of substances having a vapour pressure not exceeding 110 kPa (1.1 bar) (absolute pressure) at 50 °C shall be designed for a calculation pressure of twice the static pressure of the substance to be carried but not less than twice the static pressure of water.

(2)   Pressure-filled or pressure-discharge shells intended for the carriage of substances having a vapour pressure not exceeding 110 kPa (1.1 bar) (absolute pressure) at 50 °C shall be designed for a calculation pressure equal to 1.3 times the filling or discharge pressure.

(3)   Shells intended for the carriage of substances having a vapour pressure of more than 110 kPa (1.1 bar) but not more than 175 kPa (1.75 bar) (absolute pressure) at 50 °C shall, whatever their filling or discharge system, be designed for a calculation pressure of not less than 150 kPa (1.5 bar) (gauge pressure) or 1.3 times the filling or discharge pressure, whichever is the higher.

(4)   Shells intended for the carriage of substances having a vapour pressure of more than 175 kPa (1.75 bar) (absolute pressure) at 50 °C shall, whatever their filling or discharge system, be designed for a calculation pressure equal to 1.3 times the filling or discharge pressure but not less than 400 kPa (4 bar) (gauge pressure).

212 124   Tank-containers intended to contain certain dangerous substances shall be provided with additional protection, which may take the form of additional thickness of the shell (such additional thickness being determined in the light of the dangers inherent in the substances concerned: see the relevant classes) or of a protective device.

Appendix B.1b

212 125 At the test pressure, the stress σ (sigma) at the most severely stressed point of the shell shall not exceed the material-dependent limits prescribed below. Allowance shall be made for any weakening due to the welds.

(1) For all metals and alloys, the stress σ at the test pressure shall be lower than the smaller of the values given by the following formulae:

$$\sigma \leq 0.75 \text{ Re or } \sigma \leq 0.5 \text{ Rm}$$

where

Re = apparent yield stress, or 0.2%
or, in the case of austenitic steels, 1%

Rm = minimum tensile strength.

Ratios of Re/Rm exceeding 0.85 are not allowed for steels used in the construction of welded tanks.

The values of Re and Rm to be used shall be specified minimum values according to material standards. If no material standard exists for the metal or alloy in question, the values of Re and Rm used shall be approved by the competent authority or by a body designated by that authority.

When austenitic steels are used, the specified minimum values according to the material standards may be exceeded by up to 15% if these higher values are attested in the inspection certificate.

The values specified in the certificate shall be taken as a basis in determining the Re/Rm ratio in each case.

(2) For steel, the elongation at fracture, in per cent, shall be not less than

$$\frac{10\ 000}{\text{determined tensile strength in N/mm}^2}$$

but in any case for fine grained steels it shall be not less than 16% and not less than 20% for other steels. For aluminium alloys the elongation at fracture shall be not less than 12% [1].

212 126 All parts of a tank-container intended for the carriage of liquids having a flash-point of not more than 61 °C, or for the carriage of flammable gases, shall be capable of being electrically earthed. Any metal contact which might encourage electrochemical corrosion shall be avoided.

---

[1] *In the case of sheet metal, the axis of the tensile test-piece shall be at right angles to the direction of rolling. The permanent elongation at fracture shall be measured on test-pieces of circular cross-section in which the gauge length l is equal to five times the diameter d (l = 5d); if test-pieces of rectangular section are used, the gauge length shall be calculated by the formula*

$$l = 5,65 \sqrt{F_0}$$

where F_0 indicates the initial cross-section area of the test-piece.

- 152 -

Appendix B.1b

212 127 Tank-containers shall be capable of withstanding the stresses specified in paragraph (1) and the wall thickness of the shells shall be at least that prescribed in paragraphs (2) to (5) below.

(1)   Tank-containers and their fastenings shall, under the maximum permissible load be capable of absorbing the stresses equal to those exerted by:

- in the direction of travel: twice the total mass;

- horizontally at right angles to the direction of travel: the total mass; (where the direction of travel is not clearly determined, twice the total mass in each direction);

- vertically upwards: the total mass; and

- vertically downwards: twice the total mass.

Under each force the safety factors to be complied with shall be the following:

- for metals having a clearly-defined yield point: a safety factor of 1.5 in relation to the guaranteed apparent yield stress; or,

- for metals with no clearly-defined yield point: a safety factor of 1.5 in relation to the guaranteed 0.2% proof stress, and in the case of austenitic steels the 1% maximum elongation.

(2)   The thickness of the cylindrical wall of the shell and of the ends and cover plates shall not be less than the greater of the values determined by the following formulae:

$$e = \frac{P_{ep}\, D}{2\sigma\lambda} \quad (mm)$$

$$e = \frac{P_{cal}\, D}{2\sigma} \quad (mm)$$

where:

P_{ep}	=	test pressure in MPa
P_{cal}	=	calculation pressure in MPa as specified in marginal 212 123
D	=	internal diameter of shell in mm
σ	=	permissible stress, as defined in marginal 212 125 (1) in N/mm²
λ	=	a coefficient not exceeding or equal to 1, allowing for any weakening due to welds.

The thickness shall in no case be less than that defined in paragraphs (3) and (4) below.

212 127
(contd)

(3)   The walls, ends and cover plates of shells not more than 1.80 m in diameter [2] shall be not less than 5 mm thick if of mild steel [3] (in conformity with the provisions of marginal 212 125) or of equivalent thickness if of another metal. Where the diameter is more than 1.80 m [2], this thickness shall be increased to 6 mm except in the case of shells intended for the carriage of powdery or granular substances, if the shell is of mild steel [3] (in conformity with the provisions of marginal 212 125) or to an equivalent thickness if the tank is of another metal.

Whatever the metal used, the thickness of the shell wall shall in no case be less than 3 mm.

"*Equivalent thickness*" means the thickness obtained by the following formula:

$$e_1 = \frac{21.4 \times e_o}{\sqrt[3]{Rm_1 \times A_1}} \quad [4]$$

(4)   Where protection of the shell against damage is provided, the competent authority may allow the aforesaid minimum thicknesses to be reduced in proportion to the protection provided; however, the said thicknesses shall be not less than 3 mm in the case of mild steel, [3] or than an equivalent thickness in the case of other materials, for shells not more than 1.80 m in diameter [2]. For shells of a diameter exceeding 1.80 m [2] this minimum thickness shall be increased to 4 mm in the case of mild steel [3] and to an equivalent thickness in the case of other metals.

"*Equivalent thickness*" means the thickness obtained by the following formula:

$$e_1 = \frac{21.4 \times e_o}{\sqrt[3]{Rm_1 \times A_1}} \quad [4]$$

(5)   The protection referred to under (4) may consist of over-all external structural protection as in "sandwich" construction where the sheathing is secured to the shell, or a structure in which the shell is supported by a complete skeleton including longitudinal and transverse structural members, or double-wall construction.

---

[2]   *For shells not of circular cross-section, for example box-shaped or elliptical shells, the indicated diameters shall correspond to those calculated on the basis of a circular cross-section of the same area. For such shapes of cross-section the radius of convexity of the shell wall shall not exceed 2 000 mm at the sides or 3 000 mm at the top and bottom.*

[3]   *"Mild steel" means a steel having a minimum breaking strength between 360 N/mm² and 440 N/mm².*

[4]   *This formula is derived from the general formula:*

$$e_1 = e_o \sqrt[3]{\frac{Rm_o \times A_o}{Rm_1 \times A_1}}$$

where:

Rm_o =   *360,*
A_o =   *27 for the reference mild steel;*
Rm_1 =   *minimum tensile strength of the metal chosen, in N/mm²; and*
A_1 =   *minimum elongation of the metal chosen on fracture under tensile stress, in per cent.*

Appendix B.1b

**212 127
(contd)** Where the shells are made with double walls, the space between being evacuated of air, the aggregate thickness of the outer metal wall and the shell wall shall correspond to the minimum wall thickness prescribed in (3), the thickness of the wall of the shell itself being not less than the minimum thickness prescribed in (4).

Where shells are made with double walls with an intermediate layer of solid materials at least 50 mm thick, the outer wall shall have a thickness of not less than 0.5 mm if it is made of mild steel [5/] or at least 2 mm if it is made of a plastics material reinforced with glass fibre. Solid foam with an impact absorption capacity such as that, for example, of polyurethane foam, may be used as the intermediate layer of solid material.

(6)   The manufacturer's qualification for performing welding operations shall be one recognized by the competent authority. Welding shall be performed by skilled welders using a welding process whose effectiveness (including any heat treatments required) has been demonstrated by test. Non-destructive tests shall be carried out by radiography or by ultrasound and must confirm that the quality of the welding is appropriate to the stresses.

In determining the thickness of the shell walls in accordance with (2), the following values of the coefficient λ (lambda) should be adopted for the welds:

0.8:   where the weld beads are so far as possible inspected visually on both faces and are subjected to a non-destructive spot check with particular attention to connections;

0.9:   where all longitudinal beads throughout their length, all connections, 25% of circular beads, and welds for the assembly of large-diameter items of equipment are subjected to non-destructive checks. Beads shall be checked visually on both sides as far as possible;

1.0:   where all beads are subjected to non-destructive checks and are so far as possible inspected visually on both sides. A weld test-piece shall be taken.

Where the competent authority has doubts regarding the quality of weld beads, it may require additional checks.

(7)   Measures shall be taken to protect shells against the risk of deformation as a result of a negative internal pressure.

Unless otherwise prescribed in the special provisions for the individual classes, these shells may have valves to avoid an unacceptable negative internal pressure, without intervening bursting discs.

(8)   The thermal insulation shall be so designed as not to hinder access to, or the operation of, filling and discharge devices and safety valves.

**212 128-
212 129**

[5/]   *See footnote 3/.*

Appendix B.1b

SECTION 3.　　　　**Items of equipment**

212 130　The items of equipment shall be so arranged as to be protected against the risk of being wrenched off or damaged during carriage or handling. They shall exhibit a suitable degree of safety comparable to that of the shells themselves and shall in particular:

　　　　-　　be compatible with the substances carried;
　　　　-　　meet the requirements of marginal 212 121.

The leakproofness of the service equipment shall be ensured even in the event of the overturning of the tank-container. The gaskets shall be made of material compatible with the substance carried and shall be replaced as soon as their effectiveness is impaired, for example as a result of ageing. Gaskets ensuring the leakproofness of fittings requiring manipulation during normal use of the tank-containers shall be so designed and arranged that manipulation of the fittings incorporating them does not damage them.

212 131　Every bottom-discharge tank-container, and in the case of compartmented bottom-discharge tank-containers every compartment, shall be equipped with two mutually independent shut-off devices, the first being an internal stop-valve [6] fixed directly to the shell and the second being a sluice-valve or other equivalent device [7], mounted in series, one at each end of the discharge pipe. The bottom discharge of shells intended for the carriage of powdery or granular substances may be constituted by external piping with a stop-valve if it is made of a malleable metal material. In addition, the openings shall be capable of being closed by means of screw-threaded plugs, blank flanges or other equally effective devices.

The internal stop-valve shall be operable from above or from below. Its setting - open or closed - shall so far as possible in each case be capable of being verified from the ground. Internal stop-valve control devices shall be so designed as to prevent any unintended opening through impact or an inadvertent act.

The internal shut-off device shall continue to be effective in the event of damage to the external control device.

In order to avoid any loss of contents in the event of damage to the external discharge fittings (pipes, lateral shut-off devices), the internal stop-valve and its seating shall be protected against the danger of being wrenched off by external stresses or shall be so designed as to resist them. The filling and discharge devices (including flanges or threaded plugs) and protective caps (if any) shall be capable of being secured against any unintended opening.

The position and/or direction of closure of the valves shall be clearly apparent.

The shell or each of its compartments shall be provided with an opening large enough to permit inspection.

---

　　[6]　　*However, in the case of shells intended for the carriage of certain crystallizable or highly viscous substances, of deeply refrigerated liquefied gases and shells fitted with an ebonite or thermoplastic coating, the internal stop-valve may be replaced by an external stop-valve provided with additional protection.*

　　[7]　　*In the case of tank-containers of less than 1 m³ capacity, the sluice-valve or other equivalent device may be replaced by a blank flange.*

212 132   Tank-containers intended for the carriage of substances for which all the openings are above the surface level of the liquid may be equipped, in the lower part of the body, with a cleaning aperture (fist-hole). This aperture shall be capable of being sealed by a flange so closed as to be leakproof, the design of which shall be approved by the competent authority or by a body designated by that authority.

212 133   Tank-containers intended for the carriage of liquids having a vapour pressure of not more than 110 kPa (1.1 bar) (absolute pressure) at 50 °C shall have a venting system and a safety device to prevent the contents from escaping from the shell if the tank-container overturns; or they shall conform to the requirements of marginal 212 134 or 212 135 below.

212 134   Tank-containers intended for the carriage of liquids having a vapour pressure of more than 110 kPa (1.1 bar) and not more than 175 kPa (1.75 bar) (absolute pressure) at 50 °C shall have a safety valve set at not less than 150 kPa (1.5 bar) (gauge pressure) and such that it is fully open at a pressure not exceeding the test pressure; or shall conform to the requirements of marginal 212 135.

212 135   Tank-containers intended for the carriage of liquids having a vapour pressure of more than 175 kPa (1.75 bar) and not more than 300 kPa (3 bar) (absolute pressure) at 50 °C shall be equipped with a safety valve set at not less than 300 kPa (3 bar) (gauge pressure) and such that it is fully open at a pressure not exceeding the test pressure; or shall be hermetically closed [8].

212 136   No movable parts such as covers, closures, etc., which are liable to come into frictional or percussive contact with aluminium shells intended for the carriage of flammable liquids having a flash-point of not more than 61 °C or for the carriage of flammable gases may be made of unprotected corrodible steel.

212 137-
212 139

SECTION 4.   Type approval

212 140   The competent authority or a body designated by that authority shall issue in respect of each new type of tank-container a certificate attesting that the prototype tank-container, including fastenings, which it has inspected is suitable for the purpose for which it is intended and meets the construction requirements of Section 2, the equipment requirements of Section 3 and the special conditions for the classes of substances carried. If the tank-containers are manufactured in series without modification, this approval shall be valid for the entire series. The test results, the substances and/or the groups of substances for the carriage of which the tank-container is approved and its type approval number as a prototype shall be specified in a test report. The substances of a group of substances shall be of a similar kind and equally compatible with the characteristics of the shell. The substances or groups of substances permitted shall be specified in the test report, with their chemical names or the corresponding collective heading in the list of substances, and with their Class and item number. The approval number shall consist of the distinguishing sign [2] of the State in whose territory the approval was granted, and a registration number.

212 141-
212 149

---

[8]   *"Hermetically closed shells" means shells whose openings are hermetically closed and which are not equipped with safety valves, bursting discs or other similar safety devices. Shells having safety valves preceded by a bursting disc shall be deemed to be hermetically closed.*

[2]   *Distinguishing sign for used in international traffic prescribed by the Convention on Road Traffic (Vienna, 1968).*

SECTION 5.   **Tests**

212 150   Shells and their equipment shall either together or separately undergo an initial inspection before being put into service. This inspection shall include:

- a check of conformity to the approved prototype;
- a check of the design characteristics [10];
- an examination of the internal and external conditions;
- a hydraulic pressure test [11] at the test pressure indicated on the data plate; and
- a check of satisfactory operation of the equipment.

The hydraulic pressure test shall be carried out before the installation of such thermal insulation as may be necessary. If the shells and their equipment are tested separately, they shall be jointly subjected to a leakproofness test in accordance with marginal 212 102 (3).

212 151   Shells and their equipment shall undergo periodic inspections at fixed intervals. The periodic inspections shall include an external and internal examination and, as a general rule, a hydraulic pressure test [11]. Sheathing for thermal or other insulation shall be removed only to the extent required for reliable appraisal of the characteristics of the shell.

In the case of shells intended for the carriage of powdery or granular substances, and with the agreement of the expert approved by the competent authority, the periodic hydraulic pressure tests may be omitted and replaced by leakproofness tests in accordance with marginal 212 102 (3).

The maximum intervals for inspections shall be five years.

Tank-containers, empty, uncleaned, may also be moved after expiration of this period for the purpose of undergoing the test.

212 152   In addition, a leakproofness test of the shell with its equipment in accordance with marginal 212 102 (3) and a check of the satisfactory operation of all the equipment shall be carried out at least every two and a half years. Empty, uncleaned tank-containers may be moved after expiration of this period, for undergoing inspection.

212 153   When the safety of the shell or of its equipment may have been impaired as a result of repairs, alterations or accident, an exceptional check shall be carried out.

212 154   The tests, inspections and checks in accordance with marginals 212 150 to 212 153 shall be carried out by the expert approved by the competent authority. Certificates shall be issued showing the results of these operations. These certificates shall refer to the list of substances permitted for carriage in this shell in accordance with 212 140.

212 155-
212 159

---

[10]   *The check of the design characteristics shall also include, for shells requiring a test pressure of 1 MPa (10 bar) or higher, the taking of weld test-pieces (work samples) in accordance with the tests in Appendix B.1d.*

[11]   *In special cases and with the agreement of the expert approved by the competent authority, the hydraulic pressure test may be replaced by a pressure test using another liquid or gas, where such an operation does not entail any danger.*

SECTION 6. Marking

212 160 Each tank-container shall be fitted with a corrosion-resistant metal plate permanently attached to the shell in a place readily accessible for inspection. The following particulars at least shall be marked on the plate by stamping or by any other similar method. These particulars may be engraved directly on the walls of the shell itself if the walls are so reinforced that the strength of the shell is not impaired:

- approval number;
- manufacturer's name or mark;
- manufacturer's serial number;
- year of manufacture;
- test pressure [12] (gauge pressure);
- capacity [12] - in the case of multiple-element tank-containers: capacity of each element;
- design temperature [12] (only if above 50 °C or below -20 °C);
- date (month and year) of initial test and most recent periodic test in accordance with marginals 212 150 and 212 151; and
- stamp of the expert who carried out the tests.
- material of the shell and, when appropriate, the protective lining.

In addition the maximum working pressure shall be inscribed on pressure-filled or pressure-discharge shells.

212 161 The following particulars shall be inscribed either on the tank-container itself or on a plate:

- names of owner and of operator;
- capacity of the shell [12];
- tare [12];
- the maximum permissible laden mass [12]; and
- name of substance carried [13].

In addition, tank-containers shall bear the prescribed danger labels.

212 162-
212 169

---

[12] *The units of measurement should be indicated after numerical values.*

[13] *A collective description covering a group of substances of a similar nature and equally compatible with the characteristics of the shell may be given instead of the name.*

Appendix B.1b

SECTION 7.   **Operation**

212 170   During carriage, tank-containers shall be fixed on the carrying vehicle in such a way as to be adequately protected by the fittings of the carrying vehicle or of the tank-container itself against lateral and longitudinal impact and against overturning [14]. If the shells, including the service equipment, are so constructed as to withstand impact or overturning they need not be protected in this way. The thickness of the walls of the shell shall remain, throughout its period of use, not less than the minimum value required by marginal 212 127 (2).

212 171   Shells shall not be loaded with any dangerous substances other than those for whose carriage they have been approved and which, in contact with the materials of the shell, gaskets, equipment and protective linings, are not liable to react dangerously with them, to form dangerous products or appreciably to weaken the material. Foodstuffs shall not be carried in these shells unless the necessary steps have been taken to prevent any harm to public health.

212 172   (1)   The following degrees of filling shall not be exceeded in tank-containers intended for the carriage of liquids at ambient temperatures:

        (a)   for flammable substances without additional risks (e.g. toxicity or corrosivity), in tank-containers with a venting system or with safety valves (even where preceded by a bursting disc):

$$\text{degree of filling} = \frac{100}{1 + \alpha\,(50 - t_F)}\ \%\ \text{of capacity}$$

        (b)   for toxic or corrosive substances (whether inflammable or not) in tank-containers with a venting system or with safety valves (even where preceded by a bursting disc):

$$\text{degree of filling} = \frac{98}{1 + \alpha\,(50 - t_F)}\ \%\ \text{of capacity};$$

        (c)   for flammable substances and for slightly toxic or slightly corrosive substances (whether flammable or not) in hermetically closed shells [15] without safety device:

$$\text{degree of filling} = \frac{97}{1 + \alpha\,(50 - t_F)}\ \%\ \text{of capacity};$$

---

[14]   *Examples of protection of shells:*

    1.   protection against lateral impact may, for example, consist of longitudinal bars protecting the shell on both sides at the level of the median line.

    2.   protection against overturning may, for example, consist of reinforcing rings or bars fixed transversally in relation to the frame.

    3.   protection against rear impact may for example consist of a bumper or frame.

[15]   *See footnote 8/ to marginal 212 135.*

212 172
(contd)
(d) for highly toxic, toxic, highly corrosive or corrosive substances (whether inflammable or not) in hermetically closed shells [16] without safety device:

$$degree\ of\ filling = \frac{95}{1 + \alpha\ (50 - t_F)}\ \%\ of\ capacity.$$

(2) In these formulae, is the mean coefficient of cubical expansion of the liquid between 15 °C and 50 °C, i.e. for a maximum variation in temperature of 35 °C.

$$\alpha\ is\ calculated\ by\ the\ formula:\ \alpha = \frac{d_{15} - d_{50}}{(35 \times d_{50})}$$

where d_{15} and d_{50} are the relative densities of the liquid at 15 °C and 50 °C respectively. t_F is the mean temperature of the liquid during filling.

(3) The provisions of (1) shall not apply to shells whose contents are, by means of a heating device, maintained at a temperature above 50 °C during carriage. In this case the degree of filling at the outset shall be such, and the temperature so regulated, that the shell is not full to more than 95% of its capacity and that the filling temperature is not exceeded, at any time during carriage.

(4) Where hot substances are loaded, the temperature of the outer surface of the shell or of the thermal insulation shall not exceed 70 °C during carriage.

212 173 If the shells of tank-containers intended for the carriage of liquids [17] are not divided by partitions or surge plates into sections of not more than 7 500 litres capacity, they shall be filled to not less than 80% of their capacity unless they are nominally empty.

212 174 During loading and unloading of tanks, appropriate measures shall be taken to prevent the release of dangerous quantities of gases and vapours.

Tank-containers shall be closed so that the contents cannot spill out uncontrolled. The openings of bottom-discharge shells shall be closed by means of screw-threaded plugs, blank flanges or other equally effective devices. The leakproofness of the closures of the shells, in particular at the top of the dip-tube, shall be checked by the consignor after the shell is filled.

212 175 Where several closure systems are fitted in a series, that nearest to the substance being carried shall be closed first.

212 176 No dangerous residue of the filling substance shall adhere to the outside of a tank-container during transport either laden or empty.

212 177 To be accepted for carriage, empty tank-containers, uncleaned, shall be closed in the same manner and leakproof in the same degree as though they were full.

---

[16] See footnote 8/ to marginal 212 135.

[17] Substances whose kinematic viscosity at 20 °C is less than 2 680 mm²/s shall be deemed to be liquids for the purposes of this provision.

212 178 Substances which may react dangerously with each other shall not be carried in adjoining compartments of tanks:

The following are considered dangerous reactions:

(a)   combustion and/or giving off considerable heat

(b)   emission of flammable and/or toxic gases

(c)   formation of corrosive liquids

(d)   formation of unstable substances

(e)   dangerous rise in pressure.

Substances which may react dangerously with each other may be carried in adjoining compartments of tanks, when these compartments are separated by a partition with a wall-thickness equal to or greater than that of the tank itself. They may also be carried in compartments of the same tank separated by an empty space or an empty compartment between loaded compartments.

212 179

SECTION 8.   Transitional measures

212 180 Tank-containers constructed before the entry into force of the provisions applicable from 1 January 1988 which do not conform to those provisions but were constructed according to the requirements of ADR in force before that date may still be used.

212 181 Tank-containers constructed before the entry into force of the provisions applicable from 1 January 1993 which do not conform to those provisions but were constructed according to the requirements of ADR in force until that date may still be used.

212 182-
212 189

SECTION 9.   Use of tank-containers approved for maritime transport

212 190 Tank-containers which do not fully meet the requirements of this appendix but which have been approved in accordance with the requirements concerning maritime transport shall be accepted for carriage [18/].

In addition to the particulars already prescribed, the transport document shall bear the words: **"Carriage in accordance with marginal 212 190"**.

Only substances authorized under marginal 10 121 (1) may be carried in tank-containers.

212 191-
212 199

[18/]   *These requirements are contained in Section 13 of the General Introduction to the International Maritime Dangerous Goods (IMDG) Code published by the International Maritime Organisation, London.*

Appendix B.1b

PART II. SPECIAL REQUIREMENTS SUPPLEMENTING OR MODIFYING
THE REQUIREMENTS OF PART I

CLASS 2. GASES

212 200-
212 209

SECTION 1.   General; scope (use of tank-containers); definitions

Use

212 210 The gases of marginal 2201 listed in the tables in marginal 212 251 may be carried in tank-containers.

212 211-
212 219

SECTION 2.   Construction

212 220 (1)   Shells intended for the carriage of substances of 1°, 2° or 4° shall be made of steel. In the case of weldless shells by derogation from marginal 212 125 (3), a minimum elongation at fracture of 14% and also a stress σ (sigma) lower than or equal to limits hereafter given according to the material may be accepted:

  (a)   When the ratio Re/Rm of the minimum guaranteed characteristics after heat treatment is higher than 0.66 without exceeding 0.85:

$$\sigma \leq 0.75 \; Re;$$

  (b)   When the ratio Re/Rm of the minimum guaranteed characteristics after heat treatment is higher than 0.85:

$$\sigma \leq 0.5 \; Rm.$$

  (2)   Receptacles as defined in marginals 2211 (1), (2) and (3) and cylinders as part of bundles of cylinders as defined in marginal 2211 (5) which are elements of a multiple-element tank-container, shall be constructed according to marginal 2212.

212 221 The requirements of Appendix B.1d shall apply to the materials and construction of welded shells.

212 222 Shells intended for the carriage of 1017 chlorine or 1076 phosgene of 2°TC shall be designed for a calculation pressure [see marginal 212 127 (2)] of at least 2.2 MPa (22 bar) (gauge pressure).

212 223-
212 229

SECTION 3.   Items of equipment

212 230 The discharge pipes of shells shall be capable of being closed by blank flanges or some other equally reliable device. For shells intended for the carriage of gases of 3°, these blank flanges or other equally reliable devices may be fitted with pressure-release openings of a maximum diameter of 1.5 mm.

- 163 -

Appendix B.1b

212 231 Shells intended for the carriage of liquefied gases may, in addition to openings prescribed in marginals 212 131 and 212 132, be provided with openings for the fitting of gauges, thermometers, manometers and with bleed holes, as required for their operational safety.

212 232 Safety devices shall meet the following requirements:

(1) Filling and discharge openings of shells of a capacity exceeding 1 m^3 intended for the carriage of liquefied flammable and/or toxic gases shall be equipped with an instant-closing internal safety device which closes automatically in the event of an unintended movement of the tank-container or of fire. It shall also be possible to operate the closing device by remote control.

(2) All openings, other than those accommodating safety valves and than closed bleed holes, of shells intended for the carriage of liquefied flammable and/or toxic gases shall, if their nominal diameter is more than 1.5 mm, be equipped with an internal shut-off device.

(3) By derogation from the provisions of paragraphs (1) and (2), shells intended for the carriage of deeply refrigerated flammable and/or toxic liquefied gases may be equipped with external devices in place of internal devices if the external devices afford protection against external damage at least equivalent to that afforded by the wall of the shell.

(4) If the shells are equipped with gauges, the latter shall not be made of a transparent material in direct contact with the substance carried. If there are thermometers, they shall not project directly into the gas or liquid through the shell wall.

(5) Shells intended for the carriage of 1053 hydrogen sulphide or 1064 methyl mercaptan of 2°TF or 1017 chlorine, 1076 phosgene or 1079 sulphur dioxide of 2°TC shall not have an opening below the surface level of the liquid. In addition, the cleaning apertures (fist holes) referred to in marginal 212 132 shall not be permitted.

(6) Filling and discharge openings situated in the upper part of shells shall be equipped with, in addition to what is prescribed in paragraph (1) a second, external, closing device. This device shall be capable of being closed by a blank flange or some other equally reliable device.

(7) By derogation from the provisions in paragraphs (1), (2) and (6), for receptacles as defined in marginals 2211 (1), (2), (3) and (5) which form a multiple-element tank-container, the required closing devices may be provided for within the manifolding arrangement.

212 233 Safety valves shall meet the following requirements:

(1) Shells intended for the carriage of gases of 1°, 2° or 4° may be fitted with not more than two safety valves whose aggregate clear cross-sectional area of passage at the seating or seatings shall be not less than 20 cm^2 per 30 m^3 or part thereof of the receptacle's capacity. These valves shall be capable of opening automatically under a pressure between 0.9 and 1.0 times the test pressure of the shell to which they are fitted. They shall be of such a type as to resist dynamic stresses, including liquid surge. The use of dead weight or counter weight valves is prohibited.

Shells intended for the carriage of gases of 1° to 4° indicated by the letter T in marginal 2201, shall not have safety valves unless the safety valves are preceded by a bursting disc. In the latter case the arrangement of the bursting disc and the safety valve shall be satisfactory to the competent authority.

212 233
(contd) Where tank-containers are intended for carriage by sea, the provisions of this paragraph shall not prohibit the fitting of safety valves conforming to the regulations governing that mode of transport [19].

(2)   Shells intended for the carriage of gases of 3° shall be fitted with two independent safety valves; each valve shall be so designed as to allow the gases formed by evaporation during normal operation to escape from the shell in such a way that the pressure does not at any time exceed by more than 10% the working pressure indicated on the shell. One of the two safety valves may be replaced by a bursting disc which shall be such as to burst at the test pressure.

In the event of loss of the vacuum in a double-walled shell, or of destruction of 20% of the insulation of a single-walled shell, the safety valve and the bursting disc shall permit an outflow such that the pressure in the shell cannot exceed the test pressure.

(3)   The safety valves of shells intended for the carriage of gases of 3° shall be capable of opening at the working pressure indicated on the shell. They shall be so designed as to function faultlessly even at the lowest working temperature. The reliability of their operation at that temperature shall be established and checked either by testing each valve or by testing a specimen valve of each design type.

Thermal insulation

212 234   (1)   If shells intended for the carriage of gases of 2° are equipped with thermal insulation, such insulation shall consist of either:

-     a sun shield covering not less than the upper third but not more than the upper half of the shell surface and separated from the shell by an air space at least 4 cm across; or

-     a complete cladding, of adequate thickness, of insulating materials.

(2)   Shells intended for the carriage of gases of 3° shall be thermally insulated. The thermal insulation shall be protected by means of a continuous sheathing. If the space between the shell and the sheathing is under vacuum (vacuum insulation), the protective sheathing shall be so designed as to withstand without deformation an external pressure of at least 100 kPa (1 bar) (gauge pressure). By derogation from marginal 212 102 (2) (a) external and internal reinforcing devices may be taken into account in the calculations. If the sheathing is so closed as to be gas-tight, a device shall be provided to prevent any dangerous pressure from developing in the insulating layer in the event of inadequate gas-tightness of the shell or of its items of equipment. The device shall prevent the infiltration of moisture into the heat-insulating sheath.

(3)   Shells intended for the carriage of liquefied gases having a boiling point below -182 °C at atmospheric pressure shall not include any combustible material either in the thermal insulation or in the fastenings.

The fastening for shells of vacuum insulated tanks may, with the approval of the competent authority, contain plastics substances between the shell and the sheathing.

---

[19]   *See footnote 17/.*

212 235 (1)   A multiple-element tank-container contains elements which are linked to each other by a manifold and mounted on the frame of a multiple-element tank-container. The following elements are considered to be elements of a multiple-element tank-container:

-    cylinders as defined in marginal 2211 (1);

-    tubes as defined in marginal 2211 (2);

-    pressure drums as defined in marginal 2211 (3);

-    bundles of cylinders (also known as frames) as defined in marginal 2211 (5);

-    shells as defined in Annex B.

NOTE: Bundles of cylinders as defined in marginal 2211 (5) which are not elements of a multiple-element tank-container are subject to the requirements of marginals 2204 to 2224.

(2)   The following conditions shall be complied with for multiple-element tank-containers:

(a)   If one of the elements of a multiple-element tank-container is equipped with a safety valve and shut-off devices are provided between the elements, every element shall be so equipped.

(b)   The filling and discharge devices may be affixed to a manifold.

(c)   Each element of a multiple-element tank-container, including each individual cylinder of a bundle, as defined in marginal 2211 (5), intended for the carriage of gases designated by capital letter T in marginal 2201, shall be capable of being isolated by a shut-off valve.

(d)   The elements of a multiple-element tank-container intended for the carriage of gases designated by capital letter F in marginal 2201, when consisting of receptacles as defined in marginals 2211 (1), (2), (3) and (5), shall be combined to groups of not more than 5,000 litres which are capable of being isolated by a shut-off valve.

Each element of a multiple-element tank-container intended for the carriage of gases designated by capital letter F in marginal 2201 when consisting of shells as defined in Annex B shall be capable of being isolated by a shut-off valve.

212 236 By derogation from the provisions of marginal 212 131 shells intended for the carriage of deeply-refrigerated liquefied gases need not have an inspection aperture.

212 237-
212 239

SECTION 4.   **Type approval**

212 240-
212 249 (No special requirements)

Appendix B.1b

SECTION 5.   Tests

212 250   (1)   Receptacles as defined in marginal 2211 (1), (2) and (3) and cylinders as part of bundles of cylinders as defined in marginal 2211 (5), which are elements of a multiple-element tank-container, shall be tested according to marginal 2219.

(2)   The materials of every welded shell which do not meet the definition of paragraph (1) shall be tested according to the method described in Appendix B.1d.

212 251   (1)   The test pressure for shells intended for the carriage of gases of 1° having a critical temperature below -50 °C shall be at least one and one-half times the filling pressure at 15 °C.

(2)   The test pressure for shells intended for the carriage of:

-         gases of 1° having a critical temperature of -50 °C or above; and
-         gases of 2° having a critical temperature below 70 °C
-         gases of 4°

shall be such that, when the shell is filled to the maximum mass of the contents per litre of capacity, the pressure reached in the shell by the substance at 55°C for shells with thermal insulation or 65°C for shells without thermal insulation does not exceed the test pressure.

(3)   The test pressure for shells intended for the carriage of gases of 2° having a critical temperature of 70 °C or above will be:

(a)   If the shell is equipped with thermal insulation, at least equal to the vapour pressure, reduced by 0.1 MPa (1 bar) of the liquid at 60 °C, but not less than 1 MPa (10 bar);

(b)   If the shell is not equipped with thermal insulation, at least equal to the vapour pressure, reduced by 0.1 MPa (1 bar), of the liquid at 65 °C, but not less than 1 MPa (10 bar).

The maximum permissible mass of contents per litre of capacity in kg/litre prescribed for the degree of filling is calculated as follows:

maximum permissible mass of contents
per litre of capacity   = 0.95 × density of the liquid phase at 50 °C;

moreover the vapour phase shall not disappear below 60 °C.

If the shells are not more than 1.5 metre in diameter the values of the test pressure and maximum permissible mass of contents per litre of capacity conforming to marginal 2219 (d) shall be applicable.

(4)   The test pressure for shells intended for the carriage of gases of 3° shall be not less than 1.3 times the maximum permitted working pressure indicated on the shell, but not less than 300 kPa (3 bar) (gauge pressure); for shells with vacuum insulation the test pressure shall be not less than 1.3 times the maximum permitted working pressure increased by 100 kPa (1 bar).

212 251
(contd) (5)   Table of gases and gas mixtures which may be carried in tank-containers, minimum test pressure of the shells and as far as applicable, maximum mass of contents per litre of capacity.

In the case of gases and gas mixtures classified under n.o.s. entries, the values of the test pressure and maximum mass of contents per litre of capacity shall be prescribed by the expert approved by the competent authority.

When shells for gases of 1° or 2° having a critical temperature of -50 °C or above and below 70 °C have been subjected to a test pressure lower than shown in the table, and the shells are fitted with thermal insulation, a lower maximum load may be prescribed by the expert approved by the competent authority, provided that the pressure reached in the shell by the substance at 55 °C does not exceed the test pressure stamped on the shell.

Toxic gases and gas mixtures classified under n.o.s. entries with a LC_{50} < 200 ppm shall not be authorized for transport in tank-containers.

NOTE: 1076 Phosgene of 2°TC, 1067 Dinitrogen tetroxide (nitrogen dioxide) of 2°TOC and 1001 Acetylene, dissolved, of 4°F shall only be authorized for transport in multiple-element tank-containers.

Item No. and group	Identification number	Name of the substance	Minimum test pressure for shells				Max. filling ratio (kg/l)
			With thermal insulation		Without thermal insulation		
			MPa	bar	MPa	bar	
1°A	1002	AIR, COMPRESSED	See marginal 212 251 (1)				
	1006	ARGON, COMPRESSED	See marginal 212 251 (1)				
	1046	HELIUM, COMPRESSED	See marginal 212 251 (1)				
	1056	KRYPTON, COMPRESSED	See marginal 212 251 (1)				
	1065	NEON, COMPRESSED	See marginal 212 251 (1)				
	1066	NITROGEN, COMPRESSED	See marginal 212 251 (1)				
	1979	RARE GASES MIXTURE, COMPRESSED	See marginal 212 251 (1)				
	1980	RARE GASES AND OXYGEN MIXTURE, COMPRESSED	See marginal 212 251 (1)				
	1981	RARE GASES AND NITROGEN MIXTURE, COMPRESSED	See marginal 212 251 (1)				
	1982	TETRAFLUOROMETHANE, COMPRESSED (REFRIGERANT GAS R 14, COMPRESSED)	20 30	200 300	20 30	200 300	0.62 0.94
	2036	XENON, COMPRESSED	12	120	13	130	1.3 1.24
	2193	HEXAFLUOROETHANE, COMPRESSED (REFRIGERANT GAS R 116, COMPRESSED)	16 20	160 200	20	200	1.1 1.28 1.34
	1956	COMPRESSED GAS, N.O.S.	See marginal 212 251 (1) or (2)				
1°O	1014	CARBON DIOXIDE AND OXYGEN MIXTURE, COMPRESSED	See marginal 212 251 (1)				
	1072	OXYGEN, COMPRESSED	See marginal 212 251 (1)				
	3156	COMPRESSED GAS, OXIDIZING, N.O.S.	See marginal 212 251 (1) or (2)				
1°F	1049	HYDROGEN, COMPRESSED	See marginal 212 251 (1)				
	1957	DEUTERIUM, COMPRESSED	See marginal 212 251 (1)				
	1962	ETHYLENE, COMPRESSED	12 22.5	120 225	22.5 30	225 300	0.34 0.37 0.25 0.36
	1971 1971	METHANE, COMPRESSED or NATURAL GAS, COMPRESSED with high methane content	See marginal 212 251 (1)				
	2034	HYDROGEN AND METHANE MIXTURE, COMPRESSED	See marginal 212 251 (1)				
	2203	SILANE, COMPRESSED [2]	2.5 25	225 250	22.5 25	225 250	0.32 0.41
	1964	HYDROCARBON GAS MIXTURE, COMPRESSED, N.O.S	See marginal 212 251 (1) or (2)				
	1954	COMPRESSED GAS, FLAMMABLE, N.O.S	See marginal 212 251 (1) or (2)				

---

[2]   *Considered as pyrophoric.*

Item No. and group	Identification number	Name of the substance	Minimum test pressure for shells				Max. filling ratio (kg/l)
			With thermal insulation		Without thermal insulation		
			MPa	bar	MPa	bar	
1°T	1612	HEXAETHYL TETRAPHOSPHATE AND COMPRESSED GAS MIXTURE	See marginal 212 251 (1)				
	1955	COMPRESSED GAS, TOXIC, N.O.S.	See marginal 212 251 (1) or (2) and ²/				
1°TF	1016	CARBON MONOXIDE, COMPRESSED	See marginal 212 251 (1)				
	1023	COAL GAS, COMPRESSED	See marginal 212 251 (1)				
	1071	OIL GAS, COMPRESSED	See marginal 212 251 (1)				
	1911	DIBORANE, COMPRESSED	Not allowed				
	2600	CARBON MONOXIDE AND HYDROGEN MIXTURE, COMPRESSED	See marginal 212 251 (1)				
	1953	COMPRESSED GAS, TOXIC, FLAMMABLE, N.O.S.	See marginal 212 251 (1) or (2) and ²/				
1°TC	1008	BORON TRIFLUORIDE, COMPRESSED	22.5	225	22.5	225	0.715
			30	300	30	300	0.86
	1859	SILICON TETRAFLUORIDE, COMPRESSED	20	200	20	200	0.74
			30	300	30	300	1.1
	2198	PHOSPHORUS PENTAFLUORIDE, COMPRESSED	Not allowed				
	2417	CARBONYL FLUORIDE, COMPRESSED	20	200	20	200	0.47
			30	300	30	300	0.7
	3304	COMPRESSED GAS, TOXIC, CORROSIVE, N.O.S.	See marginal 212 251 (1) or (2) and ²/				
1°TO	2451	NITROGEN TRIFLUORIDE	20	200	20	200	0.5
			30	300	30	300	0.75
	3303	COMPRESSED GAS, TOXIC, OXIDIZING, N.O.S.	See marginal 212 251 (1) or (2) and ²/				
1°TFC	3305	COMPRESSED GAS, TOXIC, FLAMMABLE, CORROSIVE, N.O.S.	See marginal 212 251 (1) or (2) and ²/				
1°TOC	1045	FLUORINE, COMPRESSED	Not allowed				
	1660	NITRIC OXIDE, COMPRESSED	Not allowed				
	2190	OXYGEN DIFLUORIDE	Not allowed				
	3306	COMPRESSED GAS, TOXIC, OXIDIZING, CORROSIVE, N.O.S.	See marginal 212 251 (1) or (2) and ²/				
2°A	1009	BROMOTRIFLUOROMETHANE (REFRIGERANT GAS R 13B1)			4.2	42	1.13
					12	120	1.44
					25	250	1.6
			12	120			1.5
	1013	CARBON DIOXIDE			19	190	0.66
					25	250	0.75
			19	190			0.73
			22.5	225			0.78
	1015	CARBON DIOXIDE AND NITROUS OXIDE MIXTURE	See marginal 212 251 (2) or (3)				
	1018	CHLORODIFLUOROMETHANE (REFRIGERANT GAS R 22)	2.4	24	2.6	26	1.03

---

²/   *Allowed if LC₅₀ equal to or greater than 200 ppm.*

Item No. and group	Identification number	Name of the substance	Minimum test pressure for shells				Max. filling ratio (kg/l)
			With thermal insulation		Without thermal insulation		
			MPa	bar	MPa	bar	
2°A (contd)	1020	CHLOROPENTAFLUOROETHANE (REFRIGERANT GAS R 115)	2	20	2.3	23	1.06
	1021	1-CHLORO-1,2,2,2-TETRAFLUOROETHANE (REFRIGERANT GAS R 124)	1	10	1.1	11	1.2
	1022	CHLOROTRIFLUOROMETHANE (REFRIGERANT GAS R 13)			10	100	0.83
					12	120	0.9
					19	190	1.04
					25	250	1.1
			12	120			0.96
			22.5	225			1.12
	1028	DICHLORODIFLUOROMETHANE (REFRIGERANT GAS R 12)	1.5	15	1.6	16	1.15
	1029	DICHLOROFLUOROMETHANE (REFRIGERANT GAS R 21)	1	10	1	10	1.23
	1058	LIQUEFIED GASES, non-flammable, charged with nitrogen, carbon dioxide or air	1.5 × filling pressure See marginal 212 251 (2) or (3)				
	1080	SULPHUR HEXAFLUORIDE	12	120			1.34
					7	70	1.04
					14	140	1.33
					16	160	1.37
	1858	HEXAFLUOROPROPYLENE (REFRIGERANT GAS R 1216)	1.7	17	1.9	19	1.11
	1952	ETHYLENE OXIDE AND CARBON DIOXIDE MIXTURE with not more than 9% ethylene oxide	19	190	19	190	0.66
			25	250	25	250	0.75
	1958	1,2-DICHLORO-1,1,2,2-TETRAFLUOROETHANE (REFRIGERANT GAS R 114)	1	10	1	10	1.3
	1973	CHLORODIFLUOROMETHANE AND CHLOROPENTAFLUOROETHANE MIXTURE with fixed boiling point, with approximately 49% chlorodifluoromethane (REFRIGERANT GAS R 502)	2.5	25	2.8	28	1.05
	1974	CHLORODIFLUOROBROMOMETHANE (REFRIGERANT GAS R 12B1)	1	10	1	10	1.61
	1976	OCTAFLUOROCYCLOBUTANE (REFRIGERANT GAS R C318)	1	10	1	10	1.34
	1983	1-CHLORO-2,2,2-TRIFLUOROETHANE (REFRIGERANT GAS R 133a)	1	10	1	10	1.18
	1984	TRIFLUOROMETHANE (REFRIGERANT GAS R 23)	19	190			0.92
			25	250			0.99
					19	190	0.87
					25	250	0.95
	2422	OCTAFLUOROBUT-2-ENE (REFRIGERANT GAS R 1318)	1.2	12	1.2	12	1.34
	2424	OCTAFLUOROPROPANE (REFRIGERANT GAS R 218)	2.5	25	2.5	25	1.09

Item No. and group	Identification number	Name of the substance	Minimum test pressure for shells				Max. filling ratio (kg/l)
			With thermal insulation		Without thermal insulation		
			MPa	bar	MPa	bar	
2°A (contd)	2599	CHLOROTRIFLUOROMETHANE AND TRIFLUOROMETHANE, AZEOTROPIC MIXTURE with approximately 60% chlorotrifluoromethane (REFRIGERANT GAS R 503)	3.1 4.2 10	31 42 100	3.1 4.2 10	31 42 100	0.11 0.21 0.76 0.2 0.66
	2602	DICHLORODIFLUOROMETHANE AND 1,1-DIFLUOROETHANE, AZEOTROPIC MIXTURE with approximately 74% dichlorodifluoromethane (REFRIGERANT GAS R 500)	1.8	18	2	20	1.01
	3070	ETHYLENE OXIDE AND DICHLORODIFLUOROMETHANE MIXTURE with not more than 12.5% ethylene oxide	1.5	15	1.6	16	1.09
	3159	1,1,1,2-TETRAFLUOROETHANE (REFRIGERANT GAS R 134a)	1.6	16	1.8	18	1.04
	3220	PENTAFLUOROETHANE (REFRIGERANT GAS R 125)	4.1	4.1	4.9	4.9	0.95
	3296	HEPTAFLUOROPROPANE (REFRIGERANT GAS R 227)	1.5	15	1.5	15	1.2
	3297	ETHYLENE OXIDE AND CHLOROTETRAFLUORO-ETHANE MIXTURE, with not more than 8.8% ethylene oxide	1	10	1	10	1.16
	3298	ETHYLENE OXIDE AND PENTAFLUOROETHANE MIXTURE, with not more than 7.9% ethylene oxide	2.6	26	2.6	26	1.02
	3299	ETHYLENE OXIDE AND TETRAFLUOROETHANE MIXTURE, with not more than 5.6% ethylene oxide	1.7	17	1.7	17	1.03
	1078	REFRIGERANT GASES, N.O.S. such as					
		MIXTURE F1 MIXTURE F2 MIXTURE F3	1 1.5 2.4	10 15 24	1.1 1.6 2.7	11 16 27	1.23 1.15 1.03
		Other mixtures	See marginal 212 251 (2) or (3)				
	1968	INSECTICIDE GAS, N.O.S.	See marginal 212 251 (2) or (3)				
	3163	LIQUEFIED GAS, N.O.S.	See marginal 212 251 (2) or (3)				
2°O	1070	NITROUS OXIDE	22.5	225	18 22.5 25	180 225 250	0.78 0.68 0.74 0.75
	3157	LIQUEFIED GAS, OXIDIZING, N.O.S.	See marginal 212 251 (2) or (3)				
2°F	1010	1.2-BUTADIENE, INHIBITED or	1	10	1	10	0.59
	1010	1.3-BUTADIENE, INHIBITED or	1	10	1	10	0.55
	1010	MIXTURES OF 1,3-BUTADIENE AND HYDROCARBONS, INHIBITED	1	10	1	10	0.5
	1011	BUTANE	1	10	1	10	0.51
	1012	BUTYLENES MIXTURE or	1	10	1	10	0.5
	1012	1-BUTYLENE or	1	10	1	10	0.53
	1012	CIS-2-BUTENE or	1	10	1	10	0.55
	1012	TRANS-2-BUTYLENE	1	10	1	10	0.54

Item No. and group	Identification number	Name of the substance	Minimum test pressure for shells				Max. filling ratio (kg/l)
			With thermal insulation		Without thermal insulation		
			MPa	bar	MPa	bar	
2°F (contd)	1027	CYCLOPROPANE	1.6	16	1.8	18	0.53
	1030	1,1-DIFLUOROETHANE (REFRIGERANT GAS R 152a)	1.4	14	1.6	16	0.79
	1032	DIMETHYLAMINE, ANHYDROUS	1	10	1	10	0.59
	1033	DIMETHYL ETHER	1.4	14	1.6	16	0.58
	1035	ETHANE	12	120			0.32
					9.5	95	0.25
					12	120	0.29
					30	300	0.39
	1036	ETHYLAMINE	1	10	1	10	0.61
	1037	ETHYL CHLORIDE	1	10	1	10	0.8
	1039	ETHYL METHYL ETHER	1	10	1	10	0.64
	1041	ETHYLENE OXIDE AND CARBON DIOXIDE MIXTURE, with more than 9% ethylene oxide but not more than 87%	2.4	24	2.6	26	0.73
	1055	ISOBUTYLENE	1	10	1	10	0.52
	1060	METHYLACETYLENE AND PROPADIENE MIXTURE, STABILIZED	See marginal 212 251 (2) or (3)				
		PROPADIENE with 1% to 4% methylacetylene	2.2	22	2.2	22	0.5
		MIXTURE P1	2.5	25	2.8	28	0.49
		MIXTURE P2	2.2	22	2.3	23	0.47
	1061	METHYLAMINE, ANHYDROUS	1	10	1.1	11	0.58
	1063	METHYL CHLORIDE (REFRIGERANT GAS R 40)	1.3	13	1.5	15	0.81
	1077	PROPYLENE	2.5	25	2.7	27	0.43
	1081	TETRAFLUOROETHYLENE, INHIBITED	Not allowed				
	1083	TRIMETHYLAMINE, ANHYDROUS	1	10	1	10	0.56
	1085	VINYL BROMIDE, INHIBITED	1	10	1	10	1.37
	1086	VINYL CHLORIDE, INHIBITED	1	10	1.1	11	0.81
	1087	VINYL METHYL ETHER, INHIBITED	1	10	1	10	0.67
	1860	VINYL FLUORIDE, INHIBITED	12	120			0.58
			22.5	225			0.65
					25	250	0.64
	1912	METHYLCHLORIDE AND METHYLENE CHLORIDE MIXTURE	1.3	13	1.5	15	0.81
	1959	1,1-DIFLUOROETHYLENE (REFRIGERANT GAS R 1132a)	12	120			0.66
			22.5	225			0.78
					25	250	0.77
	1969	ISOBUTANE	1	10	1	10	0.49
	1978	PROPANE	2.1	21	2.3	23	0.42
	2035	1,1,1-TRIFLUOROETHANE (REFRIGERANT GAS R 143a)	2.8	28	3.2	32	0.79
	2044	2,2-DIMETHYLPROPANE	1	10	1	10	0.53

Item No. and group	Identification number	Name of the substance	Minimum test pressure for shells				Max. filling ratio (kg/l)
			With thermal insulation		Without thermal insulation		
			MPa	bar	MPa	bar	
2°F (contd)	2200	PROPADIENE, INHIBITED	2.2	22	2.2	22	0.5
	2419	BROMOTRIFLUOROETHYLENE	1	10	1	10	1.19
	2452	ETHYLACETYLENE, INHIBITED	1	10	1	10	0.57
	2453	ETHYL FLUORIDE (REFRIGERANT GAS R 161)	3	30	3	30	0.57
	2454	METHYL FLUORIDE (REFRIGERANT GAS R 41)	30	300	30	300	0.36
	2517	1-CHLORO-1,1-DIFLUOROETHANE (REFRIGERANT GAS R 142b)	1	10	1	10	0.99
	2601	CYCLOBUTANE	1	10	1	10	0.63
	3153	PERFLUORO(METHYL VINYL ETHER)	2	20	2	20	0.75
	3154	PERFLUORO(ETHYL VINYL ETHER)	1	10	1	10	0.98
	3252	DIFLUOROMETHANE (REFRIGERANT GAS R 32)	3.9	3.9	4.5	45	0.78
	1965	HYDROCARBON GAS MIXTURE, LIQUEFIED, N.O.S.					
		MIXTURE A	1	10	1	10	0.5
		MIXTURE A0	1.2	12	1.4	14	0.47
		MIXTURE A1	1.6	16	1.8	18	0.46
		MIXTURE B	2	20	2.3	23	0.43
		MIXTURE C	2.5	25	2.7	27	0.42
		Other mixtures	See marginal 212 251 (2) or (3)				
	3161	LIQUEFIED GAS, FLAMMABLE, N.O.S.	See marginal 212 251 (2) or (3)				
2°T	1062	METHYL BROMIDE	1	10	1	10	1.51
	1581	CHLOROPICRIN AND METHYL BROMIDE MIXTURE	Not allowed				
	1582	CHLOROPICRIN AND METHYL CHLORIDE MIXTURE	Not allowed				
	2191	SULPHURYL FLUORIDE	5	50	5	50	1.1
	1967	INSECTICIDE GAS, TOXIC, N.O.S.	See marginal 212 251 (2) or (3) and */				
	3162	LIQUEFIED GAS, TOXIC, N.O.S.	See marginal 212 251 (2) or (3) and */				
2°TF	1026	CYANOGEN	10	100	10	100	0.7
	1040	ETHYLENE OXIDE WITH NITROGEN up to a total pressure of 1MPa (10 bar) at 50°C	1.5	15	1.5	15	0.78
	1053	HYDROGEN SULPHIDE	4.5	45	5	50	0.67
	1064	METHYL MERCAPTAN	1	10	1	10	0.78
	1082	TRIFLUOROCHLOROETHYLENE, INHIBITED	1.5	15	1.7	17	1.13
	2188	ARSINE	Not allowed				
	2192	GERMANE **/	Not allowed				
	2199	PHOSPHINE **/	Not allowed				

*/   *Allowed if LC_{50} equal to or greater than 200 ppm.*

**/   *Considered as pyrophoric.*

Item No. and group	Identification number	Name of the substance	Minimum test pressure for shells				Max. filling ratio (kg/l)
			With thermal insulation		Without thermal insulation		
			MPa	bar	MPa	bar	
2°TF (contd)	2202	HYDROGEN SELENIDE, ANHYDROUS	Not allowed				
	2204	CARBONYL SULPHIDE	2.6	26	2.6	26	0.84
	2676	STIBINE	Not allowed				
	3300	ETHYLENE OXIDE AND CARBON DIOXIDE MIXTURE with more than 87% ethylene oxide	2.8	28	2.8	28	0.73
	3160	LIQUEFIED GAS, TOXIC, FLAMMABLE, N.O.S.	See marginal 212 251 (2) or (3) and [*]				
2°TC	1005	AMMONIA, ANHYDROUS	2.6	26	2.9	29	0.53
	1017	CHLORINE	1.7	17	1.9	19	1.25
	1048	HYDROGEN BROMIDE, ANHYDROUS	5	50	5.5	55	1.54
	1050	HYDROGEN CHLORIDE, ANHYDROUS	12	120			0.69
					10	100	0.3
					12	120	0.56
					15	150	0.67
					20	200	0.74
	1069	NITROSYL CHLORIDE	Not allowed				
	1076	PHOSGENE	Only in multiple-element tank-containers				
	1079	SULPHUR DIOXIDE	1	10	1.2	12	1.23
	1589	CYANOGEN CHLORIDE, INHIBITED	Not allowed				
	1741	BORON TRICHLORIDE	Not allowed				
	2194	SELENIUM HEXAFLUORIDE	Not allowed				
	2195	TELLURIUM HEXAFLUORIDE	Not allowed				
	2196	TUNGSTEN HEXAFLUORIDE	Not allowed				
	2197	HYDROGEN IODIDE, ANHYDROUS	2.3	23	2.3	23	2.25
	2418	SULPHUR TETRAFLUORIDE	Not allowed				
	2420	HEXAFLUOROACETONE	2.2	22	2.2	22	1.08
	3057	TRIFLUOROACETYL CHLORIDE	1.3	13	1.5	15	1.17
	3308	LIQUEFIED GAS, TOXIC, CORROSIVE, N.O.S.	See marginal 212 251 (2) or (3) and [*]				
2°TO	3083	PERCHLORYL FLUORIDE	3.3	33	3.3	33	1.21
	3307	LIQUEFIED GAS, TOXIC, OXIDIZING, N.O.S.	See marginal 212 251 (2) or (3) and [*]				
2°TFC	2189	DICHLOROSILANE	1	10	1	10	0.9
	2534	METHYLCHLOROSILANE	Not allowed				
	3309	LIQUEFIED GAS, TOXIC, FLAMMABLE, CORROSIVE, N.O.S.	See marginal 212 251 (2) or (3) and [*]				

[*] *Allowed if LC_{50} equal to or greater than 200 ppm.*

Item No. and group	Identification number	Name of the substance	Minimum test pressure for shells				Max. filling ratio (kg/l)
			With thermal insulation		Without thermal insulation		
			MPa	bar	MPa	bar	
2°TOC	1067	DINITROGEN TETROXIDE (NITROGEN DIOXIDE)	Only in multiple-element tank-containers				
	1749	CHLORINE TRIFLUORIDE	3	30	3	30	1.4
	1975	NITRIC OXIDE AND DINITROGEN TETROXIDE MIXTURE	Not allowed				
		(NITRIC OXIDE AND NITROGEN DIOXIDE MIXTURE)					
	2548	CHLORINE PENTAFLUORIDE	Not allowed				
	2901	BROMINE CHLORIDE	1	10	1	10	1.5
	3310	LIQUEFIED GAS, TOXIC, OXIDIZING, CORROSIVE, N.O.S.	See marginal 212 251 (2) or (3) and */				
3°A	1913	NEON, REFRIGERATED LIQUID	See marginal 212 251 (4)				
	1951	ARGON, REFRIGERATED LIQUID	See marginal 212 251 (4)				
	1963	HELIUM, REFRIGERATED LIQUID	See marginal 212 251 (4)				
	1970	KRYPTON, REFRIGERATED LIQUID	See marginal 212 251 (4)				
	1977	NITROGEN, REFRIGERATED LIQUID	See marginal 212 251 (4)				
	2187	CARBON DIOXIDE, REFRIGERATED LIQUID	See marginal 212 251 (4)				
	2591	XENON, REFRIGERATED LIQUID	See marginal 212 251 (4)				
	3136	TRIFLUOROMETHANE, REFRIGERATED LIQUID	See marginal 212 251 (4)				
	3158	GAS, REFRIGERATED LIQUID, N.O.S.	See marginal 212 251 (4)				
3°O	1003	AIR, REFRIGERATED LIQUID	See marginal 212 251 (4)				
	1073	OXYGEN, REFRIGERATED LIQUID	See marginal 212 251 (4)				
	2201	NITROUS OXIDE, REFRIGERATED LIQUID	See marginal 212 251 (4)				
	3311	GAS, REFRIGERATED, LIQUEFIED, OXIDIZING, N.O.S.	See marginal 212 251 (4)				
3°F	1038	ETHYLENE, REFRIGERATED LIQUID	See marginal 212 251 (4)				
	1961	ETHANE, REFRIGERATED LIQUID	See marginal 212 251 (4)				
	1966	HYDROGEN, REFRIGERATED LIQUID	See marginal 212 251 (4)				
	1972 1972	METHANE, REFRIGERATED LIQUID or NATURAL GAS, REFRIGERATED LIQUID, with high methane content	See marginal 212 251 (4)				
	3138	ETHYLENE, ACETYLENE AND PROPYLENE IN MIXTURE, REFRIGERATED LIQUID, containing at least 71.5% ethylene with not more than 22.5% acetylene and not more than 6% propylene	See marginal 212 251 (4)				
	3312	GAS, REFRIGERATED, LIQUEFIED, FLAMMABLE, N.O.S.	See marginal 212 251 (4)				

*/ *Allowed if LC$_{50}$ equal to or greater than 200 ppm.*

Item No. and group	Identification number	Name of the substance	Minimum test pressure for shells				Max. filling ratio (kg/l)
			With thermal insulation		Without thermal insulation		
			MPa	bar	MPa	bar	
4°A	2073	AMMONIA SOLUTIONS, relative density less than 0.88 at 15°C					
		with more than 35% and not more than 40% ammonia	1	10	1	10	0.8
		with more than 40% and not more than 50% ammonia	1.2	12	1.2	12	0.77
4°F	1001	ACETYLENE, DISSOLVED	Only in multiple-element tank-containers				
4°TC	3318	AMMONIA SOLUTIONS, relative density less than 0.880 at 15°C in water, with more than 50% ammonia	See marginal 212 251 (2)				

212 252   The first hydraulic pressure test shall be carried out before the thermal insulation is placed in position.

212 253   The capacity of each shell intended for the carriage of gases of 1° filled by mass, or gases of 2° or 4° shall be determined, under the supervision of an expert approved by the competent authority, by weighing or volumetric measurement of the quantity of water which fills the shell; any error in the measurement of shell capacity shall be of less than 1%. Determination by a calculation based on the dimensions of the shell is not permitted. The maximum filling masses allowed in accordance with marginals 2219 and 212 251 (3) shall be prescribed by an approved expert.

212 254   Checking of the welds shall be carried out in accordance with the lambda-coefficient 1.0 requirements of marginal 212 127 (6).

212 255   By derogation from the requirements of marginal 212 151, the periodic tests shall take place:

(1)   Every two and a half years in the case of shells intended for the carriage of 1008 boron trifluoride of 1°TC, 1053 hydrogen sulphide of 2°TF, 1048 hydrogen bromide, anhydrous, 1050 hydrogen chloride, anhydrous, 1017 chlorine, 1076 phosgene or 1079 sulphur dioxide of 2°TC, or 1067 dinitrogen tetroxide (nitrogen dioxide) of 2°TOC;

(2)   After 8 years' service and thereafter every 12 years in the case of shells intended for the carriage of gases of 3°. A leakproofness test may be performed, at the request of the competent authority, between any two successive tests.

(3)   Receptacles as defined in marginals 2211 (1), (2) and (3) and cylinders as part of bundles of cylinders as defined in marginal 2211 (5), which are elements of a multiple-element tank-container, shall have periodic inspections according to marginal 2217.

212 256   In the case of vacuum-insulated shells, the hydraulic-pressure test and the check of the internal condition may, with the consent of the approved expert, be replaced by a leakproofness test and measurement of the vacuum.

212 257   If apertures have been made, on the occasion of periodic inspections, in shells intended for the carriage of gases of 3°, the method by which they are hermetically closed before the shells are replaced in service shall be approved by the approved expert and shall ensure the integrity of the shell.

212 258 Leakproofness test of shells intended for the carriage of gases of 1°, 2° or 4° shall be performed at a pressure of not less than 400 kPa (4 bar) and not more than 800 kPa (8 bar) (gauge pressure).

212 259

SECTION 6. Marking

212 260 The following additional particulars shall be marked by stamping or by any other similar method on the plate prescribed in marginal 212 160, or directly on the walls of the shell itself if the walls are so reinforced that the strength of the shell is not impaired:

    (1)   On shells intended for the carriage of only one substance:

        -    the name of the gas in letters in accordance with marginal 2201 and, in addition for gases classified under an n.o.s. entry, the technical name [20].

This indication shall be supplemented in the case of shells intended for the carriage of compressed gases of 1° filled by volume (pressure), by an indication of the maximum filling pressure at 15 °C permitted for the shell, and in the case of shells intended for the carriage of gases of 1° filled by mass, and of gases of 2°, 3° and 4° by the maximum permissible load mass in kg and of the filling temperature if below -20 °C;

    (2)   On multi-purpose shells:

        -    the name of the gas in letters in accordance with marginal 2201 and, in addition for gases classified under an n.o.s. entry, the technical name [20], of the gases for whose carriage the shell is approved.

These particulars shall be supplemented by an indication of the maximum permissible load mass in kg for each gas;

    (3)   On shells intended for the carriage of gases of 3°:

        -    the maximum working pressure allowed; and

    (4)   On shells equipped with thermal insulation:

        -    the inscription "thermally insulated" or "thermally insulated by vacuum".

---

[20] *The technical name shall be a name currently used in scientific and technical handbooks, journals and texts. Trade names shall not be used for this purpose.*
Instead of the technical name the use of one of the following names is permitted:

    -    *For 1078 refrigerant gas, N.O.S., of 2°A: mixture F1, mixture F2, mixture F3;*

    -    *For 1060 methyl acetylene and propadiene mixtures, stabilized, of 2°F: mixture P1, mixture P2;*

    -    *For 1965 hydrocarbon gas mixture, liquefied, N.O.S., of 2°F: mixture A, mixture A0, mixture A1, mixture B, mixture C.*

The names customary in the trade and mentioned in NOTE 1 under the entry 1965 of 2°F of marginal 2201 may be used only as a complement.

Appendix B.1b

212 261 (1) The frame of a multiple-element tank-container shall bear near the filling point a plate specifying:

- the test pressure of the elements [21];

- the maximum filling pressure [21] at 15 °C allowed for elements intended for compressed gases;

- the number of elements;

- the total capacity [21] of the elements;

- the name of the gas in letters in accordance with marginal 2201 and, in addition for gases classified under an n.o.s. entry, the technical name [22];

and, in addition, in the case of liquefied gases:

- the permissible maximum load [21] per element.

(2) Receptacles as defined in marginal 2211 (1), (2), (3) and (5), which are elements of a multiple-element tank-container, shall be marked according to marginal 2223. These receptacles need not be labelled individually with the danger labels as required in marginal 2224.

Multiple-element tank-containers shall be marked and labelled according to marginal 10 500.

212 262 In addition to the particulars prescribed in marginal 212 161, the following shall be inscribed either on the tank-container itself or on a plate:

(a) - the inscription: "minimum filling temperature allowed: ...";

(b) where the shell is intended for the carriage of one substance only:

- the name of the gas in letters in accordance with marginal 2201 and, in addition for gases classified under an n.o.s. entry, the technical name [22];

- for gases of 1° filled by mass, and for gases of 2°, 3° and 4°, the maximum permissible load mass in kg;

(c) where the shell is a multi-purpose shell:

- the name of the gas in letters in accordance with marginal 2201 and, in addition for gases classified under an n.o.s. entry, the technical name [22] of all the gases to whose carriage the shell is assigned, with an indication of the maximum permissible load mass in kg for each of them;

---

[21] *The units of measurement should be indicated after numerical values.*

[22] *See footnote 19/ to marginal 212 260.*

212 262 (d) where the shell is equipped with thermal insulation:
(contd)

- the inscription "thermally insulated" or "thermally insulated by vacuum", in an official language of the country of registration and also, if that language is not English, French or German, in English, French or German, unless any agreements concluded between the countries concerned in the transport operation provide otherwise.

212 263-
212 269

SECTION 7. Operation

212 270 When shells are approved for different gases, a change of use shall include emptying, purging and evacuation operations to the extent necessary for safe operation.

212 271-
212 273

212 274 When loaded tanks or empty but uncleaned tanks are handed over for carriage, only the particulars specified in marginal 212 262 applicable to the gas loaded or just discharged shall be visible; all particulars concerning other gases shall be covered up.

212 275 All the elements of a multiple-element tank-container shall contain only one and the same gas.

212 276

212 277 The degree of filling of shells intended for the carriage of gases of 3°F shall remain below the level at which, if the contents were raised to a temperature at which the vapour pressure equalled the opening pressure of the safety valve, the volume of the liquid would reach 95% of the shell's capacity at that temperature.

Shells intended for the carriage of gases of 3°A or 3°O may be filled to 98% at the loading temperature and the loading pressure.

212 278 In the case of shells intended for the carriage of gases of 3°O, the substances used to ensure leakproofness of the joints or for the maintenance of the closures shall be compatible with the contents.

212 279 The requirement in marginal 212 175 shall not apply to gases of 3°.

SECTION 8. Transitional measures

212 280 Tank-containers intended for the carriage of substances of Class 2, built before 1 January 1997, may bear a marking conforming to the provisions of this appendix applicable until 31 December 1996 until the next periodic test.

212 280-
212 299

Appendix B.1b

CLASS 3. FLAMMABLE LIQUIDS

212 300-
212 309

SECTION 1.   General; scope (use of tank-containers); definitions

Use

212 310 The following substances of marginal 2301 may be carried in tank-containers:

(a) propyleneimine, inhibited, of 12°;

(b) substances classified under (a) of 11°, 14° to 22°, 26° and 27°, 41°;

(c) substances classified under (b) of 11°, 14° to 27°, 41°, and substances of 32° and 33°;

(d) substances of 1° to 5°, 31°, 34° and 61° (c), with the exception of isopropyl nitrate, n-propyl nitrate and nitromethane of 3° (b).

212 311-
212 319

SECTION 2.   Construction

212 320 Shells intended for the carriage of inhibited propyleneimine of 12° shall be designed for a calculation pressure [see marginal 212 127 (2)] of not less than 1.5 MPa (15 bar) (gauge pressure).

212 321 Shells intended for the carriage of the substances referred to in marginal 212 310 (b) shall be designed for a calculation pressure [see marginal 212 127 (2)] of not less than 100 kPa (10 bar) (gauge pressure).

212 322 Shells intended for the carriage of the substances referred to in marginal 212 310 (c) shall be designed for a calculation pressure [see marginal 212 127 (2)] of not less than 400 kPa (4 bar) (gauge pressure).

212 323 Shells intended for the carriage of the substances referred to in marginal 212 310 (d) shall be designed in accordance with the requirements of Part I of this Appendix.

212 324-
212 329

SECTION 3.   Items of equipment

212 330 All openings of shells intended for the carriage of the substances referred to in marginal 212 310 (a) and (b) shall be above the surface level of the liquid. No pipes or pipe connections shall pass through the walls of the shell below the surface level of the liquid. Shells shall be capable of being hermetically closed [23] and the closures shall be capable of being protected with lockable caps.

---

[23] *See footnote 8/ to marginal 212 135.*

212 331 Shells intended for the carriage of the substances referred to in marginal 212 310 (c) and (d) may also be of the bottom-discharge type. Shells intended for the carriage of the substances referred to in marginal 212 310 (c), except those of 33°, shall be capable of being hermetically closed [23].

212 332 If shells intended for the carriage of the substances referred to in marginal 212 310 (a), (b) or (c), except those of 33°, are fitted with safety valves, a bursting disc shall be placed before the valve. The arrangement of the bursting disc and safety valve shall be such as to satisfy the competent authority. If shells intended for the carriage of the substances referred to in marginal 212 310 (d) are equipped with safety valves or a venting system, these shall satisfy the requirements of marginals 212 133 to 212 135.

If shells intended for the carriage of substances of 33° are fitted with safety valves, these shall satisfy the requirements of marginals 212 134 and 212 135.

Shells intended for the carriage of the substances referred to in marginal 212 310 (d) having a flash-point not exceeding 61 °C and equipped with a venting system which cannot be closed shall have a flame-trap in the venting system or the shells shall be explosion-pressure proof.

212 333 If the shells are fitted with non-metallic protective linings (inner layers), these shall be so designed that no danger of ignition from electrostatic charges can occur.

212 334 The bottom discharge system of shells intended for the carriage of substances of 61° (c) may consist of an external pipe with a stop-valve, if it is constructed in a metallic material liable to deformation.

212 335-
212 339

SECTION 4.   **Type approval**

212 340-
212 349 (No special requirements)

SECTION 5.   **Tests**

212 350 Shells intended for the carriage of the substances referred to in marginal 212 310 (a), (b) or (c) shall be subjected to the initial and periodic hydraulic pressure tests at a gauge pressure of not less than 400 kPa (4 bar).

212 351 Shells intended for the carriage of the substances referred to in marginal 212 310 (d) shall be subjected to the initial and periodic hydraulic pressure tests at their calculation pressure as defined in marginal 212 123.

212 352-
212 359

SECTION 6.   **Marking**

212 360-
212 369 (No special requirements)

---

[23]   *See footnote 8/ to marginal 212 135.*

Appendix B.1b

SECTION 7. Operation

212 370 Shells intended for the carriage of the substances referred to in marginal 212 310 (a), (b) or (c), except those of 33°, shall be hermetically closed [23] during carriage. The closures of shells intended for the carriage of the substances referred to in marginal 212 310 (a) and (b) shall be protected by a locked cap.

212 371 Tank-containers approved for the carriage of substances of 11°, 12°, 14° to 19°, 27°, 32° and 41° shall not be used for the carriage of foodstuffs, articles of consumption or animal feeds.

212 372 An aluminium-alloy shell shall not be used for the carriage of acetaldehyde of 1° (a) unless the shell is reserved solely for such carriage and the acetaldehyde is free from acid.

212 373 The petrol (gasoline) referred to in the Note to 3° (b) of marginal 2301 may also be carried in tanks designed according to marginal 212 123 (1) and having equipment conforming to marginal 212 133.

212 374-
212 379

SECTION 8. Transitional measures

212 380 Tank-containers intended for the carriage of substances of 32° and 33° of marginal 2301, built according to the requirements of this Appendix applicable prior to 1 January 1995, but which do not, however, conform to the requirements applicable as from 1 January 1995, may still be used up to 31 December 1999.

212 381 Tank-containers which were intended for the carriage of substances of 61° (c) of marginal 2301, built before 1 January 1995, but which do not conform with the requirements applicable as from 1 January 1995, may still be used until 31 December 2004.

212 382 Tank-containers, constructed before 1 January 1997 which do not conform to the provisions of marginals 212 332 and 212 333 but were constructed according to the requirements of ADR in force until that date, may still be used.

212 383-
212 399

---

[23] *See footnote 8/ to marginal 212 135.*

CLASS 4.1. FLAMMABLE SOLIDS

CLASS 4.2. SUBSTANCES LIABLE TO SPONTANEOUS COMBUSTION

CLASS 4.3. SUBSTANCES WHICH, IN CONTACT WITH WATER, EMIT FLAMMABLE GASES

**212 400-
212 409**

SECTION 1. **General, scope (use of tank-containers); definitions**

Use

212 410 The following substances of marginals 2401, 2431 and 2471 may be carried in tank- containers:

(a) the substances listed under letter (a) of 6°, 17°, 19° and 31° to 33° of marginal 2431;

(b) the substances of 11° (a) and 22° of marginal 2431;

(c) the substances listed under letter (a) of 1°, 2°, 3°, 21°, 23° and 25° of marginal 2471;

(d) the substances of 11° (a) of marginal 2471;

(e) the substances listed under letter (b) or (c) of:

6°, 8°, 10°, 17°, 19° and 21° of marginal 2431, and
3°, 21°, 23° and 25° of marginal 2471;

(f) the substances of 5° and 15° of marginal 2401;

(g) powdery and granular substances listed under letter (b) or (c) of:

1°, 6°, 7°, 8°, 11°, 12°, 13°, 14°, 16° and 17° of marginal 2401,
1°, 5°, 7°, 9°, 12°, 13°, 14°, 15°, 16°, 18° and 20° of marginal 2431,
11°, 12°, 13°, 14°, 15°, 16°, 17°, 19°, 20°, 22° and 24° of marginal 2471.

NOTE: For the carriage in bulk of substances of

4° (c), 6° (c), 11° (c), 12° (c), 13° (c) and 14° (c) and solid mixtures (such as preparations and wastes) classified under (c) of these items of marginal 2401,

1° (c), 2° (c), 3° (c), 12° (c) and 16° (c), and solid wastes classified under (c) of these items of marginal 2431,

11° (c), 12° (c), 13° (b) and (c), 14° (c), 15° (c), 17° (b) and 20° (c) and solid mixtures (such as preparations and wastes) classified under (c) of these items of marginal 2471,

see marginals 41 111, 42 111 and 43 111.

**212 411-
212 419**

Appendix B.1b

SECTION 2. Construction

212 420 Shells intended for the carriage of the substances referred to in marginal 212 410 (a) shall be designed for a calculation pressure [see marginal 212 127 (2)] of not less than 2.1 MPa (21 bar) (gauge pressure).

The requirements of Appendix B.1d are applicable to the materials and construction of these shells.

212 421 Shells intended for the carriage of the substances referred to in marginal 212 410 (b), (c) and (d) shall be designed for a calculation pressure [see marginal 212 127 (2)] of not less than 1 MPa (10 bar) (gauge pressure).

212 422 Shells intended for the carriage of the substances referred to in marginal 212 410 (e) shall be designed for a calculation pressure (see marginal 212 127 (2)) of not less than 400 kPa (4 bar) (gauge pressure).

212 423 Shells intended for the carriage of the solids referred to in marginal 212 410 (f) and (g) shall be designed in conformity with the requirements of Part I of this Appendix.

212 424 All parts of the tank-container intended for the carriage of substances of marginal 2431, 1° (b) shall be capable of being electrically earthed.

212 425-
212 429

SECTION 3. Items of equipment

212 430 All openings of shells intended for the carriage of the substances referred to in marginal 212 410 (a), (b), (c) and (e) shall be above the surface level of the liquid. No pipes or pipe connections shall pass through the walls of the shell below the surface level of the liquid. Shells shall be capable of being hermetically closed [23] and the closure shall be capable of being protected with lockable caps. The cleaning apertures (fist-holes) referred to in marginal 212 132 shall not be permitted.

212 431 With the exception of shells intended for the carriage of caesium and rubidium of marginal 2471, 11° (a), shells intended for the carriage of substances referred to in marginal 212 410 (d), (f) and (g) may also be of the bottom-discharge type. The openings of shells intended for the carriage of caesium and rubidium of marginal 2471, 11° (a) shall be equipped with hermetically closing [23] and lockable caps.

212 432 Shells intended for the carriage of the substances referred to in marginal 212 410 (b) shall in addition meet the following requirements:

(1) The heating device shall not penetrate into, but shall be exterior to, the body of the shell. However, a pipe used for extracting the phosphorus may be equipped with a heating jacket. The device heating the jacket shall be so regulated as to prevent the temperature of the phosphorus from exceeding the filling temperature of the shell. Other piping shall enter the shell in its upper part; openings shall be situated above the highest permissible level of the phosphorus and be capable of being completely enclosed under lockable caps. In addition, the cleaning apertures (fist-holes) referred to in marginal 212 132 shall not be permitted.

---

[23] *See footnote 8/ to marginal 212 135.*

212 432   (2)   The shell shall be equipped with a gauging system for verifying the level of the phosphorus
(contd)   and, if water is used as a protective agent, with a fixed gauge mark showing the highest permissible level of the water.

212 433   If shells intended for the carriage of the substances referred to in marginal 212 410 (a), (c) and (e) are fitted with safety valves, a bursting disc shall be placed before the valve. The arrangement of the bursting disc and safety valve shall be such as to satisfy the competent authority.

212 434   Shells intended for the carriage of the substances referred to in marginal 212 410 (f) shall be equipped with thermal insulation made of materials which are not readily flammable.

212 435   If shells intended for the carriage of substances referred to in marginal 212 410 (d) are equipped with thermal insulation, such insulation shall be made of materials which are not readily flammable.

212 436   Shells intended for the carriage of the substances referred to in marginal 212 410 (f) may be equipped with valves opening automatically inwards or outwards under the effect of a difference of pressure of between 20 kPa and 30 kPa (0.2 bar and 0.3 bar).

212 437-
212 439

     SECTION 4.   **Type approval**

212 440-
212 449   (No special requirements)

     SECTION 5.   **Tests**

212 450   Shells intended for the carriage of the substances referred to in marginal 212 410 (a) shall be subjected to the initial and periodic hydraulic pressure tests at a gauge pressure of at least 1 MPa (10 bar). The materials of each of these shells shall be tested by the method described in Appendix B.1d.

212 451   Shells intended for the carriage of the substances referred to in marginal 212 410 (b) to (e) shall be subjected to the initial and periodic hydraulic pressure tests at a gauge pressure of at least 400 kPa (4 bar).

     By derogation from the requirements of marginal 212 151, shells intended for the carriage of substances referred to in marginal 212 410 (d) shall undergo periodic inspections at least every eight years which shall include a thickness check using suitable instruments. For such shells, the leakproofness test and check, for which provision is made in marginal 212 152, shall be carried out at least every four years.

212 452   Shells intended for the carriage of the substances referred to in marginal 212 410 (f) and (g) shall be subjected to the initial and periodic hydraulic pressure tests at their calculation pressure as defined in marginal 212 123.

212 453-
212 459

     SECTION 6.   **Marking**

212 460   Shells intended for the carriage of the substances referred to in marginal 212 410 (a) shall bear in addition to the particulars prescribed in marginal 212 161, the words: "Do not open during carriage. Liable to spontaneous combustion".

212 460 (contd)   Shells intended for the carriage of the substances of marginal 2471 referred to in marginal 212 410 (c) to (e) shall bear in addition to the particulars prescribed in marginal 212 161, the words: "Do not open during carriage. Gives off flammable gases on contact with water".

These particulars shall be in an official language of the country of approval, and also, if that language is not English, French or German, in English, French or German, unless any agreements concluded between the countries concerned in the transport operation provide otherwise.

212 461   Shells intended for the carriage of substances of marginal 2471, 1° (a) shall also bear, on the plate prescribed in marginal 212 160, the names of the approved substances and the maximum permissible load of the shell in kg.

212 462-
212 469

SECTION 7.   Operation

212 470   (1)   Substances of 11° and 22° of marginal 2431 shall, if water is used as a protective agent, be covered with a depth of not less than 12 cm of water at the time of filling; the degree of filling at a temperature of 60 °C shall not exceed 98%. If nitrogen is used as a protective agent, the degree of filling at a temperature of 60 °C shall not exceed 96%. The remaining space shall be filled with nitrogen in such a way that, even after cooling, the pressure at no time falls below atmospheric pressure. The shell shall be hermetically closed [23] so that no leakage of gas occurs.

(2)   Uncleaned empty shells which have contained substances of 11° and 22° of marginal 2431 shall, when handed over for carriage, either:

- be filled with nitrogen; or

- be filled with water to not less than 96% and not more than 98% of their capacity; between 1 October and 31 March, this water shall contain sufficient anti-freeze agent to make it impossible for the water to freeze during carriage; the anti-freeze agent shall be free from corrosive action and not liable to react with phosphorus.

212 471   Shells containing substances of 31° to 33° of marginal 2431 and substances of 2° (a), 3° (a) and 3° (b) of marginal 2471 shall be filled to not more than 90% of their capacity; a space of 5% shall remain empty for safety when the liquid is at an average temperature of 50 °C. During carriage, the substances shall be under a layer of inert gas, the gauge pressure of which shall not be less than 50 kPa (0.5 bar). The shells shall be hermetically closed [23] and the protective caps conforming to 212 430 shall be locked. Uncleaned empty shells shall when handed over for carriage be filled with an inert gas at a gauge pressure of at least 50 kPa (0.5 bar).

212 472   For ethyldichlorosilane, methyldichlorosilane and trichlorosilane of marginal 2471, 1°, the degree of filling shall not exceed 0.93 or 0.95 or 1.14 kg per litre of capacity respectively, if filling is by mass. If filling is by volume, and for chlorosilanes not mentioned by name (n.o.s.) of marginal 2471, 1°, the rate of filling shall not exceed 85%. The shells shall be hermetically closed [23] and the protective caps conforming to marginal 212 430 shall be locked.

---

[23]   *See footnote 8/ to marginal 212 135.*

212 473 Shells containing substances of marginal 2401, 5° and 15°, shall not be filled to more than 98% of their capacity.

212 474 For the carriage of caesium and rubidium of marginal 2471, 11° (a), the substances shall be covered by an inert gas and the caps conforming to marginal 212 431 shall be locked. Shells containing other substances of marginal 2471, 11° (a) shall not be handed over for carriage until the substance has solidified completely and been covered by an inert gas.

Uncleaned empty shells which have contained substances of marginal 2471, 11° (a) shall be filled with an inert gas. The shells shall be hermetically closed [23].

212 475 (1)   When substances of marginal 2431, 1° (b) are being loaded, the temperature of the goods being loaded shall not exceed 60 °C.

(2)   A maximum loading temperature of 80 °C is allowed provided that smoulder spots are prevented during loading and the shells are hermetically closed [23].

After loading, the shells shall be pressurized (e.g. with compressed air) to check tightness. It shall be ensured that no depressurization takes place during carriage.

Before unloading, it shall be checked if pressure is still above atmospheric. If this is not the case, an inert gas shall be introduced into the shells prior to unloading.

212 476-
212 499

---

[23]   *See footnote 8/ to marginal 212 135.*

Appendix B.1b

CLASS 5.1. OXIDIZING SUBSTANCES
CLASS 5.2. ORGANIC PEROXIDES

212 500-
212 509

SECTION 1.   General, scope (use of tank-containers); definitions

Use

212 510   The following substances of marginal 2501 may be carried in tank-containers:

(a)   substances of 5°;

(b)   substances listed under letter (a) or (b) of 1° to 4°, 11°, 13°, 16°, 17°, 22° and 23°, carried in the liquid state or in the molten state;

(c)   ammonium nitrate liquid of 20°;

(d)   substances listed under letter (c) of 1°, 11°, 13°, 16°, 18°, 22° and 23°, carried in the liquid state or in the molten state;

(e)   substances in powdery or granular form listed under letter (b) or (c) of 11°, 13° to 18°, 21° to 27°, 29° and 31°.

NOTE: For the carriage in bulk of substances of 11° to 13°, 16°, 18°, 21° and 22° (c), and of solid wastes classified in the aforementioned items of marginal 2501, see marginal 51 111.

212 511   Substances of 9° (b), 10° (b), 19° (b) or 20° (b) of marginal 2551 may be carried in tank-containers at the latest from 1 January 1995 under conditions laid down by the competent authority of the country of origin if, on the basis of tests (see marginal 212 541), the competent authority is satisfied that such a transport operation can be carried out safely. If the country of origin is not party to ADR, these conditions shall be recognized by the competent authority of the first ADR country reached by the consignment.

212 512-
212 519

SECTION 2.   Construction

212 520   Shells intended for the carriage of the substances referred to in marginal 212 510 (a) shall be designed for a calculation pressure [see marginal 212 127 (2)] of at least 1 MPa (10 bar) (gauge pressure).

212 521   Shells intended for the carriage of the substances referred to in marginal 212 510 (b) shall be designed for a calculation pressure [see marginal 212 127 (2)] of at least 400 kPa (4 bar) (gauge pressure). Shells, and their items of equipment, intended for the carriage of substances of 1° shall be made of aluminium not less than 99.5% pure or of suitable steel not liable to cause hydrogen peroxide to decompose. Where shells are made of aluminium not less than 99.5% pure, the wall thickness need not be greater than 15 mm, even where calculation in accordance with marginal 212 127 (2) gives a higher value.

Appendix B.1b

212 522 Shells intended for the carriage of the substances referred to in marginal 212 510 (c) shall be designed for a calculation pressure [see marginal 212 127 (2)] of at least 400 kPa (4 bar) (gauge pressure). The shells shall be made of austenitic steel.

212 523 Shells intended for the carriage of the liquids referred to in marginal 212 510 (d) and the powdery or granular substances referred to in marginal 212 510 (e) shall be designed in accordance with the requirements of Part I of this Appendix.

212 524 Shells intended for the carriage of substances referred to in marginal 212 511 shall be designed for a calculation pressure of at least 400 kPa (4 bar) (gauge pressure).

212 525-
212 529

SECTION 3. Items of equipment

212 530 Shells intended for the carriage of substances of 1° (a), 3° (a) and 5° of marginal 2501 shall have their openings above the surface level of the liquid. In addition, the cleaning apertures (fist holes) referred to in marginal 212 132 shall not be permitted.

For solutions containing more than 60% but not more than 70% hydrogen peroxide, openings below the surface level of the liquid shall be permissible. In this case the shell-discharge system shall be equipped with two mutually independent shut-off devices mounted in series, the first taking the form of a quick-closing internal stop-valve of an approved type and the second that of a sluice-valve, one at each end of the discharge pipe. A blank flange, or another device providing the same measure of security, shall also be fitted at the outlet of each external sluice-valve. The internal stop-valve shall be such that if the pipe is wrenched off the stop-valve will remain integral with the shell and in the closed position. The connections to the external pipe-sockets of shells shall be made of materials not liable to cause decomposition of hydrogen peroxide.

212 531

212 532 Shells intended for the carriage of substances of 1°, or of liquid ammonium nitrate of 20° of marginal 2501 shall be fitted in their upper part with a shut-off device preventing any build-up of excess pressure inside the shell, any leakage of liquid, and any entry of foreign matter into the shell. The shut-off devices of shells intended for the carriage of ammonium nitrate liquid of marginal 2501, 20°, shall be so designed as to preclude obstruction of the devices by solidified ammonium nitrate during carriage.

212 533 Where shells intended for the carriage of ammonium nitrate liquid of marginal 2501, 20°, are sheathed in thermally-insulating material, the material shall be of an inorganic nature and entirely free from combustible matter.

212 534 Shells intended for the carriage of substances referred to in marginal 212 511 shall be equipped with thermal insulation complying with the requirements of marginal 212 234 (1). If the SADT of the organic peroxide in the shell is 55 °C or less, or the shell is constructed of aluminium, the shell shall be completely insulated. The sun shield and any part of the shell not covered by it, or the outer sheathing of a complete lagging, shall be painted white or finished in bright metal. The paint shall be cleaned before each transport journey and renewed in case of yellowing or deterioration. The thermal insulation shall be free from combustible matter.

212 535 Shells intended for the carriage of substances referred to in marginal 212 511 shall be fitted with temperature sensing devices.

212 536 (1)   Shells intended for the carriage of substances referred to in marginal 212 511 shall be fitted with safety valves and pressure-relief devices.   Vacuum-relief devices may also be used. Pressure-relief devices shall operate at pressures determined according to both the properties of the organic peroxide and the construction characteristics of the tank. Fusible elements shall not be permitted in the body of the shell.

(2)   Shells intended for the carriage of substances referred to in marginal 212 511 shall be fitted with spring-loaded safety valves to prevent significant pressure build-up within the shell of the decomposition products and vapours released at a temperature of 50 °C.   The capacity and start-to-discharge pressure of the safety-valve(s) shall be based on the results of the tests specified in marginal 212 541.   The start-to-discharge pressure shall however in no case be such that liquid could escape from the valve(s) if the shell were overturned.

(3)   The pressure-relief devices of shells intended for the carriage of substances referred to in marginal 212 511 may be of the spring-loaded type or bursting disc type, designed to vent all the decomposition products and vapours evolved during a period of not less than one hour of fire engulfment (heat load 110 kW/m^2) or self-accelerating decomposition.   The start-to-discharge pressure of the pressure-relief device(s) shall be higher than that specified in paragraph (2) and based on the results of the tests referred to in marginal 212 541. The dimensions of the pressure-relief devices shall be such that the maximum pressure in the shell never exceeds the test pressure of the shell.

(4)   For shells with an insulation consisting of a complete cladding intended for the carriage of substances referred to in marginal 212 511, the capacity and setting of the pressure-relief device(s) shall be determined assuming a loss of insulation from 1% of the surface area.

(5)   Vacuum-relief devices and spring-loaded safety valves of shells for the carriage of substances referred to in marginal 212 511 shall be provided with flame arresters unless the substances to be carried and their decomposition products are non-combustible. Due attention shall be paid to the reduction of the relief capacity caused by the flame arrester.

212 537-
212 539

SECTION 4.   Type approval

212 540   Tank-containers approved for the carriage of ammonium nitrate liquid of marginal 2501, 20°, shall not be approved for the carriage of organic substances.

212 541   For the type approval of shells intended for the carriage of substances referred to in marginal 212 511, tests shall be undertaken:

- to prove the compatibility of all materials normally in contact with the substance during carriage;

- to provide data to facilitate the design of the pressure-relief devices and safety valves taking into account the design characteristics of the tank-container; and

- to establish any special requirements necessary for the safe carriage of the substance.

The test results shall be included in the report for the type approval of the shell.

212 542-
212 549

Appendix B.1b

SECTION 5.   Tests

212 550 Shells intended for the carriage of the substances referred to in marginal 212 510 (a), (b) and (c) shall be subjected to the initial and periodic hydraulic pressure tests at a pressure of not less than 400 kPa (4 bar) (gauge pressure). Shells of pure aluminium intended for the carriage of substances of marginal 2501, 1°, may be subjected to the initial and periodic hydraulic pressure tests at a pressure of only 250 kPa (2.5 bar) (gauge pressure).

Shells intended for the carriage of the substances referred to in marginal 212 510 (d) and (e) shall be subjected to the initial and periodic hydraulic pressure tests at their calculation pressure as defined in marginal 212 123.

212 551 Shells intended for the carriage of substances referred to in marginal 212 511 shall be subjected to the initial and periodic hydraulic pressure tests at the calculation pressure in accordance with marginal 212 524.

212 552-
212 559

SECTION 6.   Marking

212 560 The following additional particulars shall be marked by stamping or by any other similar method on the plate prescribed in marginal 212 161 or directly on the walls of the shell itself, if the walls are so reinforced that the strength of the shell is not impaired:

- the chemical name with the approved concentration of the substance concerned.

212 561-
212 569

SECTION 7.   Operation

212 570 The inside of the shell and all parts liable to come into contact with the substances referred to in marginals 212 510 and 212 511 shall be kept clean. No lubricant capable of combining dangerously with the substance carried shall be used for pumps, valves or other devices.

212 571 Shells intended for the carriage of substances of 1° (a), 2° (a) and 3° (a) of marginal 2501 shall be filled to not more than 95% of their capacity at a reference temperature of 15 °C. Shells intended for the carriage of substances of marginal 2501, 20°, shall be filled to not more than 97% of their capacity, and the maximum temperature after filling shall not exceed 140 °C. In the event of a change of use, shells and equipment shall be thoroughly cleansed of all residues before and after the carriage of substances of 20°.

212 572 Shells intended for the carriage of substances referred to in marginal 212 511 shall be filled as set out in the test report for the type approval of the tank but shall be filled to not more than 90% of their capacity. Shells shall be free from impurities at the time of filling.

212 573 Service equipment such as valves and external piping of shells intended for the carriage of substances referred to in marginal 212 511 shall be emptied after filling or discharging of the tank.

212 574-
212 599

Appendix B.1b

CLASS 6.1. TOXIC SUBSTANCES

CLASS 6.2. INFECTIOUS SUBSTANCES

212 600-
212 609

SECTION 1. General, scope (use of tank-containers); definitions

Use

212 610 The following substances of marginal 2601 may be carried in tank-containers:

(a) the substances listed by name in 2° to 4°;

(b) substances classified under (a) of 6° to 13° with the exception of isopropyl chloroformate of 10°, 15° to 17°, 20°, 22°, 23°, 25° to 28°, 31° to 36°, 41°, 44°, 51°, 52°, 55°, 61°, 65° to 68°, 71° to 73° and 90°, carried in the liquid state or in the molten state;

(c) substances classified under (b) or (c) of 11°, 12°, 14° to 28°, 31° to 36°, 41°, 44°, 51° to 55°, 57° to 62°, 64° to 68°, 71° to 73° and 90°, carried in the liquid state or in the molten state;

(d) substances in powdery or granular form classified under (b) or (c) of 12°, 14°, 17°, 19°, 21°, 23°, 25° to 27°, 32° to 35°, 41°, 44°, 51° to 55°, 57° to 68°, 71° to 73° and 90°.

NOTE: For the carriage in bulk of substances of 60° (c), of solids containing toxic liquids of 65° (b) (identification number 3243) and of solid substances, including mixtures (such as preparations and wastes) classified under (c) of the various items, see marginal 61 111.

(2) Substances of marginal 2651, 3° and 4° may be carried in tank-containers.

212 611-
212 619

SECTION 2. Construction

212 620 Shells intended for the carriage of substances referred to in marginal 212 610 (1) (a) shall be designed for a calculation pressure [see marginal 212 127 (2)] of not less than 1.5 MPa (15 bar) (gauge pressure).

212 621 Shells intended for the carriage of the substances referred to in marginal 212 610 (1) (b) shall be designed for a calculation pressure [see marginal 212 127 (2)] of not less than 1.0 MPa (10 bar) (gauge pressure).

212 622 Shells intended for the carriage of the substances referred to in marginals 212 610 (1) (c) and 212 610 (2) shall be designed for a calculation pressure [see marginal 212 127 (2)] of not less than 400 kPa (4 bar) (gauge pressure). Shells intended for the carriage of chloroacetic acid of 24° (b) of marginal 2601 shall be provided with an enamel or equivalent protective lining if the material of the shell is attacked by chloroacetic acid.

212 623 Shells intended for the carriage of the powdery or granular substances referred to in marginal 212 610 (1) (d) shall be designed in accordance with the requirements of Part I of this Appendix.

212 624-
212 629

SECTION 3.   Items of equipment

212 630 All openings of shells intended for the carriage of the substances referred to in marginal 212 610 (1) (a) and (b) shall be above the surface level of the liquid. No pipe or pipe connections shall pass through the walls of the shell below the surface level of the liquid. Shells shall be capable of being hermetically closed [23] and the closures shall be capable of being protected with lockable caps. The cleaning openings (fist holes) provided for in marginal 212 132 shall not however be permitted for shells intended for the carriage of solutions of hydrocyanic acid of 2°.

212 631 Shells intended for the carriage of the substances referred to in marginal 212 610 (1) (c) and (d) and (2) may also be of the bottom-discharge type. The shells shall be capable of being hermetically closed [23].

212 632 If shells are fitted with safety valves, a bursting disc shall be placed before the valve. The arrangement of the bursting disc and safety valve shall be such as to satisfy the competent authority.

212 633-
212 639

SECTION 4.   Type approval

212 640-
212 649 (No special requirements)

SECTION 5.   Tests

212 650 Shells intended for the carriage of the substances referred to in marginal 212 610 (1) (a), (b) and (c) and (2) shall be subjected to the initial and periodic hydraulic pressure tests at a gauge pressure of not less than 400 kPa (4 bar).

212 651 Shells intended for the carriage of the substances referred to in marginal 212 610 (1) (d) shall be subjected to the initial and periodic hydraulic pressure tests at their calculation pressure as defined in marginal 212 123.

212 652-
212 659

SECTION 6.   Marking

212 660-
212 669 (No special requirements)

---

[23]   *See footnote 8/ to marginal 212 135.*

SECTION 7. Operation

212 670 Shells intended for the carriage of substances of 3° of marginal 2601 shall not be filled to more than 1 kg per litre of capacity.

212 671 Shells shall be hermetically closed [23] during carriage. The closures of shells intended for the carriage of the substances referred to in marginal 212 610 (1) (a) and (b) shall be protected with locked caps.

212 672 Tank-containers approved for the carriage of the substances referred to in marginal 212 610 shall not be used for the carriage of foodstuffs, articles of consumption or animal feeds.

212 673-
212 679

SECTION 8. Transitional measures

212 680 Tank-containers intended for the carriage of substances of 6°, 8°, 9°, 10°, 13°, 15°, 16°, 18°, 20°, 25° or 27° of marginal 2601, built before 1 January 1995 in accordance with the requirements of this Appendix applicable until that date, but which do not, however, conform to the requirements applicable as from 1 January 1995, may still be used until 31 December 1999.

212 681-
212 699

---

[23] *See footnote 8/ to marginal 212 135.*

CLASS 7. RADIOACTIVE MATERIAL

**212 700-
212 709**

SECTION 1.   General, scope (use of tank-containers); definitions

Use

212 710   Materials of marginal 2704, Schedules 1, 5, 6, 9, 10 and 11, except uranium hexafluoride, may be carried in tank-containers.   The provisions of the appropriate schedule in marginal 2704 are applicable.

NOTE: There may be additional requirements for tank-containers which are designed as a Type A or Type B packaging.

**212 711-
212 719**

SECTION 2.   Construction

212 720   See marginal 3736.

**212 721-
219 729**

SECTION 3.   Items of Equipment

212 730   The openings of tank-containers for the carriage of liquid radioactive material [24] shall be above the level of the liquid.   The shell walls shall not have any piping or pipe connection below the level of the liquid.

**212 731-
212 739**

SECTION 4.   Type approval

212 740   Tank-containers approved for the carriage of radioactive material shall not be approved for the carriage of any other substance.

**212 741-
212 749**

SECTION 5.   Tests

212 750   The shells shall initially and periodically undergo a hydraulic pressure test at a pressure of at least 265 kPa (2.65 bar), (gauge pression).

Notwithstanding the provisions of marginal 212 151 the periodic internal inspection may be replaced by a programme approved by the competent authority.

**212 751-
212 759**

---

[24]   *See footnote 17/ to marginal 212 173.*

Appendix B.1b

SECTION 6.   Marking

212 760 In addition, the trefoil symbol described in marginal 2705 (5), shall be marked by stamping or by any other equivalent method on the place described in marginal 212 160. This trefoil marking may be applied directly on the walls of the shell itself, if the walls are so reinforced that the strength of the shell is not impaired.

212 761-
212 769

SECTION 7.   Operation

212 770 The degree of filling according to marginal 212 172, at the reference temperature of 15 °C shall not exceed 93% of the capacity of the shell.

212 771 Tank-containers in which radioactive material has been carried shall not be used for the carriage of other substances.

212 772-
212 799

Appendix B.1b

CLASS 8. CORROSIVE SUBSTANCES

212 800-
212 809

SECTION 1.   General, scope (use of tank-containers); definitions

Use

212 810   The following substances of marginal 2801 may be carried in tank-containers:

(a)   substances listed by name in 6° and 14°;

(b)   substances classified under (a) of 1°, 2°, 3°, 7°, 8°, 12°, 17°, 32°, 33°, 39°, 40°, 46°, 47°, 52° to 56°, 64° to 68°, 70°, 72° to 76°, carried in the liquid state or in the molten state;

(c)   substances 15° or classified under (b) or (c) of 1° to 5°, 7°, 8° 10°, 12°, 17°, 31° to 40°, 42° to 47°, 51° to 56°, 61° to 76°, carried in the liquid state or in the molten state;

(d)   substances in powdery or granular form classified under (b) or (c) of 9°, 11°, 13°, 16°, 31°, 34°, 35°, 39°, 41°, 45°, 46°, 52°, 55°, 62°, 65°, 68°, 69°, 71°, 73° and 75°.

NOTE: For the carriage in bulk of lead sulphate of 1° (b), of substances of 13° (b), of solids containing a corrosive liquid of 65° (b) of identification number 3244 and of solid substances, including mixtures (such as preparations and wastes) classified under (c) of the various items, see marginal 81 111.

212 811-
212 819

SECTION 2.   Construction

212 820   Shells intended for the carriage of substances listed by name in 6° and 14° shall be designed for a calculation pressure [see marginal 212 127 (2)] of not less than 2.1 MPa (21 bar) (gauge pressure). Shells intended for the carriage of substances of 14° shall be provided with a lead lining not less than 5 mm thick or an equivalent lining. The requirement of Appendix B.1d shall apply to the materials and construction of welded shells, intended for the carriage of substances of 6°.

212 821   Shells intended for the carriage of the substances referred to in marginal 212 810 (b) shall be designed for a calculation pressure [see marginal 212 127 (2)] of not less than 1.0 MPa (10 bar) (gauge pressure).

Where the use of aluminium is necessary for shells intended for the carriage of nitric acid of 2° (a), such shells shall be made of aluminium not less than 99.5% pure; even where the calculation pressure according to marginal 212 127 (2) gives a higher value, the wall thickness need not exceed 15 mm.

212 822   Shells intended for the carriage of the substances referred to in marginal 212 810 (c) shall be designed for a calculation pressure [see marginal 212 127 (2)] of not less than 400 kPa (4 bar) (gauge pressure).

If the shells are made of pure aluminium, the wall thickness need not be greater than 15 mm even where the calculation pressure according to marginal 212 127 (2) gives a higher value.

- 201 -

212 823 Shells intended for the carriage of the powdery or granular substances referred to in marginal 212 810 (d) shall be designed in accordance with the requirements of Part I of this Appendix.

212 824-
212 829

SECTION 3.   Items of equipment

212 830 All openings of shells intended for the carriage of substances of 6°, 7° and 14° shall be above the surface level of the liquid. No pipes or pipe connections shall pass through the walls of the shell below the surface level of the liquid. In addition, the cleaning openings (fist holes) referred to in marginal 212 132 shall not be permissible. Tank-containers shall be capable of being hermetically closed [25] and the closures shall be capable of being protected by lockable cap.

212 831 Shells intended for the carriage of the substances referred to in marginal 212 810 (b), (c) and (d) with the exception of substances of 7° may also be of the bottom-discharge type.

212 832 If shells intended for the carriage of the substances referred to in marginal 212 810 (b) are fitted with safety valves, a bursting disc shall be placed before the valve. The arrangement of the bursting disc and safety valve shall be such as to satisfy the competent authority.

212 833 Shells intended for the carriage of sulphur trioxide of 1° (a) shall be thermally insulated and fitted with a heating device on the outside.

212 834 Shells and their service equipment intended for carriage of hypochlorite solutions of 61° shall be so designed as to prevent the entry of foreign matter, leakage of liquid or any building up of dangerous excess pressure inside the shell.

212 835-
212 839

SECTION 4.   Type approval

212 840-
212 849 (No special requirements)

SECTION 5.   Tests

212 850 Shells intended for the carriage of substances of 6° shall be subjected to the initial and periodic hydraulic pressure tests at a gauge pressure of at least 1.0 MPa (10 bar) and those intended for the carriage of substances of 7° shall be subjected to initial and periodic hydraulic pressure tests at a gauge pressure of not less than 400 kPa (4 bar).

The materials of every welded shell intended for the carriage of substances of 6° shall be tested by the method described in Appendix B.1d.

212 851 Shells intended for the carriage of substances of 14° or of the substances referred to in marginal 212 810 (b) and (c) shall be subjected to the initial and periodic hydraulic pressure tests at a gauge pressure of not less than 400 kPa (4 bar). The hydraulic pressure test for shells intended for the carriage of sulphur trioxide of 1° (a) shall be repeated every two and a half years.

---

[25]   *See footnote 8/ to marginal 212 135.*

Appendix B.1b

**212 851
(contd)** Shells made of pure aluminium and intended for the carriage of nitric acid of 2° (a) need be subjected to the initial and periodic hydraulic pressure tests at a gauge pressure of only 250 kPa (2.5 bar).

The condition of the lining of shells intended for the carriage of substances of 14° shall be inspected every year by an expert approved by the competent authority, who shall inspect the inside of the shell.

212 852 Shells intended for the carriage of the substances referred to in marginal 212 810 (d) shall be subjected to the initial and periodic tests at their calculation pressure as defined in marginal 212 123.

**212 853-
212 859**

SECTION 6. Marking

212 860 Shells intended for the carriage of substances of 6° and 14°, shall bear, in addition to the particulars referred to in marginal 212 160, the date (month, year) of the most recent inspection of the internal condition.

212 861 Shells intended for the carriage of inhibited sulphur trioxide of 1° (a) and substances of 6° and 14° shall bear in addition, on the plate referred to in marginal 212 160, the maximum permissible load mass in kg of the shell.

**212 862-
212 869**

SECTION 7. Operation

212 870 Shells intended for the carriage of inhibited or stabilized sulphur trioxide of 1° (a) shall not be filled to more than 88% of their capacity; those intended for the carriage of substances of 14° shall be filled to not less than 88% and not more than 92% of their capacity or to 2.86 kg per litre of capacity. For the transport of 1829 sulphur trioxide, 99.95% pure and above, without inhibitor, the temperature of the substance shall be maintained at or above 32.5 °C.

Shells intended for the carriage of substances of 6° shall not be filled to more than 0.84 kg per litre of capacity.

212 871 Shells intended for the carriage of substances of 6°, 7° and 14° shall be hermetically closed [25/] [see marginal 212 127 (2)] during carriage and the closures shall be protected with lockable caps.

**212 872-
212 879**

SECTION 8. Transitional measures

212 880 Tank-containers intended for the carriage of substances of 3°, 12°, 33°, 40° or 54° of marginal 2801, built before 1 January 1995 in accordance with the requirements of this Appendix applicable until that date, but which do not, however, conform to the requirements applicable as from 1 January 1995, may still be used until 31 December 1999.

**212 881-
212 899**

[25/] *See footnote 8/ to marginal 212 135.*

Appendix B.1b

CLASS 9.   MISCELLANEOUS DANGEROUS SUBSTANCES AND ARTICLES

212 900-
212 909

SECTION 1.   General, scope (use of tank-containers); definitions

Use

212 910   Substances of 1°, 2° (b), 11° (c), 12° (c), 20° (c), 31° (c) to 35° (c) or 2211 polymeric beads, expandable of 4° (c) of marginal 2901 may be carried in tank-containers.

NOTE: For carriage in bulk of substances of 4° (c), 12° (c), 20° (c), 21° (c), 31°, 32° or 35° of marginal 2901, see marginal 91 111.

212 911-
212 919

SECTION 2.   Construction

212 920   Shells intended for the carriage of substances of 1°, 2° (b), 11° (c), 12° (c), 20° (c), 31° to 35° or 2211 polymeric beads, expandable, of 4° (c) of marginal 2901 shall be designed in accordance with the requirements of Part I of this Appendix.

212 921   Shells intended for the carriage of substances of 2° shall be designed for a calculation pressure [see marginal 212 127 (2)] of not less than 400 kPa (4 bar) (gauge pressure).

212 922-
212 929

SECTION 3.   Items of equipment

212 930   Shells intended for the carriage of substances of 1° and 2° shall be capable of being hermetically closed [25]. Shells intended for the carriage of 2211 polymeric beads, expandable of 4° (c) shall be equipped with a safety valve.

212 931   If shells intended for the carriage of substances of 1° and 2° are fitted with safety valves, a bursting disc shall be placed before the valves. The arrangement of the bursting disc and safety valve shall be such as to satisfy the competent authority.

212 932   Shells intended for the carriage of substances of 20° (c) shall be equipped with thermal insulation. They may also be equipped with pressure release devices opening automatically inwards or outwards under the effect of a difference of pressure of between 20 kPa and 30 kPa (0.2 bar and 0.3 bar). The thermal insulation directly in contact with the shell intended for the carriage of substances of 20° (c) shall have an ignition temperature at least 50 °C higher than the maximum temperature for which the shell was designed.

212 933   The bottom discharge system of shells intended for the carriage of substances of 20° (c) may consist of an external pipe with a stop-valve if it is constructed in a metallic material liable to deformation.

212 934-
212 939

---

[25]   *See footnote [8] to marginal 212 135.*

Appendix B.1b

SECTION 4.   **Type approval**

212 940-
212 949   (No special requirements)

SECTION 5.   **Tests**

212 950   Shells intended for the carriage of substances of 2° shall be subjected to the initial and periodic hydraulic pressure tests at a pressure of at least 400 kPa (4 bar) (gauge pressure).

212 951   Shells intended for the carriage of substances of 1°, 2° (b), 11° (c), 12° (c), 20° (c), 31° to 35° or 2211 polymeric beads, expandable, of 4° (c) of marginal 2901 shall be subject to the initial and periodic hydraulic pressure tests at the calculation pressure used in their design as defined in marginal 212 123.

212 952-
212 959

SECTION 6.   **Marking**

212 960   Shells intended for the carriage of substances of 20° (c) shall bear on both sides, in addition to the markings stipulated in marginal 212 161, the mark reproduced in Appendix B.7.

212 969   (No special requirements)

SECTION 7.   **Operation**

212 970   Shells intended for the carriage of substances of 1° and 2° shall be hermetically closed [25] during carriage.

212 971   Tank-containers approved for the carriage of substances of 1° and 2° shall not be used for the carriage of foodstuffs, articles of consumption or animal feeds.

212 972-
212 979

SECTION 8.   **Transitional measures**

212 980   Tank-containers which were intended for the carriage of substances of 20° of marginal 2901, built before 1 January 1997 but which do not conform with the requirements of this Appendix applicable as from 1 January 1997, may still be used until 31 December 2006.

212 981-
212 999

---

[25]   *See footnote 8/ to marginal 212 135.*

Appendix B.1c

PROVISIONS CONCERNING FIXED TANKS AND DEMOUNTABLE TANKS MADE OF REINFORCED PLASTICS

NOTE 1: This Appendix applies to fixed tanks and demountable tanks; it does not apply to battery-vehicles, to tank-containers, or to receptacles.

NOTE 2: For receptacles, see the requirements concerning them in Annex A (packages).

213 000-
213 009

SECTION 1. **General provisions concerning the use and construction of fixed and demountable tanks**

NOTE: In accordance with the provisions of marginal 10 121 (2) the carriage of dangerous substances in fixed or demountable tanks made of reinforced plastics complying with the requirements of this Appendix is permitted only where the use of such tanks for those substances is expressly authorized under marginal 213 010.

Use

213 010 The following substances may be carried in reinforced-plastics tanks conforming to the provisions of this Appendix:

(a) crude petroleum and other crude oils; volatile products from the distillation of crude petroleum and of other crude oils of 3° (b) of Class 3;

(b) semi-heavy products from the distillation of petroleum and of other crude oils of 31° (c) of Class 3;

(c) heating oils and diesel oils of 31° (c) of Class 3;

(d) aqueous solutions of hydrogen peroxide of 1° (b) and (c) and solutions of 11° (b) of Class 5.1;

(e) substances of 1° (b) and (c), 2° (b), 5°, 8° (b) and (c), 17° (c), 42°, 43° (c) and 61° of Class 8.

213 011-
213 099

Construction

213 100 The tanks shall comply with the following requirements of Appendix B.1a:

(1) General provisions applicable to tanks used for carriage of substances of all classes:

Marginals 211 120 (4), (5) and (6); 211 121; 211 122; 211 124; 211 126; 211 127 (7); 211 128; 211 130; 211 132; 211 140; 211 150 to 211 154; 211 160 and 211 161; 211 171; 211 172 (1) and (2); 211 173 to 211 178.

**213 100
(cont'd)** (2) Provisions applicable to tanks used for carriage of substances of Class 3: Shells which are fitted with a venting device not capable of being closed and which are intended for the carriage of inflammable liquids having a flash-point not exceeding 55 °C shall have a flame-trap in the venting device.

The leakproofness test and the internal inspection shall be performed every three years.

(3) Special provisions applicable to tanks used for the carriage of substances of Class 5.1: marginal 211 532.

(4) Provisions applicable to tanks used for carriage of substances of Class 8: marginal 211 834.

213 101 The walls of the tank must present no material defect causing a reduction in safety.

213 102 The walls of the tank must have a lasting resistance to the mechanical, thermal and chemical stresses to which they are subjected.

Tank openings

213 103 (1) Where the tank has one or more discharge openings below the level of the liquid, any pipe or valve fitted to such opening or openings shall be protected either by being recessed into the tank shell or by any other means approved by the competent authority and providing equivalent protection.

(2) The use of screwed plugs is strictly prohibited. Valves shall be of a model approved by the competent authority.

(3) Filling apertures shall be closed by a hermetic device. If the device projects outwards from the tank shell it shall be protected by a cap capable of withstanding wrenching stresses occurring through accidental overturning of the tank.

**213 104-
213 119**

SECTION 2. **Materials used for the walls of the tank**

213 120 The walls of tanks may be made of the following materials:

(1) Synthetic resin

- non-saturated polyester resins;

- epoxide resins;

- other resins with similar characteristics, provided that the safety of the wall is demonstrated.

(2) Fibre reinforcements

Glass fibres (glass of types E and C) [1] with an appropriate coating, for example with a silane base or similar products. The glass fibres may be used in the form of cut or uncut rovings including prestressed continuous rovings or filaments, mats, surface mats or woven fabric.

---

[1] *Glass of types E and C is defined in Table 1.*

Appendix B.1c

**213 120
(contd)**
(3)   Additives

(a)   Additives necessary for the treatment of resins, for example, catalysts, accelerators, monomers, hardeners, thixotropic substances, in accordance with instructions by the manufacturer of the resin.

(b)   Extenders, pigments, colorants and other products enabling the required properties to be obtained, for example, the increase of fire-resistant properties, provided that they cause no reduction in the safety of use of the walls of the tank.

**213 121-
213 129**

SECTION 3.   Structure of the walls of the tank

213 130   The external surface layer of the walls of the tank must be resistant to atmospheric effects and also to brief contact with the substance to be carried.

213 131   The walls of the tank and the sealed joints must satisfy the mechanical resistance requirements listed in section 4.

213 132   The internal surface layer of the walls must be resistant to the lasting effects of the substance to be carried. This layer must be made of reinforced resin having a minimum thickness of 1 mm. The fibres used must not reduce the chemical resistance of the layer. The inner part of the layer must be rich in resins and must have a minimum thickness of 0.2 mm.

The requirements detailed in marginals 213 140 (6) and 213 142 (2) of section 4 must be satisfied.

213 133   The finished walls must satisfy the requirements detailed in marginal 213 140 (3) of section 4.

213 134   The minimum thickness of the wall shall be

- 3.5 mm if the capacity of the tank does not exceed 3 m^3
- 5.0 mm if the capacity of the tank is more than 3 m^3.

**213 135-
213 139**

SECTION 4.   Test methods and qualities required

Tests and qualities required for materials for the prototype tank

213 140   (1)   *Taking of specimens*

The specimens required for the test must wherever possible be taken from the walls of the tank. For this purpose cut-out parts resulting from the making of apertures, etc. may be used.

(2)   *Percentage of glass fibre*

The test must be conducted in accordance with the methods prescribed in ISO Recommendation R1172 1970.

The fiberglass content of the specimen must be higher than 25% and lower than 75% by mass.

Appendix B.1c

213 140 **(3)** *Degree of polymerization*
(contd)

(a) Wall in polyester resins

The residual styrene content may not be higher than 2%, calculated on the total quantity of resins. The test shall be conducted in accordance with a suitable method [2].

(b) Wall in epoxide resins

The acetone extract may not be higher than 2% calculated on the total quantity of resins. The test shall be conducted in accordance with a suitable method [3].

(4) *Bending and tensile strength*

The mechanical properties must be determined:

- for the shell, in the axial and circumferential directions;
- for the ends and walls of compartments, in any direction.

If the principal directions of the reinforcement do not coincide with the axial and circumferential directions (for example in the case of biaxial winding), the strength must be determined in the principal directions of the reinforcement and calculated for the axial and circumferential directions by applying the following formulae:

Tensile

$$\sigma_{T,c} = 2\,\sigma_{T,H}\,\sin^2\alpha$$

$$\sigma_{T,a} = 2\,\sigma_{T,H}\,\cos^2\alpha$$

T = tensile
c = circumferential
a = axial

Bending

$$\sigma_{F,c} = 2\,\sigma_{F,H}\,\sin^2\alpha$$

$$\sigma_{F,a} = 2\,\sigma_{F,H}\,\cos^2\alpha$$

H = helicoidal
F = bending
α = preferential winding angle

The tensile strength must be tested in accordance with the methods prescribed in document ISO/TC61/WG2/TG "Tests of glass reinforced plastics" No. 4 of February 1971.

The bending strength must be tested in accordance with the methods prescribed in Recommendation ISO/TC61 No. 1540 of April 1970.

---

[2] The method prescribed in standard DIN 16945 of June 1969, paragraph 6.4.3. is regarded as suitable.

[3] The method prescribed in standard DIN 16945 of June 1969, paragraph 6.4.2. is regarded as suitable.

213 140   *Requirements*
(contd)

New tanks must meet the following safety factors against rupture:

safety factor for static loading: 7.5
safety factor for dynamic loading: 5.5

The acceleration values to be applied in computing the dynamic load are as follows:

2 g in direction of travel;
1 g at right angles to direction of travel;
1 g vertically upwards; and
2 g vertically downwards.

As the characteristics of a reinforced plastics laminate may vary according to its structure, minimum values are not prescribed for bending and tensile strength but for loads:

$A = e \, \sigma_T$ where σ_T is the tensile strength at break;

$B = e^2 \, \sigma_F$ where σ_F is the bending strength at break;

where e is the thickness of the wall.

The minimum values for forces A and B are:

For bending:

Capacity of tank $\leq 3 \text{ m}^3$

- circumferential direction   B = 600 daN
- axial direction   B = 300 daN

Capacity of tank $> 3 \text{ m}^3$

- circumferential direction   B = 600 daN
- axial direction   B = 600 daN

For tensile:

- circumferential direction   A = 100 daN/mm
- axial direction   A = 70 daN/mm

Module E on bending is measured at -40 °C and at +60 °C. The two values may not differ by more than 30% from the value obtained at 20 °C. Behaviour of wall material during a tensile test lasting more than 1 000 hours.

The test tension is: $\dfrac{\sigma_T}{7,5}$

During the test the factor $K = \dfrac{\epsilon_{1\,000}}{\epsilon_0}$ may not be higher than 1.6.

ϵ_0 = elongation of loaded specimen at beginning of test
$\epsilon_{1\,000}$ = elongation of loaded specimen at end of test

- 211 -

213 140 (5)   *Impact behaviour*
(contd)

(a)   *Nature of test*

Impact behaviour is determined on a sample of laminate corresponding to the structural material used for the construction of the tank. The test is carried out by dropping a 5 kg steel mass onto the surface of the laminate corresponding to the external surface of the tank.

(b)   *Apparatus*

The apparatus consists of a 5 kg steel mass, a guidance device for this mass and a specimen-bearing chassis. A general diagram of the apparatus is given in figure 1. The mass is in the form of a steel cylinder provided with two guide channels, the lower extremity being spherically shaped, 90 mm diameter. The guidance device is fitted vertically to a wall.

The specimen-bearer is composed of two angle-bars of 100 x 100 x 25 mm and 300 mm long, welded to a 400 x 400 mm metal support. The gap between the two bars is 175 mm. The specimen-bearer, fixed to the ground, is provided with a 50 mm deep cavity to allow flexion of the specimen.

(c)   *Preparation of specimens*

From the sample, three specimens are taken, each measuring 200 x 200 mm x thickness of the sample.

(d)   *Operating method*

The specimen is placed symmetrically on the specimen-bearer; if possible it rests on the support following two basic straight lines of the surface, in such a way that the mass strikes the centre of the face of the specimen corresponding to the external surface of the tank.

The mass is allowed to fall from a determined height, care being taken to ensure that it does not rebound and strike the specimen a second time.

The test must be conducted at ambient temperature.

The height to which the mass is raised in the guidance device is noted.

The other two specimens are tested in the same way.

(e)   *Requirement*

The drop height for a 5 kg mass shall be 1 metre; the specimen must not allow leakage of more than 1 litre per 24 hours when subjected to a column of water of 1 m.

213 140 (6)
(contd)

Resistance to chemical agents

Flat reinforced plastics test plates, prepared in the laboratory, are subjected to attack by the dangerous substance at a temperature of 50 °C for 30 days in accordance with the following procedure:

(a)   *Description of the test apparatus (shown in figure 2)*

The test apparatus comprises a glass cylinder, diameter 140 x 150 mm, 150 mm high with two nozzles positioned at 135° one fitted with an NS 29 joint to take an intermediate pipe for a reflux condenser (1), the other nozzle fitted with an NS 14.5 joint to take a thermometer (2), an intermediate pipe for a reflux condenser and a reflux condenser not shown in the diagram. The glass part of the apparatus shall be in glass resistant to changes of temperature.

The specimens taken from the test plates form the base and the top of the glass cylinder. They are sealed to the sides of the cylinder by a PTFE collar. The cylinder with the two specimens is clamped between two pressure plates in corrosion-resistant steel with six threaded bolts tightened by means of wing nuts. An asbestos washer must be placed between the pressure plates and the specimens. These washers are not shown in figure 2. Heating is effected from outside by means of an automatically controlled sleeve heater. The temperature is measured in the chamber containing the liquid.

(b)   *Operation of the test apparatus*

The test apparatus allows only flat plates of uniform thickness to be tested. The test plates should, if possible, be 4 mm thick. Should these plates be covered with a gel coating, they must be tested in condition as for practical use. Six hexagonal specimens, each side measuring 100 mm, are cut from the test plate.

For each test, three specimens are prepared per apparatus. One of these samples is used as a reference and the other two are used for checking in the liquid zone, and vapour zone of the device respectively.

(c)   *Test procedure*

The specimens to be tested are placed on the apparatus with the surface which may be gel-coated facing inwards. 1 200 ml of test liquid is poured into the glass cylinder. The apparatus is then heated to the test temperature. A constant temperature is maintained during the test. After the test the apparatus is cooled to the ambient temperature and the test liquid removed. The specimens tested are immediately washed with distilled water. Liquids which are not soluble in water are removed with a solvent which does not attack the specimens. Mechanical cleaning of the plates cannot be performed because of the danger of damaging the surface of the specimens.

(d)   *Evaluation*

A visual examination is made:

-       if the visual examination reveals excessive attack (cracks, bubbles, pores, peeling off, swelling, or roughness), the test is conclusive negatively;

213 140   -   if the visual examination reveals no abnormality, bending tests are made by the
(contd)   methods specified in marginal 213 140 (4) on the two specimens subjected to
                        chemical attack and on the reference specimen. In this case the bending
                        strength shall not be more than 20% lower than the value ascertained for the
                        test plate not subjected to any stress.

Test and quality required for the prototype unit

213 141   The prototype tank shall be subjected to a hydraulic pressure test conducted by an expert approved
              by the competent authorities of a Contracting Party.

If the prototype tank is divided into compartments either by bulkheads or by baffle plates, the test
shall be conducted on a unit made for this purpose with the same external ends as the entire tank
and which represents the part of the tank subjected, under normal conditions of use, to the greatest
stresses.

This test should not be conducted if there has already been a successful test on another prototype
unit of the same section or a section with larger dimensions, geometrically similar to that of the
prototype unit in question, even if that unit has a different internal surface layer.

This test must demonstrate that the prototype unit has, under normal conditions of use, a factor of
not less than 7.5 so far as rupture is concerned.

It must be proved, e.g. by calculation, that safety factors against fracture given in
marginal 213 140 (4) are complied with for each section of the tank.

Rupture occurs when the test liquid escapes from the tank in the form of jets. Consequently,
before this rupture, the presence of delaminations and losses of liquid through these delaminations
in the form of droplets is permitted.

The prototype unit shall be submitted to a hydraulic pressure.

$$H = 7.5 \times d \times h$$

where H is the height of the column of water

  h is the height of the tank
  d is the density of the substance to be carried.

If a rupture occurs with a water-column height H_1 less than H, there must still be

$$H_1 \geq 7.5 \times d \times (h-h_1)$$

where h_1 is the height of the highest point where the first jet of liquid appears.

Should the flow of liquid at point h_1 be too great, it is essential to make a temporary repair and
temporary local strengthening to enable the test to continue to height H.

Appendix B.1c

Conformity check on tanks produced in series

213 142 (1) The inspection of conformity on tanks produced in series shall be carried out by conducting one or more of the tests listed in marginal 213 140. However, the measurement of the degree of polymerization is replaced by Barcol hardness measurement.

(2) Barcol hardness

The test must be conducted in accordance with suitable procedures [4]. Barcol hardness measured on the internal surface of the finished tank shall not be less than 75% of the value obtained in the laboratory on pure hardened resin.

(3) The percentage of glass fibre must be within the limits prescribed in marginal 213 140 (2) and, in addition, must not deviate by more than 10% of the figure for the prototype tank.

Tests and qualities required for all tanks before being put into service

213 143 *Leakproofness test*

The leakproofness test shall be conducted in accordance with the provisions of marginals 211 150, 211 151 and 211 152 and the expert's stamp shall be applied to the tank.

213 144-
213 149

SECTION 5. **Special provisions for tanks used for the carriage of substances with a flash-point of 55 °C or lower**

213 150 The tank must be constructed so as to ensure the elimination of static electricity from the various component parts so as to avoid the accumulation of dangerous electric charges.

213 151 All metal parts of the tank and the transport unit and also wall layers conducting electricity must be interconnected.

213 152 The resistance between each conducting part and the chassis must not be higher than 10^6 ohms.

Elimination of hazards due to charges generated by friction

213 153 The surface resistance and the discharge resistance to earth of the entire surface of the tank shall conform with the requirements of marginal 213 154.

213 154 The surface resistance and discharge resistance to earth measured in accordance with marginal 213 155 must satisfy the following requirements.

(1) Walls not equipped with electrically conducting elements:

(a) Surfaces upon which one can walk:

the discharge resistance to earth shall not be higher than 10^8 ohms.

(b) Other surfaces:

the surface resistance shall not be higher than 10^9 ohms.

---

[4] *The procedures prescribed in standard ASTM-D 2583-67 are regarded as suitable.*

213 154
(contd)
(2)   Walls equipped with electrically conducting elements:

(a)   Surfaces on which one can walk:

the discharge resistance to earth shall not be higher than 10^8 ohms.

(b)   Other surfaces:

conductance shall be considered as sufficient if the maximum thickness of non-conducting layers on conducting elements, for example conducting sheets, metal netting or other appropriate material, connected to the earthing connexion, does not exceed 2 mm, and that, in the case of a metal netting, the surface area of the mesh does not exceed 64 cm^2.

(3)   Any measurement of surface resistance or discharge resistance to earth must be carried out on the tank itself shall be replaced at intervals of not more than one year to ensure that the specified resistances are not exceeded.

Test methods

213 155   (1)   Surface resistance (R_{100}) - (insulating resistance) in ohms, electrodes of conducting paint in accordance with figure 3 of Recommendation IEC 167 of 1964, measured in the standard 23/50 atmosphere according to Recommendation ISO R291, paragraph 3.1, of 1963.

(2)   The discharge resistance to earth in ohms is the ratio between the direct voltage measured between an electrode described below in contact with the surface of the tank of the vehicle and the earthed chassis of the vehicle, and the total current.

The conditioning of the specimens is the same as in paragraph 1. The electrode is a disc with a surface area of 20 cm^2 and a diameter of 50 mm. Its close contact with the surface of the tank must be ensured, for example by using damp paper or a damp sponge or any other suitable substance. The earthed chassis of the vehicle is used as the other electrode. A direct voltage in the range of 100 volts-500 volts shall be applied. The measurement shall be carried out after the test voltage has been applied for one minute. The electrode may be placed on any point of the internal or external surface of the tank.

If measuring is impossible on the tank, it may also be carried out, under the same conditions, in the laboratory, on a specimen of the material.

Elimination of hazards due to charges generated during filling

213 156   Metallic components bonded to earth shall be provided and so disposed that at any stage of the filling or emptying process there is an area of not less than 0.04 sq. metres of earthed metal in contact with the product per cubic metre of product contained in the tank at that instant, and that no part of the product shall be more than 2.0 metres from the nearest earthed metal component. Such metallic components may take the form of:

(a)   A metal foot valve, pipe outlet, or plate provided the total area of metal in contact with the liquid is not less than that specified, or

(b)   A metallic grill with wire thickness not less than 1 mm diameter and hole area not greater than 4 sq. centimetres, provided that the total area of the grill in contact with the liquid is not less than that specified.

Appendix B.1c

213 157 Marginal 213 156 shall not apply to reinforced-plastics tanks equipped with any other system for eliminating the hazard from charges generated during filling, provided it has been demonstrated by a practical comparative test in accordance with marginal 213 158 that the relaxation time of the charge generated within the tank during filling is equivalent to that obtained for a metal tank of comparable dimensions.

Comparative test

213 158 (1)   A comparative test of the electrostatic charge relaxation time in accordance with the conditions of test described in paragraph (2) shall be carried out on a prototype reinforced-plastics tank and steel tank in the following manner (see figure 3).

      (a)   The reinforced-plastics tank shall be mounted in the same manner as it would be in use, for example, on a steel support simulating a vehicle's chassis, and shall be filled to not less than 75% capacity with automotive diesel fuel, a proportion of which is passed through a suitable microfilter in such a manner that the charge density of the total flow is approximately 100 uC/m^3.

      (b)   The field strength in the tank vapour space shall be measured by a suitable continuous reading field meter mounted with its axis vertical and placed at least 20 cm from the vertical fill pipe.

      (c)   A similar test shall be carried out on a steel tank whose width, length, breadth, and volume are within 15% of those of the reinforced-plastics tank, or on a reinforced-plastics tank of similar dimensions, coated internally with metal foil connected to earth.

    (2)   The following conditions of test shall be met:

      (a)   the test shall be carried out in a covered area in conditions of relative humidity less than 80%.

      (b)   The automotive diesel fuel used in the test shall have a residual conductivity at the temperature of measurement between 3 and 5 pS/m. This shall be measured in a cell in which

$$\frac{VT}{d^2} \text{ is less than or equal to } 2.5 \times 10^6$$

        where   V   =   applied voltage
                d   =   spacing between electrodes in metres
                T   =   duration of measurement in seconds

        The residual conductivity measured on samples of the product taken from the test tank after filling shall not differ in successive tests on plastics and metal tanks by more than 0.5 pS/m

      (c)   Filling shall be at a constant rate within the range 1 to 2 m^3/min and shall be the same for the reinforced-plastics tank and for the steel tank. At the end of filling, the flow should be stopped in a time which is shorter than the relaxation time for the charge in the steel tank.

Appendix B.1c

213 158
(contd)

(d) The charge density shall be measured by a suitable continuous reading field meter (for example, a field mill type) immersed in the product and placed as close as possible to the filling pipe.

(e) The supply pipes and the vertical filling pipe shall be of 10 cm internal diameter and shall terminate in a "T" type filling pipe outlet.

(f) A suitable microfilter [5], with an adjustable by-pass enabling the proportion of flow passing through it to be regulated, shall be fitted not more than 5 m from the filling pipe outlet.

(g) The liquid level shall not reach the bottom of the filling pipe or the field meter.

Comparison of relaxation times

(3) The initial value of the field strength shall be that recorded at the earliest point of time after the cessation of flow of the fuel when a smooth decay curve has been established. The relaxation time in both tests shall be expressed as the time taken for the field strength to decay from the initial value to 37% of the initial value.

(4) The relaxation time of the reinforced-plastics tank shall not exceed that of the steel tank.

213 159-
213 999

---

[5]   *A Rellumit 5 has been found to be suitable.*

- 218 -

Appendix B.1c

Table 1

COMPOSITION OF GLASS

Glass E: **Composition by mass:**

Silica	$(Si\ O_2)$	52	to	55	%
Alumina	(AL_2O_3)	14	to	15.5	%
Lime	$(Ca\ O)$	16.5	to	18	%
Magnesia	$(Mg\ O)$	4	to	5.5	%
Boric oxide	(B_2O_3)	6.5	to	21	%
Fluorine	(F)	0.2	to	0.6	%
Ferric oxide	(Fe_2O_3)	)			
		)	< 1		%
Titanium oxide	$(Ti\ O_2)$	)			
Alkaline oxides	$(Na_2O + K_2O)$		< 1		%

Glass C: **Composition by masse:**

Silica	$(Si\ O_2)$	63.5	to	65	%
Alumina	(AL_2O_3)	4	to	4.5	%
Lime	$(Ca\ O)$	14	to	14.5	%
Magnesia	$(Mg\ O)$	2.5	to	3	%
Boric oxide	(B_2O_3)	5	to	6.5	%
Iron	(Fe_2O_3)			0.3	%
Sodium oxide	(Na_2O)	7	to	9	%
Potassium oxide	(K_2O)	0.7	to	1	%

Figure 1

Device for measuring impact resistance by means of a spherically-ended falling weight

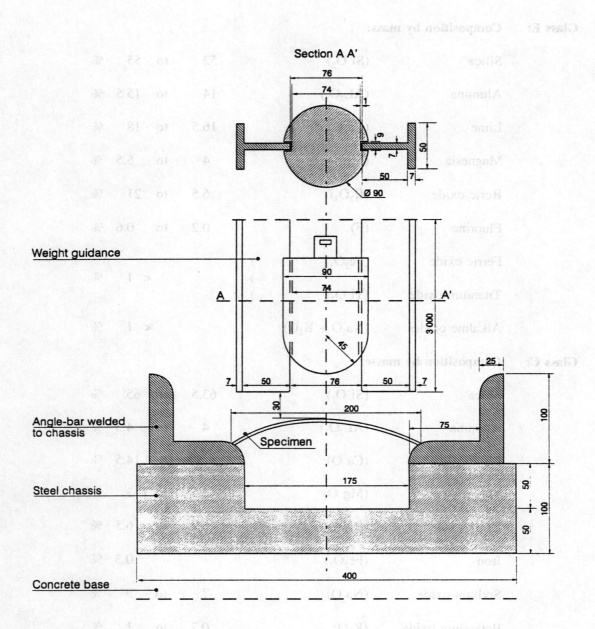

Appendix B.1c

Figure 2

Device to test resistance to chemical agents

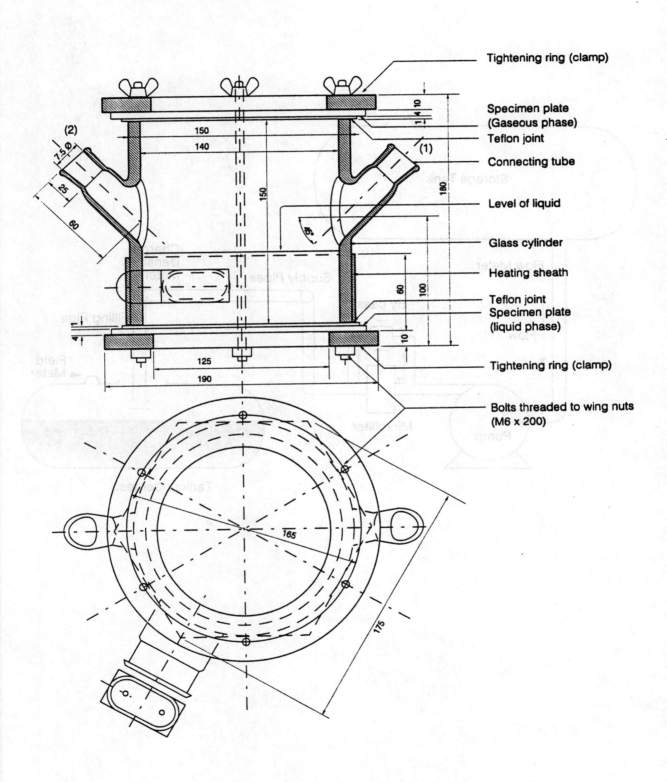

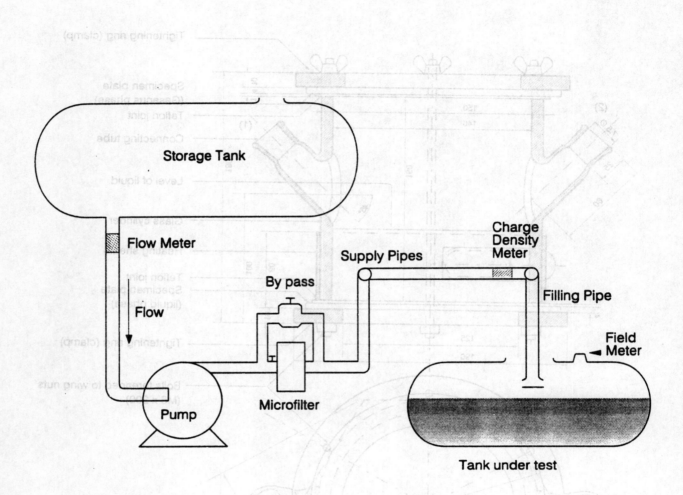

Appendix B.1d

REQUIREMENTS CONCERNING THE MATERIALS AND CONSTRUCTION OF FIXED WELDED TANKS, DEMOUNTABLE WELDED TANKS, AND WELDED SHELLS OF TANK-CONTAINERS FOR WHICH A TEST PRESSURE OF NOT LESS THAN 1 MPa (10 BAR) IS REQUIRED, AND OF FIXED WELDED TANKS, DEMOUNTABLE WELDED TANKS AND WELDED SHELLS OF TANK-CONTAINERS INTENDED FOR THE CARRIAGE OF DEEPLY-REFRIGERATED LIQUEFIED GASES OF CLASS 2

214 000-
214 249

1. Materials and shells

214 250 (1) Shells intended for the carriage of substances of Class 2, 1°, 2° and 4°, Class 4.2, 6° (a), 17° (a), 19° (a) and 31° (a) to 33° (a), or Class 8, 6°, shall be made of steel.

(2) For shells constructed of fine-grained steels for the carriage of:

- substances of Class 2 which are classified as corrosive and substances of 4°A of marginal 2201, and

- substances of marginal 2801, 6°

the steel shall have a guaranteed yield strength of not more than 460 N/mm^2 and a maximum ultimate tensile strength of 725 N/mm^2. Such shells shall be heat-treated for thermal stress relief.

(3) Shells intended for the carriage of deeply-refrigerated liquefied gases of Class 2 shall be made of steel, aluminium, aluminium alloy, copper or copper alloy, e.g., brass. However, shells made of copper or copper alloy shall be allowed only for gases containing no acetylene; ethylene, however, may contain not more than 0.005% acetylene.

(4) Only materials appropriate to the lowest and highest working temperatures of the shells and of their fittings and accessories may be used.

214 251 The following materials shall be allowed for the manufacture of shells:

(a) steels not subject to brittle fracture at the lowest working temperature (see marginal 214 265), the following may be used:

1. mild steels (except for gases of marginal 2201, 3°);

2. fine-grained unalloyed steels, down to a temperature of -60 °C;

3. nickel steels (with a nickel content of 0.5 to 9%), down to a temperature of -196 °C, depending on the nickel content;

4. austenitic chrome-nickel steels, down to a temperature of -270 °C;

(b) aluminium not less than 99.5% pure, or aluminium alloys (see marginal 214 266);

(c) deoxidized copper not less than 99.9% pure, or copper alloys having a copper content of over 56% (see marginal 214 267).

Appendix B.1d

214 252 (1) Shells made of steel, aluminium or aluminium alloys shall be either seamless or welded.

(2) Shells made of austenitic steel, copper or copper alloys may be hard-soldered.

214 253 The fittings and accessories may either be screwed to the shells or be secured thereto as follows:

(a) shells made of steel, aluminium or aluminium alloy: by welding;

(b) shells made of austenitic steel, of copper or of copper alloy: by welding or hard-soldering.

214 254 The construction of shells and their attachment to the vehicle, to the underframe or in the container frame shall be such as to preclude with certainty any such reduction in the temperature of the load-bearing components as would be likely to render them brittle. The means of attachment of shells shall themselves be so designed that even when the shell is at its lowest working temperature they still possess the necessary mechanical properties.

214 255-
214 264

2. Test requirements

(a) *Steel shells*

214 265 The materials used for the manufacture of shells and the weld beads shall, at their lowest working temperature, but at least at -20 °C, meet at least the following requirements as to impact strength.

The tests shall be carried out with test-pieces having a V-shaped notch.

The minimum impact strength (see marginals 214 275 to 214 277) for test-pieces with their longitudinal axis at right angles to the direction of rolling and a V-shaped notch (conforming to ISO R 148) perpendicular to the plate surface, shall be 34 J/cm^2 for mild steel (which, because of existing ISO standards, may be tested with test-pieces having the longitudinal axis in the direction of rolling); fine-grained steel; ferritic alloy steel Ni < 5%, ferritic alloy steel 5% ≤ Ni ≤ 9%; or austenitic Cr - Ni steel.

In the case of austenitic steels, only the weld bead need be subjected to an impact-strength test.

For working temperatures below -196 °C the impact-strength test is not performed at the lowest working temperature, but at -196 °C.

(b) *Shells made of aluminium or aluminium alloy*

214 266 The seams of shells shall meet the requirements laid down by the competent authority.

(c) *Shells made of copper or copper alloy*

214 267 It is not necessary to carry out tests to determine whether the impact strength is adequate.

214 268-
214 274

Appendix B.1d

3. Test methods

(a) *Impact-strength tests*

214 275 For sheets less than 10 mm but not less than 5 mm thick, test-pieces having a cross-section of 10 mm x e mm, where "e" represents the thickness of the sheet, shall be used. Machining to 7.5 mm or 5 mm is permitted if it is necessary. The minimum value of 34 J/cm^2 shall be required in every case.

NOTE: No impact-strength test shall be carried out on sheets less than 5 mm thick, or on their weld seams.

214 276 (1) For the purpose of testing sheets, the impact strength shall be determined on three test-pieces. Test-pieces shall be taken at right angles to the direction of rolling; however, for mild steel they may be taken in the direction of rolling.

(2) For testing weld seams the test-pieces shall be taken as follows:

when e ≤ 10 mm:

three test-pieces with the notch at the centre of the weld;

three test-pieces with the notch in the centre of the heat affected zone; (the V-notch to cross the fusion boundary at the centre of the specimen)

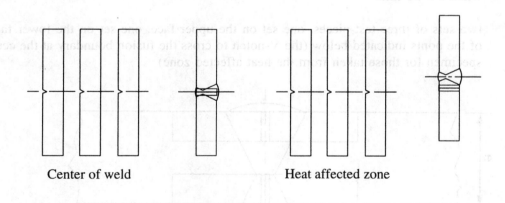

Center of weld   Heat affected zone

**214 276
(contd)**

when 10 mm <e ≤20 mm:

three test-pieces from the centre of the weld;

three test-pieces from the heat affected zone; (the V-notch to cross the fusion boundary at the centre of the specimen)

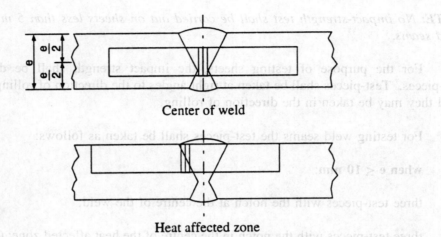

Center of weld

Heat affected zone

when e > 20 mm:

two sets of three test-pieces, one set on the upper face, one set on the lower face at each of the ponts indicated below (the V-notch to cross the fusion boundary at the centre of the specimen for those taken from the heat affected zone)

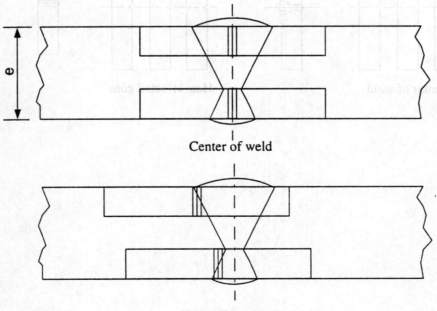

Center of weld

Heat affected zone

214 277 (1)   For sheets, the average of the three tests shall meet the minimum value of 34 J/cm^2 indicated in marginal 214 265; not more than one of the individual values may be below the minimum value and then not below 24 J/cm^2.

(2)   For welds, the average value obtained from the three test-pieces taken at the centre of the weld shall not be below the minimum value of 34 J/cm^2; not more than one of the individual values may be below the minimum value and then not below 24 J/cm^2.

(3)   For the heat affected zone (the V-notch to cross the fusion boundary at the centre of the specimen) the value obtained from not more than one of the three test-pieces may be below the minimum value of 34 J/cm^2, though not below 24 J/cm^2.

214 278   If the requirements prescribed in marginal 214 277 are not met, one retest only may be done if:

(a)   the average value of the first three tests is below the minimum value of 34 J/cm^2, or

(b)   more than one of the individual values is less than the minimum value of 34 J/cm^2 but not below 24 J/cm^2.

214 279   In a repeated impact test on sheets or welds, none of the individual values may be below 34 J/cm^2. The average value of all the results of the original test and of the retest should be equal to or more than the minimum of 34 J/cm^2.

On a repeated impact-strength test on the heat-affected zone, none of the individual values may be below 34 J/cm^2.

214 280-
219 999

APPENDIX B.2

UNIFORM PROVISIONS CONCERNING THE CONSTRUCTION OF VEHICLES INTENDED FOR THE CARRIAGE OF DANGEROUS GOODS INCLUDING PROVISIONS FOR THEIR TYPE APPROVAL WHERE APPROPRIATE

220 000-
220 099

SECTION 1.   Scope

220 100   (1)   The provisions of this Appendix apply to the construction of base vehicles of motor vehicles and their trailers intended for the carriage of dangerous goods, which are subject to approval according to marginals 10 282, 11 282 and to their type approval.

(2)   For the type-approval of a vehicle type in accordance with marginal 10 281, all sections of this Appendix shall apply.

(3)   In the case of single vehicles which have not been subject to the type-approval procedure in accordance with marginal 10 281, only the provisions of section 5 of this Appendix apply.

220 101-
220 199

SECTION 2.   Definitions

220 200   For the purpose of this Appendix:

(1)   "*Vehicle*" means a chassis-cab vehicle, a tractor for semi-trailer or a trailer-chassis or a trailer with a self-supporting body intended for the transport of dangerous goods;

(2)   "*Vehicle type*" means vehicles which do not differ essentially with regard to the constructional features specified in this Appendix.

SECTION 3.   Application for type-approval

220 300   The application for type-approval of a vehicle type with regard to its specific constructional features shall be submitted by the vehicle manufacturer or by his duly accredited representative.

220 301   The application for type-approval shall be accompanied by the under-mentioned documents in triplicate and by the following particulars:

(1)   a detailed description of the vehicle type with respect to its relevant structure, engine (compression-ignition, positive-ignition), dimensions, configuration and constituent materials;

(2)   the type of vehicle according to the dangerous goods which the vehicle is intended to transport, i.e.:

        Type EX/II   for vehicles intended for the carriage of explosives as type II transport units (see marginal 11 204);

        Type EX/III   for vehicles intended for the carriage of explosives as type III transport units (see marginal 11 204);

220 301 **(contd)**	TYPE FL:	for vehicles intended for the carriage of liquids with a flash-point of not more than 61 °C or flammable gases, in tank-containers of more than 3000 litres capacity, fixed tanks or demountable tanks and for battery vehicles of more than 1000 litres capacity intended for the carriage of flammable gases;
	TYPE OX:	for vehicles intended for the carriage of substances of class 5.1, marginal 2501, item 1° (a) in tank-containers of more than 3000 litres capacity, fixed tanks or demountable tanks;
	TYPE AT:	for vehicles, other than those of types FL or OX, intended for the carriage of dangerous goods in tank-containers of more than 3000 litres capacity, fixed tanks or demountable tanks, and for battery vehicles of more than 1000 litres capacity other than those of type FL.

(3)   drawings of the vehicle; and

(4)   particulars of:

    (a)   the technical maximum mass (kg);

    (b)   the type(s) of endurance braking system(s).

220 302   A vehicle representative of the type to be approved shall be submitted to the technical service responsible for conducting the approval tests.

220 303   The competent authority shall verify the existence of satisfactory arrangements for ensuring effective control of the conformity of production before type approval is granted.

220 304-
220 399

SECTION 4.   **Type-approval**

220 400   If the vehicle submitted for approval pursuant to this Appendix meets the provisions of Section 5 below, approval of that vehicle type shall be granted.

220 401   An approval number shall be assigned to each type approved. Its first two digits (00 for the Appendix in its present form) shall indicate the series of amendments incorporating the most recent major technical amendments made to the provisions at the time of issue of the approval. The same Contracting Party may not assign the same number to another vehicle type within the meaning of marginal 220 200 (2) above.

220 402   Notice of approval or of extension of approval of a vehicle type pursuant to this Appendix shall be communicated to the Contracting Parties by means of a form conforming to the model reproduced in marginal 221 000.

220 403   There shall be affixed, conspicuously and in a readily accessible place specified on the approval form, to every vehicle conforming to a vehicle type approved under this Appendix an international approval mark consisting of:

220 403 (1) a circle surrounding the letters "ADR" followed by the distinguishing number of the
(contd) State which has granted approval [1];

(2) the approval number to the right of the circle prescribed in paragraph (1); and

(3) an additional symbol separated from the approval number and consisting of the symbol identifying the vehicle type approved in accordance with marginal 220 301(2).

220 404 The approval mark shall be clearly legible and be indelible.

220 405 The approval mark shall be placed close to or on the vehicle data plate affixed by the manufacturer.

220 406-
220 499

SECTION 5. **Technical provisions**

220 500 Motor vehicles and trailers intended for use as transport units for dangerous goods shall, depending on their category and type, comply with the following provisions according to the table below.

---

[1] *1 for Germany, 2 for France, 3 for Italy, 4 for the Netherlands, 5 for Sweden, 6 for Belgium, 7 for Hungary, 8 for the Czech Republic, 9 for Spain, 10 for Yugoslavia, 11 for the United Kingdom, 12 for Austria, 13 for Luxembourg, 14 for Switzerland, 15 (free), 16 for Norway, 17 for Finland, 18 for Denmark, 19 for Romania, 20 for Poland, 21 for Portugal, 22 for the Russian Federation, 23 for Greece, 24 (reserved), 25 for Croatia, 26 for Slovenia, 27 for Slovakia, 28 for Belarus, 29 for Estonia, 30 (reserved), 31 for Bosnia Herzegovina, 32 for Latvia, 33 for Liechtenstein, 34 for Bulgaria, 35 (reserved) and 36 for Lithuania. Subsequent numbers shall be assigned by the Secretary General of the United Nations to other States which become Contracting Parties to the ADR.*

TECHNICAL SPECIFICATIONS	TYPE OF VEHICLE ACCORDING TO MARGINAL 220 301 (2)				
	EX/II	EX/III	AT	FL	OX
220 510 ELECTRICAL EQUIPMENT					
220 511 - wiring		X	X	X	X
220 512 - battery master switch		X		X	
220 513 - batteries	X			X	
220 514 - tachographs		X		X	
220 515 - permanently energized installations		X		X	
220 516 - electrical installation behind cab		X		X	
220 520 BRAKING	X	X	X	X	X
220 521 - Anti-lock		X	X	X	X
220 522 - endurance		X	X	X	X
220 530 FIRE RISKS					
220 531 - cab: materials	X	X			
- cab: thermal shield				X	X
220 532 - fuel tanks	X	X		X	X
220 533 - engine	X	X		X	X
220 534 - exhaust system	X	X	X	X	X
220 535 - endurance braking system		X		X	X
220 536 - auxiliary heating	X	X		X	X
220 540 SPEED LIMITATION	X	X	X	X	X

220 501-
220 509

Electrical equipment

General provisions

220 510   The electrical installation as a whole shall meet the provisions of marginal 220 511 to 220 515 in accordance with the table of marginal 220 500.

Wiring

220 511   (1)   The size of conductors shall be large enough to avoid overheating. Conductors shall be adequately insulated. All circuits shall be protected by fuses or automatic circuit breakers, except for the following:

-   from the battery to cold start and stopping systems of the engine
-   from the battery to the alternator
-   from the alternator to the fuse or circuit breaker box
-   from the battery to the starter motor
-   from the battery to the power control housing of the endurance braking system (see marginal 220 522 below), if this system is electrical or electromagnetic
-   from the battery to the electrical lifting mechanism for lifting the bogie axle.

The above unprotected circuits shall be as short as possible.

(2)   Cables shall be securely fastened and positioned in such a way that the conductors are adequately protected against mechanical and thermal stresses.

Battery master switch

220 512   (1)   A switch for breaking the electrical circuits shall be placed as close to the battery as possible.

(2)   Direct or indirect control devices shall be installed, one in the driver's cab and a second on the outside of the vehicle. They shall be readily accessible and distinctively marked. The control device located in the driver's cab shall be within immediate reach of the driver seated in the driver's seat. It shall be protected against inadvertent operation by either adding a protective cover, or by using a dual movement control device or by other suitable means.

(3)   It shall be possible to open the switch while the engine is running, without causing any dangerous excess voltage. Operation of the switch shall not constitute a fire hazard in an explosive atmosphere; this can be ensured by using a switch having a casing with protection degree IP65 in accordance with IEC Standard 529.

(4)   The cable connections on the battery master switch shall have a protection degree IP54. However, this does not apply if these connections are contained in a housing which may be the battery box. In this case it is sufficient to insulate the connections against short circuits, for example with a rubber cap.

Batteries

220 513 The battery terminals shall be electrically insulated or covered by the insulating battery box cover. If the batteries are not located under the engine bonnet, they shall be fitted in a vented box.

Tachographs

220 514 The electrical supply to the tachograph shall be provided via a safety barrier connected directly to the battery. The tachograph and the safety barrier shall meet the requirements for associated electrical equipment according to European Standard EN 50 020.

Permanently energized installations

220 515 Those parts of the electrical installation, other than the tachograph, which remain energized when the battery master-switch is open, shall be suitable for use in a hazardous area and shall meet the appropriate requirements of European Standard EN 50 014 and one of European Standards EN 50 015 to 50 020 or EN 50 028. The requirements for the relevant gas group according to the product being carried shall be met.

Provisions concerning that part of the electrical installation situated to the rear of the driver's cab

220 516 The whole installation shall be so designed, constructed and protected such that it cannot provoke any ignition or short-circuit under normal conditions of use of vehicles and that these risks can be minimized in the event of an impact or deformation. In particular:

(1) *Wiring*

The wiring located behind the driver's cab shall be protected against impact, abrasion and chafing during normal vehicle operation. Examples of appropriate protection are given in the figures 1, 2, 3 and 4 below. However, the sensor cables of anti-lock braking devices do not need additional protection.

(2) *Lighting*

Lamp bulbs with a screw cap shall not be used.

Electrical lifting mechanism

220 517 The electrical equipment of the mechanism for lifting a bogie axle shall be installed outside the chassis frame in a sealed housing.

220 518-
220 519

Appendix B.2

FIGURES

Figure No.1

Corrugated polyamide conduit

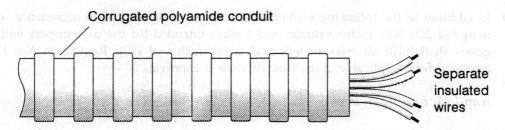

Separate insulated wires

Figure No.2

Corrugated polyamide conduit   Insulating sheath

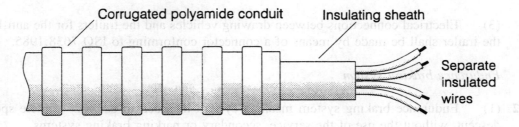

Separate insulated wires

Figure No.3

Polyurethane sheath   With inner sheath

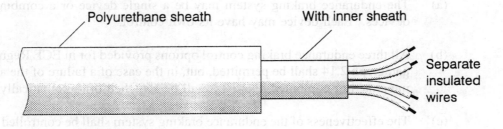

Separate insulated wires

Figure No.4

Outer layer   Inner layer

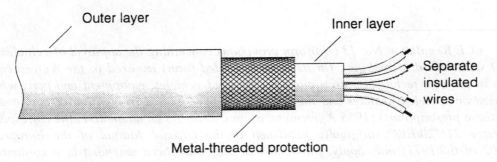

Separate insulated wires

Metal-threaded protection

Appendix B.2

Braking equipment

General provisions

220 520   In addition to the following technical provisions, to be applied in accordance with the table of marginal 220 500, motor vehicles and trailers intended for use as transport units for dangerous goods shall fulfil all relevant technical requirements of ECE Regulation No. 13 [2] in its latest amended form applicable at the time of vehicle approval.

Anti-lock Braking System

220 521   (1)   Motor vehicles having a maximum mass exceeding 16 tonnes, or authorized to tow a trailer with a maximum mass exceeding 10 tonnes, shall be equipped with an anti-lock braking system of category 1 according to ECE Regulation No. 13 [2], Annex 13.

(2)   Trailers having a maximum mass exceeding 10 tonnes shall be equipped with an anti-lock braking system of category A according to ECE Regulation No.13 [2], Annex 13.

(3)   Electrical connections between drawing vehicles and the trailers for the anti-lock system in the trailer shall be made by means of a connector conforming to ISO 7638:1985.

Endurance braking system

220 522   (1)   Endurance braking system means a system intended to stabilize vehicle speed on a long descent, without the use of the service, secondary or parking braking systems.

(2)   Motor vehicles having a maximum mass exceeding 16 tonnes or authorized to tow a trailer with a maximum mass exceeding 10 tonnes shall be fitted with an endurance braking system which complies with the following requirements:

(a)   The endurance braking system may be a single device or a combination of several devices. Each device may have its own control.

(b)   All three endurance braking control options provided for in ECE Regulation No. 13 [2], paragraph 2.14 shall be permitted, but, in the case of a failure of the anti-lock system, integrated or combined retarders shall be switched off automatically.

(c)   The effectiveness of the endurance braking system shall be controlled by the anti-lock braking system such that the axle(s) braked by the endurance braking system cannot be locked by the endurance braking system at speeds above 15 km/h. However, this provision shall not apply to that part of the braking system constituted by natural engine braking.

---

[2]   *ECE Regulation No. 13 (Uniform provisions concerning the approval of vehicles of categories M, N and O with regard to braking), (in its latest amended form) annexed to the Agreement concerning the adoption of uniform technical prescriptions for wheeled vehicles, equipment and parts which can be fitted and/or used on wheeled vehicles and the conditions for reciprocal recognition of approvals granted on the basis of these prescriptions) (1958 Agreement, as amended). As an alternative, the corresponding provisions of Directive 71/320/EEC (originally published in the Official Journal of the European Communities No. L 202 of 6.9.1971) may apply, provided that they have been amended in accordance with the latest amended form of ECE Regulation No. 13 applicable at the time of the vehicle approval.*

220 522
(contd)

(d) The endurance braking system shall comprise several stages of effectiveness, including a low stage appropriate for the unladen condition. Where the endurance braking system of a motor vehicle is constituted by its engine, the different gear ratios shall be considered to provide the different stages of effectiveness.

(e) The performance of the endurance braking system must be such that it fulfils the requirements of ECE Regulation No. 13 [3], Annex 5 (Type II A test), with a laden vehicle mass comprising the laden mass of the motor vehicle and its authorized maximum towed mass but not exceeding a total of 44 tonnes.

(f) If the motor vehicle does not fulfil the performance requirements for the endurance braking system as defined in paragraph (2) (e) above, it shall at least fulfil the requirements of ECE Regulation No. 13 [3], Annex 5, and shall be restricted to be coupled only to a trailer fitted with an endurance braking system. Such a motor vehicle must be fitted with a control device for the endurance braking system on the trailer.

(3) If a trailer is equipped with an endurance braking system it shall fulfil the requirements of ECE Regulation No. 13 [3], Annex 5, and the provisions of paragraphs (2) (a) to (2) (d) above.

220 523-
220 529

Prevention of fire risks

General provisions

220 530 The following technical provisions shall apply in accordance with the table of marginal 220 500.

Vehicle cab

220 531 (1) Only material not readily flammable shall be used in the construction of the driver's cab. This provision will be deemed to be met if, in accordance with the procedure specified in ISO standard 3795:1989, samples of the following cab components have a burn rate not exceeding 100 mm/min: seat cushions, seat backs, safety belts, head lining, opening roofs, arm rests, all trim panels including door, front, rear, and side panels, compartment shelves, head restraints, floor coverings, sun visors, curtains, shades, wheel housing covers, engine compartment covers, mattress covers and any other interior materials, including padding and crash-deployed elements, that are designed to absorb energy on contact by occupants in the event of a crash.

(2) Unless the driver's cab is made of not readily flammable materials, a shield made of metal or other suitable material of the same width as the tank shall be fitted at the back of the cab. Any windows in the back of the cab or in the shield shall be hermetically closed and made of fire resistant safety glass with fire resistant frames. Furthermore, there shall be a clear space of not less than 15 cm between the tank and the cab or the shield.

Fuel tanks

220 532 The fuel tanks for supplying the engine of the vehicle shall meet the following requirements:

(1) The fuel tanks shall be so placed as to be protected as far as possible against any collision.

---

[3]   *See footnote 2/.*

220 532
(contd)
(2) In the event of any leakage, the fuel shall drain to the ground without coming into contact with hot parts of the vehicle or the load.

(3) Fuel tanks containing petrol shall be equipped with an effective flame trap at the filler opening or with a closure with which the opening can be kept hermetically sealed.

Engine

220 533 The engine propelling the vehicle shall be so equipped and situated to avoid any danger to the load through heating or ignition. In the case of transport of explosive substances or articles (vehicle types EX/II and EX/III) the engine shall be placed forward of the front wall of the body: it may nevertheless be placed under the body, provided this is done in such a way as to avoid any heating, even localized, of the load.

Exhaust system

220 534 The exhaust system as well as the exhaust pipes shall be so directed or protected to avoid any danger to the load through heating or ignition. Parts of the exhaust system situated directly below the fuel tank (diesel) shall have a clearance of at least 100 mm or be protected by a thermal shield. In the case of transport of explosive substances or articles (vehicle types EX/II and EX/III) the exhaust system shall be placed forward of the front wall of the body or separated from the load-carrying part of the vehicle by a fire-resistant and heat-insulating screen. In this case the exhaust pipe outlet shall be directed outwards from the vehicle.

Vehicle endurance braking

220 535 Vehicles equipped with endurance braking systems emitting high temperatures placed behind the rear wall of the driver's cab shall be equipped with a thermal shield securely fixed and located between this system and the tank or load so as to avoid any heating, even local, of the tank shell or the load.

In addition, the thermal shield shall protect the braking system against any outflow or leakage, even accidental, of the load. For instance, a protection including a twin-shell shield shall be considered satisfactory.

Auxiliary heating device

220 536 The heating devices and their exhaust gas routing shall be designed, located, protected or covered so as to prevent any risks caused by overheating or ignition of the load. No explosive atmosphere shall be allowed to penetrate into the heating device.

The heating device may not be put into operation except by actuating a manual switch located in the driver's cab. This operation shall be indicated to the driver. The heating controls elements shall be capable of putting the heating device into operation only if the above switch is in the "on" position and the device shall not be considered as "out of operation" unless the switch is in the "off" position. The heating device shall be put out of operation by at least the following methods:

(a) intentional manual switching off from the driver's cab; or

(b) intentional or accidental stopping of the vehicle engine (in this case the heating device may be restarted by manual switching); or

(c) putting into operation of a feed pump for the dangerous goods transported.

220 536
(contd)
The heating device may continue to run for a time after being switched off. For the methods (b) and (c) above, the supply of combustion air shall be interrupted by appropriate means within not more than 40 seconds after the device has been switched off.

Only appliances with a means of restricting the operating time of the combustion air ventilator after cut-off to a short interval (maximum 20 s) may be used.

220 537-
220 539

Speed limitation device

220 540
Motor vehicles (rigid vehicles and tractors for semi-trailers) with a maximum mass exceeding 12 tonnes, shall be equipped in accordance with marginal 10 261 with a speed limitation device according to the provisions of ECE Regulation No. 89 [4]. The set speed V as defined in paragraph 2.1.2 of ECE Regulation No. 89 [4] shall not exceed 85 km/h.

220 541-
220 599

SECTION 6. Modification of the vehicle type and extension of approval

220 600
Every modification of the vehicle type shall be notified to the administrative department which approved the vehicle type. The department may then either:

(1) Consider that the modifications made are unlikely to have an appreciable adverse effect and that in any case the vehicle still complies with the requirements, or

(2) Require a further test report from the technical service responsible for conducting the tests.

220 601
Confirmation or refusal of approval, specifying the alteration, shall be communicated by the procedure specified in marginal 220 402 to the Contracting Parties.

220 602
The competent authority issuing an extension of approval shall assign a series number to each communication form drawn up for such an extension and inform thereof the other Parties by means of a communication form conforming to the model in marginal 221 000.

220 603-
220 699

---

[4] *ECE Regulation No. 89 (Uniform provisions concerning the approval of: I. vehicles with regard to limitation of their maximum speed; II. vehicles with regard to the installation of a speed limitation device (SLD) of an approved type; III. speed limitation devices (SLD)), as amended, annexed to the Agreement concerning the adoption of uniform technical prescriptions for wheeled vehicles, equipment and parts which can be fitted and/or used on wheeled vehicles and the conditions for reciprocal recognition of approvals granted on the basis of these prescriptions (1958 Agreement, as amended). As an alternative, the corresponding provisions of directives 92/6/EEC and 92/24/EEC, as amended, may apply provided that they have been amended in accordance with the latest amended form of ECE Regulation No.89 applicable at the time of the vehicle approval.*

Appendix B.2

SECTION 7.   Conformity of production

Initial assessment

220 700   The approval authority of a Contracting Party shall verify - before granting type approval - the existence of satisfactory arrangements and procedures for ensuring effective control so that vehicles when in production conform to the approved type.

220 701   The requirement in marginal 220 700 shall be verified to the satisfaction of the authority granting type approval but may also be verified, on behalf of the authority granting type approval, by the approval authority of another Contracting Party. In that case, the latter approval authority prepares a statement of compliance outlining the areas and production facilities it has covered as relevant to the vehicle(s) to be type approved.

220 702   The approval authority shall also accept the manufacturer's registration to harmonized standard ISO 9002 (the scope of which/covers the vehicle(s) to be approved) or an equivalent accreditation standard as satisfying the requirements of marginal 220 700. The manufacturer shall provide details of the registration and undertake to inform the approval authority of any revisions to its validity or scope.

220 703   On receiving an application from the authority of another Contracting Party the approval authority shall send forthwith the statement of compliance mentioned in the last sentence of marginal 220 701 or advise that it is not in a position to provide such a statement.

220 704-
220 709

Conformity of production

220 710   Every vehicle approved under this Appendix shall be so manufactured as to conform to the type approved by meeting the provisions set out in Section 5 above.

220 711   The approval authority of a Contracting Party granting a type approval pursuant to this Appendix shall verify the existence of adequate arrangements and documented control plans, to be agreed with the manufacturer for each approval, to carry out at specified intervals those tests or associated checks necessary to verify continued conformity with the approved type including specifically, where applicable, tests specified in this Appendix.

220 712   The holder of the approval shall in particular:

(1)   Ensure the existence of procedures for effective control of the conformity of vehicles to the type approval;

(2)   Have access to the testing equipment necessary for checking the conformity to each approved type;

(3)   Ensure that test results data are recorded and that annexed documents remain available for a period to be determined in agreement with the approval authority. This period shall not exceed 10 years;

- 240 -

220 712
(contd) (4)   Analyse results of each type of test, in order to verify and ensure the stability of the vehicle characteristics, making allowance for variation of an industrial production;

(5)   Ensure that for each type of vehicle, at least the checks and tests prescribed in this Appendix are carried out;

(6)   Ensure that any set of samples or test pieces giving evidence of non-conformity in the type of test in question gives rise to a further sampling and test. All the necessary steps shall be taken to restore conformity of the corresponding production.

220 713 The authority which has granted type approval may at any time verify the conformity control methods applied in each production facility. The normal frequency of these verifications shall be consistent with the arrangements (if any) accepted under marginals 220 701 or 220 702 of this Appendix and be such as to ensure that the relevant controls are reviewed over a period consistent with the climate of trust established by the approval authority.

(1)   At every inspection, the test records and production records shall be available to the visiting inspector.

(2)   Where the nature of the test is appropriate, the inspector may select samples at random to be tested in the manufacturer's laboratory or by the Technical Service according to section 9 below. The minimum number of samples may be determined according to the results of the manufacturer's own verification.

(3)   Where the level of control appears unsatisfactory, or when it seems necessary to verify the validity of the tests carried out in application of paragraph (2) above, the inspector shall select samples to be sent to the Technical Service which conducts the type approval tests.

(4)   The approval authority may carry out any check or test prescribed in this Appendix.

(5)   In cases where unsatisfactory results are found during an inspection, the approval authority shall ensure that all necessary steps are taken to restore conformity of production as rapidly as possible.

220 714-
220 719

Penalties for non-conformity of production

220 720 The approval granted in respect of a vehicle type pursuant to this Appendix may be withdrawn if the provisions laid down in section 5 above are not complied with.

220 721 If a Contracting Party withdraws an approval it has previously granted, it shall forthwith so notify the other Contracting Parties by means of a communication form conforming to the model in marginal 221 000.

220 722-
220 799

Appendix B.2

SECTION 8.   **Production definitely discontinued**

220 800   If the holder of the approval completely ceases to manufacture a type of vehicle approved in accordance with this Appendix, he shall so inform the authority which granted the approval. Upon receiving the relevant communication, that authority shall inform thereof the other Parties by means of a communication form conforming to the model in marginal 221 000.

220 801-
220 899

SECTION 9.   **Names and addresses of technical services responsible for conducting approval tests and of administrative departments**

220 900   The Contracting Parties shall communicate to the United Nations secretariat the names and addresses of the technical services responsible for conducting approval tests and of the administrative departments which grant approval and to which forms certifying approval or extension, or refusal or withdrawal of approval or production definitely discontinued, issued in other States, are to be sent.

220 901-
220 999

221 000

COMMUNICATION

[maximum format: A4 (210 mm x 297 mm)]

ADR...   issued by: Name of Administration:

....

....

concerning [2]:   **APPROVAL GRANTED**
APPROVAL EXTENDED
APPROVAL REFUSED
APPROVAL WITHDRAWN
PRODUCTION DEFINITELY DISCONTINUED OF A VEHICLE TYPE WITH REGARD TO SPECIFIC CONSTRUCTIONAL FEATURES FOR THE TRANSPORT OF DANGEROUS GOODS

Approval N° . . . .   Extension N° . . . .

1.   Trade name or mark of vehicle: . . . .

2.   Vehicle type: Chassis-cab, tractor for semi-trailer, trailer, semi-trailer, trailer with self-supporting body [2] . . . .

3.   Type of vehicle according to marginal 220 301 (2) (EX/II, EX/III, FL, OX, AT) . . . .

4.   Manufacturer's name and address: . . . .

5.   If applicable, name and address of manufacturer's representative: . . . .

6.   Mass of vehicle: . . . .

6.1   Technical maximum mass of complete vehicle: . . . .

7.   Specific equipment of vehicle: . . . .

7.1   The vehicle is/is not equipped with specific electrical devices.

Summary description: . . . .

7.2   The vehicle is/is not equipped with a brake anti-lock device.

Approval number: . . . .

Category of device: . . . .

_____

   [1]   _Distinguishing number of the State which has granted/extended/refused/withdrawn approval (see footnote 1/ to marginal 220 403 (1)]._

   [2]   _Strike out what does not apply._

7.3   The vehicle is/is not equipped with an endurance braking system.

        Approval number: . . . .

        Technical maximum mass of the vehicle corresponding to the performance of the endurance braking system . . . .

        Summary description: . . . .

7.4   The vehicle is/is not equipped with devices for the prevention of fire risks

        Summary description: . . . .

7.5   In the case of a motor vehicle:

        7.5.1   Type of engine: positive-ignition; compression ignition: . . . .

        7.5.2   The vehicle is/is not equipped with a device to limit the speed by construction adjusted to a speed of . . . . km/h.

        Approval number: . . . .

8.   Vehicle submitted for approval on: . . . .

9.   Technical service responsible for carrying out approval inspections . . . .

10.   Date of report issued by that service: . . . .

11.   Number of report issued by that service: . . . .

12.   Approval granted/extended/withdrawn [3/]

13.   Position of approval mark on the vehicle: . . . .

14.   Place: . . . .

15.   Date: . . . .

16.   Signature: . . . .

221 001-
229 999

[3/]   *Strike out what does not apply.*

CERTIFICATE OF APPROVAL FOR VEHICLES
CARRYING CERTAIN DANGEROUS GOODS

(see marginal 10 282)

230 000 *NOTE: The dimensions of the certificate shall be 210 x 297 mm (format A 4). Both front and back shall be used. The colour shall be white, with a pink diagonal stripe.*

CERTIFICATE OF APPROVAL FOR VEHICLES CARRYING CERTAIN DANGEROUS GOODS

1. Certificate No.

    testifying that the vehicle specified below fulfils the conditions prescribed by the European Agreement concerning the International Carriage of Dangerous Goods by Road (ADR) for its acceptance for the international carriage of dangerous goods by road.

2. Manufacturer and type of vehicle . . . .

    . . . .

3. Registration number (if any) and Chassis number . . . .

    . . . .

4. Name and business address of carrier, operator or owner . . . .

    . . . .

    . . . .

5. The vehicle specified above has undergone the inspections prescribed in ADR, Annex B, marginals 10 282/10 283 [1] and fulfils the conditions required for its acceptance for the international carriage by road of dangerous goods of the following classes, items numbers and letters (where necessary the name of the substances or the substance identification number shall be given):

6. Remarks

    . . . .

    . . . .

7. Valid until . . . .   Stamp of issuing service at:

    Date:

    Signature:

---

[1] *Delete if not applicable.*

8.   Validity extended until ....   **Stamp of issuing service at:**

                                                           Date:

                                                           Signature:

9.   Validity extended until ....   **Stamp of issuing service at:**

                                                           Date:

                                                           Signature:

10.   Validity extended until ....   **Stamp of issuing service at:**

                                                           Date:

                                                           Signature

11.   Validity extended until   **Stamp of issuing service at:**

                                                           Date:

                                                           Signature:

NOTE 1: Every vehicle shall be the subject of a separate certificate unless otherwise required e.g. for Class 1.

NOTE 2: This certificate must be returned to the issuing service when the vehicle is taken out of service; if the vehicle is transferred to another carrier, operator or owner, as specified in item 4; on expiry of the validity of the certificate; and if there is a material change in one or more essential characteristics of the vehicle.

230 001-
239 999

Appendix B.4

PROVISIONS CONCERNING THE TRAINING FOR DRIVERS OF VEHICLES CARRYING DANGEROUS GOODS

240 000-
240 099

SECTION 1. General, structure of the training and training programme

240 100 (1) Training shall be given in accordance with the provisions of this Appendix on the basis of marginals 10 315, 11 315 and 71 315.

(2) The necessary knowledge and skills shall be imparted by training covering theoretical courses and practical exercises. The knowledge shall be tested in an examination.

Structure

240 101 Initial and refresher training shall be given in the form of a basic course and, when applicable, specialization courses.

240 102 Subjects to be covered by the basic course will be, at least:

    (a) the general requirements governing the carriage of dangerous goods;

    (b) the main types of hazard;

    (c) information on environmental protection in the control of the transfer of wastes;

    (d) preventive and safety measures appropriate to the various types of hazard;

    (e) what to do after an accident (first aid, road safety, basic knowledge about the use of protective equipment, etc.);

    (f) labelling and marking to indicate danger;

    (g) what a driver should and should not do during the carriage of dangerous goods;

    (h) the purpose and the method of operation of technical equipment on vehicles;

    (i) prohibitions on mixed loading in the same vehicle or container;

    (j) precautions to be taken during loading and unloading of dangerous goods;

    (k) general information concerning civil liability;

    (l) information on multimodal transport operation;

    (m) handling and stowage of packages.

240 103 Special subjects to be covered by the specialization course for transport in tanks shall be, at least:

    (a) the behaviour of vehicles on the road, including movements of the load;

    (b) specific requirements of the vehicles;

    (c) general theoretical knowledge of the various and different loading and discharge systems;

    (d) specific additional provisions applicable to the use of those vehicles (certificates of approval, approval marking, marking and labelling, etc.).

240 104 Special subjects to be covered by the specialization course for the transport of substances and articles of class 1 shall be, at least:

    (a)   specific hazards related to explosive and pyrotechnic substances and articles;

    (b)   specific requirements concerning mixed loading of substances and articles of class 1.

240 105 Special subjects to be covered by the specialization course for the transport of radioactive material of class 7 shall be, at least:

    (a)   specific hazards related to ionizing radiation;

    (b)   specific requirements concerning packing, handling, mixed loading and stowage of radioactive material;

    (c)   special measures to be taken in the event of an accident involving radioactive material.

Initial training programme

240 106 (1)   The minimum duration of the theoretical element of each initial course or part of the comprehensive course shall be as follows:

Basic course	18 teaching units [1]
Specialization course for transport in tanks	12 teaching units [1]
Specialization course for transport of substances and articles of Class 1	8 teaching units
Specialization course for transport of radioactive material	8 teaching units

The total duration of the comprehensive course may be determined by the competent authority, who shall maintain the duration of the basic course and the specialized course for tanks, but may supplement it with shortened specialised courses for classes 1 and 7.

(2)   Teaching units are intended to last 45 minutes.

(3)   Normally, not more than 8 teaching units are permitted on each day of the course.

(4)   The individual practical exercises shall take place in connection with the theoretical training, and shall at least cover first aid, fire-fighting and what to do in case of an incident or accident.

Refresher training programme

240 107 (1)   Refresher training courses undertaken at regular intervals serve the purpose of bringing the drivers' knowledge up to date; they shall cover new technical, legal and substance-related developments.

(2)   Refresher courses shall have been completed before the period referred to in marginal 10 315 (3) has expired.

---

[1]   *Additional teaching units are required for practical exercises referred to in (4) below which will vary depending on the number of drivers under instruction.*

240 107   (3)   The duration of each refresher course shall be of at least one day.
(contd)

         (4)   Normally, not more than 8 teaching units shall be permitted on each day of the course.

240 108-
240 199

SECTION 2.   Approval of training

Procedure

240 200   The training courses shall be subject to approval by the competent authority.

240 201   (1)   Approval shall only be given with regard to applications submitted in writing.

         (2)   The following documents shall be attached to the application for approval:

             (a)   a detailed training programme specifying the subjects taught and indicating the time schedule and planned teaching methods;

             (b)   qualifications and fields of activities of the teaching personnel;

             (c)   information on the premises where the courses take place and on the teaching materials as well as on the facilities for the practical exercises;

             (d)   conditions of participation in the courses, such as number of participants.

         (3)   The competent authority shall organize the supervision of training and examinations.

Granting of approval

240 202   (1)   Approval shall be granted in writing by the competent authority subject to the following conditions, in particular:

             (a)   the training shall be given in conformity with the application documents;

             (b)   the competent authority shall be granted the right to send authorized persons to be present at the training courses and examinations;

             (c)   the competent authority shall be advised in time of the dates and the places of the individual training courses;

             (d)   the approval may be withdrawn if the conditions of approval are not complied with.

         (2)   The approval document shall indicate whether the courses concerned are basic or specialization courses, initial or refresher courses or comprehensive courses.

240 203   If the training body, after a training course has been given approval, intends to make any alterations with respect to such details as were relevant to the approval, it shall seek permission in advance from the competent authority. This applies in particular to changes concerning the training programme.

240 204-
240 299

Appendix B.4

SECTION 3. **Requirements applicable to the training**

240 300 The training provider shall ensure that the training instructors have a good knowledge of, and take into consideration, developments in regulations and training requirements relating to the transport of dangerous goods. The training shall be as practice-related as possible. The training programme shall conform with the approval, on the subjects set out in marginals 240 102 to 240 105. The initial training and refresher training shall also include individual practical exercises (see marginal 240 106).

240 301-
240 399

SECTION 4. **Examinations**

Initial Basic course

240 400 (1) After completion of the training, including the practical exercises, an examination shall be held on the basic course.

(2) In the examination, the candidate has to prove that he has the knowledge, insight and skill for the practice of professional driver of vehicles carrying dangerous goods as provided in the basic training course.

(3) For this purpose the competent authority, or the examination body approved by that authority, shall prepare a catalogue of questions which refer to the items summarized in marginal 240 102. Questions in the examination shall be drawn from this catalogue. The candidates shall not have any knowledge of the specific questions that are selected from the catalogue prior to the relevant examination.

(4) A single examination for comprehensive courses may be held.

(5) Each competent authority shall supervise the modalities of the examination.

(6) The examination shall take the form of a written examination or a combination of a written and oral examination. Each candidate shall be asked at least 25 written questions. The duration of the examination shall be of at least 45 minutes. The questions may be of a varying degree of difficulty and be allocated a different weighting.

Initial specialization courses for transport in tanks and for the transport of explosive substances and articles and radioactive material

204 401 (1) After having sat the examination on the basic course and after having attended the specialization course for carriage in tanks and/or for the carriage of explosive or radioactive materials, the candidate shall be allowed to take part in the corresponding examination.

(2) This examination shall be held and supervised on the same basis as in marginal 240 400 above.

(3) At least 15 questions shall be asked with respect to each specialization course.

Refresher Courses

240 402 (1)   After having undertaken a refresher training course the candidate shall be allowed to take part in the corresponding examination.

(2)   The examination shall be held and supervised on the same basis as set out in marginal 240 400 above.

(3)   At least 15 questions shall be asked with respect to the refresher training course.

240 403-
240 499

SECTION 5.   Certificate of driver's training

240 500 (1)   According to paragraph (9) of marginal 10 315, the certificate shall be issued:

(a)   after completion of a basic training course, provided the candidate has successfully passed the examination in accordance with marginal 240 000 above;

(b)   if applicable, after completion of a specialization course for transport in tanks or transport of explosive substances or articles or of radioactive material, or after having acquired the knowledge according marginal 11 315 (3) or marginal 71 315 (3), provided the candidate has successfully passed an examination in accordance with marginal 240 401 above.

(2)   The certificate shall be renewed if the candidate furnishes proof of his participation in a refresher course in accordance with marginal 10 315 (3) and if he has successfully passed an examination in accordance with marginal 240 402 above.

240 501-
249 999

APPENDIX B.5

250 000 List of substances and identification numbers

(1)   The hazard identification number consists of two or three figures. In general, the figures indicate the following hazards:

2   Emission of gas due to pressure or to chemical reaction
3   Flammability of liquids (vapours) and gases or self-heating liquid
4   Flammability of solids or self-heating solid
5   Oxidizing (fire-intensifying) effect
6   Toxicity or risk of infection
7   Radioactivity
8   Corrosivity
9   Risk of spontaneous violent reaction

NOTE: The risk of spontaneous violent reaction within the meaning of figure 9 include the possibility following from the nature of a substance of a risk of explosion, disintegration and polymerization reaction following the release of considerable heat or flammable and/or toxic gases.

Doubling of a figure indicates an intensification of that particular hazard.

Where the hazard associated with a substance can be adequately indicated by a single figure, this is followed by zero.

The following combinations of figures, however, have a special meaning: 22, 323, 333, 362, 382, 423, 44, 446, 462, 482, 539, 606, 623, 642, 823, 842 and 90, see (2) below.

If a hazard identification number is prefixed by the letter "X", this indicates that the substance will react dangerously with water. For such substances, water may only be used by approval of experts.

(2)   The hazard identification numbers listed in paragraph (3) have the following meanings:

20   asphyxiant gas or gas with no subsidiary risk
22   refrigerated liquefied gas, asphyxiant
223   refrigerated liquefied gas, flammable
225   refrigerated liquefied gas, oxidizing (fire-intensifying)
23   flammable gas
239   flammable gas, which can spontaneously lead to violent reaction
25   oxidizing (fire-intensifying) gas
26   toxic gas
263   toxic gas, flammable
265   toxic gas, oxidizing (fire-intensifying)
268   toxic gas, corrosive

30   flammable liquid (flash-point between 23 °C and 61 °C, inclusive) or flammable liquid or solid in the molten state with a flash-point above 61 °C, heated to a temperature equal to or above its flash-point, or self-heating liquid
323   flammable liquid which reacts with water, emitting flammable gases
X323   flammable liquid which reacts dangerously with water, emitting flammable gases [2]
33   highly flammable liquid (flash-point below 23 °C)

---

[2]   *Water not to be used except by approval of experts.*

- 253 -

333	pyrophoric liquid
333	pyrophoric liquid which reacts dangerously with water [2]
336	highly flammable liquid, toxic
338	highly flammable liquid, corrosive
X338	highly flammable liquid, corrosive, which reacts dangerously with water [2]
339	highly flammable liquid which can spontaneously lead to violent reaction
36	flammable liquid (flash-point between 23 °C and 61 °C inclusive), slightly toxic, or self-heating liquid, toxic
362	flammable liquid, toxic, which reacts with water, emitting flammable gases
X362	flammable liquid toxic, which reacts dangerously with water, emitting flammable gases [2]
368	flammable liquid, toxic, corrosive
38	flammable liquid (flash-point between 23 °C and 61 °C, inclusive), corrosive
382	flammable liquid, corrosive, which reacts with water, emitting flammable gases
X382	flammable liquid, corrosive, which reacts dangerously with water, emitting flammable gases [2]
39	flammable liquid, which can spontaneously lead to violent reaction
40	flammable solid, or self-reactive substance, or self-heating substance
423	solid which reacts with water, emitting flammable gases
X423	flammable solid which reacts dangerously with water, emitting flammable gases [2]
43	spontaneously flammable (pyrophoric) solid
44	flammable solid, in the molten state at an elevated temperature
446	flammable solid, toxic, in the molten state, at an elevated temperature
46	flammable or self-heating solid, toxic
462	toxic solid which reacts with water, emitting flammable gases
X462	solid which, reacts dangerously with water, emitting toxic gases [2]
48	flammable or self-heating solid, corrosive
482	corrosive solid which reacts with water, emitting flammable gases
X482	solid which, reacts dangerously with water, emitting corrosive gases [2]
50	oxidizing (fire-intensifying) substance
539	flammable organic peroxide
55	strongly oxidizing (fire-intensifying) substance
556	strongly oxidizing (fire-intensifying) substance, toxic
558	strongly oxidizing (fire-intensifying) substance, corrosive
559	strongly oxidizing (fire-intensifying) substance, which can spontaneously lead to violent reaction
56	oxidizing substance (fire-intensifying), toxic
568	oxidizing substance (fire-intensifying), toxic, corrosive
58	oxidizing substance (fire-intensifying), corrosive
59	oxidizing substance (fire-intensifying) which can spontaneously lead to violent reaction
60	toxic or slightly toxic substance
606	infectious substance
623	toxic liquid, which reacts with water, emitting flammable gases
63	toxic substance, flammable (flash-point between 23 °C and 61 °C inclusive)

---

[2]   *Water not to be used except by approval of experts.*

638	toxic substance, flammable (flash-point between 23 °C and 61 °C inclusive), corrosive
639	toxic substance, flammable (flash-point not above 61 °C) which can spontaneously lead to violent reaction
64	toxic solid, flammable or self-heating
642	toxic solid, which reacts with water, emitting flammable gases
65	toxic substance, oxidizing (fire-intensifying)
66	highly toxic substance
663	highly toxic substance, flammable (flash-point not above 61 °C)
664	highly toxic solid, flammable or self-heating
665	highly toxic substance, oxidizing (fire-intensifying)
668	highly toxic substance, corrosive
669	highly toxic substance which can spontaneously lead to violent reaction
68	toxic substance, corrosive
69	toxic or slightly toxic substance, which can spontaneously lead to violent reaction
70	radioactive material
72	radioactive gas
723	radioactive gas, flammable
73	radioactive liquid, flammable (flash-point not above 61 °C)
74	radioactive solid, flammable
75	radioactive material, oxidizing (fire-intensifying)
76	radioactive material, toxic
78	radioactive material, corrosive
80	corrosive or slightly corrosive substance
X80	corrosive or slightly corrosive substance, which reacts dangerously with water [*]
823	corrosive liquid which reacts with water, emitting flammable gases
83	corrosive or slightly corrosive substance, flammable (flash-point between 23 °C and 61 °C inclusive)
X83	corrosive or slightly corrosive substance, flammable, (flash-point between 23 °C and 61 °C inclusive), which reacts dangerously with water [*]
839	corrosive or slightly corrosive substance, flammable (flash-point between 23 °C and 61 °C inclusive) which can spontaneously lead to violent reaction
X839	corrosive or slightly corrosive substance, flammable (flash-point between 23 °C and 61 °C inclusive), which can spontaneously lead to violent reaction and which reacts dangerously with water [*]
84	corrosive solid, flammable or self-heating
842	corrosive solid which reacts with water, emitting flammable gases
85	corrosive or slightly corrosive substance, oxidizing (fire-intensifying)
856	corrosive or slightly corrosive substance, oxidizing (fire-intensifying) and toxic
86	corrosive or slightly corrosive substance, toxic
88	highly corrosive substance
X88	highly corrosive substance, which reacts dangerously with water [*]
883	highly corrosive substance, flammable (flash-point between 23 °C and 61 °C inclusive)
884	highly corrosive solid, flammable or self-heating
885	highly corrosive substance, oxidizing (fire-intensifying)
886	highly corrosive substance, toxic

---

[*]   *Water not to be used except by approval of experts.*

X886	highly corrosive substance, toxic, which reacts dangerously with water [*]
89	corrosive or slightly corrosive substance, which can spontaneously lead to violent reaction
90	environmentally hazardous substance; miscellaneous dangerous substances
99	Miscellaneous dangerous substance carried at an elevated temperature.

(3)   The identification numbers referred to in marginal 10 500 are listed in Tables I, II and III below.

NOTE 1: The identification numbers to be shown on the orange plates should be looked for first in Table 1. If in the case of substances of classes 3, 4.1, 4.2, 4.3, 5.1, 5.2, 6.1, 6.2, 7, 8 and 9 the name of the substance to be carried or the collective heading which covers it is not listed in Table 1, the identification numbers are to be taken from Table 2.

NOTE 2: Table 3 contains all the entries in Tables 1 and 2 in substance identification number order.

---

[*]   *Water not to be used except by approval of experts.*

Table 1

List of substances described under their chemical names or under collective headings which are given a specific "substance identification number" [column (b)]. [For solutions and mixtures of substances (such as preparations and wastes), see also marginal 2002 (8) and (9)].

This table also includes substances not shown in the class lists of substances, but which nevertheless fall within the classes and item numbers shown in column (e).

NOTE: For substances of Classes 3, 4.1, 4.2, 4.3, 5.1, 6.1, 6.2, 7, 8 and 9 not mentioned in this table, see Table 2. Substances are listed in alphabetical order.

Name of substance (a)	Substance Identification No. (Lower part) (b)	Hazard Identification No. (Upper part) (c)	Label (d)	Class and item number (e)
Acetal	1088	33	3	3, 3° (b)
Acetaldehyde	1089	33	3	3, 1° (a)
Acetaldehyde ammonia	1841	90	9	9, 31° (c)
Acetaldehyde oxime	2332	30	3	3, 31° (c)
Acetic acid, glacial	2789	83	8 + 3	8, 32° (b)2.
Acetic acid, solution	2789	83	8 + 3	8, 32° (b)2.
Acetic acid, solution	2790	80	8	8, 32° (b)1., (c)
Acetic anhydride	1715	83	8 + 3	8, 32° (b)2.
Acetone	1090	33	3	3, 3° (b)
Acetone cyanohydrin, stabilized	1541	66	6.1	6.1, 12° (a)
Acetone oils	1091	33	3	3, 3° (b)
Acetonitrile (methyl cyanide)	1648	33	3	3, 3° (b)
Acetyl bromide	1716	80	8	8, 35° (b)1.
Acetyl chloride	1717	X338	3 + 8	3, 25° (b)
Acetylene, dissolved	1001	239	3	2, 4°F
Acetyl iodide	1898	80	8	8, 35° (b)1.
Acetyl methyl carbinol	2621	30	3	3, 31° (c)
Acridine	2713	60	6.1	6.1, 12° (c)
Acrolein, dimer, stabilized	2607	39	3	3, 31° (c)
Acrolein, inhibited	1092	663	6.1 + 3	6.1, 8° (a)2.
Acrylamide	2074	60	6.1	6.1, 12° (c)
Acrylic acid, inhibited	2218	839	8 + 3	8, 32° (b)2.
Acrylonitrile, inhibited	1093	336	3 + 6.1	3, 11° (a)
Adhesives	1133	33	3	3, 5° (a), (b), (c)
Adhesives	1133	30	3	3, 31°(c)
Adiponitrile	2205	60	6.1	6.1, 12° (c)

Name of substance (a)	Substance Identification No. (Lower part) (b)	Hazard Identification No. (Upper part) (c)	Label (d)	Class and item number (e)
Air, compressed	1002	20	2	2, 1°A
Air, refrigerated liquid	1003	225	2 + 05	2, 3°O
Alcoholic beverages	3065	30	3	3, 31° (c)
Alcoholic beverages	3065	33	3	3, 3° (b)
Aldol	2839	60	6.1	6.1, 14° (b)
Alkali metal amalgam	1389	X423	4.3	4.3, 11° (a)
Alkali metal amides	1390	423	4.3	4.3, 19° (b)
Alkali metal dispersion	1391	X423	4.3	4.3, 11° (a)
Alkaline earth metal amalgam	1392	X423	4.3	4.3, 11° (a)
Alkaline earth metal dispersion	1391	X423	4.3	4.3, 11° (a)
Alkylsulphonic acids, liquid	2584	80	8	8, 1° (b)
Alkylsulphonic acids, liquid	2586	80	8	8, 34° (c)
Alkylsulphonic acids, solid	2583	80	8	8, 1° (b)
Alkylsulphonic acids, solid	2585	80	8	8, 34° (c)
Alkylsulphuric acids	2571	80	8	8, 34° (b)
Allyl acetate	2333	336	3 + 6.1	3, 17° (b)
Allyl alcohol	1098	663	6.1 + 3	6.1, 8° (a)2.
Allyl bromide	1099	336	3 + 6.1	3, 16° (a)
Allyl chloride	1100	336	3 + 6.1	3, 16° (a)
Allyl chloroformate	1722	638	6.1 + 8 + 3	6.1, 28° (a)
Allyl ethyl ether	2335	336	3 + 6.1	3, 17° (b)
Allyl formate	2336	336	3 + 6.1	3. 17° (a)
Allyl glycidyl ether	2219	30	3	3, 31° (c)
Allyl iodide	1723	338	3 + 8	3, 25° (b)
Allyl isothiocyanate, inhibited	1545	639	6.1 + 3	6.1, 20° (b)
Allylamine	2334	663	6.1 + 3	6.1, 7° (a)2.
Allyltrichlorosilane, stabilised	1724	X839	8 + 3	8, 37° (b)
Aluminium alkyl halides	3052	X333	4.2 + 4.3	4.2, 32° (a)
Aluminium alkyl hydrides	3076	X333	4.2 + 4.3	4.2. 32° (a)
Aluminium alkyls	3051	X333	4.2 + 4.3	4.2, 31° (a)
Aluminium borohydride	2870	X333	4.2 + 4.3	4.2, 17° (a)
Aluminium borohydride in devices	2870	X333	4.2 + 4.3	4.2, 17° (a)
Aluminium bromide solution	2580	80	8	8, 5° (c)
Aluminium bromide, anhydrous	1725	80	8	8, 11° (b)
Aluminium carbide	1394	423	4.3	4.3, 17° (b)
Aluminium chloride solution	2581	80	8	8, 5° (c)
Aluminium chloride, anhydrous	1726	80	8	8, 11° (b)

Name of substance (a)	Substance Identification No. (Lower part) (b)	Hazard Identification No. (Upper part) (c)	Label (d)	Class and item number (e)
Aluminium smelting by-products or aluminium remelting by-products	3170	423	4.3	4.3, 13° (b), (c)
Aluminium ferrosilicon powder	1395	462	4.3 + 6.1	4.3, 15° (b)
Aluminium nitrate	1438	50	5.1	5.1, 22° (c)
Aluminium powder, coated	1309	40	4.1	4.1, 13° (b), (c)
Aluminium powder, uncoated	1396	423	4.3	4.3, 13° (b)
Aluminium resinate	2715	40	4.1	4.1, 12° (c)
Aluminium silicon powder, uncoated	1398	423	4.3	4.3, 13° (c)
2-Amino-4-chlorophenol	2673	60	6.1	6.1, 12° (b)
2-Amino-5-diethylaminopentane	2946	60	6.1	6.1, 12° (c)
2-(2-Aminoethoxy) ethanol	3055	80	8	8, 53° (c)
N-Aminoethylpiperazine	2815	80	8	8, 53° (c)
Aminophenols (o-, m-, p-)	2512	60	6.1	6.1, 12° (c)
Aminopyridines (o-, m-, p-)	2671	60	6.1	6.1, 12° (b)
Ammonia, anhydrous	1005	268	6.1 + 8	2, 2°TC
Ammonia solution containing between 10 and 35% ammonia	2672	80	8	8, 43° (c)
Ammonia solution with more than 35% and not more than 40% ammonia	2073	20	2	2, 4°A
Ammonia solution with more than 40% and not more than 50% ammonia	2073	20	2	2, 4°A
Ammonia solution with more than 50 % ammonia	3318	268	6.1 + 8	2, 4°TC
Ammonium arsenate	1546	60	6.1	6.1, 51° (b)
Ammonium dichromate	1439	50	5.1	5.1, 27° (b)
Ammonium dinitro-o-cresolate	1843	60	6.1	6.1, 12° (b)
Ammonium fluoride	2505	60	6.1	6.1, 63° (c)
Ammonium fluorosilicate	2854	60	6.1	6.1, 64° (c)
Ammonium hydrogendifluoride, solid	1727	80	8	8, 9° (b)
Ammonium hydrogendifluoride solution	2817	86	8 + 6.1	8, 7° (b), (c)
Ammonium hydrogen sulphate	2506	80	8	8, 13° (b)
Ammonium metavanadate	2859	60	6.1	6.1, 58° (b)
Ammonium nitrate	1942	50	5.1	5.1, 21° (c)
Ammonium nitrate fertilizers, type A1	2067	50	5.1	5.1, 21° (c)
Ammonium nitrate fertilizers, type A2	2068	50	5.1	5.1, 21° (c)
Ammonium nitrate fertilizers, type A3	2069	50	5.1	5.1, 21° (c)
Ammonium nitrate fertilizers, type A4	2070	50	5.1	5.1, 21° (c)
Ammonium nitrate, liquid (hot concentrated solution)	2426	59	5.1	5.1, 20°
Ammonium perchlorate	1442	50	5.1	5.1, 12° (b)

Name of substance (a)	Substance Identification No. (Lower part) (b)	Hazard Identification No. (Upper part) (c)	Label (d)	Class and item number (e)
Ammonium persulphate	1444	50	5.1	5.1, 18° (c)
Ammonium polysulphide solution	2818	86	8 + 6.1	8, 45° (c)
Ammonium polysulphide solution	2818	86	8 + 6.1	8, 45° (b)1.
Ammonium polyvanadate	2861	60	6.1	6.1, 58° (b)
Ammonium sulphide, solution	2683	86	8 + 6.1 + 3	8, 45° (b)2.
Amyl acetates	1104	30	3	3, 31° (c)
Amyl acid phosphate	2819	80	8	8, 38° (c)
Amyl alcohols	1105	30	3	3, 31° (c)
Amyl alcohols	1105	33	3	3, 3° (b)
Amyl butyrates	2620	30	3	3, 31° (c)
Amyl chloride	1107	33	3	3, 3° (b)
Amyl formates	1109	30	3	3, 31° (c)
Amyl mercaptan	1111	33	3	3, 3° (b)
n-Amyl methyl ketone	1110	30	3	3, 31° (c)
Amyl nitrate	1112	30	3	3, 31° (c)
Amyl nitrite	1113	33	3	3, 3° (b)
Amylamines (n-amylamine, tert-amylamine)	1106	338	3 + 8	3, 22° (b)
Amylamine (sec-amylamine)	1106	38	3 + 8	3, 33° (c)
Amyltrichlorosilane	1728	X80	8	8, 36° (b)
Aniline	1547	60	6.1	6.1, 12° (b)
Aniline hydrochloride	1548	60	6.1	6.1, 12° (c)
Anisidines	2431	60	6.1	6.1, 12° (c)
Anisole (phenyl methyl ether)	2222	30	3	3, 31° (c)
Anisoyl chloride	1729	80	8	8, 35° (b)1.
Antimony lactate	1550	60	6.1	6.1, 59° (c)
Antimony pentachloride solution	1731	80	8	8, 12° (b), (c)
Antimony pentachloride, liquid	1730	X80	8	8, 12° (b)
Antimony pentafluoride	1732	86	8 + 6.1	8, 10° (b)
Antimony potassium tartrate	1551	60	6.1	6.1, 59° (c)
Antimony powder	2871	60	6.1	6.1, 59° (c)
Antimony trichloride	1733	80	8	8, 11° (b)
Argon, compressed	1006	20	2	2, 1°A
Argon, refrigerated liquid	1951	22	2	2, 3°A
Arsenic	1558	60	6.1	6.1, 51° (b)
Arsenic acid, liquid	1553	66	6.1	6.1, 51° (a)
Arsenic acid, solid	1554	60	6.1	6.1, 51° (b)
Arsenic bromide	1555	60	6.1	6.1, 51° (b)
Arsenic pentoxide	1559	60	6.1	6.1, 51° (b)

Name of substance (a)	Substance Identification No. (Lower part) (b)	Hazard Identification No. (Upper part) (c)	Label (d)	Class and item number (e)
Arsenic trichloride	1560	66	6.1	6.1, 51° (a)
Arsenic trioxide	1561	60	6.1	6.1, 51° (b)
Arsenical dust	1562	60	6.1	6.1, 51° (b)
Arylsulphonic acids, liquid	2584	80	8	8, 1° (b)
Arylsulphonic acids, liquid	2586	80	8	8, 34° (c)
Arylsulphonic acids, solid	2583	80	8	8, 1° (b)
Arylsulphonic acids, solid	2585	80	8	8, 34° (c)
Barium	1400	423	4.3	4.3, 11° (b)
Barium bromate	2719	56	5.1 + 6.1	5.1, 29° (b)
Barium chlorate	1445	56	5.1 + 6.1	5.1, 29° (b)
Barium hypochlorite	2741	56	5.1 + 6.1	5.1, 29° (b)
Barium nitrate	1446	56	5.1 + 6.1	5.1, 29° (b)
Barium oxide	1884	60	6.1	6.1, 60° (c)
Barium perchlorate	1447	56	5.1 + 6.1	5.1, 29° (b)
Barium permanganate	1448	56	5.1 + 6.1	5.1, 29° (b)
Barium peroxide	1449	56	5.1 + 6.1	5.1, 29° (b)
Batteries, dry containing potassium hydroxide solid, electric storage	3028	80	8	8, 81° (c)
Batteries, wet, filled with acid, electric storage	2794	80	8	8, 81° (c)
Batteries, wet, filled with alkali, electric storage	2795	80	8	8, 81° (c)
Batteries, wet, non-spillable, electric storage	2800	80	8	8, 81° (c)
Battery fluid, alkali	2797	80	8	8, 42° (b)
Battery fluid, acid	2796	80	8	8, 1° (b)
Benzaldehyde	1990	90	9	9, 34 (c)
Benzene	1114	33	3	3, 3° (b)
Benzenesulphonyl chloride	2225	80	8	8, 35° (c)
Benzidine	1885	60	6.1	6.1, 12° (b)
Benzonitrile	2224	60	6.1	6.1, 12° (b)
Benzoquinone	2587	60	6.1	6.1, 14° (b)
Benzotrichloride	2226	80	8	8, 66° (b)
Benzotrifluoride	2338	33	3	3, 3° (b)
Benzoyl chloride	1736	80	8	8, 35° (b)1.
Benzyl bromide	1737	68	6.1 + 8	6.1, 27° (b)
Benzyl chloride	1738	68	6.1 + 8	6.1, 27° (b)
Benzyl chloroformate	1739	88	8	8, 64° (a)
Benzyl iodide	2653	60	6.1	6.1, 15° (b)
Benzyldimethylamine	2619	83	8 + 3	8, 54° (b)
Benzylidene chloride	1886	60	6.1	6.1, 15° (b)

Name of substance (a)	Substance Identification No. (Lower part) (b)	Hazard Identification No. (Upper part) (c)	Label (d)	Class and item number (e)
Beryllium nitrate	2464	56	5.1 + 6.1	5.1, 29° (b)
Beryllium powder	1567	64	6.1 + 4.1	6.1, 54° (b)1.
Bisulphates, aqueous solution	2837	80	8	8, 1° (b), (c)
Blue asbestos (Crocidolite)	2212	90	9	9, 1° (b)
Borneol	1312	40	4.1	4.1, 6° (c)
Boron tribromide (boron bromide)	2692	X88	8	8, 12° (a)
Boron trifluoride acetic acid complex	1742	80	8	8, 33° (b)
Boron trifluoride, compressed	1008	268	6.1 + 8	2, 1°TC
Boron trifluoride diethyl etherate	2604	883	8 + 3	8, 33° (a)
Boron trifluoride dihydrate	2851	80	8	8, 10° (b)
Boron trifluoride dimethyl etherate	2965	382	4.3 + 3 + 8	4.3, 2° (a)
Boron trifluoride propionic acid complex	1743	80	8	8, 33° (b)
Bromine or bromine solution	1744	886	8 + 6.1	8, 14°
Bromine chloride	2901	265	6.1 + 05 + 8	2, 2°TOC
Bromine pentafluoride	1745	568	5.1 + 6.1 + 8	5.1, 5°
Bromine trifluoride	1746	568	5.1 + 6.1 + 8	5.1, 5°
1-Bromo-3-chloropropane	2688	60	6.1	6.1, 15° (c)
1-Bromo-3-methylbutane	2341	30	3	3, 31° (c)
Bromoacetic acid	1938	80	8	8, 31° (b)
Bromoacetone	1569	63	6.1 + 3	6.1, 16° (b)
Bromoacetyl bromide	2513	X80	8	8, 35° (b)1.
Bromobenzene	2514	30	3	3, 31° (c)
Bromobenzyl cyanides	1694	66	6.1	6.1, 17° (a)
1-Bromobutane	1126	33	3	3, 3° (b)
2-Bromobutane	2339	33	3	3, 3° (b)
Bromochloromethane	1887	60	6.1	6.1, 15° (c)
2-Bromoethyl ethyl ether	2340	33	3	3, 3° (b)
Bromoform	2515	60	6.1	6.1, 15° (c)
Bromomethylpropanes	2342	33	3	3, 3° (b)
2-Bromopentane	2343	33	3	3, 3° (b)
Bromopropanes	2344	33	3	3, 3° (b)
3-Bromopropyne	2345	33	3	3, 3° (b)
Bromotrifluoroethylene	2419	23	3	2, 2°F
Bromotrifluoromethane (R 13B1)	1009	20	2	2, 2°A
Brown asbestos (Amosite or Mysorite)	2212	90	9	9, 1° (b)
Brucine	1570	66	6.1	6.1, 90° (a)
1,3-Butadiene, inhibited	1010	239	3	2, 2°F
1,2-Butadiene, inhibited	1010	239	3	2, 2°F

Name of substance (a)	Substance Identification No. (Lower part) (b)	Hazard Identification No. (Upper part) (c)	Label (d)	Class and item number (e)
Butane	1011	23	3	2, 2°F
Butane (trade name): see Mixture A, A0	1965	23	3	2, 2°F
Butanedione (diacetyl)	2346	33	3	3, 3° (b)
Butanols	1120	33	3	3, 3° (b)
Butanols	1120	30	3	3, 31° (c)
Butyl acetates	1123	30	3	3, 31° (c)
Butyl acetates	1123	33	3	3, 3° (b)
Butyl acid phosphate	1718	80	8	8, 38° (c)
Butyl acrylates, inhibited	2348	39	3	3, 31° (c)
n-Butyl bromide	1126	33	3	3, 3° (b)
n-Butyl chloroformate	2743	638	6.1 + 3 + 8	6.1, 28° (b)
n-Butyl formate	1128	33	3	3, 3° (b)
tert-Butyl isocyanate	2484	663	6.1 + 3	6.1, 6° (a)
n-Butyl isocyanate	2485	663	6.1 + 3	6.1, 6° (a)
Butyl mercaptan	2347	33	3	3, 3° (b)
n-Butyl methacrylate, inhibited	2227	39	3	3, 31° (c)
Butyl methyl ether	2350	33	3	3, 3° (b)
Butyl nitrites	2351	33	3	3, 3° (b)
Butyl nitrites	2351	30	3	3, 31° (c)
Butyl propionates	1914	30	3	3, 31° (c)
Butyl vinyl ether, inhibited	2352	339	3	3, 3° (b)
n-Butylamine	1125	338	3 + 8	3, 22° (b)
N-Butylaniline	2738	60	6.1	6.1, 12° (b)
Butylbenzenes	2709	30	3	3, 31° (c)
tert-Butylcyclohexyl chloroformate	2747	60	6.1	6.1, 17° (c)
1-Butylene	1012	23	3	2, 2°F
cis-2-Butylene	1012	23	3	2, 2°F
trans-2-Butylene	1012	23	3	2, 2°F
1,2-Butylene oxide, stabilized	3022	339	3	3, 3° (b)
Butylenes mixture	1012	23	3	2, 2°F
N,n-Butylimidazole	2690	60	6.1	6.1, 12° (b)
Butyltoluenes	2667	60	6.1	6.1, 25° (c)
Butyltrichlorosilane	1747	X83	8 + 3	8, 37° (b)
1,4-Butynediol	2716	60	6.1	6.1, 14° (c)
Butyraldehyde	1129	33	3	3, 3° (b)
Butyraldoxime	2840	30	3	3, 31° (c)
Butyric acid	2820	80	8	8, 32° (c)
Butyric anhydride	2739	80	8	8, 32° (c)

Name of substance (a)	Substance Identification No. (Lower part) (b)	Hazard Identification No. (Upper part) (c)	Label (d)	Class and item number (e)
Butyronitrile	2411	336	3 + 6.1	3, 11° (b)
Butyryl chloride	2353	338	3 + 8	3, 25° (b)
Cacodylic acid	1572	60	6.1	6.1, 51° (b)
Caesium	1407	X423	4.3	4.3, 11° (a)
Caesium hydroxide	2682	80	8	8, 41° (b)
Caesium hydroxide, solution	2681	80	8	8, 42° (b), (c)
Caesium nitrate	1451	50	5.1	5.1, 22° (c)
Calcium	1401	423	4.3	4.3, 11° (b)
Calcium arsenate	1573	60	6.1	6.1, 51° (b)
Calcium arsenate and calcium arsenite mixture, solid	1574	60	6.1	6.1, 51° (b)
Calcium carbide	1402	423	4.3	4.3, 17° (b)
Calcium chlorate	1452	50	5.1	5.1, 11° (b)
Calcium chlorate, aqueous solution	2429	50	5.1	5.1, 11° (b), (c)
Calcium chlorite	1453	50	5.1	5.1, 14° (b)
Calcium cyanamide	1403	423	4.3	4.3, 19° (c)
Calcium dithionite	1923	40	4.2	4.2, 13° (b)
Calcium hypochlorite mixture, dry	2208	50	5.1	5.1, 15° (c)
Calcium hypochlorite, dry	1748	50	5.1	5.1, 15° (b)
Calcium hypochlorite, hydrated	2880	50	5.1	5.1, 15° (b)
Calcium hypochlorite, hydrated mixture	2880	50	5.1	5.1, 15° (b)
Calcium hypochlorite, mixture, dry	1748	50	5.1	5.1, 15° (b)
Calcium manganese silicon	2844	423	4.3	4.3, 12° (c)
Calcium nitrate	1454	50	5.1	5.1, 22° (c)
Calcium perchlorate	1455	50	5.1	5.1, 13° (b)
Calcium permanganate	1456	50	5.1	5.1, 17° (b)
Calcium peroxide	1457	50	5.1	5.1, 25° (b)
Calcium resinate	1313	40	4.1	4.1, 12° (c)
Calcium resinate, fused	1314	40	4.1	4.1, 12° (c)
Calcium silicide	1405	423	4.3	4.3, 12° (b), (c)
Camphor oil	1130	30	3	3, 31° (c)
Camphor, synthetic	2717	40	4.1	4.1, 6° (c)
Caproic acid	2829	80	8	8, 32° (c)
Carbon	1361	40	4.2	4.2, 1° (b), (c)
Carbon black	1361	40	4.2	4.2, 1° (b), (c)
Carbon dioxide	1013	20	2	2, 2°A
Carbon dioxide and nitrous oxide, mixture	1015	20	2	2, 2°A
Carbon dioxide, refrigerated liquid	2187	22	2	2, 3°A

Name of substance (a)	Substance Identification No. (Lower part) (b)	Hazard Identification No. (Upper part) (c)	Label (d)	Class and item number (e)
Carbon disulphide	1131	336	3 + 6.1	3, 18° (a)
Carbon monoxide, compressed	1016	263	6.1 + 3	2, 1°TF
Carbon monoxide and hydrogen mixture, compressed	2600	263	6.1 + 3	2, 1°TF
Carbon tetrabromide	2516	60	6.1	6.1, 15° (c)
Carbon tetrachloride	1846	60	6.1	6.1, 15° (b)
Carbon sulphide	1131	336	3 + 6.1	3, 18° (a)
Carbon, activated	1362	40	4.2	4.2, 1° (c)
Carbonyl fluoride, compressed	2417	268	6.1 + 8	2, 1°TC
Carbonyl sulphide	2204	263	6.1 + 3	2, 2°TF
Castor beans	2969	90	9	9, 35° (c)
Castor flake	2969	90	9	9, 35° (c)
Castor meal	2969	90	9	9, 35° (c)
Castor pomace	2969	90	9	9, 35° (c)
Cerium	3078	423	4.3	4.3, 13° (b)
Chloral, anhydrous, inhibited	2075	60	6.1	6.1, 17° (b)
Chlorate and borate mixture	1458	50	5.1	5.1, 11° (b)
Chlorate and magnesium chloridemixture	1459	50	5.1	5.1, 11° (b)
Chloric acid, aqueous solution	2626	50	5.1	5.1, 4° (b)
Chlorine	1017	268	6.1 + 8	2, 2°TC
Chlorine trifluoride	1749	265	6.1 + 05 + 8	2, 2°TOC
Chlorite solution	1908	80	8	8, 61° (b), (c)
1-Chloro-1, 1-difluoroethane (R 142b)	2517	23	3	2, 2°F
1-Chloro-1,2,2,2-tetrafluoroethane (R 124)	1021	20	2	2, 2°A
1-Chloro-2,2,2-trifluoroethane (R 133a)	1983	20	2	2, 2°A
3-Chloro-4-methylphenyl isocyanate	2236	60	6.1	6.1, 19° (b)
4-Chloro-o-toluidine hydrochloride	1579	60	6.1	6.1, 17° (c)
Chloroacetaldehyde	2232	66	6.1	6.1, 17° (a)
Chloroacetic acid solution	1750	68	6.1 + 8	6.1, 27° (b)
Chloroacetic acid, molten	3250	68	6.1 + 8	6.1, 24° (b)
Chloroacetic acid, solid	1751	68	6.1 + 8	6.1, 27° (b)
Chloroacetone, stabilized	1695	663	6.1 + 3 + 8	6.1, 10° (a)
Chloroacetonitrile	2668	63	6.1 + 3	6.1, 11° (b)2.
Chloroacetophenone	1697	60	6.1	6.1, 17° (b)
Chloroacetyl chloride	1752	668	6.1 + 8	6.1, 27° (a)
Chloroanilines, liquid	2019	60	6.1	6.1, 12° (b)
Chloroanilines, solid	2018	60	6.1	6.1, 12° (b)
Chloroanisidines	2233	60	6.1	6.1, 17° (c)

Name of substance (a)	Substance Identification No. (Lower part) (b)	Hazard Identification No. (Upper part) (c)	Label (d)	Class and item number (e)
Chlorobenzene	1134	30	3	3, 31° (c)
Chlorobenzotrifluorides (o-, m-, p-)	2234	30	3	3, 31° (c)
Chlorobenzyl chlorides	2235	60	6.1	6.1, 17° (c)
Chlorobutanes	1127	33	3	3, 3° (b)
Chlorocresols	2669	60	6.1	6.1, 14° (b)
Chlorodifluorobromomethane (R 12B1)	1974	20	2	2, 2°A
Chlorodifluoromethane (R 22)	1018	20	2	2, 2°A
Chlorodifluoromethane and chloropentafluoroethane mixture (R 502)	1973	20	2	2, 2°A
Chlorodinitrobenzenes	1577	60	6.1	6.1, 12° (b)
Chloroform	1888	60	6.1	6.1, 15° (c)
Chloromethyl chloroformate	2745	68	6.1 + 8	6.1, 27° (b)
Chloromethyl ethyl ether	2354	336	3 + 6.1	3, 16° (b)
Chloronitroanilines	2237	60	6.1	6.1, 17° (c)
Chloronitrobenzenes	1578	60	6.1	6.1, 12° (b)
Chloronitrotoluenes	2433	60	6.1	6.1, 17° (c)
Chloropentafluoroethane (R 115)	1020	20	2	2, 2°A
Chlorophenolates, liquid	2904	80	8	8, 62° (c)
Chlorophenolates, solid	2905	80	8	8, 62° (c)
Chlorophenols, liquid	2021	60	6.1	6.1, 17° (c)
Chlorophenols, solid	2020	60	6.1	6.1, 17° (c)
Chlorophenyltrichlorosilane	1753	X80	8	8, 36° (b)
Chloropicrin	1580	66	6.1	6.1, 17° (a)
Chloroplatinic acid, solid	2507	80	8	8, 16° (c)
Chloroprene, inhibited	1991	336	3 + 6.1	3, 16° (a)
2-Chloropropane	2356	33	3	3, 2° (a)
1-Chloropropane (Propyl chloride)	1278	33	3	3, 2° (b)
3-Chloropropanol-1	2849	60	6.1	6.1, 17° (c)
2-Chloropropene	2456	33	3	3, 1° (a)
2-Chloropropionic acid	2511	80	8	8, 32° (c)
2-Chloropyridine	2822	60	6.1	6.1, 12° (b)
Chlorosulphonic acid	1754	X88	8	8, 12° (a)
Chlorotoluenes (o-, m-, p-)	2238	30	3	3, 31° (c)
Chlorotoluidines	2239	60	6.1	6.1, 17° (c)
Chlorotrifluoromethane (R 13)	1022	20	2	2, 2°A
Chlorotrifluoromethane and trifluoromethane, azeotropic mixture (R 503)	2599	20	2	2, 2°A
Chromic acid, solution	1755	80	8	8, 17° (b), (c)

Name of substance (a)	Substance Identification No. (Lower part) (b)	Hazard Identification No. (Upper part) (c)	Label (d)	Class and item number (e)
Chromic fluoride, solid	1756	80	8	8, 9° (b)
Chromic fluoride, solution	1757	80	8	8, 8° (b), (c)
Chromium nitrate	2720	50	5.1	5.1, 22° (c)
Chromium oxychloride	1758	X88	8	8, 12° (a)
Chromium trioxide, anhydrous	1463	58	5.1 + 8	5.1, 31° (b)
Chromosulphuric acid	2240	88	8	8, 1° (a)
Coal gas, compressed	1023	263	6.1 + 3	2, 1°TF
Coal tar distillates	1136	33	3	3, 3° (b)
Coal tar distillates	1136	30	3	3, 31° (c)
Coating solution	1139	33	3	3, 5° (a), (b), (c)
Coating solution	1139	30	3	3, 31° (c)
Cobalt naphthenates, powder	2001	40	4.1	4.1, 12° (c)
Cobalt resinate, precipitated	1318	40	4.1	4.1, 12° (c)
Copper acetoarsenite	1585	60	6.1	6.1, 51° (b)
Copper arsenite	1586	60	6.1	6.1, 51° (b)
Copper chlorate	2721	50	5.1	5.1, 11° (b)
Copper chloride	2802	80	8	8, 11° (c)
Copper cyanide	1587	60	6.1	6.1, 41° (b)
Copra	1363	40	4.2	4.2, 2° (c)
Cotton waste, oily	1364	40	4.2	4.2, 3° (c)
Cotton, wet	1365	40	4.2	4.2, 3° (c)
Cresols (o-, m-,p-)	2076	68	6.1 + 8	6.1, 27° (b)
Cresylic acid	2022	68	6.1 + 8	6.1, 27° (b)
Crotonaldehyde, stabilized	1143	663	6.1 + 3	6.1, 8° (a)2.
Crotonic acid	2823	80	8	8, 31° (c)
Crotonylene (2-Butyne)	1144	339	3	3, 1° (a)
Cupriethylenediamine, solution	1761	86	8 + 6.1	8, 53° (b)(c)
Cyanogen	1026	263	6.1 + 3	2, 2TF
Cyanogen bromide	1889	668	6.1 + 8	6.1, 27° (a)
Cyanuric chloride	2670	80	8	8, 39° (b)
Cyclobutane	2601	23	3	2, 2°F
Cyclobutyl chloroformate	2744	638	6.1 + 3 + 8	6.1, 28° (b)
1,5,9-Cyclododecatriene	2518	60	6.1	6.1, 25° (c)
Cycloheptane	2241	33	3	3, 3° (b)
Cycloheptatriene	2603	336	3 + 6.1	3, 19° (b)
Cycloheptene	2242	33	3	3, 3° (b)
Cyclohexane	1145	33	3	3, 3° (b)
Cycloheptene	2242	33	3	3, 3° (b)

Name of substance (a)	Substance Identification No. (Lower part) (b)	Hazard Identification No. (Upper part) (c)	Label (d)	Class and item number (e)
Cyclohexanone	1915	30	3	3, 31° (c)
Cyclohexene	2256	33	3	3, 3° (b)
Cyclohexenyltrichlorosilane	1762	X80	8	8, 36° (b)
Cyclohexyl acetate	2243	30	3	3, 31° (c)
Cyclohexyl isocyanate	2488	663	6.1 + 3	6.1, 18° (a)
Cyclohexyl mercaptan	3054	30	3	3, 31° (c)
Cyclohexylamine	2357	83	8 + 3	8, 54° (b)
Cyclohexyltrichlorosilane	1763	X80	8	8, 36° (b)
Cyclooctadienes	2520	30	3	3, 31° (c)
Cyclooctatetraene	2358	33	3	3, 3° (b)
Cyclopentane	1146	33	3	3, 3° (b)
Cyclopentanol	2244	30	3	3, 31° (c)
Cyclopentanone	2245	30	3	3, 31° (c)
Cyclopentene	2246	33	3	3, 2° (b)
Cyclopropane	1027	23	3	2, 2°F
Cymenes (o-, m-, p-) (Methyl isopropyl benzenes)	2046	30	3	3, 31° (c)
Decaborane	1868	46	4.1 + 6.1	4.1, 16° (b)
Decahydronaphthalene	1147	30	3	3, 31° (c)
n-Decane	2247	30	3	3, 31° (c)
Deuterium, compressed	1957	23	3	2, 1°F
1,2-Di-(dimethylamino) ethane	2372	33	3	3, 3° (b)
Di-n-amylamine	2841	36	3 + 6.1	3, 32° (c)
Di-n-butylamine	2248	83	8 + 3	8, 54° (b)
Di-n-propyl ether	2384	33	3	3, 3° (b)
Diacetone alcohol, chemically pure	1148	30	3	3, 31° (c)
Diacetone alcohol, technically-pure	1148	33	3	3, 3° (b)
Diallyl ether	2360	336	3 + 6.1	3, 17° (b)
Diallylamine	2359	338	3 + 8 + 6.1	3, 27° (b)
4,4'-Diaminodiphenylmethane	2651	60	6.1	6.1, 12° (c)
Dibenzyldichlorosilane	2434	X80	8	8, 36° (b)
Dibromodifluoromethane	1941	90	9	9, 33 (c)
1,2-Dibromobutan-3-one	2648	60	6.1	6.1, 17° (b)
Dibromochloropropanes	2872	60	6.1	6.1, 15° (c)
Dibromomethane	2664	60	6.1	6.1, 15° (c)
Dibutyl ethers	1149	30	3	3, 31° (c)
Dibutylaminoethanol	2873	60	6.1	6.1, 12° (c)
1,2-Dichloro-1,1,2,2-tetrafluoroethane (R 114)	1958	20	2	2, 2°A
1,1-Dichloro-1-nitroethane	2650	60	6.1	6.1, 17° (b)

Name of substance (a)	Substance Identification No. (Lower part) (b)	Hazard Identification No. (Upper part) (c)	Label (d)	Class and item number (e)
Dichloroacetic acid	1764	80	8	8, 32° (b)1.
1,3-Dichloroacetone	2649	60	6.1	6.1, 17° (b)
Dichloroacetyl chloride	1765	X80	8	8, 35° (b)1.
Dichloroanilines	1590	60	6.1	6.1, 12° (b)
o-Dichlorobenzene	1591	60	6.1	6.1, 15° (c)
2,2'-Dichlorodiethyl ether	1916	63	6.1 + 3	6.1, 16° (b)
Dichlorodifluoromethane (R 12)	1028	20	2	2, 2°A
Dichlorodifluoromethane and 1,1-difluoroethane, azeotropic mixture (R 500)	2602	20	2	2, 2°A
Dichlorodifluoromethane and ethylene oxide mixture	3070	20	2	2, 2°A
1,2-Dichloroethane (Ethylene dichloride)	1184	336	3 + 6.1	3, 16° (b)
1,1-Dichloroethane (Ethylidene chloride)	2362	33	3	3, 3° (b)
1,2-Dichloroethylene	1150	33	3	3, 3° (b)
Dichlorofluoromethane (R 21)	1029	20	2	2, 2°A
Dichloroisocyanuric acid salts	2465	50	5.1	5.1, 26° (b)
Dichloroisocyanuric acid, dry	2465	50	5.1	5.1, 26° (b)
Dichloroisopropyl ether	2490	60	6.1	6.1, 17° (b)
Dichloromethane	1593	60	6.1	6.1, 15° (c)
Dichloropentanes	1152	30	3	3, 31° (c)
Dichlorophenyl isocyanates	2250	60	6.1	6.1, 19° (b)
Dichlorophenyltrichlorosilane	1766	X80	8	8, 36° (b)
1,2-Dichloropropane	1279	33	3	3, 3° (b)
1,3-Dichloropropanol-2	2750	60	6.1	6.1, 17° (b)
Dichloropropenes	2047	30	3	3, 31° (c)
Dichloropropenes	2047	33	3	3, 3° (b)
Dichlorosilane	2189	263	6.1 + 05 + 8	2, 2°TFC
Dicyclohexylamine	2565	80	8	8, 53° (c)
Dicyclohexylammonium nitrite	2687	40	4.1	4.1, 11° (c)
Dicyclopentadiene	2048	30	3	3, 31° (c)
Didymium nitrate	1465	50	5.1	5.1, 22° (c)
Diesel fuel	1202	30	3	3, 31° (c)
Diethoxymethane	2373	33	3	3, 3° (b)
3,3-Diethoxypropene	2374	33	3	3, 3° (b)
Diethyl carbonate (Ethyl carbonate)	2366	30	3	3, 31° (c)
Diethyl ether (ethyl ether)	1155	33	3	3, 2° (a)
Diethyl ketone	1156	33	3	3, 3° (b)
Diethyl sulphate	1594	60	6.1	6.1, 14° (b)

Name of substance (a)	Substance Identification No. (Lower part) (b)	Hazard Identification No. (Upper part) (c)	Label (d)	Class and item number (e)
Diethyl sulphide	2375	33	3	3, 3° (b)
Diethylamine	1154	338	3 + 8	3, 22° (b)
2-Diethylaminoethanol	2686	83	8 + 3	3, 54° (b)
Diethylaminopropylamine	2684	38	3 + 8	3, 33° (c)
N,N-Diethylaniline	2432	60	6.1	6.1, 12° (c)
Diethylbenzenes (o-, m-, p-)	2049	30	3	3, 31° (c)
Diethyldichlorosilane	1767	X83	8 + 3	8, 37° (b)
Diethylenetriamine	2079	80	8	8, 53° (b)
N,N-Diethylethylenediamine	2685	83	8 + 3	8, 54° (b)
Diethylthiophosphoryl chloride	2751	80	8	8, 35° (b)1.
Diethylzinc	1366	X333	4.2 + 4.3	4.2, 31° (a)
1,1-Difluoroethane (R 152a)	1030	23	3	2, 2°F
1,1-Difluoroethylene (R 1132a)	1959	239	3	2, 2°F
Difluorophosphoric acid, anhydrous	1768	80	8	8, 8° (b)
Difluoromethane	3252	23	3	2, 2°F
2,3-Dihydropyran	2376	33	3	3, 3° (b)
Diisobutyl ketone	1157	30	3	3, 31° (c)
Diisobutylamine	2361	38	3 + 8	3, 33° (c)
2-Dimethylaminoethyl acrylate	3302	60	6.1	6.1, 12° (b)
Diisobutylene, isomeric compounds	2050	33	3	3, 3° (b)
Diisooctyl acid phosphate	1902	80	8	8, 38° (c)
Diisopropyl ether	1159	33	3	3, 3° (b)
Diisopropylamine	1158	338	3 + 8	3, 22° (b)
Diketene, inhibited	2521	663	6.1 + 3	6.1, 13° (a)
1,2-Dimethoxyethane	2252	33	3	3, 3° (b)
1,1-Dimethoxyethane	2377	33	3	3, 3° (b)
Dimethyl carbonate	1161	33	3	3, 3° (b)
Dimethyl disulphide	2381	33	3	3, 3° (b)
Dimethyl ether	1033	23	3	2, 2°F
Dimethyl sulphate	1595	668	6.1 + 8	6.1, 27° (a)
Dimethyl sulphide	1164	33	3	3, 2° (b)
Dimethyl thiophosphoryl chloride	2267	68	6.1 + 8	6.1, 27° (b)
Dimethylamine, anhydrous	1032	23	3	2, 2°F
Dimethylamine aqueous solution	1160	338	3 + 8	3, 22° (b)
2-Dimethylaminoacetonitrile	2378	336	3 + 6.1	3, 11° (b)
2-Dimethylaminoethanol	2051	83	8 + 3	8, 54° (b)
2-Dimethylaminoethyl methacrylate	2522	69	6.1	6.1, 12° (b)
N,N-Dimethylaniline	2253	60	6.1	6.1, 12° (b)

Name of substance (a)	Substance Identification No. (Lower part) (b)	Hazard Identification No. (Upper part) (c)	Label (d)	Class and item number (e)
2,3-Dimethylbutane	2457	33	3	3, 3° (b)
1,3-Dimethylbutylamine	2379	338	3 + 8	3, 22° (b)
Dimethylcarbamoyl chloride	2262	80	8	8, 35° (b)1.
Dimethylcyclohexanes	2263	33	3	3, 3° (b)
Dimethylcyclohexylamine	2264	83	8 + 3	8, 54° (b)
Dimethyldichlorosilane	1162	X338	3 + 8	3, 21° (b)
Dimethyldiethoxysilane	2380	33	3	3, 3° (b)
Dimethyldioxanes	2707	33	3	3, 3° (b)
Dimethyldioxanes	2707	30	3	3, 31° (c)
N,N-Dimethylformamide	2265	30	3	3, 31° (c)
Dimethylhydrazine, symmetrical	2382	663	6.1 + 3	6.1, 7° (a)2.
Dimethylhydrazine, unsymmetrical	1163	663	6.1 + 3 + 8	6.1, 7° (a)1.
2,2-Dimethylpropane	2044	23	3	2, 2°F
Dimethyl-N-propylamine	2266	338	3 + 8	3, 22° (b)
Dimethylzinc	1370	X333	4.2 + 4.3	4.2, 31° (a)
Dinitro-o-cresol	1598	60	6.1	6.1, 12° (b)
Dinitroanilines	1596	60	6.1	6.1, 12° (b)
Dinitrobenzenes	1597	60	6.1	6.1, 12° (b)
Dinitrogen tetroxide (nitrogen dioxide)	1067	265	6.1 + 05 + 8	2, 2°TOC
Dinitrophenol solutions	1599	60	6.1	6.1, 12° (b), (c)
Dinitrotoluenes	2038	60	6.1	6.1, 12° (b)
Dinitrotoluenes, molten	1600	60	6.1	6.1, 24° (b)1.
Dioxane	1165	33	3	3, 3° (b)
Dioxolane	1166	33	3	3, 3° (b)
Dipentene	2052	30	3	3, 31° (c)
Diphenylamine chloroarsine	1698	66	6.1	6.1, 34° (a)
Diphenylchloroarsine	1699	66	6.1	6.1, 34° (a)
Diphenyldichlorosilane	1769	X80	8	8, 36° (b)
Diphenylmethyl bromide	1770	80	8	8, 65° (b)
Dipropyl ketone	2710	30	3	3, 31° (c)
Dipropylamine	2383	338	3 + 8	3, 22° (b)
Disodium trioxosilicate	3253	80	8	8, 41° (c)
Divinyl ether inhibited	1167	339	3	3, 2° (a)
Dodecyltrichlorosilane	1771	X80	8	8, 36° (b)
Epibromohydrin	2558	663	6.1 + 3	6.1, 16° (a)
Epichlorohydrin	2023	63	6.1 + 3	6.1, 16° (b)
1,2-Epoxy-3-ethoxypropane	2752	30	3	3, 31° (c)
Ethane	1035	23	3	2, 2°F

Name of substance (a)	Substance Identification No. (Lower part) (b)	Hazard Identification No. (Upper part) (c)	Label (d)	Class and item number (e)
Ethane, refrigerated liquid	1961	223	3	2, 3°F
Ethanol (Ethyl alcohol) or ethanol (Ethyl alcohol) solution containing more than 70 vol.-% alcohol	1170	33	3	3, 3° (b)
Ethanolamine or ethanolamine solution	2491	80	8	8, 53° (c)
Ethanol solution (Ethyl alcohol solution) containing more than 24 vol.-% and not more than 70 vol.-% alcohol	1170	30	3	3, 31° (c)
Ethyl acetate	1173	33	3	3, 3° (b)
Ethyl acrylate, inhibited	1917	339	3	3, 3° (b)
Ethyl amyl ketones	2271	30	3	3, 31° (c)
Ethyl borate	1176	33	3	3, 3° (b)
Ethyl bromide	1891	60	6.1	6.1, 15° (b)
Ethyl bromoacetate	1603	63	6.1 + 3	6.1, 16° (b)
Ethyl butyl ether	1179	33	3	3, 3° (b)
Ethyl butyrate	1180	30	3	3, 31° (c)
Ethyl chloride	1037	23	3	2, 2°F
Ethyl chloroacetate	1181	63	6.1 + 3	6.1, 16° (b)
Ethyl chloroformate	1182	663	6.1 + 3 + 8	6.1, 10° (a)
Ethyl chlorothioformate	2826	80	8	8, 64° (b)
Ethyl crotonate	1862	33	3	3, 3° (b)
Ethyl cyanoacetate	2666	60	6.1	6.1, 12° (c)
Ethyl fluoride (R161)	2453	23	3	2, 2°F
Ethyl formate	1190	33	3	3, 3° (b)
Ethyl isobutyrate	2385	33	3	3, 3° (b)
Ethyl lactate	1192	30	3	3, 31° (c)
Ethyl mercaptan	2363	33	3 + 6.1	3, 2° (a)
Ethyl methacrylate	2277	339	3	3, 3° (b)
Ethyl methyl ether	1039	23	3	2, 2°F
Ethyl methyl ketone (methyl ethyl ketone)	1193	33	3	3, 3° (b)
Ethyl nitrite solution	1194	336	3 + 6.1	3, 15° (a)
Ethyl orthoformate	2524	30	3	3, 31° (c)
Ethyl oxalate	2525	60	6.1	6.1, 14° (c)
Ethyl propionate	1195	33	3	3, 3° (b)
Ethyl propyl ether	2615	33	3	3, 3° (b)
Ethyl 2-chloropropionate	2935	30	3	3, 31° (c)
N-Ethyl-N-benzylaniline	2274	60	6.1	6.1, 12° (c)
Ethylacetylene, inhibited	2452	239	3	2, 2°F
Ethylamine	1036	23	3	2, 2°F
Ethylamine, aqueous solution	2270	338	3 + 8	3, 22° (b)

Name of substance (a)	Substance Identification No. (Lower part) (b)	Hazard Identification No. (Upper part) (c)	Label (d)	Class and item number (e)
N-Ethylaniline	2272	60	6.1	6.1, 12° (c)
2-Ethylaniline	2273	60	6.1	6.1, 12° (c)
Ethylbenzene	1175	33	3	3, 3° (b)
N-Ethylbenzyltoluidines	2753	60	6.1	6.1, 12° (c)
2-Ethylbutanol	2275	30	3	3, 31° (c)
Ethylbutyl acetate	1177	30	3	3, 31° (c)
2-Ethylbutyraldehyde	1178	33	3	3, 3° (b)
Ethyldichloroarsine	1892	66	6.1	6.1, 34° (a)
Ethyldichlorosilane	1183	X338	4.3 + 3 + 8	4.3, 1° (a)
Ethylene, compressed	1962	23	3	2, 1°F
Ethylene chlorohydrin	1135	663	6.1 + 3	6.1, 16° (a)
Ethylene dibromide	1605	66	6.1	6.1, 15° (a)
Ethylene glycol diethyl ether	1153	30	3	3, 31° (c)
Ethylene glycol monoethyl ether	1171	30	3	3, 31° (c)
Ethylene glycol monoethyl ether acetate	1172	30	3	3, 31° (c)
Ethylene glycol monomethyl ether	1188	30	3	3, 31° (c)
Ethylene glycol monomethyl ether acetate	1189	30	3	3, 31° (c)
Ethylene oxide and carbon dioxide mixture with more than 87 % ethylene oxide	3300	263	6.1 + 3	2, 2°TF
Ethylene oxide and chlorotetrafluoroethane mixture	3297	20	2	2, 2°A
Ethylene oxide and carbon dioxide mixture, with not more than 9% ethylene oxide	1952	20	2	2, 2°A
Ethylene oxide and carbon dioxide mixture, with more than 9 % but not more than 87% ethylene oxide	1041	239	3	2, 2°F
Ethylene oxide and pentafluoroethane mixture	3298	20	2	2, 2°A
Ethylene oxide and tetrafluoroethane mixture	3299	20	2	2, 2°A
Ethylene oxide and propylene oxide mixture	2983	336	3 + 6.1	3, 17° (a)
Ethylene oxide with nitrogen	1040	263	6.1 + 3	2, 2°TF
Ethylene, acetylene and propylene mixture, refrigerated liquid	3138	223	3	2, 3°F
Ethylene, refrigerated liquid	1038	223	3	2, 3°F
Ethylenediamine	1604	83	8 + 3	8, 54° (b)
Ethyleneimine, inhibited	1185	663	6.1 + 3	6.1, 4°
2-Ethylhexyl chloroformate	2748	68	6.1 + 8	6.1, 27° (b)
2-Ethylhexylamine	2276	38	3 + 8	3, 33° (c)
Ethylphenyldichlorosilane	2435	X80	8	8, 36° (b)
1-Ethylpiperidine	2386	338	3 + 8	3, 23° (b)
N-Ethyltoluidines	2754	60	6.1	6.1, 12° (b)

Name of substance (a)	Substance Identification No. (Lower part) (b)	Hazard Identification No. (Upper part) (c)	Label (d)	Class and item number (e)
Ethyltrichlorosilane	1196	X338	3 + 8	3, 21° (b)
Extracts, aromatic, liquid	1169	30	3	3, 31° (c)
Extracts, aromatic, liquid	1169	33	3	3, 5° (a), (b), (c)
Extracts, flavouring, liquid	1197	33	3	3, 5° (a), (b), (c)
Extracts, flavouring, liquid	1197	30	3	3, 31° (c)
Ferric arsenate	1606	60	6.1	6.1, 51° (b)
Ferric arsenite	1607	60	6.1	6.1, 51° (b)
Ferric chloride, anhydrous	1773	80	8	8, 11° (c)
Ferric chloride solution	2582	80	8	8, 5° (c)
Ferric nitrate	1466	50	5.1	5.1, 22° (c)
Ferrocerium	1323	40	4.1	4.1, 13° (b)
Ferrosilicon	1408	462	4.3 + 6.1	4.3, 15° (c)
Ferrous arsenate	1608	60	6.1	6.1, 51° (b)
Ferrous metal borings, shavings, turnings or cuttings	2793	40	4.2	4.2, 12° (c)
Fluoroboric acid	1775	80	8	8, 8° (b)
Fluoroacetic acid	2642	66	6.1	6.1, 17° (a)
Fluoroanilines	2941	60	6.1	6.1, 12° (c)
Fluorobenzene	2387	33	3	3, 3° (b)
Fluorophosphoric acid, anhydrous	1776	80	8	8, 8° (b)
Fluorosilicic acid	1778	80	8	8, 8° (b)
Fluorosulphonic acid	1777	88	8	8, 8° (a)
Fluorotoluenes	2388	33	3	3, 3° (b)
Formaldehyde solution	2209	80	8	8, 63° (c)
Formaldehyde solution, flammable	1198	38	3 + 8	3, 33° (c)
Formic acid	1779	80	8	8, 32° (b)1.
Fuel, aviation, turbine engine	1863	33	3	3, 1° (a), 2° (a), (b), 3° (b)
Fuel, aviation, turbine engine	1863	30	3	3, 31° (c)
Fumaryl chloride	1780	80	8	8, 35° (b)1.
Furan	2389	33	3	3, 1°a)
Furaldehydes	1199	63	6.1 + 3	6.1, 13° (b)
Furfuryl alcohol	2874	60	6.1	6.1, 14°c)
Furfurylamine	2526	38	3 + 8	3, 33° (c)
Fusel oil	1201	33	3	3, 3° (b)
Fusel oil	1201	30	3	3, 31° (c)
Gallium	2803	80	8	8, 65° (c)
Gas oil	1202	30	3	3, 31° (c)

Name of substance (a)	Substance Identification No. (Lower part) (b)	Hazard Identification No. (Upper part) (c)	Label (d)	Class and item number (e)
Glycerol alpha-monochlorohydrin	2689	60	6.1	6.1, 17° (c)
Glycidaldehyde	2622	336	3 + 6.1	3, 17° (b)
Guanidine nitrate	1467	50	5.1	5.1, 22° (c)
Hafnium powder, dry	2545	40	4.2	4.2, 12° (b), (c)
Hafnium powder, wetted	1326	40	4.1	4.1, 13° (b)
Heating oil (light)	1202	30	3	3, 31° (c)
Helium, compressed	1046	20	2	2, 1°A
Helium, refrigerated liquid	1963	22	2	2, 3°A
Heptafluoropropane (R 227)	3296	20	2	2, 2°A
n-Heptaldehyde	3056	30	3	3, 31° (c)
Heptanes	1206	33	3	3, 3° (b)
n-Heptene	2278	33	3	3, 3° (b)
Hexachloroacetone	2661	60	6.1	6.1, 17° (c)
Hexachlorobenzene	2729	60	6.1	6.1, 15° (c)
Hexachlorobutadiene	2279	60	6.1	6.1, 15° (c)
Hexachlorocyclopentadiene	2646	66	6.1	6.1, 15° (a)
Hexachlorophene	2875	60	6.1	6.1, 17° (c)
Hexadecyltrichlorosilane	1781	X80	8	8, 36° (b)
Hexadiene	2458	33	3	3, 3° (b)
Hexaethyl tetraphosphate	1611	60	6.1	6.1, 23° (b)
Hexaethyl tetraphosphate and compressed gas mixture	1612	26	6.1	2, 1°T
Hexafluoroacetone	2420	268	6.1 + 8	2, 2°TC
Hexafluoroacetone hydrate	2552	60	6.1	6.1, 17° (b)
Hexafluoroethane (R 116), compressed	2193	20	2	2, 1°A
Hexafluorophosphoric acid	1782	80	8	8, 8° (b)
Hexafluoropropylene (R 1216)	1858	20	2	2, 2°A
Hexaldehyde	1207	30	3	3, 31° (c)
Hexamethylene diisocyanate	2281	60	6.1	6.1, 19° (b)
Hexamethylenediamine, solid	2280	80	8	8, 52° (c)
Hexamethylenediamine, solution	1783	80	8	8, 53° (b), (c)
Hexamethyleneimine	2493	338	3 + 8	3, 23° (b)
Hexamethylenetetramine	1328	40	4.1	4.1, 6° (c)
Hexanes	1208	33	3	3, 3° (b)
Hexanols	2282	30	3	3, 31° (c)
1-Hexene	2370	33	3	3, 3° (b)
Hexyltrichlorosilane	1784	X80	8	8, 36° (b)
Hydrazine, aqueous solution	2030	86	8 + 6.1	8, 44° (b)

Name of substance (a)	Substance Identification No. (Lower part) (b)	Hazard Identification No. (Upper part) (c)	Label (d)	Class and item number (e)
Hydrazine hydrate	2030	86	8 + 6.1	8, 44° (b)
Hydrazine, aqueous solution	3293	60	6.1	6.1, 65° (c)
Hydriodic acid, solution	1787	80	8	8, 5° (b), (c)
Hydrobromic acid, solution	1788	80	8	8, 5° (b), (c)
Hydrochloric acid, solution	1789	80	8	8, 5° (b), (c)
Hydrofluoric acid and sulphuric acid mixture	1786	886	8 + 6.1	8, 7° (a)
Hydrofluoric acid solution containing between 60 and 85% hydrogen fluoride	1790	886	8 + 6.1	8, 7° (a)
Hydrofluoric acid solution containing less than 60% hydrogen fluoride	1790	86	8 + 6.1	8, 7° (b)
Hydrofluoric acid solution containing more than 85% hydrogen fluoride	1790	886	8 + 6.1	8, 6°
Hydrogen and methane mixture, compressed	2034	23	3	2, 1°F
Hydrogen bromide, anhydrous	1048	268	6.1 + 8	2, 2°TC
Hydrogen chloride, anhydrous	1050	268	6.1 + 8	2, 2°TC
Hydrogen cyanide, aqueous solution (Hydrocyanic acid)	1613	663	6.1 + 3	6.1, 2°
Hydrogen cyanide, solution in alcohol	3294	663	6.1 + 3	6.1, 2°
Hydrogen fluoride, anhydrous	1052	886	8 + 6.1	8, 6°
Hydrogen iodide, anhydrous	2197	268	6.1 + 8	2, 2°TC
Hydrogen peroxide and peroxyacetic acid mixture, stabilized	3149	58	5.1 + 8	5.1, 1° (b)
Hydrogen peroxide, aqueous solution	2014	58	5.1 + 8	5.1, 1° (b)
Hydrogen peroxide, aqueous solution	2984	50	5.1	5.1, 1° (c)
Hydrogen peroxide, aqueous solution, stabilized	2015	559	5.1 + 8	5.1, 1° (a)
Hydrogen peroxide, stabilized	2015	559	5.1 + 8	5.1, 1° (a)
Hydrogen sulphide	1053	263	6.1 + 3	2, 2°TF
Hydrogen, compressed	1049	23	3	2, 1°F
Hydrogen, refrigerated liquid	1966	223	3	2, 3°F
Hydroquinone	2662	60	6.1	6.1, 14° (c)
Hydroxylamine sulphate	2865	80	8	8, 16° (c)
Hypochlorite solution	1791	80	8	8, 61° (b), (c)
3,3'-Iminodipropylamine	2269	80	8	8, 53° (c)
Iodine monochloride	1792	80	8	8, 12° (b)
Iodine pentafluoride	2495	568	5.1 + 6.1 + 8	5.1, 5°
2-Iodobutane	2390	33	3	3, 3° (b)
Iodomethylpropanes	2391	33	3	3, 3° (b)
Iodopropanes	2392	30	3	3, 31° (c)
Iron oxide, spent	1376	40	4.2	4.2, 16° (c)

Name of substance (a)	Substance Identification No. (Lower part) (b)	Hazard Identification No. (Upper part) (c)	Label (d)	Class and item number (e)
Iron pentacarbonyl	1994	663	6.1 + 3	6.1, 3°
Iron sponge, spent	1376	40	4.2	4.2, 16° (c)
Isobutane	1969	23	3	2, 2°F
Isobutanol	1212	30	3	3, 31° (c)
Isobutyl acetate	1213	33	3	3, 3° (b)
Isobutyl acrylate, inhibited	2527	39	3	3, 31° (c)
Isobutyl formate	2393	33	3	3, 3° (b)
Isobutyl isobutyrate	2528	30	3	3, 31° (c)
Isobutyl isocyanate	2486	336	3 + 6.1	3, 14° (b)
Isobutyl methacrylate, inhibited	2283	39	3	3, 31° (c)
Isobutyl propionate	2394	33	3	3, 3° (b)
Isobutylamine	1214	338	3 + 8	3, 22° (b)
Isobutylene	1055	23	3	2, 2°F
Isobutyraldehyde	2045	33	3	3, 3° (b)
Isobutyric acid	2529	38	3 + 8	3, 33° (c)
Isobutyric anhydride	2530	38	3 + 8	3, 33° (c)
Isobutyronitrile	2284	336	3 + 6.1	3, 11° (b)
Isobutyryl chloride	2395	338	3 + 8	3, 25° (b)
Isocyanatobenzotrifluorides	2285	63	6.1 + 3	6.1, 18° (b)
Isoheptene	2287	33	3	3, 3° (b)
Isohexene	2288	33	3	3, 3° (b)
Isooctenes	1216	33	3	3, 3° (b)
Isopentenes	2371	33	3	3, 1° (a)
Isophorone diisocyanate	2290	60	6.1	6.1, 19° (c)
Isophoronediamine	2289	80	8	8, 53° (c)
Isoprene, inhibited	1218	339	3	3, 2° (a)
Isopropanol (Isopropyl alcohol)	1219	33	3	3, 3° (b)
Isopropenyl acetate	2403	33	3	3, 3° (b)
Isopropenylbenzene	2303	30	3	3, 31° (c)
Isopropyl 2-chloropropionate	2934	30	3	3, 31° (c)
Isopropyl acetate	1220	33	3	3, 3° (b)
Isopropyl acid phosphate	1793	80	8	8, 38° (c)
Isopropyl butyrate	2405	30	3	3, 31° (c)
Isopropyl chloroacetate	2947	30	3	3, 31° (c)
Isopropyl isobutyrate	2406	33	3	3, 3° (b)
Isopropyl isocyanate	2483	336	3 + 6.1	3, 14° (a)
Isopropyl propionate	2409	33	3	3, 3° (b)
Isopropylamine	1221	338	3 + 8	3, 22° (a)

Name of substance (a)	Substance Identification No. (Lower part) (b)	Hazard Identification No. (Upper part) (c)	Label (d)	Class and item number (e)
Isopropylbenzene (Cumene)	1918	30	3	3, 31° (c)
Kerosene	1223	30	3	3, 31° (c)
Krypton, compressed	1056	20	2	2, 1°A
Krypton, refrigerated liquid	1970	22	2	2, 3°A
Lead acetate	1616	60	6.1	6.1, 62° (c)
Lead arsenates	1617	60	6.1	6.1, 51° (b)
Lead arsenites	1618	60	6.1	6.1, 51° (b)
Lead cyanide	1620	60	6.1	6.1, 41° (b)
Lead dioxide	1872	56	5.1 + 6.1	5.1, 29° (c)
Lead nitrate	1469	56	5.1 + 6.1	5.1, 29° (c)
Lead perchlorate	1470	56	5.1 + 6.1	5.1, 29° (b)
Lead phosphite, dibasic	2989	40	4.1	4.1, 11° (b), (c)
Lead sulphate	1794	80	8	8, 1° (b)
Liquefied gases, non-flammable, charged with nitrogen, carbon dioxide or air	1058	20	2	2, 2°A
Lithium	1415	X423	4.3	4.3, 11° (a)
Lithium alkyls	2445	X333	4.2 + 4.3	4.2, 31° (a)
Lithium ferrosilicon	2830	423	4.3	4.3, 12° (b)
Lithium hydride, fused solid	2805	423	4.3	4.3, 16° (b)
Lithium hydroxide, monohydrate	2680	80	8	8, 41° (b)
Lithium hydroxide, solution	2679	80	8	8, 42° (b), (c)
Lithium hypochlorite, mixture or dry	1471	50	5.1	5.1, 15° (b)
Lithium nitrate	2722	50	5.1	5.1, 22° (c)
Lithium peroxide	1472	50	5.1	5.1, 25° (b)
Lithium silicon	1417	423	4.3	4.3, 12° (b)
London purple	1621	60	6.1	6.1, 51° (b)
Magnesium	1869	40	4.1	4.1, 13° (c)
Magnesium alkyls	3053	X333	4.2 + 4.3	4.2, 31° (a)
Magnesium alloys	1869	40	4.1	4.1, 13° (c)
Magnesium arsenate	1622	60	6.1	6.1, 51° (b)
Magnesium bromate	1473	50	5.1	5.1, 16° (b)
Magnesium chlorate	2723	50	5.1	5.1, 11° (b)
Magnesium diamide	2004	40	4.2	4.2, 16° (b)
Magnesium diphenyl	2005	X333	4.2 + 4.3	4.2, 31° (a)
Magnesium fluorosilicate	2853	60	6.1	6.1, 64° (c)
Magnesium granules, coated	2950	423	4.3	4.3, 11° (c)
Magnesium nitrate	1474	50	5.1	5.1, 22° (c)
Magnesium perchlorate	1475	50	5.1	5.1, 13° (b)

Name of substance (a)	Substance Identification No. (Lower part) (b)	Hazard Identification No. (Upper part) (c)	Label (d)	Class and item number (e)
Magnesium peroxide	1476	50	5.1	5.1, 25° (b)
Magnesium powder	1418	423	4.3 + 4.2	4.3, 14° (b)
Magnesium silicide	2624	423	4.3	4.3, 12° (b)
Maleic anhydride	2215	80	8	8, 31° (c)
Malononitrile	2647	60	6.1	6.1, 12° (b)
Maneb	2210	40	4.2 + 4.3	4.2, 16° (c)
Maneb preparation	2210	40	4.2 + 4.3	4.2, 16° (c)
Maneb preparation, stabilized	2968	423	4.3	4.3, 20° (c)
Maneb, stabilized	2968	423	4.3	4.3, 20° (c)
Manganese nitrate	2724	50	5.1	5.1, 22° (c)
Manganese resinate	1330	40	4.1	4.1, 12° (c)
Mercuric arsenate	1623	60	6.1	6.1, 51° (b)
Mercuric chloride	1624	60	6.1	6.1, 52° (b)
Mercuric nitrate	1625	60	6.1	6.1, 52° (b)
Mercurous nitrate	1627	60	6.1	6.1, 52° (b)
Mercury	2809	80	8	8, 66° (c)
Mercury acetate	1629	60	6.1	6.1, 52° (b)
Mercury ammonium chloride	1630	60	6.1	6.1, 52° (b)
Mercury benzoate	1631	60	6.1	6.1, 52° (b)
Mercury bromides	1634	60	6.1	6.1, 52° (b)
Mercury cyanide	1636	60	6.1	6.1, 41° (b)
Mercury gluconate	1637	60	6.1	6.1, 52° (b)
Mercury iodide	1638	60	6.1	6.1, 52° (b)
Mercury nucleate	1639	60	6.1	6.1, 52° (b)
Mercury oleate	1640	60	6.1	6.1, 52° (b)
Mercury oxide	1641	60	6.1	6.1, 52° (b)
Mercury oxycyanide, desensitized	1642	60	6.1	6.1, 41° (b)
Mercury potassium iodide	1643	60	6.1	6.1, 52° (b)
Mercury salicylate	1644	60	6.1	6.1, 52° (b)
Mercury sulphate	1645	60	6.1	6.1, 52° (b)
Mercury thiocyanate	1646	60	6.1	6.1, 52° (b)
Mesityl oxide	1229	30	3	3, 31° (c)
Metal catalyst, dry	2881	40	4.2	4.2, 12° (b), (c)
Metal catalyst, wetted	1378	40	4.2	4.2, 12° (b)
Metaldehyde	1332	40	4.1	4.1, 6° (c)
Methacrylaldehyde, inhibited	2396	336	3 + 6.1	3, 17° (b)
Methacrylic acid, inhibited	2531	89	8	8, 32° (c)
Methacrylonitrile, inhibited	3079	336	3 + 6.1	3, 11° (a)

Name of substance (a)	Substance Identification No. (Lower part) (b)	Hazard Identification No. (Upper part) (c)	Label (d)	Class and item number (e)
Methallyl alcohol	2614	30	3	3, 31° (c)
Methane, compressed	1971	23	3	2, 1°F
Methane gas, refrigerated liquid	1972	223	3	2, 3°F
Methanesulphonyl chloride	3246	668	6.1 + 8	6.1, 27° (a)
Methanol	1230	336	3 + 6.1	3, 17° (b)
1-Methoxy-2-propanol	3092	30	3	3, 31° (c)
4-Methoxy-4-methylpentan-2-one	2293	30	3	3, 31° (c)
Methoxymethyl isocyanate	2605	336	3 + 6.1	3, 14° (a)
Methyl acetate	1231	33	3	3, 3° (b)
Methyl acrylate, inhibited	1919	339	3	3, 3° (b)
Methyl bromide	1062	26	6.1	2, 2°T
Methyl bromide and ethylene dibromide mixture, liquid	1647	66	6.1	6.1, 15° (a)
Methyl bromoacetate	2643	60	6.1	6.1, 17° (b)
Methyl butyrate	1237	33	3	3, 3° (b)
Methyl chloride	1063	23	3	2, 2°F
Methyl chloride and methylene chloride mixture	1912	23	3	2, 2°F
Methyl chloroacetate	2295	663	6.1 + 3	6.1, 16° (a)
Methyl chloroformate	1238	663	6.1 + 3 + 8	6.1, 10° (a)
Methyl chloromethyl ether	1239	663	6.1 + 3	6.1, 9° (a)
Methyl dichloroacetate	2299	60	6.1	6.1, 17° (c)
Methyl formate	1243	33	3	3, 1° (a)
Methyl fluoride (R41)	2454	23	3	2, 2°F
Methyl iodide	2644	66	6.1	6.1, 15° (a)
Methyl isobutyl carbinol	2053	30	3	3, 31° (c)
Methyl isobutyl ketone	1245	33	3	3, 3° (b)
Methyl isopropenyl ketone, inhibited	1246	339	3	3, 3° (b)
Methyl isothiocyanate	2477	663	6.1 + 3	6.1, 20° (a)
Methyl isovalerate	2400	33	3	3, 3° (b)
Methyl magnesium bromide in ethyl ether	1928	X323	4.3 + 3	4.3, 3° (a)
Methyl mercaptan	1064	263	6.1 + 3	2, 2°TF
Methyl methacrylate monomer, inhibited	1247	339	3	3, 3° (b)
Methyl orthosilicate (Tetramethoxysilane)	2606	663	6.1 + 3	6.1, 8° (a)2.
Methyl propionate	1248	33	3	3, 3° (b)
Methyl propyl ether	2612	33	3	3, 2° (b)
Methyl propyl ketone	1249	33	3	3, 3° (b)
Methyl tert-butyl ether	2398	33	3	3, 3° (b)
Methyl trichloroacetate	2533	60	6.1	6.1, 17° (c)

Name of substance (a)	Substance Identification No. (Lower part) (b)	Hazard Identification No. (Upper part) (c)	Label (d)	Class and item number (e)
Methyl vinyl ketone, stabilized	1251	639	6.1 + 3	6.1, 8° (a)1.
2-Methyl-1-butene	2459	33	3	3, 1° (a)
3-Methyl-1-butene (Isopropylethylene)	2561	33	3	3, 1° (a)
2-Methyl-2-butene	2460	33	3	3, 2° (b)
Methyl 2-chloropropionate	2933	30	3	3, 31° (c)
2-Methyl-2-heptanethiol	3023	663	6.1 + 3	6.1, 20° (a)
2-Methyl-5-ethylpyridine	2300	60	6.1	6.1, 12° (c)
Methylacetylene and propadiene mixtures, stabilized	1060	239	3	2, 2°F
Methylal	1234	33	3	3, 2° (b)
Methylallyl chloride	2554	33	3	3, 3° (b)
Methylamine, anhydrous	1061	23	3	2, 2°F
Methylamine, aqueous solution	1235	338	3 + 8	3, 22° (b)
Methylamyl acetate	1233	30	3	3, 31° (c)
N-Methylaniline	2294	60	6.1	6.1, 12° (c)
alpha-Methylbenzyl alcohol	2937	60	6.1	6.1, 14° (c)
3-Methylbutan-2-one	2397	33	3	3, 3° (b)
N-Methylbutylamine	2945	338	3 + 8	3, 22° (b)
Methylcyclohexane	2296	33	3	3, 3° (b)
Methylcyclohexanols	2617	30	3	3, 31° (c)
Methylcyclohexanones	2297	30	3	3, 31° (c)
Methylcyclopentane	2298	33	3	3, 3° (b)
Methyldichlorosilane	1242	X338	4.3 + 3 + 8	4.3, 1° (a)
2-Methylfuran	2301	33	3	3, 3° (b)
5-Methylhexan-2-one	2302	30	3	3, 31° (c)
Methylhydrazine	1244	663	6.1 + 3 + 8	6.1, 7° (a)1.
4-Methylmorpholine	2535	338	3 + 8	3, 23° (b)
Methylpentadiene	2461	33	3	3, 3° (b)
2-Methylpentan-2-ol	2560	30	3	3, 31° (c)
Methylphenyldichlorosilane	2437	X80	8	8, 36° (b)
1-Methylpiperidine	2399	338	3 + 8	3, 23° (b)
Methyltetrahydrofuran	2536	33	3	3, 3° (b)
Methyltrichlorosilane	1250	X338	3 + 8	3, 21° (a)
alpha-Methylvaleraldehyde	2367	33	3	3, 3° (b)
Mixture A, A0, A1, B, C: see Hydrocarbon gas mixture liquefied, n.o.s.	1965	239	3	2, 2°F
Mixture P1, P2: see methylacetylene and propadiene, mixtures, stabilized	1060	23	3	2, 2°F
Mixture F1, F2, F3: see Refrigerant gas, n.o.s.	1078	20	2	2, 2°A

Name of substance (a)	Substance Identification No. (Lower part) (b)	Hazard Identification No. (Upper part) (c)	Label (d)	Class and item number (e)
Mixtures of 1,3-butadiene and hydrocarbons, inhibited	1010	239	3	2, 2°F
Molybdenum pentachloride	2508	80	8	8, 11° (c)
Morpholine	2054	30	3	3, 31° (c)
Motor fuel anti-knock mixture	1649	66	6.1	6.1, 31° (a)
Motor spirit	1203	33	3	3, 3° (b)
Naphthalene, crude or refined	1334	40	4.1	4.1, 6° (c)
Naphthalene, molten	2304	44	4.1	4.1, 5°
beta-Naphthylamine	1650	60	6.1	6.1, 12° (b)
alpha-Naphthylamine	2077	60	6.1	6.1, 12° (c)
Naphthylthiourea	1651	60	6.1	6.1, 21° (b)
Naphthylurea	1652	60	6.1	6.1, 12° (b)
Natural gas, compressed	1971	23	3	2, 1°F
Natural gas, refrigerated liquid	1972	223	3	2, 3°F
Neon, compressed	1065	20	2	2, 1°A
Neon, refrigerated liquid	1913	22	2	2, 3°A
Nickel carbonyl	1259	663	6.1 + 3	6.1, 3°
Nickel cyanide	1653	60	6.1	6.1, 41° (b)
Nickel nitrate	2725	50	5.1	5.1, 22° (c)
Nickel nitrite	2726	50	5.1	5.1, 23° (c)
Nicotine	1654	60	6.1	6.1, 90° (b)
Nicotine hydrochloride or nicotine hydrochloride solution	1656	60	6.1	6.1, 90° (b)
Nicotine salicylate	1657	60	6.1	6.1, 90° (b)
Nicotine sulphate, solid	1658	60	6.1	6.1, 90° (b)
Nicotine sulphate, solution	1658	60	6.1	6.1, 90° (b)
Nicotine tartrate	1659	60	6.1	6.1, 90° (b)
Nitrating acid mixture, spent, containing less than 50% nitric acid	1826	80	8	8, 3° (b)
Nitrating acid mixture, spent, containing more than 50% nitric acid	1826	885	8 + 05	8, 3° (a)
Nitrating acid, mixture containing less than 50% nitric acid	1796	80	8	8, 3° (b)
Nitrating acid, mixture containing more than 50% nitric acid	1796	885	8 + 05	8, 3° (a)
Nitric acid containing less than 70% pure acid	2031	80	8	8, 2° (b)
Nitric acid containing more than 70% pure acid	2031	885	8	8, 2° (a)1.
Nitric acid, red fuming	2032	856	8 + 05 + 6.1	8, 2° (a)2.
3-Nitro-4-chlorobenzotrifluoride	2307	60	6.1	6.1, 12° (b)
Nitroanilines (o-, m-, p-)	1661	60	6.1	6.1, 12° (b)

Name of substance (a)	Substance Identification No. (Lower part) (b)	Hazard Identification No. (Upper part) (c)	Label (d)	Class and item number (e)
Nitroanisole	2730	60	6.1	6.1, 12° (c)
Nitrobenzene	1662	60	6.1	6.1, 12° (b)
Nitrobenzenesulphonic acid	2305	80	8	8, 34° (b)
Nitrobenzotrifluorides	2306	60	6.1	6.1, 12° (b)
Nitrobromobenzene	2732	60	6.1	6.1, 12° (c)
Nitrocellulose solution, flammable	2059	33	3	3, 4° (a), (b)
Nitrocellulose solution, flammable	2059	30	3	3, 34° (c)
Nitrocresols (o-, m-, p-)	2446	60	6.1	6.1, 12° (c)
Nitroethane	2842	30	3	3, 31° (c)
Nitrogen, compressed	1066	20	2	2, 1°A
Nitrogen, refrigerated liquid	1977	22	2	2, 3°A
Nitrogen trifluoride, compressed	2451	265	6.1 + 05	2, 1°TO
Nitronaphthalene	2538	40	4.1	4.1, 6° (c)
Nitrophenols	1663	60	6.1	6.1, 12° (c)
Nitropropanes	2608	30	3	3, 31° (c)
p-Nitrosodimethylaniline	1369	40	4.2	4.2, 5° (b)
Nitrosylsulphuric acid	2308	X80	8	8, 1° (b)
Nitrotoluenes (o-, m-, p-)	1664	60	6.1	6.1, 12° (b)
Nitrotoluidines (mono)	2660	60	6.1	6.1, 12° (c)
Nitrous oxide	1070	25	2 + 05	2, 2°O
Nitrous oxide, refrigerated liquid	2201	225	2 + 05	2, 3°O
Nitroxylenes (o-, m-, p-)	1665	60	6.1	6.1, 12° (b)
Nonanes	1920	30	3	3, 31° (c)
Nonyltrichlorosilane	1799	X80	8	8, 36° (b)
2,5-Norbornadiene (Dicycloheptadiene), inhibited	2251	339	3	3, 3° (b)
Octadecyltrichlorosilane	1800	X80	8	8, 36° (b)
Octadiene	2309	33	3	3, 3° (b)
Octafluorobut-2-ene (R 1318)	2422	20	2	2, 2°A
Octafluorocyclobutane (RC 318)	1976	20	2	2, 2°A
Octafluoropropane (R 218)	2424	20	2	2, 2°A
Octanes	1262	33	3	3, 3° (b)
Octyl aldehydes (ethyl hexaldehydes)	1191	30	3	3, 31° (c)
2-Methyl-2-heptanethiol	3023	663	6.1 + 3	6.1, 20° (a)
Octyltrichlorosilane	1801	X80	8	8, 36° (b)
Oil gas, compressed	1071	263	6.1 + 3	2, 1°TF
Organic pigments, self-heating	3313	40	4.2	4.2, 5° (b), (c)
Oxygen and carbon dioxide mixture, compressed (max. 30% CO2)	1014	25	2 + 05	2, 1°O

Name of substance (a)	Substance Identification No. (Lower part) (b)	Hazard Identification No. (Upper part) (c)	Label (d)	Class and item number (e)
Oxygen, compressed	1072	25	2 + 05	2, 1°O
Oxygen, refrigerated liquid	1073	225	2 + 05	2, 3°O
Paint	1263	30	3	3, 31° (c)
Paint	1263	33	3	3, 5° (a), (b), (c)
Paint or paint related material	3066	80	8	8, 66° (b), (c)
Paint related material	1263	30	3	3, 31° (c)
Paint related material	1263	33	3	3, 5° (a), (b), (c)
Paper, unsaturated oil treated	1379	40	4.2	4.2, 3° (c)
Paraformaldehyde	2213	40	4.1	4.1, 6° (c)
Paraldehyde	1264	30	3	3, 31° (c)
Pentaborane	1380	333	4.2 + 6.1	4.2, 19° (a)
Pentachloroethane	1669	60	6.1	6.1, 15° (b)
Pentachlorophenol	3155	60	6.1	6.1, 17° (b)
Pentafluoroethane (R 125)	3220	20	2	2, 2°A
Pentamethylheptane (Isododecane)	2286	30	3	3, 31° (c)
Pentan-2,4-dione	2310	36	3 + 6.1	3, 32° (c)
Pentanes, liquid	1265	33	3	3, 1° (a)
Pentanes, liquid	1265	33	3	3, 2° (b)
1-Pentene (n-Amylene)	1108	33	3	3, 1° (a)
1-Pentol	2705	80	8	8, 66° (b)
Perchloric acid	1802	85	8	8, 4° (b)
Perchloric acid, with more than 50% but not more than 72% acid, by mass	1873	558	5.1 + 8	5.1, 3° (a)
Perchloromethyl mercaptan	1670	66	6.1	6.1, 17° (a)
Perfluoroethylvinyl ether	3154	23	3	2, 2°F
Perfluoromethylvinyl ether	3153	23	3	2, 2°F
Perchloryl fluoride	3083	265	6.1 + 05	2, 2°TO
Perfumery products	1266	33	3	3, 5° (a), (b), (c)
Perfumery products	1266	30	3	3, 31° (c)
Petroleum crude oil	1267	33	3	3, 1° (a), 2° (a), (b), 3° (b)
Petroleum crude oil	1267	30	3	3, 31° (c)
Phenacyl bromide	2645	60	6.1	6.1, 17° (b)
Phenetidines	2311	60	6.1	6.1, 12° (c)
Phenol solution	2821	60	6.1	6.1, 14° (b), (c)
Phenol, molten	2312	60	6.1	6.1, 24° (b)
Phenol, solid	1671	60	6.1	6.1, 14° (b)
Phenolates, liquid	2904	80	8	8, 62° (c)

Name of substance (a)	Substance Identification No. (Lower part) (b)	Hazard Identification No. (Upper part) (c)	Label (d)	Class and item number (e)
Phenolates, solid	2905	80	8	8, 62° (c)
Phenolsulphonic acid, liquid	1803	80	8	8, 34° (b)
Phenyl chloroformate	2746	68	6.1 + 8	6.1, 27° (b)
Phenyl isocyanate	2487	663	6.1 + 3	6.1, 18° (a)
Phenyl mercaptan	2337	663	6.1 + 3	6.1, 20° (a)
Phenylacetonitrile, liquid	2470	60	6.1	6.1, 12° (c)
Phenylacetyl chloride	2577	80	8	8, 35° (b)1.
Phenylcarbylamine chloride	1672	66	6.1	6.1, 17° (a)
Phenylenediamines (o-, m-, p-)	1673	60	6.1	6.1, 12° (c)
Phenylhydrazine	2572	60	6.1	6.1, 12° (b)
Phenylmercuric acetate	1674	60	6.1	6.1, 33° (b)
Phenylmercuric hydroxide	1894	60	6.1	6.1, 33° (b)
Phenylmercuric nitrate	1895	60	6.1	6.1, 33° (b)
Phenylphosphorus dichloride	2798	80	8	8, 35° (b)1.
Phenylphosphorus thiodichloride	2799	80	8	8, 35° (b)1.
Phenyltrichlorosilane	1804	X80	8	8, 36° (b)
Phosgene	1076	268	6.1 + 8	2, 2°TC
9-Phosphabicyclononanes (cyclooctadiene phosphines)	2940	40	4.2	4.2, 5° (b)
Phosphoric acid	1805	80	8	8, 17° (c)
Phosphorous acid	2834	80	8	8, 16° (c)
Phosphorus oxychloride	1810	X80	8	8, 12° (b)
Phosphorus, white or yellow, dry	1381	46	4.2 + 6.1	4.2, 11° (a)
Phosphorus heptasulphide	1339	40	4.1	4.1, 11° (b)
Phosphorus oxybromide	1939	80	8	8, 11° (b)
Phosphorus oxybromide, molten	2576	80	8	8, 15°
Phosphorus pentabromide	2691	80	8	8, 11° (b)
Phosphorus pentachloride	1806	80	8	8, 11° (b)
Phosphorus pentasulphide	1340	423	4.3	4.3, 20° (b)
Phosphorus pentoxide	1807	80	8	8, 16° (b)
Phosphorus sesquisulphide	1341	40	4.1	4.1, 11° (b)
Phosphorus tribromide	1808	X80	8	8, 12° (b)
Phosphorus trichloride	1809	668	6.1 + 8	8, 67° (a)
Phosphorus trioxide	2578	80	8	8, 16° (c)
Phosphorus trisulphide	1343	40	4.1	4.1, 11° (b)
Phosphorus, amorphous	1338	40	4.1	4.1, 11° (c)
Phosphorus, white or yellow, molten	2447	446	4.2 + 6.1	4.2, 22°
Phthalic anhydride	2214	80	8	8, 31° (c)

Name of substance (a)	Substance Identification No. (Lower part) (b)	Hazard Identification No. (Upper part) (c)	Label (d)	Class and item number (e)
Picolines	2313	30	3	3, 31° (c)
Pine oil	1272	30	3	3, 31° (c)
alpha-Pinene	2368	30	3	3, 31° (c)
Piperazine	2579	80	8	8, 52° (c)
Piperidine	2401	338	3 + 8	3, 23° (b)
Plastics moulding compound	3314	90	9	9, 4° (c)
Polychlorinated biphenyls	2315	90	9	9, 2° (b)
Polyhalogenated biphenyls, liquid	3151	90	9	9, 2° (b)
Polyhalogenated biphenyls, solid	3152	90	9	9, 2° (b)
Polyhalogenated terphenyls, liquid	3151	90	9	9, 2° (b)
Polyhalogenated terphenyls, solid	3152	90	9	9, 2° (b)
Polymeric beads, expandable	2211	90	9	9, 4° (c)
Potassium	2257	X423	4.3	4.3, 11° (a)
Potassium arsenate	1677	60	6.1	6.1, 51° (b)
Potassium arsenite	1678	60	6.1	6.1, 51° (b)
Potassium bromate	1484	50	5.1	5.1, 16° (b)
Potassium chlorate	1485	50	5.1	5.1, 11° (b)
Potassium chlorate aqueous solution	2427	50	5.1	5.1, 11° (b), (c)
Potassium cuprocyanide	1679	60	6.1	6.1, 41° (b)
Potassium dithionite	1929	40	4.2	4.2, 13° (b)
Potassium fluoride	1812	60	6.1	6.1, 63° (c)
Potassium fluoroacetate	2628	66	6.1	6.1, 17° (a)
Potassium fluorosilicate	2655	60	6.1	6.1, 64° (c)
Potassium hydrogen sulphate	2509	80	8	8, 13° (b)
Potassium hydrogendifluoride	1811	86	8 + 6.1	8, 9° (b)
Potassium hydroxide solution	1814	80	8	8, 42° (b), (c)
Potassium hydroxide, solid	1813	80	8	8, 41° (b)
Potassium metal alloys	1420	X423	4.3	4.3, 11° (a)
Potassium metavanadate	2864	60	6.1	6.1, 58° (b)
Potassium monoxide	2033	80	8	8, 41° (b)
Potassium nitrate	1486	50	5.1	5.1, 22° (c)
Potassium nitrate and sodium nitrite mixtures	1487	50	5.1	5.1, 24° (b)
Potassium nitrite	1488	50	5.1	5.1, 23° (b)
Potassium perchlorate	1489	50	5.1	5.1, 13° (b)
Potassium permanganate	1490	50	5.1	5.1, 17° (b)
Potassium persulphate	1492	50	5.1	5.1, 18° (c)
Potassium sodium alloys	1422	X423	4.3	4.3, 11° (a)
Potassium sulphide, anhydrous	1382	40	4.2	4.2, 13° (b)

Name of substance (a)	Substance Identification No. (Lower part) (b)	Hazard Identification No. (Upper part) (c)	Label (d)	Class and item number (e)
Potassium sulphide, hydrated	1847	80	8	8, 45° (b)1.
Potassium sulphide, with less than 30% water of crystallisation	1382	40	4.2	4.2, 13° (b)
Printing ink	1210	33	3	3, 5° (a), (b), (c)
Printing ink	1210	30	3	3, 31° (c)
Propadiene, inhibited	2200	239	3	2, 2°F
Propane	1978	23	3	2, 2°F
Propane (trade name): see Mixture C	1965	23	3	2, 2°F
Propanethiols (propyl mercaptans)	2402	33	3	3, 3° (b)
n-Propanol	1274	33	3	3, 3° (b)
n-Propanol	1274	30	3	3, 31° (c)
Propionaldehyde	1275	33	3	3, 3° (b)
Propionic acid	1848	80	8	8, 32° (c)
Propionic anhydride	2496	80	8	8, 32° (c)
Propionitrile	2404	336	3 + 6.1	3, 11° (b)
Propionyl chloride	1815	338	3 + 8	3, 25° (b)
n-Propyl acetate	1276	33	3	3, 3° (b)
n-Propyl chloroformate	2740	668	6.1 + 8 + 3	6.1, 28° (a)
Propyl formates	1281	33	3	3, 3° (b)
n-Propyl isocyanate	2482	663	6.1 + 3	6.1, 6° (a)
Propylamine	1277	338	3 + 8	3, 22° (b)
n-Propylbenzene	2364	30	3	3, 31° (c)
Propylene	1077	23	3	2, 2°F
Propylene chlorohydrin	2611	63	6.1 + 3	6.1, 16° (b)
Propylene oxide	1280	339	3	3, 2° (a)
Propylene tetramer	2850	30	3	3, 31° (c)
1,2-Propylenediamine	2258	83	8 + 3	8, 54° (b)
Propyleneimine, inhibited	1921	336	3 + 6.1	3, 12°
Propyltrichlorosilane	1816	X83	8 + 3	8, 37° (b)
Pyridine	1282	33	3	3, 3° (b)
Pyrosulphuryl chloride	1817	X80	8	8, 12° (b)
Pyrrolidine	1922	338	3 + 8	3, 23° (b)
Quinoline	2656	60	6.1	6.1, 12° (c)
Rare gases and nitrogen mixture, compressed	1981	20	2	2, 1°A
Rare gases and oxygen mixture, compressed	1980	20	2	2, 1°A
Rare gases mixture, compressed	1979	20	2	2, 1°A
Resin solution, flammable	1866	33	3	3, 5° (a), (b), (c)
Resin solution, flammable	1866	30	3	3, 31° (c)

Name of substance (a)	Substance Identification No. (Lower part) (b)	Hazard Identification No. (Upper part) (c)	Label (d)	Class and item number (e)
Resorcinol	2876	60	6.1	6.1, 14° (c)
Rosin oil	1286	30	3	3, 31° (c)
Rosin oil	1286	33	3	3, 5° (a), (b), (c)
Rubber scrap or shoddy	1345	40	4.1	4.1, 1° (b)
Rubber solution	1287	33	3	3, 5° (a), (b), (c)
Rubber solution	1287	30	3	3, 31° (c)
Rubidium	1423	X423	4.3	4.3, 11° (a)
Rubidium hydroxide	2678	80	8	8, 41° (b)
Rubidium hydroxide solution	2677	80	8	8, 42° (b), (c)
Seed cake	1386	40	4.2	4.2, 2° (c)
Seed cake	2217	40	4.2	4.2, 2° (c)
Selenium disulphide	2657	60	6.1	6.1, 55° (b)
Selenium oxychloride	2879	X886	8 + 6.1	8, 12° (a)
Shale oil	1288	30	3	3, 31° (c)
Shale oil	1288	33	3	3, 3° (b)
Silane, compressed	2203	23	3	2, 1°F
Silicon powder, amorphous	1346	40	4.1	4.1, 13° (c)
Silicon tetrachloride	1818	X80	8	8, 12° (b)
Silicon tetrafluoride, compressed	1859	268	6.1 + 8	2, 1°TC
Silver arsenite	1683	60	6.1	6.1, 51° (b)
Silver cyanide	1684	60	6.1	6.1, 41° (b)
Silver nitrate	1493	50	5.1	5.1, 22° (b)
Sludge acid	1906	80	8	8, 1° (b)
Soda lime	1907	80	8	8, 41° (c)
Sodium	1428	X423	4.3	4.3, 11° (a)
Sodium aluminate, solution	1819	80	8	8, 42° (b), (c)
Sodium aluminium hydride	2835	423	4.3	4.3, 16° (b)
Sodium ammonium vanadate	2863	60	6.1	6.1, 58° (b)
Sodium arsanilate	2473	60	6.1	6.1, 34° (c)
Sodium arsenate	1685	60	6.1	6.1, 51° (b)
Sodium arsenite, aqueous solution	1686	60	6.1	6.1, 51° (b), (c)
Sodium arsenite, solid	2027	60	6.1	6.1, 51° (b)
Sodium borohydride and sodium hydroxide solution, with not more than 12% sodium borohydride and not more than 40% sodium hydroxide by mass	3320	80	8	8, 42° (b), (c)
Sodium bromate	1494	50	5.1	5.1, 16° (b)
Sodium cacodylate	1688	60	6.1	6.1, 51° (b)
Sodium chlorate	1495	50	5.1	5.1, 11° (b)

Name of substance (a)	Substance Identification No. (Lower part) (b)	Hazard Identification No. (Upper part) (c)	Label (d)	Class and item number (e)
Sodium chlorate, aqueous solution	2428	50	5.1	5.1, 11° (b), (c)
Sodium chlorite	1496	50	5.1	5.1, 14° (b)
Sodium chloroacetate	2659	60	6.1	6.1, 17° (c)
Sodium cuprocyanide solution	2317	66	6.1	6.1, 41° (a)
Sodium dithionite (Sodium hydrosulphite)	1384	40	4.2	4.2, 13° (b
Sodium fluoride	1690	60	6.1	6.1, 63° (c)
Sodium fluoroacetate	2629	66	6.1	6.1, 17° (a)
Sodium fluorosilicate	2674	60	6.1	6.1, 64° (c)
Sodium hydrogendifluoride	2439	80	8	8, 9° (b)
Sodium hydrosulphide hydrated	2318	40	4.2	4.2, 13° (b)
Sodium hydrosulphide	2949	80	8	8, 45° (b)1.
Sodium hydroxide solution	1824	80	8	8, 42° (b), (c)
Sodium hydroxide, solid	1823	80	8	8, 41° (b)
Sodium methylate	1431	48	4.2 + 8	4.2, 15° (b)
Sodium methylate solution	1289	338	3 + 8	3, 24° (b)
Sodium methylate solution	1289	38	3 + 8	3, 33° (c)
Sodium monoxide	1825	80	8	8, 41° (b)
Sodium nitrate	1498	50	5.1	5.1, 22° (c)
Sodium nitrate and potassium nitrate mixture	1499	50	5.1	5.1, 22° (c)
Sodium nitrite	1500	50	5.1	5.1, 23° (c)
Sodium pentachlorophenate	2567	60	6.1	6.1, 17° (b)
Sodium perchlorate	1502	50	5.1	5.1, 13° (b)
Sodium permanganate	1503	50	5.1	5.1, 17° (b)
Sodium peroxoborate, anhydrous	3247	50	5.1	5.1, 27° (b)
Sodium persulphate	1505	50	5.1	5.1, 18° (c)
Sodium sulphide, anhydrous	1385	40	4.2	4.2, 13° (b)
Sodium sulphide, hydrated	1849	80	8	8, 45° (b)1.
Sodium sulphide, with less than 30% water of crystallisation	1385	40	4.2	4.2, 13° (b)
Stannic chloride pentahydrate	2440	80	8	8, 11° (c)
Stannic chloride, anhydrous	1827	X80	8	8, 12° (b)
Strontium arsenite	1691	60	6.1	6.1, 51° (b)
Strontium chlorate	1506	50	5.1	5.1, 11° (b)
Strontium nitrate	1507	50	5.1	5.1, 22° (c)
Strontium perchlorate	1508	50	5.1	5.1, 13° (b)
Strontium peroxide	1509	50	5.1	5.1, 25° (b)
Strychnine or strychnine, salts	1692	66	6.1	6.1, 90° (a)
Styrene monomer, inhibited (Vinylbenzene)	2055	39	3	3, 31° (c)

Name of substance (a)	Substance Identification No. (Lower part) (b)	Hazard Identification No. (Upper part) (c)	Label (d)	Class and item number (e)
Sulphamic acid	2967	80	8	8, 16° (c)
Sulphur	1350	40	4.1	4.1, 11° (c)
Sulphur chlorides	1828	X88	8	8, 12° (a)
Sulphur dioxide	1079	268	6.1 + 8	2, 2°TC
Sulphur hexafluoride	1080	20	2	2, 2°A
Sulphur trioxide, inhibited or sulphur trioxide, stabilized	1829	X88	8	8, 1° (a)
Sulphur, molten	2448	44	4.1	4.1, 15°
Sulphuric acid, containing more than 51% acid	1830	80	8	8, 1° (b)
Sulphuric acid, fuming	1831	X886	8 + 6.1	8, 1° (a)
Sulphuric acid, spent	1832	80	8	8, 1° (b)
Sulphuric acid, with more than 51% acid	2796	80	8	8, 1° (b)
Sulphurous acid	1833	80	8	8, 1° (b)
Sulphuryl chloride	1834	X88	8	8, 12° (a)
Sulphuryl fluoride	2191	26	6.1	2, 2°T
Tars, liquid	1999	30	3	3, 31° (c)
Tars, liquid	1999	33	3	3, 5° (b), (c)
Terpinolene	2541	30	3	3, 31° (c)
Tetrabromoethane	2504	60	6.1	6.1, 15° (c)
1,1,2,2-Tetrachloroethane	1702	60	6.1	6.1, 15° (b)
Tetrachloroethylene	1897	60	6.1	6.1, 15° (c)
Tetraethyl dithiopyrophosphate	1704	60	6.1	6.1, 23° (b)
Tetraethyl silicate	1292	30	3	3, 31° (c)
Tetraethylenepentamine	2320	80	8	8, 53° (c)
Tetrafluorethylene, inhibited	1081	239	3	2, 2°F
1,1,1,2-Tetrafluoroethane (R 134a)	3159	20	2	2, 2°A
Tetrafluoromethane (R 14), compressed	1982	20	2	2, 1°A
1,2,3,6-Tetrahydrobenzaldehyde	2498	30	3	3, 31° (c)
Tetrahydrofuran	2056	33	3	3, 3° (b)
Tetrahydrofurfurylamine	2943	30	3	3, 31° (c)
Tetrahydrophthalic anhydrides	2698	80	8	8, 31° (c)
1,2,3,6-Tetrahydropyridine	2410	33	3	3, 3° (b)
Tetrahydrothiophene (thiolanne)	2412	33	3	3, 3° (b)
Tetramethylammonium hydroxide	1835	80	8	8, 51° (b)
Tetramethylsilane	2749	33	3	3, 1° (a)
Tetranitromethane	1510	559	5.1 + 6.1	5.1, 2° (a)
Tetrapropyl orthotitanate	2413	30	3	3, 31° (c)
Thallium chlorate	2573	56	5.1 + 6.1	5.1, 29° (b)

Name of substance (a)	Substance Identification No. (Lower part) (b)	Hazard Identification No. (Upper part) (c)	Label (d)	Class and item number (e)
Thallium nitrate	2727	65	6.1 + 05	6.1, 68° (b)
Thioacetic acid	2436	33	3	3, 3° (b)
Thioglycol	2966	60	6.1	6.1, 21° (b)
Thioglycolic acid	1940	80	8	8, 32° (b)1.
Thiolactic acid	2936	60	6.1	6.1, 21° (b)
Thionyl chloride	1836	X88	8	8, 12° (a)
4-Thiapentanal	2785	60	6.1	6.1, 21° (c)
Thiophene	2414	33	3	3, 3° (b)
Thiophosgene	2474	60	6.1	6.1, 21° (b)
Thiophosphoryl chloride	1837	X80	8	8, 12° (b)
Tinctures, medicinal	1293	30	3	3, 31° (c)
Tinctures, medicinal	1293	33	3	3, 3° (b)
Titanium disulphide	3174	40	4.2	4.2, 13° (c)
Titanium hydride	1871	40	4.1	4.1, 14° (b)
Titanium powder, dry	2546	40	4.2	4.2, 12° (b), (c)
Titanium powder, wetted	1352	40	4.1	4.1, 13° (b)
Titanium sponge, powder or granules	2878	40	4.1	4.1, 13° (c)
Titanium tetrachloride	1838	X80	8	8, 12° (b)
Titanium trichloride mixture	2869	80	8	8, 11° (b), (c)
Toluene	1294	33	3	3, 3° (b)
Toluene diisocyanate	2078	60	6.1	6.1, 19° (b)
Toluidines	1708	60	6.1	6.1, 12° (b)
2,4-Toluylenediamine	1709	60	6.1	6.1, 12° (c)
Triallyl borate	2609	60	6.1	6.1, 14° (c)
Triallylamine	2610	38	3 + 8	3, 33° (c)
Tributylamine	2542	60	6.1	6.1, 12° (b)
Trichloroacetic acid	1839	80	8	8, 31° (b)
Trichloroacetic acid solution	2564	80	8	8, 32° (c)
Trichloroacetic acid solution	2564	80	8	8, 32° (b)1.
Trichloroacetyl chloride	2442	X80	8	8, 35° (b)1.
Trichlorobenzenes, liquid	2321	60	6.1	6.1, 15° (c)
Trichlorobutene	2322	60	6.1	6.1, 15° (b)
1,1,1-Trichloroethane	2831	60	6.1	6.1, 15° (c)
Trichloroethylene	1710	60	6.1	6.1, 15° (c)
Trichloroisocyanuric acid, dry	2468	50	5.1	5.1, 26° (b)
Trichlorosilane	1295	X338	4.3 + 3 + 8	4.3, 1° (a)
Tricresyl phosphate	2574	60	6.1	6.1, 23° (b)
Triethyl phosphite	2323	30	3	3, 31° (c)

Name of substance (a)	Substance Identification No. (Lower part) (b)	Hazard Identification No. (Upper part) (c)	Label (d)	Class and item number (e)
Triethylamine	1296	338	3 + 8	3, 22° (b)
Triethylenetetramine	2259	80	8	8, 53° (b)
Trifluoracetyl chloride	3057	268	6.1 + 8	2, 2°TC
Trifluoroacetic acid	2699	88	8	8, 32° (a)
Trifluorochloroethylene, inhibited (R 1113)	1082	263	6.1 + 3	2, 2°TF
1,1,1-Trifluoroethane (R 143a)	2035	23	3	2, 2°F
Trifluoromethane (R 23)	1984	20	2	2, 2°A
Trifluoromethane, refrigerated liquid	3136	22	2	2, 3°A
2-Trifluoromethylaniline	2942	60	6.1	6.1, 12° (c)
3-Trifluoromethylaniline	2948	60	6.1	6.1, 17° (b)
Tris-(1-aziridinyl) phosphine oxide solution	2501	60	6.1	6.1, 23° (b), (c)
Triisobutylene (Isobutylene trimer)	2324	30	3	3, 31° (c)
Triisopropyl borate	2616	30	3	3, 31° (c)
Triisopropyl borate	2616	33	3	3, 3° (b)
Trimethyl borate	2416	33	3	3, 3° (b)
Trimethyl phosphite	2329	30	3	3, 31° (c)
Trimethylacetyl chloride	2438	663	6.1 + 3 + 8	6.1, 10° (a)
Trimethylamine, anhydrous	1083	23	3	2, 2°F
Trimethylamine, aqueous solution	1297	338	3 + 8	3, 22° (a), (b)
Trimethylamine, aqueous solution	1297	38	3 + 8	3, 33° (c)
1,3,5-Trimethylbenzene	2325	30	3	3, 31° (c)
Trimethylchlorosilane	1298	X338	3 + 8	3, 21° (b)
Trimethylcyclohexylamine	2326	80	8	8, 53° (c)
Trimethylhexamethylene diisocyanate	2328	60	6.1	6.1, 19° (c)
Trimethylhexamethylenediamine	2327	80	8	8, 53° (c)
Tripropylamine	2260	38	3 + 8	3, 33° (c)
Tripropylene	2057	33	3	3, 3° (b)
Tripropylene	2057	30	3	3, 31° (c)
Turpentine	1299	30	3	3, 31° (c)
Turpentine substitute	1300	33	3	3, 3° (b)
Turpentine substitute	1300	30	3	3, 31° (c)
Undecane	2330	30	3	3, 31° (c)
Uranyl nitrate hexahydrate solution	2980	78	7A, 7B or 7C+8	7, Sch 5, 6 or 13
Urea hydrogen peroxide	1511	58	5.1 + 8	5.1, 31° (c)
Valeraldehyde	2058	33	3	3, 3° (b)
Valeryl chloride	2502	83	8 + 3	8, 35° (b)2.
Vanadium oxytrichloride	2443	80	8	8, 12° (b)
Vanadium pentoxide	2862	60	6.1	6.1, 58° (b)

Name of substance (a)	Substance Identification No. (Lower part) (b)	Hazard Identification No. (Upper part) (c)	Label (d)	Class and item number (e)
Vanadium tetrachloride	2444	X88	8	8, 12° (a)
Vanadium trichloride	2475	80	8	8, 11° (c)
Vanadyl sulphate	2931	60	6.1	6.1, 58° (b)
Vinyl acetate, inhibited	1301	339	3	3, 3° (b)
Vinyl bromide, inhibited	1085	239	3	2, 2°F
Vinyl butyrate, inhibited	2838	339	3	3, 3° (b)
Vinyl chloride, inhibited or stabilized	1086	239	3	2, 2°F
Vinyl chloroacetate	2589	63	6.1 + 3	6.1, 16° (b)
Vinyl ethyl ether, inhibited	1302	339	3	3, 2° (a)
Vinyl methyl ether, inhibited	1087	239	3	2, 2°F
Vinyl fluoride, inhibited	1860	239	3	2, 2°F
Vinyl isobutyl ether, inhibited	1304	339	3	3, 3° (b)
Vinylidene chloride, inhibited	1303	339	3	3, 1° (a)
Vinyltoluene, inhibited (o-,m-,p-)	2618	39	3	3, 31° (c)
Vinylpyridines, inhibited	3073	639	6.1 + 3 + 8	6.1, 11° (b)1.
Vinyltrichlorosilane, inhibited	1305	X338	3 + 8	3, 21° (a)
White asbestos (Actinolite, Anthophyllite, Chrysotile or Tremolite)	2590	90	9	9, 1° (c)
Wood preservatives, liquid	1306	33	3	3, 5° (b), (c)
Wood preservatives, liquid	1306	30	3	3, 31° (c)
Xenon, compressed	2036	20	2	2, 1°A
Xenon, refrigerated liquid	2591	22	2	2, 3°A
Xylenes	1307	30	3	3, 31° (c)
Xylenes	1307	33	3	3, 3° (b)
Xylenols	2261	60	6.1	6.1, 14° (b)
Xylidines	1711	60	6.1	6.1, 12° (b)
Xylyl bromide	1701	60	6.1	6.1, 15° (b)
Zinc ammonium nitrite	1512	50	5.1	5.1, 23° (b)
Zinc arsenate	1712	60	6.1	6.1, 51° (b)
Zinc arsenate and zinc arsenite mixture	1712	60	6.1	6.1, 51° (b)
Zinc arsenite	1712	60	6.1	6.1, 51° (b)
Zinc ashes	1435	423	4.3	4.3, 13° (c)
Zinc bromate	2469	50	5.1	5.1, 16° (c)
Zinc chlorate	1513	50	5.1	5.1, 11° (b)
Zinc chloride solution	1840	80	8	8, 5° (c)
Zinc chloride, anhydrous	2331	80	8	8, 11° (c)
Zinc cyanide	1713	66	6.1	6.1, 41° (a)
Zinc dithionite	1931	90	9	9, 32° (c)

Name of substance (a)	Substance Identification No. (Lower part) (b)	Hazard Identification No. (Upper part) (c)	Label (d)	Class and item number (e)
Zinc dust	1436	423	4.3 + 4.2	4.3, 14° (b), (c)
Zinc fluorosilicate	2855	60	6.1	6.1, 64° (c)
Zinc nitrate	1514	50	5.1	5.1, 22° (b)
Zinc permanganate	1515	50	5.1	5.1, 17° (b)
Zinc peroxide	1516	50	5.1	5.1, 25° (b)
Zinc powder	1436	423	4.3 + 4.2	4.3, 14° (b), (c)
Zinc resinate	2714	40	4.1	4.1, 12° (c)
Zirconium hydride	1437	40	4.1	4.1, 14° (b)
Zirconium nitrate	2728	50	5.1	5.1, 22° (c)
Zirconium powder, dry	2008	40	4.2	4.2, 12° (b), (c)
Zirconium powder, wetted	1358	40	4.1	4.1, 13° (b)
Zirconium scrap	1932	40	4.2	4.2, 12° (c)
Zirconium suspended in a flammable liquid	1308	33	3	3, 1° (a), 2° (a), (b), 3° (b)
Zirconium suspended in a flammable liquid	1308	30	3	3, 31° (c)
Zirconium tetrachloride	2503	80	8	8, 11° (c)
Zirconium, dry	2858	40	4.1	4.1, 13° (c)

Table 2

List of collective headings or n.o.s. entries which are not listed by name, or which do not fall under a collective heading in Table 1.

This table includes two types of collective headings or n.o.s. entries:

- specific collective headings or n.o.s. entries applicable to groups of chemical compounds of the same type;

- general collective headings or n.o.s. entries applicable to groups of substances which present similar primary and secondary hazards.

Substances may only be classified under a general collective heading or n.o.s. entry if they cannot be classified under a specific collective heading or n.o.s. entry.

NOTE: This table applies only to substances not included in Table 1.

Group of substances (a)	Substance Identification No. (Lower part) (b)	Hazard Identification No. (Upper part) (c)	Label (d)	Class and item number (e)
Class 2: Gases				
Specific n.o.s entries				
Hydrocarbon gas mixture, compressed, n.o.s.	1964	23	3	2, 1°F
Insecticide gas, toxic, n.o.s.	1967	26	6.1	2, 2°T
Insecticide gas, n.o.s.	1968	20	2	2, 2°A
Refrigerant gas, n.o.s.	1078	20	2	2, 2°A
Hydrocarbon gas mixture, liquefied, n.o.s.	1965	23	3	2, 2°F
General n.o.s entries				
Compressed gas, n.o.s.	1956	20	2	2, 1°A
Compressed gas, oxidizing, n.o.s.	3156	25	2 + 05	2, 1°O
Compressed gas, flammable, n.o.s.	1954	23	3	2, 1°F
Compressed gas, toxic, n.o.s.	1955	26	6.1	2, 1°T
Compressed gas, toxic, flammable, n.o.s.	1953	263	6.1 + 3	2, 1°TF
Compressed gas, toxic, corrosive, n.o.s.	3304	268	6.1 + 8	2, 1°TC
Compressed gas, toxic, oxidizing, n.o.s.	3303	265	6.1 + 05	2, 1°TO
Compressed gas, toxic, flammable, corrosive, n.o.s.	3305	263	6.1 + 3 + 8	2, 1°TFC
Compressed gas, toxic, oxidizing, corrosive, n.o.s.	3306	265	6.1 + 05 + 8	2, 1°TOC
Liquefied gas, n.o.s.	3163	20	2	2, 2°A
Liquefied gas, oxidizing, n.o.s.	3157	25	2 + 05	2, 2°O
Liquefied gas, flammable, n.o.s.	3161	23	3	2, 2°F
Liquefied gas, toxic, n.o.s.	3162	26	6.1	2, 2°T
Liquefied gas, toxic, flammable, n.o.s.	3160	263	6.1 + 3	2, 2°TF

Group of substances (a)	Substance Identification No. (Lower part) (b)	Hazard Identification No. (Upper part) (c)	Label (d)	Class and item number (e)
Liquefied gas, toxic, corrosive, n.o.s.	3308	268	6.1 + 8	2, 2°TC
Liquefied gas, toxic, flammable, corrosive, n.o.s.	3309	263	6.1 + 3 + 8	2, 2TFC
Liquefied gas, toxic, oxidizing, n.o.s.	3307	265	6.1 + 05	2, 2°TO
Liquefied gas, toxic, oxidizing, corrosive, n.o.s.	3310	265	6.1 + 05 + 8	2, 2°TOC
Gas, refrigerated liquid, n.o.s.	3158	22	2	2, 3°A
Gas, refrigerated liquid, oxidizing, n.o.s.	3311	225	2 + 05	2, 3°O
Gas, refrigerated liquid, flammable, n.o.s.	3312	223	3	2, 3°F
Class 3: Flammable liquids **Specific n.o.s. entries or specific collective headings**				
Petroleum distillates, n.o.s.	1268 1268 1268 1268 1268	33 33 33 33 30	3 3 3 3 3	3, 1° (a) 3, 2° (a) 3, 2° (b) 3, 3° (b) 3, 31° (c)
Petroleum products, n.o.s.	1268 1268 1268 1268 1268	33 33 33 33 33	3 3 3 3 3	3, 1° (a) 3, 2° (a) 3, 2° (b) 3, 3° (b) 3, 31° (c)
Hydrocarbons, liquid, n.o.s.	3295 3295 3295 3295 3295	33 33 33 33 33	3 3 3 3 3	3, 1° (a) 3, 2° (a) 3, 2° (b) 3, 3° (b) 3, 31° (c)
Aldehydes, flammable, n.o.s.	1989 1989 1989	33 33 30	3 3 3	3, 2° (b) 3, 3° (b) 3, 31° (c)
Alcohols, flammable, n.o.s.	1987 1987 1987	33 33 30	3 3 3	3, 2° (b) 3, 3° (b) 3, 31° (c)
Ketones, n.o.s.	1224 1224 1224	33 33 30	3 3 3	3, 2° (b) 3, 3° (b) 3, 31° (c)
Ethers, n.o.s.	3271 3271	33 30	3 3	3, 3° (b) 3, 31° (c)
Esters, n.o.s.	3272 3272	33 30	3 3	3, 3° (b) 3, 31° (c)
Nitriles, flammable, toxic, n.o.s.	3273	336	3 + 6.1	3, 11° (a), (b)
Isocyanates or isocyanate solution, flammable, toxic, n.o.s.	2478 2478	336 36	3 + 6.1 3 + 6.1	3, 14° (b) 3, 32° (c)
Alcohols, flammable, toxic, n.o.s.	1986 1986	336 36	3 + 6.1 3 + 6.1	3, 17° (a), (b) 3, 32° (c)
Aldehydes, flammable, toxic, n.o.s.	1988 1988	336 36	3 + 6.1 3 + 6.1	3, 17° (a), (b) 3, 32° (c)

Group of substances (a)	Substance Identification No. (Lower part) (b)	Hazard Identification No. (Upper part) (c)	Label (d)	Class and item number (e)
Mercaptans or mercaptan mixture, liquid, flammable, toxic n.o.s.	1228 1228	336 36	3 + 6.1 3 + 6.1	3, 18° (b) 3, 32° (c)
Medicine, liquid, flammable, toxic, n.o.s.	3248 3248	336 36	3 + 6.1 3 + 6.1	3, 19° (b) 3, 32° (c)
Chlorosilanes, flammable, corrosive, n.o.s.	2985	338	3 + 8	3, 21° (b)
Amines or polyamines, flammable, corrosive, n.o.s.	2733 2733	338 38	3 + 8 3 + 8	3, 22° (a), (b) 3, 33° (c)
Alcoholates solution, n.o.s.	3274	338	3 + 8	3, 24° (b)
Terpene hydrocarbons, n.o.s.	2319	30	3	3, 31° (c)
Pesticides				
Organophosphorous pesticide, liquid, flammable, toxic	2784	336	3 + 6.1	3, 41° (a), (b)
Organochlorine pesticide, liquid, flammable, toxic	2762	336	3 + 6.1	3, 41° (a), (b)
Phenoxy pesticide, liquid, flammable, toxic	2766	336	3 + 6.1	3, 41° (a), (b)
Carbamate pesticide, liquid, flammable, toxic	2758	336	3 + 6.1	3, 41° (a), (b)
Mercury based pesticide, liquid, flammable, toxic	2778	336	3 + 6.1	3, 41° (a), (b)
Organotin pesticide, liquid, flammable, toxic	2787	336	3 + 6.1	3, 41° (a), (b)
Coumarin derivative pesticide, liquid, flammable, toxic	3024	336	3 + 6.1	3, 41° (a), (b)
Bipyridilium pesticide, liquid, flammable, toxic	2782	336	3 + 6.1	3, 41° (a), (b)
Arsenical pesticide, liquid, flammable, toxic	2760	336	3 + 6.1	3, 41° (a), (b)
Copper based pesticide, liquid, flammable, toxic	2776	336	3 + 6.1	3, 41° (a), (b)
Substituted nitrophenol pesticide, liquid, flammable, toxic	2780	336	3 + 6.1	3, 41° (a), (b)
Triazine pesticide, liquid, flammable, toxic	2764	336	3 + 6.1	3, 41° (a), (b)
Benzoic derivative pesticide, liquid, flammable, toxic	2770	336	3 + 6.1	3, 41° (a), (b)
Phthalimide derivative pesticide, liquid, flammable, toxic	2774	336	3 + 6.1	3, 41° (a), (b)
Phenyl urea pesticide, liquid, flammable, toxic	2768	336	3 + 6.1	3, 41° (a), (b)
Dithiocarbamate pesticide, liquid, flammable, toxic	2772	336	3 + 6.1	3, 41° (a), (b)
Pesticide, liquid, flammable, toxic, n.o.s.	3021	336	3 + 6.1	3, 41° (a), (b)
General n.o.s. entries				
Flammable liquid, n.o.s.	1993 1993 1993 1993 1993 1993	33 33 33 33 33 30	3 3 3 3 3 3	3, 1° (a) 3, 2° (a) 3, 2° (b) 3, 3° (b) 3, 5° (c) 3, 31° (c)
Flammable liquid, toxic, n.o.s.	1992 1992	36 336	3 + 6.1 3 + 6.1	3, 32° (c) 3, 19° (a), (b)

Group of substances (a)	Substance Identification No. (Lower part) (b)	Hazard Identification No. (Upper part) (c)	Label (d)	Class and item number (e)
Flammable liquid, corrosive, n.o.s.	2924	338	3 + 8	3, 26° (a), (b)
	2924	38	3 + 8	3, 33° (c)
Flammable liquid, toxic, corrosive, n.o.s.	3286	368	3 + 6.1 + 8	3, 27° (a), (b)
Elevated temperature liquid, flammable, n.o.s.	3256	30	3	3, 61° (c)
Class 4.1: Flammable solids				
Specific n.o.s. entries				
Metal hydrides, flammable, n.o.s.	3182	40	4.1	4.1, 14° (b), (c)
General n.o.s entries				
Solids containing flammable liquid, n.o.s.	3175	40	4.1	4.1, 4° (c)
Flammable solid, organic, molten, n.o.s.	3176	44	4.1	4.1, 5°
Flammable solid, organic, n.o.s.	1325	40	4.1	4.1, 6° (b), (c)
Flammable solid, toxic, organic, n.o.s.	2926	46	4.1 + 6.1	4.1, 7° (b), (c)
Flammable solid, corrosive, organic, n.o.s.	2925	48	4.1 + 8	4.1, 8° (b), (c)
Flammable solid, inorganic, n.o.s.	3178	40	4.1	4.1, 11° (b), (c)
Metal salts of organic compounds, flammable, n.o.s.	3181	40	4.1	4.1, 12° (b), (c)
Metal powder, flammable, n.o.s.	3089	40	4.1	4.1, 13° (b), (c)
Flammable solid, toxic, inorganic, n.o.s.	3179	46	4.1 + 6.1	4.1, 16° (b), (c)
Flammable solid, corrosive, inorganic, n.o.s.	3180	48	4.1 + 8	4.1, 17° (b), (c)
Class 4.2: Substances liable to spontaneous combustion				
Specific n.o.s. entries				
Fibres, animal, vegetable or synthetic, n.o.s.	1373	40	4.2	4.2, 3° (c)
Fabrics, animal, vegetable or synthetic, n.o.s.	1373	40	4.2	4.2, 3° (c)
Alkaline-earth metal alcoholates, n.o.s.	3205	40	4.2	4.2, 14° (b), (c)
Alkali metal alcoholates, n.o.s.	3206	48	4.2 + 8	4.2, 15° (b), (c)
Metal alkyls, n.o.s. or metal aryls, n.o.s.	2003	X333	4.2 + 4.3	4.2, 31° (a)
Metal alkyl halides, n.o.s. or metal aryl halides, n.o.s.	3049	X333	4.2 + 4.3	4.2, 32° (a)
Metal alkyl hydrides, n.o.s. or metal aryl hydrides, n.o.s.	3050	X333	4.2 + 4.3	4.2, 32° (a)
General n.o.s entries				
Self-heating solid, organic, n.o.s.	3088	40	4.2	4.2, 5° (b), (c)
Pyrophoric liquid, organic, n.o.s.	2845	333	4.2	4.2, 6° (a)
Self-heating liquid, organic, n.o.s.	3183	30	4.2	4.2, 6° (b), (c)
Self-heating solid, toxic, organic, n.o.s.	3128	46	4.2 + 6.1	4.2, 7° (b), (c)
Self-heating liquid, toxic, organic, n.o.s.	3184	36	4.2 + 6.1	4.2, 8° (b), (c)
Self-heating solid, corrosive, organic, n.o.s.	3126	48	4.2 + 8	4.2, 9° (b), (c)
Self-heating liquid, corrosive, organic, n.o.s.	3185	38	4.2 + 8	4.2, 10° (b), (c)

Group of substances (a)	Substance Identification No. (Lower part) (b)	Hazard Identification No. (Upper part) (c)	Label (d)	Class and item number (e)
Metal powder, self-heating, n.o.s.	3189	40	4.2	4.2, 12° (b), (c)
Self-heating solid, inorganic, n.o.s.	3190	40	4.2	4.2, 16° (b), (c)
Pyrophoric liquid, inorganic, n.o.s.	3194	333	4.2	4.2, 17° (a)
Self-heating liquid, inorganic, n.o.s.	3186	30	4.2	4.2, 17° (b), (c)
Self-heating solid, toxic, inorganic, n.o.s.	3191	46	4.2 + 6.1	4.2, 18° (b), (c)
Self-heating liquid, toxic, inorganic, n.o.s.	3187	36	4.2 + 6.1	4.2, 19° (b), (c)
Self-heating solid, corrosive, inorganic, n.o.s.	3192	48	4.2 + 8	4.2, 20° (b), (c)
Self-heating liquid, corrosive, inorganic, n.o.s.	3188	38	4.2 + 8	4.2, 21° (b), (c)
Pyrophoric organometallic compound, n.o.s.	3203	X333	4.2 + 4.3	4.2, 33° (a)
Class 4.3: Substances, which, in contact with water, emit flammable gases				
Specific n.o.s. entries				
Chlorosilanes, water-reactive, flammable, corrosive, n.o.s.	2988	X338	4.3 + 3 + 8	4.3, 1° (a)
Alkali metal alloy, liquid, n.o.s.	1421	X423	4.3	4.3, 11° (a)
Alkaline-earth metal alloy, n.o.s.	1393	423	4.3	4.3, 11° (b)
Metal hydrides, water-reactive, n.o.s.	1409	423	4.3	4.3, 16° (b)
General n.o.s. entries				
Organometallic compound, or solution, or dispersion, water-reactive, flammable, n.o.s.	3207 3207	X323 323	4.3 + 3 4.3 + 3	4.3, 3° (a) 4.3, 3° (b), (c)
Metallic substance, water-reactive, n.o.s.	3208	423	4.3	4.3, 13° (b), (c)
Metallic substance, water-reactive, self-heating, n.o.s.	3209	423	4.3 + 4.2	4.3, 14° (b), (c)
Water-reactive solid, n.o.s.	2813	423	4.3	4.3, 20° (b), (c)
Water-reactive liquid, n.o.s.	3148 3148	X323 323	4.3 4.3	4.3, 21° (a) 4.3, 21° (b), (c)
Water-reactive solid, toxic, n.o.s.	3134	462	4.3 + 6.1	4.3, 22° (b), (c)
Water-reactive liquid, toxic, n.o.s.	3130 3130	X362 362	4.3 + 6.1 4.3 + 6.1	4.3, 23° (a) 4.3, 23° (b), (c)
Water-reactive solid, corrosive, n.o.s.	3131	482	4.3 + 8	4.3, 24° (b), (c)
Water-reactive liquid, corrosive, n.o.s.	3129 3129	X382 382	4.3 + 8 4.3 + 8	4.3, 25° (a) 4.3, 25° (b), (c)
Class 5.1: Oxidizing substances				
Specific n.o.s. entries				
Chlorates, inorganic, n.o.s.	1461	50	5.1	5.1, 11° (b)
Chlorates, inorganic, aqueous solution, n.o.s.	3210	50	5.1	5.1, 11° (b), (c)
Perchlorates, inorganic, n.o.s.	1481	50	5.1	5.1, 13° (b)
Perchlorates, inorganic, aqueous solution, n.o.s.	3211	50	5.1	5.1, 13° (b), (c)
Chlorites, inorganic, n.o.s.	1462	50	5.1	5.1, 14° (b)
Hypochlorites, inorganic, n.o.s.	3212	50	5.1	5.1, 15° (b)

Group of substances (a)	Substance Identification No. (Lower part) (b)	Hazard Identification No. (Upper part) (c)	Label (d)	Class and item number (e)
Bromates, inorganic, n.o.s.	1450	50	5.1	5.1, 16° (b)
Bromates, inorganic, aqueous solution n.o.s.	3213	50	5.1	5.1, 16° (b), (c)
Permanganates, inorganic, aqueous solution, n.o.s.	3214	50	5.1	5.1, 17° (b)
Permanganates, inorganic, n.o.s.	1482	50	5.1	5.1, 17° (b)
Persulphates, inorganic, n.o.s.	3215	50	5.1	5.1, 18° (c)
Persulphates, inorganic, aqueous solution, n.o.s.	3216	50	5.1	5.1, 18° (c)
Nitrates, inorganic, n.o.s.	1477	50	5.1	5.1, 22° (b), (c)
Nitrates, inorganic, aqueous solution, n.o.s.	3218	50	5.1	5.1, 22° (b), (c)
Nitrites, inorganic, n.o.s.	2627	50	5.1	5.1, 23° (b)
Nitrites, inorganic, aqueous solution, n.o.s.	3219	50	5.1	5.1, 23° (b), (c)
Peroxides, inorganic, n.o.s.	1483	50	5.1	5.1, 25° (b)
General n.o.s entries				
Oxidizing solid, n.o.s.	1479	50	5.1	5.1, 27° (b), (c)
Oxidizing solid, toxic, n.o.s.	3087	56	5.1 + 6.1	5.1, 29° (b), (c)
Oxidizing solid, corrosive, n.o.s.	3085	58	5.1 + 8	5.1, 31° (b), (c)
Class 5.2: Organic peroxides				
Specific collective headings				
Organic peroxide, type F, liquid	3109	539	5.2 + (8) */	5.2, 9° (b)
Organic peroxide, type F, liquid, temperature controlled	3119	539	5.2	5.2, 19° (b)
Organic peroxide, type F, solid	3110	539	5.2	5.2, 10° (b)
Organic peroxide, type F, solid, temperature controlled	3120	539	5.2	5.2, 20° (b)
Class 6.1: Toxic substances				
Specific n.o.s. entries or Specific collective headings				
Organic substances				
Nitriles, toxic, flammable, n.o.s.	3275 / 3275	663 / 63	6.1 + 3 / 6.1 + 3	6.1, 11° (a) / 6.1, 11° (b)2.
Nitriles, toxic, n.o.s.	3276 / 3276	66 / 60	6.1 / 6.1	6.1, 12° (a) / 6.1, 12° (b), (c)
Chloropicrin mixture, n.o.s.	1583 / 1583	66 / 60	6.1 / 6.1	6.1, 17° (a) / 6.1, 17° (b), (c)
Chloroformates, toxic, corrosive, n.o.s.	3277	68	6.1 + 8	6.1, 27° (b)
Chloroformates, toxic, corrosive, flammable, n.o.s.	2742	638	6.1 + 3 + 8	6.1, 28° (b)
Isocyanates, toxic, flammable, n.o.s.	3080	63	6.1 + 3	6.1, 18° (b)

*/ As the case may be.

Group of substances (a)	Substance Identification No. (Lower part) (b)	Hazard Identification No. (Upper part) (c)	Label (d)	Class and item number (e)
Isocyanate solution, toxic, flammable, n.o.s.	3080	63	6.1 + 3	6.1, 18° (b)
Isocyanates, toxic, n.o.s.	2206	60	6.1	6.1, 19° (b), (c)
Isocyanate solution, toxic, n.o.s.	2206	60	6.1	6.1, 19° (b), (c)
Mercaptans, liquid, toxic, flammable, n.o.s.	3071	63	6.1 + 3	6.1, 20° (b)
Mercaptan mixture, liquid, toxic, flammable, n.o.s.	3071	63	6.1 + 3	6.1, 20° (b)
Organophosphorus compound, toxic, flammable, n.o.s.	3279 3279 3279	663 663 63	6.1 + 3 6.1 + 3 6.1 + 3	6.1, 9° (a) 6.1, 22° (a) 6.1, 22° (b)
Organophosphorus compound, toxic, n.o.s.	3278 3278	66 60	6.1 6.1	6.1, 23° (a) 6.1, 23° (b), (c)
Disinfectant, liquid, toxic, n.o.s.	3142 3142	66 60	6.1 6.1	6.1, 25° (a) 6.1, 25° (b), (c)
Disinfectant, solid, toxic, n.o.s.	1601 1601	66 60	6.1 6.1	6.1, 25° (a) 6.1, 25° (b), (c)
Dye, liquid, toxic, n.o.s.	1602 1602	66 60	6.1 6.1	6.1, 25° (a) 6.1, 25° (b), (c)
Dye intermediate, liquid, toxic, n.o.s.	1602 1602	66 60	6.1 6.1	6.1, 25° (a) 6.1, 25° (b), (c)
Dye, solid, toxic, n.o.s.	3143 3143	66 60	6.1 6.1	6.1, 25° (a) 6.1, 25° (b), (c)
Dye intermediate, solid, toxic, n.o.s.	3143 3143	66 60	6.1 6.1	6.1, 25° (a) 6.1, 25° (b), (c)
Tear gas substance, liquid or solid, n.o.s.	1693 1693	66 60	6.1 6.1	6.1, 25° (a) 6.1, 25° (b)
Organometallic substances				
Organotin compound, liquid, n.o.s.	2788 2788	66 60	6.1 6.1	6.1, 32° (a) 6.1, 32° (b), (c)
Organotin compound, solid, n.o.s.	3146 3146	66 60	6.1 6.1	6.1, 32° (a) 6.1, 32° (b), (c)
Phenylmercuric compound, n.o.s.	2026 2026	66 60	6.1 6.1	6.1, 33° (a) 6.1, 33° (b), (c)
Organoarsenic compound, n.o.s.	3280 3280	66 60	6.1 6.1	6.1, 34° (a) 6.1, 34° (b), (c)
Metal carbonyls, n.o.s.	3281 3281	66 60	6.1 6.1	6.1, 36° (a) 6.1, 36° (b), (c)
Inorganic substances				
Cyanides, inorganic, solid, n.o.s.	1588 1588	66 60	6.1 6.1	6.1, 41° (a) 6.1, 41° (b), (c)
Cyanide solution, n.o.s.	1935 1935	66 60	6.1 6.1	6.1, 41° (a) 6.1, 41° (b), (c)
Arsenic compound, liquid, n.o.s., inorganic (arsenates, arsenites and arsenic sulphide)	1556 1556	66 60	6.1 6.1	6.1, 51° (a) 6.1, 51° (b), (c)
Arsenic compound, solid, n.o.s., inorganic (arsenates, arsenites and arsenic sulphide)	1557 1557	66 60	6.1 6.1	6.1, 51° (a) 6.1, 51° (b), (c)

Group of substances (a)	Substance Identification No. (Lower part) (b)	Hazard Identification No. (Upper part) (c)	Label (d)	Class and item number (e)
Mercury compound, liquid, n.o.s.	2024 2024	66 60	6.1 6.1	6.1, 52° (a) 6.1, 52° (b), (c)
Mercury compound, solid, n.o.s.	2025 2025	66 60	6.1 6.1	6.1, 52° (a) 6.1, 52° (b), (c)
Thallium compound, n.o.s.	1707	60	6.1	6.1, 53° (b)
Beryllium compound, n.o.s.	1566	60	6.1	6.1, 54° (b)2., (c)
Selenium compound, n.o.s.	3283 3283	66 60	6.1 6.1	6.1, 55° (a) 6.1, 55° (b), (c)
Tellurium compound, n.o.s.	3284	60	6.1	6.1, 57° (b), (c)
Vanadium compound, n.o.s.	3285	60	6.1	6.1, 58° (b), (c)
Antimony compound, inorganic, liquid, n.o.s.	3141	60	6.1	6.1, 59° (c)
Antimony compound, inorganic, solid, n.o.s.	1549	60	6.1	6.1, 59° (c)
Barium compound, n.o.s.	1564	60	6.1	6.1, 60° (b), (c)
Lead compound, soluble, n.o.s.	2291	60	6.1	6.1, 62° (c)
Fluorosilicates, n.o.s.	2856	60	6.1	6.1, 64° (c)
Cadmium compound	2570 2570	66 60	6.1 6.1	6.1, 61° (a) 6.1, 61° (b), (c)
Pesticides				
Organophosphorus pesticide, solid, toxic	2783 2783	66 60	6.1 6.1	6.1, 73° (a) 6.1, 73° (b), (c)
Organophosphorus pesticide, liquid, toxic, flammable	3017 3017	663 63	6.1 + 3 6.1 + 3	6.1, 72° (a) 6.1, 72° (b), (c)
Organophosphorus pesticide, liquid, toxic	3018 3018	66 60	6.1 6.1	6.1, 71° (a) 6.1, 71° (b), (c)
Organochlorine pesticide, solid, toxic	2761 2761	66 60	6.1 6.1	6.1, 73° (a) 6.1, 73° (b), (c)
Organochlorine pesticide, liquid, toxic, flammable	2995 2995	663 63	6.1 + 3 6.1 + 3	6.1, 72° (a) 6.1, 72° (b), (c)
Organochlorine pesticide, liquid, toxic	2996 2996	66 60	6.1 6.1	6.1, 71° (a) 6.1, 71° (b), (c)
Phenoxy pesticide, solid, toxic	2765 2765	66 60	6.1 6.1	6.1, 73° (a) 6.1, 73° (b), (c)
Phenoxy pesticide, liquid, toxic, flammable	2999 2999	663 63	6.1 + 3 6.1 + 3	6.1, 72° (a) 6.1, 72° (b), (c)
Phenoxy pesticide, liquid, toxic	3000 3000	66 60	6.1 6.1	6.1, 71° (a) 6.1, 71° (b), (c)
Carbamate pesticide, solid, toxic	2757 2757	66 60	6.1 6.1	6.1, 73° (a) 6.1, 73° (b), (c)
Carbamate pesticide, liquid, toxic, flammable	2991 2991	663 63	6.1 + 3 6.1 + 3	6.1, 72° (a) 6.1, 72° (b), (c)
Carbamate pesticide, liquid, toxic	2992 2992	66 60	6.1 6.1	6.1, 71° (a) 6.1, 71° (b), (c)
Mercury based pesticide, solid, toxic	2777 2777	66 60	6.1 6.1	6.1, 73° (a) 6.1, 73° (b), (c)

Group of substances (a)	Substance Identification No. (Lower part) (b)	Hazard Identification No. (Upper part) (c)	Label (d)	Class and item number (e)
Mercury based pesticide, liquid, toxic, flammable	3011 3011	663 63	6.1 + 3 6.1 + 3	6.1, 72° (a) 6.1, 72° (b), (c)
Mercury based pesticide, liquid, toxic	3012 3012	66 60	6.1 6.1	6.1, 71° (a) 6.1, 71° (b), (c)
Organotin pesticide, solid, toxic	2786 2786	66 60	6.1 6.1	6.1, 73° (a) 6.1, 73° (b), (c)
Organotin pesticide, liquid, toxic, flammable	3019 3019	663 63	6.1 + 3 6.1 + 3	6.1, 72° (a) 6.1, 72° (b), (c)
Organotin pesticide, liquid, toxic	3020 3020	66 60	6.1 6.1	6.1, 71° (a) 6.1, 71° (b), (c)
Coumarin derivative pesticide, liquid, toxic, flammable	3025 3025	663 63	6.1 + 3 6.1 + 3	6.1, 72° (a) 6.1, 72° (b), (c)
Coumarin derivative pesticide, liquid, toxic	3026 3026	66 60	6.1 6.1	6.1, 71° (a) 6.1, 71° (b), (c)
Coumarin derivative pesticide, solid, toxic	3027 3027	66 60	6.1 6.1	6.1, 73° (a) 6.1, 73° (b), (c)
Bipyridilium pesticide, solid, toxic	2781 2781	66 60	6.1 6.1	6.1, 73° (a) 6.1, 73° (b), (c)
Bipyridilium pesticide, liquid, toxic, flammable	3015 3015	663 63	6.1 + 3 6.1 + 3	6.1, 72° (a) 6.1, 72° (b), (c)
Bipyridilium pesticide, liquid, toxic	3016 3016	66 60	6.1 6.1	6.1, 71° (a) 6.1, 71° (b), (c)
Arsenical pesticide, solid, toxic	2759 2759	66 60	6.1 6.1	6.1, 73° (a) 6.1, 73° (b), (c)
Arsenical pesticide, liquid, toxic, flammable	2993 2993	663 63	6.1 + 3 6.1 + 3	6.1, 72° (a) 6.1, 72° (b), (c)
Arsenical pesticide, liquid, toxic	2994 2994	66 60	6.1 6.1	6.1, 71° (a) 6.1, 71° (b), (c)
Copper based pesticide, solid, toxic	2775 2775	66 60	6.1 6.1	6.1, 73° (a) 6.1, 73° (b), (c)
Copper based pesticide, liquid, toxic, flammable	3009 3009	663 63	6.1 + 3 6.1 + 3	6.1, 72° (a) 6.1, 72° (b), (c)
Copper based pesticide, liquid, toxic	3010 3010	66 60	6.1 6.1	6.1, 71° (a) 6.1, 71° (b), (c)
Substituted nitrophenol pesticide, solid, toxic	2779 2779	66 60	6.1 6.1	6.1, 73° (a) 6.1, 73° (b), (c)
Substituted nitrophenol pesticide, liquid, toxic, flammable	3013 3013	663 63	6.1 + 3 6.1 + 3	6.1, 72° (a) 6.1, 72° (b), (c)
Substituted nitrophenol pesticide, liquid, toxic	3014 3014	66 60	6.1 6.1	6.1, 71° (a) 6.1, 71° (b), (c)
Triazine pesticide, solid, toxic	2763 2763	66 60	6.1 6.1	6.1, 73° (a) 6.1, 73° (b), (c)
Triazine pesticide, liquid, toxic, flammable	2997 2997	663 63	6.1 + 3 6.1 + 3	6.1, 72° (a) 6.1, 72° (b), (c)
Triazine pesticide, liquid, toxic	2998 2998	66 60	6.1 6.1	6.1, 71° (a) 6.1, 71° (b), (c)

Group of substances (a)	Substance Identification No. (Lower part) (b)	Hazard Identification No. (Upper part) (c)	Label (d)	Class and item number (e)
Benzoic derivative pesticide, solid, toxic	2769 2769	66 60	6.1 6.1	6.1, 73° (a) 6.1, 73° (b), (c)
Benzoic derivative pesticide, liquid, toxic, flammable	3003 3003	663 63	6.1 + 3 6.1 + 3	6.1, 72° (a) 6.1, 72° (b), (c)
Benzoic derivative pesticide, liquid, toxic	3004 3004	66 60	6.1 6.1	6.1, 71° (a) 6.1, 71° (b), (c)
Phthalimide derivative pesticide, solid, toxic	2773 2773	66 60	6.1 6.1	6.1, 73° (a) 6.1, 73° (b), (c)
Phthalimide derivative pesticide, liquid, toxic, flammable	3007 3007	663 63	6.1 + 3 6.1 + 3	6.1, 72° (a) 6.1, 72° (b), (c)
Phthalimide derivative pesticide, liquid, toxic	3008 3008	66 60	6.1 6.1	6.1, 71° (a) 6.1, 71° (b), (c)
Phenyl urea pesticide, solid, toxic	2767 2767	66 60	6.1 6.1	6.1, 73° (a) 6.1, 73° (b), (c)
Phenyl urea pesticide, liquid, toxic, flammable	3001 3001	663 63	6.1 + 3 6.1 + 3	6.1, 72° (a) 6.1, 72° (b), (c)
Phenyl urea pesticide, liquid, toxic	3002 3002	66 60	6.1 6.1	6.1, 71° (a) 6.1, 71° (b), (c)
Dithiocarbamate pesticide, solid, toxic	2771 2771	66 60	6.1 6.1	6.1, 73° (a) 6.1, 73° (b), (c)
Dithiocarbamate pesticide, liquid, toxic, flammable	3005 3005	663 63	6.1 + 3 6.1 + 3	6.1, 72° (a) 6.1, 72° (b), (c)
Dithiocarbamate pesticide, liquid, toxic	3006 3006	66 60	6.1 6.1	6.1, 71° (a) 6.1, 71° (b), (c)
Pesticide, solid, toxic, n.o.s.	2588 2588	66 60	6.1 6.1	6.1, 73° (a) 6.1, 73° (b), (c)
Pesticide, liquid, toxic, n.o.s.	2902 2902	66 60	6.1 6.1	6.1, 71° (a) 6.1, 71° (b), (c)
Pesticide, liquid, toxic, flammable, n.o.s.	2903 2903	663 63	6.1 + 3 6.1 + 3	6.1, 72° (a) 6.1, 72° (b), (c)
Active substances				
Alkaloids or alcaloid salts, liquid, n.o.s.	3140 3140	66 60	6.1 6.1	6.1, 90° (a) 6.1, 90° (b), (c)
Alkaloids or alcaloid salts, solid, n.o.s.	1544 1544	66 60	6.1 6.1	6.1, 90° (a) 6.1, 90° (b), (c)
Nicotine compound or nicotine preparation, liquid, n.o.s.	3144 3144	66 60	6.1 6.1	6.1, 90° (a) 6.1, 90° (b), (c)
Nicotine compound or nicotine preparation, solid, n.o.s.	1655 1655	66 60	6.1 6.1	6.1, 90° (a) 6.1, 90° (b), (c)
Toxins, extracted from living sources, n.o.s.	3172 3172	66 60	6.1 6.1	6.1, 90° (a) 6.1, 90° (b), (c)
Medicine, liquid, toxic, n.o.s.	1851	60	6.1	6.1, 90° (b), (c)
Medicine, solid, toxic, n.o.s.	3249	60	6.1	6.1, 90° (b), (c)
General n.o.s. entries				
Organic substances				

Group of substances (a)	Substance Identification No. (Lower part) (b)	Hazard Identification No. (Upper part) (c)	Label (d)	Class and item number (e)
Toxic liquid, organic, n.o.s.	2810 2810	66 60	6.1 6.1	6.1, 25° (a) 6.1, 25° (b), (c)
Toxic solid, organic, n.o.s.	2811 2811	66 60	6.1 6.1	6.1, 25° (a) 6.1, 25° (b), (c)
Toxic liquid, flammable, organic, n.o.s.	2929 2929	663 63	6.1 + 3 6.1 + 3	6.1, 9° (a), 26° (a)1. 6.1, 26° (b)1.
Toxic solid, flammable, organic, n.o.s.	2930 2930	664 64	6.1 + 4.1 6.1 + 4.1	6.1, 26° (a)2. 6.1, 26° (b)2.
Toxic liquid, corrosive, organic, n.o.s.	2927 2927	668 68	6.1 + 8 6.1 + 8	6.1, 27° (a) 6.1, 27° (b)
Toxic solid, corrosive, organic, n.o.s.	2928 2928	668 68	6.1 + 8 6.1 + 8	6.1, 27° (a) 6.1, 27° (b)
Organometallic substances				
Organometallic compound, toxic, n.o.s.	3282 3282	66 60	6.1 6.1	6.1, 35° (a) 6.1, 35° (b), (c)
Inorganic substances				
Toxic liquid, water-reactive, n.o.s.	3123	623	6.1 + 4.3	6.1, 44° (a), (b)
Toxic solid, water-reactive, n.o.s.	3125	642	6.1 + 4.3	6.1, 44° (b), (c)
Solids containing toxic liquid, n.o.s.	3243	60	6.1	6.1, 65° (b)
Toxic liquid, inorganic, n.o.s.	3287 3287	66 60	6.1 6.1	6.1, 65° (a) 6.1, 65° (b), (c)
Toxic solid, inorganic, n.o.s.	3288 3288	66 60	6.1 6.1	6.1, 65° (a) 6.1, 65° (b), (c)
Toxic solid, self-heating, n.o.s.	3124 3124	664 64	6.1 + 4.2 6.1 + 4.2	6.1, 66° (a) 6.1, 66° (b)
Toxic liquid, corrosive, inorganic, n.o.s.	3289 3289	668 68	6.1 + 8 6.1 + 8	6.1, 67° (a) 6.1, 67° (b)
Toxic solid, corrosive, inorganic, n.o.s.	3290 3290	668 68	6.1 + 8 6.1 + 8	6.1, 67° (a) 6.1, 67° (b)
Toxic liquid, oxidizing, n.o.s.	3122 3122	665 65	6.1 + 05 6.1 + 05	6.1, 68° (a) 6.1, 68° (b)
Toxic solid, oxidizing, n.o.s.	3086 3086	665 65	6.1 + 05 6.1 + 05	6.1, 68° (a) 6.1, 68° (b)
Class 6.2: Infectious substances **Specific collective headings**				
Infectious substance, affecting humans	2814	606	6.2	6.2, 3° (b)
Infectious substance, affecting animals only	2900	606	6.2	6.2, 3° (b)
General n.o.s. entries				
Clinical waste, unspecified, n.o.s.	3291	606	6.2	6.2, 4° (b)
Class 7: Radioactive material **Specific n.o.s. entries**				

Group of substances (a)	Substance Identification No. (Lower part) (b)	Hazard Identification No. (Upper part) (c)	Label (d)	Class and item number (e)
Radioactive material, low specific activity (LSA), n.o.s.	2912	70	7A, 7B or 7C	7, Sch 5, 6 or 13
Radioactive material, low specific activity (LSA), n.o.s., gas	2912	72	7A, 7B or 7C	7, Sch 5, 6 or 13
Radioactive material, low specific activity (LSA), n.o.s., gas, flammable	2912	723	7A, 7B or 7C + 3	7, Sch 5, 6 or 13
Radioactive material, low specific activity (LSA), n.o.s., liquid, flammable, with a flash-point not above 61 °C	2912	73	7A, 7B or 7C + 3	7, Sch 5, 6 or 13
Radioactive material, low specific activity (LSA), n.o.s., solid, flammable	2912	74	7A, 7B or 7C + 4.1	7, Sch 5, 6 or 13
Radioactive material, low specific activity (LSA), n.o.s., oxidizing	2912	75	7A, 7B or 7C + 05	7, Sch 5, 6 or 13
Radioactive material, low specific activity (LSA), n.o.s., toxic	2912	76	7A, 7B or 7C + 6.1	7, Sch 5, 6 or 13
Radioactive material, low specific activity (LSA), n.o.s., corrosive	2912	78	7A, 7B or 7C + 8	7, Sch 5, 6 or 13
General n.o.s. entries				
Radioactive material, n.o.s.	2982	70	7A, 7B or 7C	7, Sch 9, 10, 11 or 13
Radioactive material, n.o.s., gas	2982	72	7A, 7B or 7C	7, Sch 9, 10, 11 or 13
Radioactive material, n.o.s., gas, flammable	2982	723	7A, 7B or 7C + 3	7, Sch 9, 10, 11 or 13
Radioactive material, n.o.s., liquid, flammable, with a flash-point not above 61 °C	2982	73	7A, 7B or 7C + 3	7, Sch 9, 10, 11 or 13
Radioactive material, n.o.s., solid, flammable	2982	74	7A, 7B or 7C + 4.1	7, Sch 9, 10, 11 or 13
Radioactive material, n.o.s., oxidizing	2982	75	7A, 7B or 7C + 05	7, Sch 9, 10, 11 or 13
Radioactive material, n.o.s., toxic	2982	76	7A, 7B or 7C + 6.1	7, Sch 9, 10, 11 or 13
Radioactive material, n.o.s., corrosive	2982	78	7A, 7B or 7C + 8	7, Sch 9, 10, 11 or 13
Class 8: Corrosive substances				
Specific n.o.s. entries				
Inorganic substances				
Hydrogendifluorides, n.o.s.	1740	80	8	8, 9° (b), (c)
Bisulphites, aqueous solution, n.o.s.	2693	80	8	8, 17° (c)
Organic substances				
Chlorosilanes, corrosive, n.o.s.	2987	80	8	8, 36° (b)
Chlorosilanes, corrosive, flammable, n.o.s.	2986	X83	8 + 3	8, 37° (b)
Alkylphenols, solid, n.o.s.	2430	88	8	8, 39° (a)
	2430	80	8	8, 39° (b), (c)

Group of substances (a)	Substance Identification No. (Lower part) (b)	Hazard Identification No. (Upper part) (c)	Label (d)	Class and item number (e)
Alkylphenols, liquid, n.o.s.	3145 3145	88 80	8 8	8, 40° (a) 8, 40° (b), (c)
Amines or polyamines, solid, corrosive, n.o.s.	3259 3259	88 80	8 8	8, 52° (a) 8, 52° (b), (c)
Amines or polyamines, liquid, corrosive, n.o.s.	2735 2735	88 80	8 8	8, 53° (a) 8, 53° (b), (c)
Amines or polyamines, liquid, corrosive, flammable, n.o.s.	2734 2734	883 83	8 + 3 8 + 3	8, 54° (a) 8, 54° (b)
Dye or dye intermediate, solid, corrosive, n.o.s.	3147	80	8	8, 65° (b), (c)
Dye or dye intermediate, liquid, corrosive, n.o.s	2801 2801	88 80	8 8	8, 66° (a) 8, 66° (b), (c)
Disinfectant, liquid, corrosive, n.o.s.	1903 1903	88 80	8 8	8, 66° (a) 8, 66° (b), (c)
General n.o.s. entries **Acid substances**				
Corrosive solid, acidic, inorganic, n.o.s.	3260 3260	88 80	8 8	8, 16° (a) 8, 16° (b), (c)
Corrosive liquid, acidic, inorganic, n.o.s.	3264 3264	88 80	8 8	8, 17° (a) 8, 17° (b), (c)
Organic substances				
Corrosive solid, acidic, organic, n.o.s.	3261 3261	88 80	8 8	8, 39° (a) 8, 39° (b), (c)
Corrosive liquid, acidic, organic, n.o.s.	3265 3265	88 80	8 8	8, 40° (a) 8, 40° (b), (c)
Basic substances **Inorganic substances**				
Caustic alkali liquid, n.o.s.	1719	80	8	8, 42° (b), (c)
Corrosive solid, basic, inorganic, n.o.s.	3262 3262	88 80	8 8	8, 46° (a) 8, 46° (b), (c)
Corrosive liquid, basic, inorganic, n.o.s.	3266 3266	80 88	8 8	8, 47° (a) 8, 47° (b), (c)
Organic substances				
Corrosive solid, basic, organic, n.o.s.	3263 3263	88 80	8 8	8, 55° (a) 8, 55° (b), (c)
Corrosive liquid, basic, organic, n.o.s.	3267 3267	88 80	8 8	8, 56° (a) 8, 56° (b), (c)
Other corrosive substances				
Solids containing corrosive liquid, n.o.s.	3244	80	8	8, 65° (b)
Corrosive solid, n.o.s.	1759 1759	88 80	8 8	8, 65° (a) 8, 65° (b), (c)
Corrosive liquid, n.o.s.	1760 1760	88 80	8 8	8, 66° (a) 8, 66° (b), (c)
Corrosive solid, flammable, n.o.s.	2921 2921	884 84	8 + 4.1 8 + 4.1	8, 67° (a) 8, 67° (b)

Group of substances (a)	Substance Identification No. (Lower part) (b)	Hazard Identification No. (Upper part) (c)	Label (d)	Class and item number (e)
Corrosive liquid, flammable, n.o.s.	2920 2920	883 83	8 + 3 8 + 3	8, 68° (a) 8, 68° (b)
Corrosive solid, self-heating, n.o.s.	3095	84	8 + 4.2	8, 69° (b)
Corrosive liquid, self-heating, n.o.s.	3301 3301	884 84	8 + 4.2 8 + 4.2	8, 70° (a) 8, 70° (b)
Corrosive solid, water-reactive, n.o.s.	3096	842	8 + 4.3	8, 71° (b)
Corrosive liquid, water-reactive n.o.s.	3094	823	8 + 4.3	8, 72° (a), (b)
Corrosive solid, oxidizing, n.o.s.	3084 3084	885 85	8 + 05 8 + 05	8, 73° (a) 8, 73° (b)
Corrosive liquid, oxidizing, n.o.s.	3093 3093	885 85	8 + 05 8 + 05	8, 74° (a) 8, 74° (b)
Corrosive solid, toxic, n.o.s.	2923 2923	886 86	8 + 6.1 8 + 6.1	8, 75° (a) 8, 75° (b), (c)
Corrosive liquid, toxic, n.o.s.	2922 2922	886 86	8 + 6.1 8 + 6.1	8, 76° (a) 8, 76° (b), (c)
Class 9: Miscellaneous dangerous substances and articles **Enviromentally hazardous substances**				
Environmentally hazardous substance, liquid, n.o.s.	3082	90	9	9, 11° (c)
Environmentally hazardous substance, solid, n.o.s.	3077	90	9	9, 12° (c)
Elevated temperature liquid, n.o.s	3257	99	9	9, 20° (c)
Elevated temperature solid, n.o.s.	3258	99	9	9, 21° (c)

Table 3

Numerical list - this table contains all the entries of tables 1 and 2 in substance identification number order

Substance Identification No. (Lower part)	Name of substance	Hazard Identification No. (Upper part)	Label	Class and item number
(a)	(b)	(c)	(d)	(e)
1001	Acetylene, dissolved	239	3	2, 4°F
1002	Air, compressed	20	2	2, 1°A
1003	Air, refrigerated liquid	225	2 + 05	2, 3°O
1005	Ammonia, anhydrous	268	6.1 + 8	2, 2°TC
1006	Argon, compressed	20	2	2, 1°A
1008	Boron trifluoride, compressed	268	6.1 + 8	2, 1°TC
1009	Bromotrifluoromethane (R 13B1)	20	2	2, 2°A
1010	1,2-Butadiene, inhibited	239	3	2, 2°F
1010	1,3-Butadiene, inhibited	239	3	2, 2°F
1010	Mixtures of 1,3-butadiene and hydrocarbons, inhibited	239	3	2, 2°F
1011	Butane	23	3	2, 2°F
1012	1-Butylene	23	3	2, 2°F
1012	Butylenes mixture	23	3	2, 2°F
1012	cis-2-Butylene	23	3	2, 2°F
1012	trans-2-Butylene	23	3	2, 2°F
1013	Carbon dioxide	20	2	2, 2°A
1014	Oxygen and carbon dioxide mixture, compressed (max. 30% CO2)	25	2 + 05	2, 1°O
1015	Carbon dioxide and nitrous oxide, mixture	20	2	2, 2°A
1016	Carbon monoxide, compressed	263	6.1 + 3	2, 1°TF
1017	Chlorine	268	6.1 + 8	2, 2°TC
1018	Chlorodifluoromethane (R 22)	20	2	2, 2°A
1020	Chloropentafluoroethane (R 115)	20	2	2, 2°A
1021	1-Chloro-1,2,2,2-tetrafluoroethane (R 124)	20	2	2, 2°A
1022	Chlorotrifluoromethane (R 13)	20	2	2, 2°A
1023	Coal gas, compressed	263	6.1 + 3	2, 1°TF
1026	Cyanogen	263	6.1 + 3	2, 2TF
1027	Cyclopropane	23	3	2, 2°F
1028	Dichlorodifluoromethane (R 12)	20	2	2, 2°A
1029	Dichlorofluoromethane (R 21)	20	2	2, 2°A
1030	1,1-Difluoroethane (R 152a)	23	3	2, 2°F
1032	Dimethylamine, anhydrous	23	3	2, 2°F
1033	Dimethyl ether	23	3	2, 2°F
1035	Ethane	23	3	2, 2°F

Substance Identification No. (Lower part) (a)	Name of substance (b)	Hazard Identification No. (Upper part) (c)	Label (d)	Class and item number (e)
1036	Ethylamine	23	3	2, 2°F
1037	Ethyl chloride	23	3	2, 2°F
1038	Ethylene, refrigerated liquid	223	3	2, 3°F
1039	Ethyl methyl ether	23	3	2, 2°F
1040	Ethylene oxide with nitrogen	263	6.1 + 3	2, 2°TF
1041	Ethylene oxide and carbon dioxide mixture, with more than 9 % but not more than 87% ethylene oxide	239	3	2, 2°F
1046	Helium, compressed	20	2	2, 1°A
1048	Hydrogen bromide, anhydrous	268	6.1 + 8	2, 2°TC
1049	Hydrogen, compressed	23	3	2, 1°F
1050	Hydrogen chloride, anhydrous	268	6.1 + 8	2, 2°TC
1052	Hydrogen fluoride, anhydrous	886	8 + 6.1	8, 6°
1053	Hydrogen sulphide	263	6.1 + 3	2, 2°TF
1055	Isobutylene	23	3	2, 2°F
1056	Krypton, compressed	20	2	2, 1°A
1058	Liquefied gases, non-flammable, charged with nitrogen, carbon dioxide or air	20	2	2, 2°A
1060	Methylacetylene and propadiene mixtures, stabilized	239	3	2, 2°F
1060	Mixture P1, P2: see methylacetylene and propadiene, mixtures, stabilized	239	3	2, 2°F
1061	Methylamine, anhydrous	23	3	2, 2°F
1062	Methyl bromide	26	6.1	2, 2°T
1063	Methyl chloride	23	3	2, 2°F
1064	Methyl mercaptan	263	6.1 + 3	2, 2°TF
1065	Neon, compressed	20	2	2, 1°A
1066	Nitrogen, compressed	20	2	2, 1°A
1067	Dinitrogen tetroxide (nitrogen dioxide)	265	6.1 + 05 + 8	2, 2°TOC
1070	Nitrous oxide	25	2 + 05	2, 2°O
1071	Oil gas, compressed	263	6.1 + 3	2, 1°TF
1072	Oxygen, compressed	25	2 + 05	2, 1°O
1073	Oxygen, refrigerated liquid	225	2 + 05	2, 3°O
1076	Phosgene	268	6.1 + 8	2, 2°TC
1077	Propylene	23	3	2, 2°F
1078	Mixture F1, F2, F3: see Refrigerant gas, n.o.s.	20	2	2, 2°A
1078	Refrigerant gas, n.o.s.	20	2	2, 2°A
1079	Sulphur dioxide	268	6.1 + 8	2, 2°TC
1080	Sulphur hexafluoride	20	2	2, 2°A

Substance Identification No. (Lower part) (a)	Name of substance (b)	Hazard Identification No. (Upper part) (c)	Label (d)	Class and item number (e)
1081	Tetrafluorethylene, inhibited	239	3	2, 2°F
1082	Trifluorochloroethylene, inhibited (R 1113)	263	6.1 + 3	2, 2°TF
1083	Trimethylamine, anhydrous	23	3	2, 2°F
1085	Vinyl bromide, inhibited	239	3	2, 2°F
1086	Vinyl chloride, inhibited or stabilized	239	3	2, 2°F
1087	Vinyl methyl ether, inhibited	239	3	2, 2°F
1088	Acetal	33	3	3, 3° (b)
1089	Acetaldehyde	33	3	3, 1° (a)
1090	Acetone	33	3	3, 3° (b)
1091	Acetone oils	33	3	3, 3° (b)
1092	Acrolein, inhibited	663	6.1 + 3	6.1, 8° (a)2.
1093	Acrylonitrile, inhibited	336	3 + 6.1	3, 11° (a)
1098	Allyl alcohol	663	6.1 + 3	6.1, 8° (a)2.
1099	Allyl bromide	336	3 + 6.1	3, 16° (a)
1100	Allyl chloride	336	3 + 6.1	3, 16° (a)
1104	Amyl acetates	30	3	3, 31° (c)
1105	Amyl alcohols	33	3	3, 3° (b)
1105	Amyl alcohols	30	3	3, 31° (c)
1106	Amylamines (n-amylamine, tert-amylamine)	338	3 + 8	3, 22° (b)
1106	Amylamine (sec-amylamine)	38	3 + 8	3, 33° (c)
1107	Amyl chloride	33	3	3, 3° (b)
1108	1-Pentene (n-Amylene)	33	3	3, 1° (a)
1109	Amyl formates	30	3	3, 31° (c)
1110	n-Amyl methyl ketone	30	3	3, 31° (c)
1111	Amyl mercaptan	33	3	3, 3° (b)
1112	Amyl nitrate	30	3	3, 31° (c)
1113	Amyl nitrite	33	3	3, 3° (b)
1114	Benzene	33	3	3, 3° (b)
1120	Butanols	33	3	3, 3° (b)
1120	Butanols	30	3	3, 31° (c)
1123	Butyl acetates	33	3	3, 3° (b)
1123	Butyl acetates	30	3	3, 31° (c)
1125	n-Butylamine	338	3 + 8	3, 22° (b)
1126	1-Bromobutane	33	3	3, 3° (b)
1126	n-Butyl bromide	33	3	3, 3° (b)
1127	Chlorobutanes	33	3	3, 3° (b)
1128	n-Butyl formate	33	3	3, 3° (b)
1129	Butyraldehyde	33	3	3, 3° (b)

Substance Identification No. (Lower part) (a)	Name of substance (b)	Hazard Identification No. (Upper part) (c)	Label (d)	Class and item number (e)
1130	Camphor oil	30	3	3, 31° (c)
1131	Carbon disulphide	336	3 + 6.1	3, 18° (a)
1131	Carbon sulphide	336	3 + 6.1	3, 18° (a)
1133	Adhesives	33	3	3, 5° (a), (b), (c)
1133	Adhesives	30	3	3, 31° (c)
1134	Chlorobenzene	30	3	3, 31° (c)
1135	Ethylene chlorohydrin	663	6.1 + 3	6.1, 16° (a)
1136	Coal tar distillates	33	3	3, 3° (b)
1136	Coal tar distillates	30	3	3, 31° (c)
1139	Coating solution	33	3	3, 5° (a), (b), (c)
1139	Coating solution	30	3	3, 31° (c)
1143	Crotonaldehyde, stabilized	663	6.1 + 3	6.1, 8° (a)2.
1144	Crotonylene (2-Butyne)	339	3	3, 1° (a)
1145	Cyclohexane	33	3	3, 3° (b)
1146	Cyclopentane	33	3	3, 3° (b)
1147	Decahydronaphthalene	30	3	3, 31° (c)
1148	Diacetone alcohol, technically-pure	33	3	3, 3° (b)
1148	Diacetone alcohol, chemically pure	30	3	3, 31° (c)
1149	Dibutyl ethers	30	3	3, 31° (c)
1150	1,2-Dichloroethylene	33	3	3, 3° (b)
1152	Dichloropentanes	30	3	3, 31° (c)
1153	Ethylene glycol diethyl ether	30	3	3, 31° (c)
1154	Diethylamine	338	3 + 8	3, 22° (b)
1155	Diethyl ether (ethyl ether)	33	3	3, 2° (a)
1156	Diethyl ketone	33	3	3, 3° (b)
1157	Diisobutyl ketone	30	3	3, 31° (c)
1158	Diisopropylamine	338	3 + 8	3, 22° (b)
1159	Diisopropyl ether	33	3	3, 3° (b)
1160	Dimethylamine aqueous solution	338	3 + 8	3, 22° (b)
1161	Dimethyl carbonate	33	3	3, 3° (b)
1162	Dimethyldichlorosilane	X338	3 + 8	3, 21° (b)
1163	Dimethylhydrazine, unsymmetrical	663	6.1 + 3 + 8	6.1, 7° (a)1.
1164	Dimethyl sulphide	33	3	3, 2° (b)
1165	Dioxane	33	3	3, 3° (b)
1166	Dioxolane	33	3	3, 3° (b)
1167	Divinyl ether inhibited	339	3	3, 2° (a)
1169	Extracts, aromatic, liquid	33	3	3, 5° (a), (b), (c)
1169	Extracts, aromatic, liquid	30	3	3, 31° (c)

Substance Identification No. (Lower part) (a)	Name of substance (b)	Hazard Identification No. (Upper part) (c)	Label (d)	Class and item number (e)
1170	Ethanol (Ethyl alcohol) or ethanol (Ethyl alcohol) solution containing more than 70 vol.-% alcohol	33	3	3, 3° (b)
1170	Ethanol solution (Ethyl alcohol solution) containing more than 24 vol.-% and not more than 70 vol.-% alcohol	30	3	3, 31° (c)
1171	Ethylene glycol monoethyl ether	30	3	3, 31° (c)
1172	Ethylene glycol monoethyl ether acetate	30	3	3, 31° (c)
1173	Ethyl acetate	33	3	3, 3° (b)
1175	Ethylbenzene	33	3	3, 3° (b)
1176	Ethyl borate	33	3	3, 3° (b)
1177	Ethylbutyl acetate	30	3	3, 31° (c)
1178	2-Ethylbutyraldehyde	33	3	3, 3° (b)
1179	Ethyl butyl ether	33	3	3, 3° (b)
1180	Ethyl butyrate	30	3	3, 31° (c)
1181	Ethyl chloroacetate	63	6.1 + 3	6.1, 16° (b)
1182	Ethyl chloroformate	663	6.1 + 3 + 8	6.1, 10° (a)
1183	Ethyldichlorosilane	X338	4.3 + 3 + 8	4.3, 1° (a)
1184	1,2-Dichloroethane (Ethylene dichloride)	336	3 + 6.1	3, 16° (b)
1185	Ethyleneimine, inhibited	663	6.1 + 3	6.1, 4°
1188	Ethylene glycol monomethyl ether	30	3	3, 31° (c)
1189	Ethylene glycol monomethyl ether acetate	30	3	3, 31° (c)
1190	Ethyl formate	33	3	3, 3° (b)
1191	Octyl aldehydes (ethyl hexaldehydes)	30	3	3, 31° (c)
1192	Ethyl lactate	30	3	3, 31° (c)
1193	Ethyl methyl ketone (methyl ethyl ketone)	33	3	3, 3° (b)
1194	Ethyl nitrite solution	336	3 + 6.1	3, 15° (a)
1195	Ethyl propionate	33	3	3, 3° (b)
1196	Ethyltrichlorosilane	X338	3 + 8	3, 21° (b)
1197	Extracts, flavouring, liquid	33	3	3, 5° (a), (b), (c)
1197	Extracts, flavouring, liquid	30	3	3, 31° (c)
1198	Formaldehyde solution, flammable	38	3 + 8	3, 33° (c)
1199	Furaldehydes	63	6.1 + 3	6.1, 13° (b)
1201	Fusel oil	33	3	3, 3° (b)
1201	Fusel oil	30	3	3, 31° (c)
1202	Diesel fuel	30	3	3, 31° (c)
1202	Gas oil	30	3	3, 31° (c)
1202	Heating oil (light)	30	3	3, 31° (c)
1203	Motor spirit	33	3	3, 3° (b)
1206	Heptanes	33	3	3, 3° (b)

Substance Identification No. (Lower part) (a)	Name of substance (b)	Hazard Identification No. (Upper part) (c)	Label (d)	Class and item number (e)
1207	Hexaldehyde	30	3	3, 31° (c)
1208	Hexanes	33	3	3, 3° (b)
1210	Printing ink	33	3	3, 5° (a), (b), (c)
1210	Printing ink	30	3	3, 31° (c)
1212	Isobutanol	30	3	3, 31° (c)
1213	Isobutyl acetate	33	3	3, 3° (b)
1214	Isobutylamine	338	3 + 8	3, 22° (b)
1216	Isooctenes	33	3	3, 3° (b)
1218	Isoprene, inhibited	339	3	3, 2° (a)
1219	Isopropanol (Isopropyl alcohol)	33	3	3, 3° (b)
1220	Isopropyl acetate	33	3	3, 3° (b)
1221	Isopropylamine	338	3 + 8	3, 22° (a)
1223	Kerosene	30	3	3, 31° (c)
1224	Ketones, n.o.s.	33	3	3, 2° (b), 3° (b)
1224	Ketones, n.o.s.	30	3	3, 31° (c)
1228	Mercaptans or mercaptan mixture, liquid, flammable, toxic n.o.s.	336	3 + 6.1	3, 18° (b)
1228	Mercaptans or mercaptans mixture, liquid, flammable, toxic, n.o.s.	36	3 + 6.1	3, 32° (c)
1229	Mesityl oxide	30	3	3, 31° (c)
1230	Methanol	336	3 + 6.1	3, 17° (b)
1231	Methyl acetate	33	3	3, 3° (b)
1233	Methylamyl acetate	30	3	3, 31° (c)
1234	Methylal	33	3	3, 2° (b)
1235	Methylamine, aqueous solution	338	3 + 8	3, 22° (b)
1237	Methyl butyrate	33	3	3, 3° (b)
1238	Methyl chloroformate	663	6.1 + 3 + 8	6.1, 10° (a)
1239	Methyl chloromethyl ether	663	6.1 + 3	6.1, 9° (a)
1242	Methyldichlorosilane	X338	4.3 + 3 + 8	4.3, 1° (a)
1243	Methyl formate	33	3	3, 1° (a)
1244	Methylhydrazine	663	6.1 + 3 + 8	6.1, 7° (a)1.
1245	Methyl isobutyl ketone	33	3	3, 3° (b)
1246	Methyl isopropenyl ketone, inhibited	339	3	3, 3° (b)
1247	Methyl methacrylate monomer, inhibited	339	3	3, 3° (b)
1248	Methyl propionate	33	3	3, 3° (b)
1249	Methyl propyl ketone	33	3	3, 3° (b)
1250	Methyltrichlorosilane	X338	3 + 8	3, 21° (a)
1251	Methyl vinyl ketone, stabilized	639	6.1 + 3	6.1, 8° (a)1.

Substance Identification No. (Lower part) (a)	Name of substance (b)	Hazard Identification No. (Upper part) (c)	Label (d)	Class and item number (e)
1259	Nickel carbonyl	663	6.1 + 3	6.1, 3°
1262	Octanes	33	3	3, 3° (b)
1263	Paint	33	3	3, 5° (a), (b), (c)
1263	Paint	30	3	3, 31° (c)
1263	Paint related material	33	3	3, 5° (a), (b), (c)
1263	Paint related material	30	3	3, 31° (c)
1264	Paraldehyde	30	3	3, 31° (c)
1265	Pentanes, liquid	33	3	3, 1° (a)
1265	Pentanes, liquid	33	3	3, 2° (b)
1266	Perfumery products	33	3	3, 5° (a), (b), (c)
1266	Perfumery products	30	3	3, 31° (c)
1267	Petroleum crude oil	33	3	3, 1° (a), 2° (a), (b), 3° (b)
1267	Petroleum crude oil	30	3	3, 31° (c)
1268	Petroleum distillates, n.o.s.	33	3	3, 1° (a), 2° (a), (b), 3° (b)
1268	Petroleum distillates, n.o.s.	30	3	3, 31° (c)
1268	Petroleum products, n.o.s.	33	3	3, 1° (a), 2° (a), (b), 3° (b)
1268	Petroleum products, n.o.s.	30	3	3, 31° (c)
1272	Pine oil	30	3	3, 31° (c)
1274	n-Propanol	33	3	3, 3° (b)
1274	n-Propanol	30	3	3, 31° (c)
1275	Propionaldehyde	33	3	3, 3° (b)
1276	n-Propyl acetate	33	3	3, 3° (b)
1277	Propylamine	338	3 + 8	3, 22° (b)
1278	1-Chloropropane (Propyl chloride)	33	3	3, 2° (b)
1279	1,2-Dichloropropane	33	3	3, 3° (b)
1280	Propylene oxide	339	3	3, 2° (a)
1281	Propyl formates	33	3	3, 3° (b)
1282	Pyridine	33	3	3, 3° (b)
1286	Rosin oil	33	3	3, 5° (a), (b), (c)
1286	Rosin oil	30	3	3, 31° (c)
1287	Rubber solution	33	3	3, 5° (a), (b), (c)
1287	Rubber solution	30	3	3, 31° (c)
1288	Shale oil	33	3	3, 3° (b)
1288	Shale oil	30	3	3, 31° (c)
1289	Sodium methylate solution	338	3 + 8	3, 24° (b)
1289	Sodium methylate solution	38	3 + 8	3, 33° (c)

Substance Identification No. (Lower part) (a)	Name of substance (b)	Hazard Identification No. (Upper part) (c)	Label (d)	Class and item number (e)
1292	Tetraethyl silicate	30	3	3, 31° (c)
1293	Tinctures, medicinal	33	3	3, 3° (b)
1293	Tinctures, medicinal	30	3	3, 31° (c)
1294	Toluene	33	3	3, 3° (b)
1295	Trichlorosilane	X338	4.3 + 3 + 8	4.3, 1° (a)
1296	Triethylamine	338	3 + 8	3, 22° (b)
1297	Trimethylamine, aqueous solution	338	3 + 8	3, 22° (a), (b)
1297	Trimethylamine, aqueous solution	38	3 + 8	3, 33° (c)
1298	Trimethylchlorosilane	X338	3 + 8	3, 21° (b)
1299	Turpentine	30	3	3, 31° (c)
1300	Turpentine substitute	33	3	3, 3° (b)
1300	Turpentine substitute	30	3	3, 31° (c)
1301	Vinyl acetate, inhibited	339	3	3, 3° (b)
1302	Vinyl ethyl ether, inhibited	339	3	3, 2° (a)
1303	Vinylidene chloride, inhibited	339	3	3, 1° (a)
1304	Vinyl isobutyl ether, inhibited	339	3	3, 3° (b)
1305	Vinyltrichlorosilane, inhibited	X338	3 + 8	3, 21° (a)
1306	Wood preservatives, liquid	33	3	3, 5° (b), (c)
1306	Wood preservatives, liquid	30	3	3, 31° (c)
1307	Xylenes	33	3	3, 3° (b)
1307	Xylenes	30	3	3, 31° (c)
1308	Zirconium suspended in a flammable liquid	33	3	3, 1° (a), 2° (a), (b), 3° (b)
1308	Zirconium suspended in a flammable liquid	30	3	3, 31° (c)
1309	Aluminium powder, coated	40	4.1	4.1, 13° (b), (c)
1312	Borneol	40	4.1	4.1, 6° (c)
1313	Calcium resinate	40	4.1	4.1, 12° (c)
1314	Calcium resinate, fused	40	4.1	4.1, 12° (c)
1318	Cobalt resinate, precipitated	40	4.1	4.1, 12° (c)
1323	Ferrocerium	40	4.1	4.1, 13° (b)
1325	Flammable solid, organic, n.o.s.	40	4.1	4.1, 6° (b), (c)
1326	Hafnium powder, wetted	40	4.1	4.1, 13° (b)
1328	Hexamethylenetetramine	40	4.1	4.1, 6° (c)
1330	Manganese resinate	40	4.1	4.1, 12° (c)
1332	Metaldehyde	40	4.1	4.1, 6° (c)
1334	Naphthalene, crude or refined	40	4.1	4.1, 6° (c)
1338	Phosphorus, amorphous	40	4.1	4.1, 11° (c)
1339	Phosphorus heptasulphide	40	4.1	4.1, 11° (b)

Substance Identification No. (Lower part) (a)	Name of substance (b)	Hazard Identification No. (Upper part) (c)	Label (d)	Class and item number (e)
1340	Phosphorus pentasulphide	423	4.3	4.3, 20° (b)
1341	Phosphorus sesquisulphide	40	4.1	4.1, 11° (b)
1343	Phosphorus trisulphide	40	4.1	4.1, 11° (b)
1345	Rubber scrap or shoddy	40	4.1	4.1, 1° (b)
1346	Silicon powder, amorphous	40	4.1	4.1, 13° (c)
1350	Sulphur	40	4.1	4.1, 11° (c)
1352	Titanium powder, wetted	40	4.1	4.1, 13° (b)
1358	Zirconium powder, wetted	40	4.1	4.1, 13° (b)
1361	Carbon	40	4.2	4.2, 1° (b), (c)
1361	Carbon black	40	4.2	4.2, 1° (b), (c)
1362	Carbon, activated	40	4.2	4.2, 1° (c)
1363	Copra	40	4.2	4.2, 2° (c)
1364	Cotton waste, oily	40	4.2	4.2, 3° (c)
1365	Cotton, wet	40	4.2	4.2, 3° (c)
1366	Diethylzinc	X333	4.2 + 4.3	4.2, 31° (a)
1369	p-Nitrosodimethylaniline	40	4.2	4.2, 5° (b)
1370	Dimethylzinc	X333	4.2 + 4.3	4.2, 31° (a)
1373	Fibres, animal, vegetable or synthetic, n.o.s.	40	4.2	4.2, 3° (c)
1373	Fabrics, animal, vegetable or synthetic, n.o.s.	40	4.2	4.2, 3° (c)
1376	Iron oxide, spent	40	4.2	4.2, 16° (c)
1376	Iron sponge, spent	40	4.2	4.2, 16° (c)
1378	Metal catalyst, wetted	40	4.2	4.2, 12° (b)
1379	Paper, unsaturated oil treated	40	4.2	4.2, 3° (c)
1380	Pentaborane	333	4.2 + 6.1	4.2, 19° (a)
1381	Phosphorus, white or yellow, dry	46	4.2 + 6.1	4.2, 11° (a)
1382	Potassium sulphide, anhydrous	40	4.2	4.2, 13° (b)
1382	Potassium sulphide, with less than 30% water of crystallisation	40	4.2	4.2, 13° (b)
1384	Sodium dithionite (Sodium hydrosulphite)	40	4.2	4.2, 13° (b
1385	Sodium sulphide, anhydrous	40	4.2	4.2, 13° (b)
1385	Sodium sulphide, with less than 30% water of crystallisation	40	4.2	4.2, 13° (b)
1386	Seed cake	40	4.2	4.2, 2° (c)
1389	Alkali metal amalgam	X423	4.3	4.3, 11° (a)
1390	Alkali metal amides	423	4.3	4.3, 19° (b)
1391	Alkali metal dispersion	X423	4.3	4.3, 11° (a)
1391	Alkaline earth metal dispersion	X423	4.3	4.3, 11° (a)
1392	Alkaline earth metal amalgam	X423	4.3	4.3, 11° (a)

Substance Identification No. (Lower part) (a)	Name of substance (b)	Hazard Identification No. (Upper part) (c)	Label (d)	Class and item number (e)
1393	Alkaline-earth metal alloy, n.o.s.	423	4.3	4.3, 11° (b)
1394	Aluminium carbide	423	4.3	4.3, 17° (b)
1395	Aluminium ferrosilicon powder	462	4.3 + 6.1	4.3, 15° (b)
1396	Aluminium powder, uncoated	423	4.3	4.3, 13° (b)
1398	Aluminium silicon powder, uncoated	423	4.3	4.3, 13° (c)
1400	Barium	423	4.3	4.3, 11° (b)
1401	Calcium	423	4.3	4.3, 11° (b)
1402	Calcium carbide	423	4.3	4.3, 17° (b)
1403	Calcium cyanamide	423	4.3	4.3, 19° (c)
1405	Calcium silicide	423	4.3	4.3, 12° (b), (c)
1407	Caesium	X423	4.3	4.3, 11° (a)
1408	Ferrosilicon	462	4.3 + 6.1	4.3, 15° (c)
1409	Metal hydrides, water-reactive, n.o.s.	423	4.3	4.3, 16° (b)
1415	Lithium	X423	4.3	4.3, 11° (a)
1417	Lithium silicon	423	4.3	4.3, 12° (b)
1418	Magnesium powder	423	4.3 + 4.2	4.3, 14° (b)
1420	Potassium metal alloys	X423	4.3	4.3, 11° (a)
1421	Alkali metal alloy, liquid, n.o.s.	X423	4.3	4.3, 11° (a)
1422	Potassium sodium alloys	X423	4.3	4.3, 11° (a)
1423	Rubidium	X423	4.3	4.3, 11° (a)
1428	Sodium	X423	4.3	4.3, 11° (a)
1431	Sodium methylate	48	4.2 + 8	4.2, 15° (b)
1435	Zinc ashes	423	4.3	4.3, 13° (c)
1436	Zinc dust	423	4.3 + 4.2	4.3, 14° (b), (c)
1436	Zinc powder	423	4.3 + 4.2	4.3, 14° (b), (c)
1437	Zirconium hydride	40	4.1	4.1, 14° (b)
1438	Aluminium nitrate	50	5.1	5.1, 22° (c)
1439	Ammonium dichromate	50	5.1	5.1, 27° (b)
1442	Ammonium perchlorate	50	5.1	5.1, 12° (b)
1444	Ammonium persulphate	50	5.1	5.1, 18° (c)
1445	Barium chlorate	56	5.1 + 6.1	5.1, 29° (b)
1446	Barium nitrate	56	5.1 + 6.1	5.1, 29° (b)
1447	Barium perchlorate	56	5.1 + 6.1	5.1, 29° (b)
1448	Barium permanganate	56	5.1 + 6.1	5.1, 29° (b)
1449	Barium peroxide	56	5.1 + 6.1	5.1, 29° (b)
1450	Bromates, inorganic, n.o.s.	50	5.1	5.1, 16° (b)
1451	Caesium nitrate	50	5.1	5.1, 22° (c)
1452	Calcium chlorate	50	5.1	5.1, 11° (b)

Substance Identification No. (Lower part) (a)	Name of substance (b)	Hazard Identification No. (Upper part) (c)	Label (d)	Class and item number (e)
1453	Calcium chlorite	50	5.1	5.1, 14° (b)
1454	Calcium nitrate	50	5.1	5.1, 22° (c)
1455	Calcium perchlorate	50	5.1	5.1, 13° (b)
1456	Calcium permanganate	50	5.1	5.1, 17° (b)
1457	Calcium peroxide	50	5.1	5.1, 25° (b)
1458	Chlorate and borate mixture	50	5.1	5.1, 11° (b)
1459	Chlorate and magnesium chloridemixture	50	5.1	5.1, 11° (b)
1461	Chlorates, inorganic, n.o.s.	50	5.1	5.1, 11° (b)
1462	Chlorites, inorganic, n.o.s.	50	5.1	5.1, 14° (b)
1463	Chromium trioxide, anhydrous	58	5.1 + 8	5.1, 31° (b)
1465	Didymium nitrate	50	5.1	5.1, 22° (c)
1466	Ferric nitrate	50	5.1	5.1, 22° (c)
1467	Guanidine nitrate	50	5.1	5.1, 22° (c)
1469	Lead nitrate	56	5.1 + 6.1	5.1, 29° (c)
1470	Lead perchlorate	56	5.1 + 6.1	5.1, 29° (b)
1471	Lithium hypochlorite, mixture or dry	50	5.1	5.1, 15° (b)
1472	Lithium peroxide	50	5.1	5.1, 25° (b)
1473	Magnesium bromate	50	5.1	5.1, 16° (b)
1474	Magnesium nitrate	50	5.1	5.1, 22° (c)
1475	Magnesium perchlorate	50	5.1	5.1, 13° (b)
1476	Magnesium peroxide	50	5.1	5.1, 25° (b)
1477	Nitrates, inorganic, n.o.s.	50	5.1	5.1, 22° (b), (c)
1479	Oxidizing solid, n.o.s.	50	5.1	5.1, 27° (b), (c)
1481	Perchlorates, inorganic, n.o.s.	50	5.1	5.1, 13° (b)
1482	Permanganates, inorganic, n.o.s.	50	5.1	5.1, 17° (b)
1483	Peroxides, inorganic, n.o.s.	50	5.1	5.1, 25° (b)
1484	Potassium bromate	50	5.1	5.1, 16° (b)
1485	Potassium chlorate	50	5.1	5.1, 11° (b)
1486	Potassium nitrate	50	5.1	5.1, 22° (c)
1487	Potassium nitrate and sodium nitrite mixtures	50	5.1	5.1, 24° (b)
1488	Potassium nitrite	50	5.1	5.1, 23° (b)
1489	Potassium perchlorate	50	5.1	5.1, 13° (b)
1490	Potassium permanganate	50	5.1	5.1, 17° (b)
1492	Potassium persulphate	50	5.1	5.1, 18° (c)
1493	Silver nitrate	50	5.1	5.1, 22° (b)
1494	Sodium bromate	50	5.1	5.1, 16° (b)
1495	Sodium chlorate	50	5.1	5.1, 11° (b)
1496	Sodium chlorite	50	5.1	5.1, 14° (b)

Substance Identification No. (Lower part) (a)	Name of substance (b)	Hazard Identification No. (Upper part) (c)	Label (d)	Class and item number (e)
1498	Sodium nitrate	50	5.1	5.1, 22° (c)
1499	Sodium nitrate and potassium nitrate mixture	50	5.1	5.1, 22° (c)
1500	Sodium nitrite	50	5.1	5.1, 23° (c)
1502	Sodium perchlorate	50	5.1	5.1, 13° (b)
1503	Sodium permanganate	50	5.1	5.1, 17° (b)
1505	Sodium persulphate	50	5.1	5.1, 18° (c)
1506	Strontium chlorate	50	5.1	5.1, 11° (b)
1507	Strontium nitrate	50	5.1	5.1, 22° (c)
1508	Strontium perchlorate	50	5.1	5.1, 13° (b)
1509	Strontium peroxide	50	5.1	5.1, 25° (b)
1510	Tetranitromethane	559	5.1 + 6.1	5.1, 2° (a)
1511	Urea hydrogen peroxide	58	5.1 + 8	5.1, 31° (c)
1512	Zinc ammonium nitrite	50	5.1	5.1, 23° (b)
1513	Zinc chlorate	50	5.1	5.1, 11° (b)
1514	Zinc nitrate	50	5.1	5.1, 22° (b)
1515	Zinc permanganate	50	5.1	5.1, 17° (b)
1516	Zinc peroxide	50	5.1	5.1, 25° (b)
1541	Acetone cyanohydrin, stabilized	66	6.1	6.1, 12° (a)
1544	Alkaloids or alcaloid salts, solid, n.o.s.	66	6.1	6.1, 90° (a)
1544	Alkaloids or alcaloid salts, solid, n.o.s.	60	6.1	6.1, 90° (b), (c)
1545	Allyl isothiocyanate, inhibited	639	6.1 + 3	6.1, 20° (b)
1546	Ammonium arsenate	60	6.1	6.1, 51° (b)
1547	Aniline	60	6.1	6.1, 12° (b)
1548	Aniline hydrochloride	60	6.1	6.1, 12° (c)
1549	Antimony compound, inorganic, solid, n.o.s.	60	6.1	6.1, 59° (c)
1550	Antimony lactate	60	6.1	6.1, 59° (c)
1551	Antimony potassium tartrate	60	6.1	6.1, 59° (c)
1553	Arsenic acid, liquid	66	6.1	6.1, 51° (a)
1554	Arsenic acid, solid	60	6.1	6.1, 51° (b)
1555	Arsenic bromide	60	6.1	6.1, 51° (b)
1556	Arsenic compound, liquid, n.o.s., inorganic (arsenates, arsenites and arsenic sulphide)	66	6.1	6.1, 51° (a)
1556	Arsenic compound, liquid, n.o.s., inorganic (arsenates, arsenites and arsenic sulphide)	60	6.1	6.1, 51° (b), (c)
1557	Arsenic compound, solid, n.o.s., inorganic (arsenates, arsenites and arsenic sulphide)	66	6.1	6.1, 51° (a)
1557	Arsenic compound, solid, n.o.s., inorganic (arsenates, arsenites and arsenic sulphide)	60	6.1	6.1, 51° (b), (c)
1558	Arsenic	60	6.1	6.1, 51° (b)

Substance Identification No. (Lower part) (a)	Name of substance (b)	Hazard Identification No. (Upper part) (c)	Label (d)	Class and item number (e)
1559	Arsenic pentoxide	60	6.1	6.1, 51° (b)
1560	Arsenic trichloride	66	6.1	6.1, 51° (a)
1561	Arsenic trioxide	60	6.1	6.1, 51° (b)
1562	Arsenical dust	60	6.1	6.1, 51° (b)
1564	Barium compound, n.o.s.	60	6.1	6.1, 60° (b), (c)
1566	Beryllium compound, n.o.s.	60	6.1	6.1, 54° (b)2., (c)
1567	Beryllium powder	64	6.1 + 4.1	6.1, 54° (b)1.
1569	Bromoacetone	63	6.1 + 3	6.1, 16° (b)
1570	Brucine	66	6.1	6.1, 90° (a)
1572	Cacodylic acid	60	6.1	6.1, 51° (b)
1573	Calcium arsenate	60	6.1	6.1, 51° (b)
1574	Calcium arsenate and calcium arsenite mixture, solid	60	6.1	6.1, 51° (b)
1577	Chlorodinitrobenzenes	60	6.1	6.1, 12° (b)
1578	Chloronitrobenzenes	60	6.1	6.1, 12° (b)
1579	4-Chloro-o-toluidine hydrochloride	60	6.1	6.1, 17° (c)
1580	Chloropicrin	66	6.1	6.1, 17° (a)
1583	Chloropicrin mixture, n.o.s.	66	6.1	6.1, 17° (a)
1583	Chloropicrin mixture, n.o.s.	60	6.1	6.1, 17° (b), (c)
1585	Copper acetoarsenite	60	6.1	6.1, 51° (b)
1586	Copper arsenite	60	6.1	6.1, 51° (b)
1587	Copper cyanide	60	6.1	6.1, 41° (b)
1588	Cyanides, inorganic, solid, n.o.s.	66	6.1	6.1, 41° (a)
1588	Cyanides, inorganic, solid, n.o.s.	60	6.1	6.1, 41° (b), (c)
1590	Dichloroanilines	60	6.1	6.1, 12° (b)
1591	o-Dichlorobenzene	60	6.1	6.1, 15° (c)
1593	Dichloromethane	60	6.1	6.1, 15° (c)
1594	Diethyl sulphate	60	6.1	6.1, 14° (b)
1595	Dimethyl sulphate	668	6.1 + 8	6.1, 27° (a)
1596	Dinitroanilines	60	6.1	6.1, 12° (b)
1597	Dinitrobenzenes	60	6.1	6.1, 12° (b)
1598	Dinitro-o-cresol	60	6.1	6.1, 12° (b)
1599	Dinitrophenol solutions	60	6.1	6.1, 12° (b), (c)
1600	Dinitrotoluenes, molten	60	6.1	6.1, 24° (b)1.
1601	Disinfectant, solid, toxic, n.o.s.	66	6.1	6.1, 25° (a)
1601	Disinfectant, solid, toxic, n.o.s.	60	6.1	6.1, 25° (b), (c)
1602	Dye, liquid, toxic, n.o.s.	66	6.1	6.1, 25° (a)
1602	Dye, liquid, toxic, n.o.s.	60	6.1	6.1, 25° (b), (c)

Substance Identification No. (Lower part) (a)	Name of substance (b)	Hazard Identification No. (Upper part) (c)	Label (d)	Class and item number (e)
1602	Dye intermediate, liquid, toxic, n.o.s.	66	6.1	6.1, 25° (a)
1602	Dye intermediate, liquid, toxic, n.o.s.	60	6.1	6.1, 25° (b), (c)
1603	Ethyl bromoacetate	63	6.1 + 3	6.1, 16° (b)
1604	Ethylenediamine	83	8 + 3	8, 54° (b)
1605	Ethylene dibromide	66	6.1	6.1, 15° (a)
1606	Ferric arsenate	60	6.1	6.1, 51° (b)
1607	Ferric arsenite	60	6.1	6.1, 51° (b)
1608	Ferrous arsenate	60	6.1	6.1, 51° (b)
1611	Hexaethyl tetraphosphate	60	6.1	6.1, 23° (b)
1612	Hexaethyl tetraphosphate and compressed gas mixture	26	6.1	2, 1°T
1613	Hydrogen cyanide, aqueous solution (Hydrocyanic acid)	663	6.1 + 3	6.1, 2°
1616	Lead acetate	60	6.1	6.1, 62° (c)
1617	Lead arsenates	60	6.1	6.1, 51° (b)
1618	Lead arsenites	60	6.1	6.1, 51° (b)
1620	Lead cyanide	60	6.1	6.1, 41° (b)
1621	London purple	60	6.1	6.1, 51° (b)
1622	Magnesium arsenate	60	6.1	6.1, 51° (b)
1623	Mercuric arsenate	60	6.1	6.1, 51° (b)
1624	Mercuric chloride	60	6.1	6.1, 52° (b)
1625	Mercuric nitrate	60	6.1	6.1, 52° (b)
1627	Mercurous nitrate	60	6.1	6.1, 52° (b)
1629	Mercury acetate	60	6.1	6.1, 52° (b)
1630	Mercury ammonium chloride	60	6.1	6.1, 52° (b)
1631	Mercury benzoate	60	6.1	6.1, 52° (b)
1634	Mercury bromides	60	6.1	6.1, 52° (b)
1636	Mercury cyanide	60	6.1	6.1, 41° (b)
1637	Mercury gluconate	60	6.1	6.1, 52° (b)
1638	Mercury iodide	60	6.1	6.1, 52° (b)
1639	Mercury nucleate	60	6.1	6.1, 52° (b)
1640	Mercury oleate	60	6.1	6.1, 52° (b)
1641	Mercury oxide	60	6.1	6.1, 52° (b)
1642	Mercury oxycyanide, desensitized	60	6.1	6.1, 41° (b)
1643	Mercury potassium iodide	60	6.1	6.1, 52° (b)
1644	Mercury salicylate	60	6.1	6.1, 52° (b)
1645	Mercury sulphate	60	6.1	6.1, 52° (b)
1646	Mercury thiocyanate	60	6.1	6.1, 52° (b)

Substance Identification No. (Lower part) (a)	Name of substance (b)	Hazard Identification No. (Upper part) (c)	Label (d)	Class and item number (e)
1647	Methyl bromide and ethylene dibromide mixture, liquid	66	6.1	6.1, 15° (a)
1648	Acetonitrile (methyl cyanide)	33	3	3, 3° (b)
1649	Motor fuel anti-knock mixture	66	6.1	6.1, 31° (a)
1650	beta-Naphthylamine	60	6.1	6.1, 12° (b)
1651	Naphthylthiourea	60	6.1	6.1, 21° (b)
1652	Naphthylurea	60	6.1	6.1, 12° (b)
1653	Nickel cyanide	60	6.1	6.1, 41° (b)
1654	Nicotine	60	6.1	6.1, 90° (b)
1655	Nicotine compound or nicotine preparation, solid, n.o.s.	66	6.1	6.1, 90° (a)
1655	Nicotine compound or nicotine preparation, solid, n.o.s.	60	6.1	6.1, 90° (b), (c)
1656	Nicotine hydrochloride or nicotine hydrochloride solution	60	6.1	6.1, 90° (b)
1657	Nicotine salicylate	60	6.1	6.1, 90° (b)
1658	Nicotine sulphate, solid	60	6.1	6.1, 90° (b)
1658	Nicotine sulphate, solution	60	6.1	6.1, 90° (b)
1659	Nicotine tartrate	60	6.1	6.1, 90° (b)
1661	Nitroanilines (o-, m-, p-)	60	6.1	6.1, 12° (b)
1662	Nitrobenzene	60	6.1	6.1, 12° (b)
1663	Nitrophenols	60	6.1	6.1, 12° (c)
1664	Nitrotoluenes (o-, m-, p-)	60	6.1	6.1, 12° (b)
1665	Nitroxylenes (o-, m-, p-)	60	6.1	6.1, 12° (b)
1669	Pentachloroethane	60	6.1	6.1, 15° (b)
1670	Perchloromethyl mercaptan	66	6.1	6.1, 17° (a)
1671	Phenol, solid	60	6.1	6.1, 14° (b)
1672	Phenylcarbylamine chloride	66	6.1	6.1, 17° (a)
1673	Phenylenediamines (o-, m-, p-)	60	6.1	6.1, 12° (c)
1674	Phenylmercuric acetate	60	6.1	6.1, 33° (b)
1677	Potassium arsenate	60	6.1	6.1, 51° (b)
1678	Potassium arsenite	60	6.1	6.1, 51° (b)
1679	Potassium cuprocyanide	60	6.1	6.1, 41° (b)
1683	Silver arsenite	60	6.1	6.1, 51° (b)
1684	Silver cyanide	60	6.1	6.1, 41° (b)
1685	Sodium arsenate	60	6.1	6.1, 51° (b)
1686	Sodium arsenite, aqueous solution	60	6.1	6.1, 51° (b), (c)
1688	Sodium cacodylate	60	6.1	6.1, 51° (b)
1690	Sodium fluoride	60	6.1	6.1, 63° (c)

Substance Identification No. (Lower part) (a)	Name of substance (b)	Hazard Identification No. (Upper part) (c)	Label (d)	Class and item number (e)
1691	Strontium arsenite	60	6.1	6.1, 51° (b)
1692	Strychnine or strychnine, salts	66	6.1	6.1, 90° (a)
1693	Tear gas substance, liquid or solid, n.o.s.	66	6.1	6.1, 25° (a)
1693	Tear gas substance, liquid or solid, n.o.s.	60	6.1	6.1, 25° (b)
1694	Bromobenzyl cyanides	66	6.1	6.1, 17° (a)
1695	Chloroacetone, stabilized	663	6.1 + 3 + 8	6.1, 10° (a)
1697	Chloroacetophenone	60	6.1	6.1, 17° (b)
1698	Diphenylamine chloroarsine	66	6.1	6.1, 34° (a)
1699	Diphenylchloroarsine	66	6.1	6.1, 34° (a)
1701	Xylyl bromide	60	6.1	6.1, 15° (b)
1702	1,1,2,2-Tetrachloroethane	60	6.1	6.1, 15° (b)
1704	Tetraethyl dithiopyrophosphate	60	6.1	6.1, 23° (b)
1707	Thallium compound, n.o.s.	60	6.1	6.1, 53° (b)
1708	Toluidines	60	6.1	6.1, 12° (b)
1709	2,4-Toluylenediamine	60	6.1	6.1, 12° (c)
1710	Trichloroethylene	60	6.1	6.1, 15° (c)
1711	Xylidines	60	6.1	6.1, 12° (b)
1712	Zinc arsenate	60	6.1	6.1, 51° (b)
1712	Zinc arsenate and zinc arsenite mixture	60	6.1	6.1, 51° (b)
1712	Zinc arsenite	60	6.1	6.1, 51° (b)
1713	Zinc cyanide	66	6.1	6.1, 41° (a)
1715	Acetic anhydride	83	8 + 3	8, 32° (b)2.
1716	Acetyl bromide	80	8	8, 35° (b)1.
1717	Acetyl chloride	X338	3 + 8	3, 25° (b)
1718	Butyl acid phosphate	80	8	8, 38° (c)
1719	Caustic alkali liquid, n.o.s.	80	8	8, 42° (b), (c)
1722	Allyl chloroformate	638	6.1 + 8 + 3	6.1, 28° (a)
1723	Allyl iodide	338	3 + 8	3, 25° (b)
1724	Allyltrichlorosilane, stabilised	X839	8 + 3	8, 37° (b)
1725	Aluminium bromide, anhydrous	80	8	8, 11° (b)
1726	Aluminium chloride, anhydrous	80	8	8, 11° (b)
1727	Ammonium hydrogendifluoride, solid	80	8	8, 9° (b)
1728	Amyltrichlorosilane	X80	8	8, 36° (b)
1729	Anisoyl chloride	80	8	8, 35° (b)1.
1730	Antimony pentachloride, liquid	X80	8	8, 12° (b)
1731	Antimony pentachloride solution	80	8	8, 12° (b), (c)
1732	Antimony pentafluoride	86	8 + 6.1	8, 10° (b)
1733	Antimony trichloride	80	8	8, 11° (b)

Substance Identification No. (Lower part) (a)	Name of substance (b)	Hazard Identification No. (Upper part) (c)	Label (d)	Class and item number (e)
1736	Benzoyl chloride	80	8	8, 35° (b)1.
1737	Benzyl bromide	68	6.1 + 8	6.1, 27° (b)
1738	Benzyl chloride	68	6.1 + 8	6.1, 27° (b)
1739	Benzyl chloroformate	88	8	8, 64° (a)
1740	Hydrogendifluorides, n.o.s.	80	8	8, 9° (b), (c)
1742	Boron trifluoride acetic acid complex	80	8	8, 33° (b)
1743	Boron trifluoride propionic acid complex	80	8	8, 33° (b)
1744	Bromine or bromine solution	886	8 + 6.1	8, 14°
1745	Bromine pentafluoride	568	5.1 + 6.1 + 8	5.1, 5°
1746	Bromine trifluoride	568	5.1 + 6.1 + 8	5.1, 5°
1747	Butyltrichlorosilane	X83	8 + 3	8, 37° (b)
1748	Calcium hypochlorite, dry	50	5.1	5.1, 15° (b)
1748	Calcium hypochlorite, mixture, dry	50	5.1	5.1, 15° (b)
1749	Chlorine trifluoride	265	6.1 + 05 + 8	2, 2°TOC
1750	Chloroacetic acid solution	68	6.1 + 8	6.1, 27° (b)
1751	Chloroacetic acid, solid	68	6.1 + 8	6.1, 27° (b)
1752	Chloroacetyl chloride	668	6.1 + 8	6.1, 27° (a)
1753	Chlorophenyltrichlorosilane	X80	8	8, 36° (b)
1754	Chlorosulphonic acid	X88	8	8, 12° (a)
1755	Chromic acid, solution	80	8	8, 17° (b), (c)
1756	Chromic fluoride, solid	80	8	8, 9° (b)
1757	Chromic fluoride, solution	80	8	8, 8° (b), (c)
1758	Chromium oxychloride	X88	8	8, 12° (a)
1759	Corrosive solid, n.o.s.	88	8	8, 65° (a)
1759	Corrosive solid, n.o.s.	80	8	8, 65° (b), (c)
1760	Corrosive liquid, n.o.s.	88	8	8, 66° (a)
1760	Corrosive liquid, n.o.s.	80	8	8, 66° (b), (c)
1761	Cupriethylenediamine, solution	86	8 + 6.1	8, 53° (b)(c)
1762	Cyclohexenyltrichlorosilane	X80	8	8, 36° (b)
1763	Cyclohexyltrichlorosilane	X80	8	8, 36° (b)
1764	Dichloroacetic acid	80	8	8, 32° (b)1.
1765	Dichloroacetyl chloride	X80	8	8, 35° (b)1.
1766	Dichlorophenyltrichlorosilane	X80	8	8, 36° (b)
1767	Diethyldichlorosilane	X83	8 + 3	8, 37° (b)
1768	Difluorophosphoric acid, anhydrous	80	8	8, 8° (b)
1769	Diphenyldichlorosilane	X80	8	8, 36° (b)
1770	Diphenylmethyl bromide	80	8	8, 65° (b)
1771	Dodecyltrichlorosilane	X80	8	8, 36° (b)

Substance Identification No. (Lower part) (a)	Name of substance (b)	Hazard Identification No. (Upper part) (c)	Label (d)	Class and item number (e)
1773	Ferric chloride, anhydrous	80	8	8, 11° (c)
1775	Fluoroboric acid	80	8	8, 8° (b)
1776	Fluorophosphoric acid, anhydrous	80	8	8, 8° (b)
1777	Fluorosulphonic acid	88	8	8, 8° (a)
1778	Fluorosilicic acid	80	8	8, 8° (b)
1779	Formic acid	80	8	8, 32° (b)1.
1780	Fumaryl chloride	80	8	8, 35° (b)1.
1781	Hexadecyltrichlorosilane	X80	8	8, 36° (b)
1782	Hexafluorophosphoric acid	80	8	8, 8° (b)
1783	Hexamethylenediamine, solution	80	8	8, 53° (b), (c)
1784	Hexyltrichlorosilane	X80	8	8, 36° (b)
1786	Hydrofluoric acid and sulphuric acid mixture	886	8 + 6.1	8, 7° (a)
1787	Hydriodic acid, solution	80	8	8, 5° (b), (c)
1788	Hydrobromic acid, solution	80	8	8, 5° (b), (c)
1789	Hydrochloric acid, solution	80	8	8, 5° (b), (c)
1790	Hydrofluoric acid solution containing more than 85% hydrogen fluoride	886	8 + 6.1	8, 6°
1790	Hydrofluoric acid solution containing between 60 and 85% hydrogen fluoride	886	8 + 6.1	8, 7° (a)
1790	Hydrofluoric acid solution containing less than 60% hydrogen fluoride	86	8 + 6.1	8, 7° (b)
1791	Hypochlorite solution	80	8	8, 61° (b), (c)
1792	Iodine monochloride	80	8	8, 12° (b)
1793	Isopropyl acid phosphate	80	8	8, 38° (c)
1794	Lead sulphate	80	8	8, 1° (b)
1796	Nitrating acid, mixture containing more than 50% nitric acid	885	8 + 05	8, 3° (a)
1796	Nitrating acid, mixture containing less than 50% nitric acid	80	8	8, 3° (b)
1799	Nonyltrichlorosilane	X80	8	8, 36° (b)
1800	Octadecyltrichlorosilane	X80	8	8, 36° (b)
1801	Octyltrichlorosilane	X80	8	8, 36° (b)
1802	Perchloric acid	85	8	8, 4° (b)
1803	Phenolsulphonic acid, liquid	80	8	8, 34° (b)
1804	Phenyltrichlorosilane	X80	8	8, 36° (b)
1805	Phosphoric acid	80	8	8, 17° (c)
1806	Phosphorus pentachloride	80	8	8, 11° (b)
1807	Phosphorus pentoxide	80	8	8, 16° (b)
1808	Phosphorus tribromide	X80	8	8, 12° (b)

Substance Identification No. (Lower part) (a)	Name of substance (b)	Hazard Identification No. (Upper part) (c)	Label (d)	Class and item number (e)
1809	Phosphorus trichloride	668	6.1 + 8	8, 67° (a)
1810	Phosphorus oxychloride	X80	8	8, 12° (b)
1811	Potassium hydrogendifluoride	86	8 + 6.1	8, 9° (b)
1812	Potassium fluoride	60	6.1	6.1, 63° (c)
1813	Potassium hydroxide, solid	80	8	8, 41° (b)
1814	Potassium hydroxide solution	80	8	8, 42° (b), (c)
1815	Propionyl chloride	338	3 + 8	3, 25° (b)
1816	Propyltrichlorosilane	X83	8 + 3	8, 37° (b)
1817	Pyrosulphuryl chloride	X80	8	8, 12° (b)
1818	Silicon tetrachloride	X80	8	8, 12° (b)
1819	Sodium aluminate, solution	80	8	8, 42° (b), (c)
1823	Sodium hydroxide, solid	80	8	8, 41° (b)
1824	Sodium hydroxide solution	80	8	8, 42° (b), (c)
1825	Sodium monoxide	80	8	8, 41° (b)
1826	Nitrating acid mixture, spent, containing more than 50% nitric acid	885	8 + 05	8, 3° (a)
1826	Nitrating acid mixture, spent, containing less than 50% nitric acid	80	8	8, 3° (b)
1827	Stannic chloride, anhydrous	X80	8	8, 12° (b)
1828	Sulphur chlorides	X88	8	8, 12° (a)
1829	Sulphur trioxide, inhibited or sulphur trioxide, stabilized	X88	8	8, 1° (a)
1830	Sulphuric acid, containing more than 51% acid	80	8	8, 1° (b)
1831	Sulphuric acid, fuming	X886	8 + 6.1	8, 1° (a)
1832	Sulphuric acid, spent	80	8	8, 1° (b)
1833	Sulphurous acid	80	8	8, 1° (b)
1834	Sulphuryl chloride	X88	8	8, 12° (a)
1835	Tetramethylammonium hydroxide	80	8	8, 51° (b)
1836	Thionyl chloride	X88	8	8, 12° (a)
1837	Thiophosphoryl chloride	X80	8	8, 12° (b)
1838	Titanium tetrachloride	X80	8	8, 12° (b)
1839	Trichloroacetic acid	80	8	8, 31° (b)
1840	Zinc chloride solution	80	8	8, 5° (c)
1841	Acetaldehyde ammonia	90	9	9, 31° (c)
1843	Ammonium dinitro-o-cresolate	60	6.1	6.1, 12° (b)
1846	Carbon tetrachloride	60	6.1	6.1, 15° (b)
1847	Potassium sulphide, hydrated	80	8	8, 45° (b)1.
1848	Propionic acid	80	8	8, 32° (c)
1849	Sodium sulphide, hydrated	80	8	8, 45° (b)1.

Substance Identification No. (Lower part) (a)	Name of substance (b)	Hazard Identification No. (Upper part) (c)	Label (d)	Class and item number (e)
1851	Medicine, liquid, toxic, n.o.s.	60	6.1	6.1, 90° (b), (c)
1858	Hexafluoropropylene (R 1216)	20	2	2, 2°A
1859	Silicon tetrafluoride, compressed	268	6.1 + 8	2, 1°TC
1860	Vinyl fluoride, inhibited	239	3	2, 2°F
1862	Ethyl crotonate	33	3	3, 3° (b)
1863	Fuel, aviation, turbine engine	33	3	3, 1° (a), 2° (a), (b), 3° (b)
1863	Fuel, aviation, turbine engine	30	3	3, 31° (c)
1866	Resin solution, flammable	33	3	3, 5° (a), (b), (c)
1866	Resin solution, flammable	30	3	3, 31° (c)
1868	Decaborane	46	4.1 + 6.1	4.1, 16° (b)
1869	Magnesium	40	4.1	4.1, 13° (c)
1869	Magnesium alloys	40	4.1	4.1, 13° (c)
1871	Titanium hydride	40	4.1	4.1, 14° (b)
1872	Lead dioxide	56	5.1 + 6.1	5.1, 29° (c)
1873	Perchloric acid, with more than 50% but not more than 72% acid, by mass	558	5.1 + 8	5.1, 3° (a)
1884	Barium oxide	60	6.1	6.1, 60° (c)
1885	Benzidine	60	6.1	6.1, 12° (b)
1886	Benzylidene chloride	60	6.1	6.1, 15° (b)
1887	Bromochloromethane	60	6.1	6.1, 15° (c)
1888	Chloroform	60	6.1	6.1, 15° (c)
1889	Cyanogen bromide	668	6.1 + 8	6.1, 27° (a)
1891	Ethyl bromide	60	6.1	6.1, 15° (b)
1892	Ethyldichloroarsine	66	6.1	6.1, 34° (a)
1894	Phenylmercuric hydroxide	60	6.1	6.1, 33° (b)
1895	Phenylmercuric nitrate	60	6.1	6.1, 33° (b)
1897	Tetrachloroethylene	60	6.1	6.1, 15° (c)
1898	Acetyl iodide	80	8	8, 35° (b)1.
1902	Diisooctyl acid phosphate	80	8	8, 38° (c)
1903	Disinfectant, liquid, corrosive, n.o.s.	88	8	8, 66° (a)
1903	Disinfectant, liquid, corrosive, n.o.s.	80	8	8, 66° (b), (c)
1906	Sludge acid	80	8	8, 1° (b)
1907	Soda lime	80	8	8, 41° (c)
1908	Chlorite solution	80	8	8, 61° (b), (c)
1912	Methyl chloride and methylene chloride mixture	23	3	2, 2°F
1913	Neon, refrigerated liquid	22	2	2, 3°A
1914	Butyl propionates	30	3	3, 31° (c)

Substance Identification No. (Lower part) (a)	Name of substance (b)	Hazard Identification No. (Upper part) (c)	Label (d)	Class and item number (e)
1915	Cyclohexanone	30	3	3, 31° (c)
1916	2,2'-Dichlorodiethyl ether	63	6.1 + 3	6.1, 16° (b)
1917	Ethyl acrylate, inhibited	339	3	3, 3° (b)
1918	Isopropylbenzene (Cumene)	30	3	3, 31° (c)
1919	Methyl acrylate, inhibited	339	3	3, 3° (b)
1920	Nonanes	30	3	3, 31° (c)
1921	Propyleneimine, inhibited	336	3 + 6.1	3, 12°
1922	Pyrrolidine	338	3 + 8	3, 23° (b)
1923	Calcium dithionite	40	4.2	4.2, 13° (b)
1928	Methyl magnesium bromide in ethyl ether	X323	4.3 + 3	4.3, 3° (a)
1929	Potassium dithionite	40	4.2	4.2, 13° (b)
1931	Zinc dithionite	90	9	9, 32° (c)
1932	Zirconium scrap	40	4.2	4.2, 12° (c)
1935	Cyanide solution, n.o.s.	66	6.1	6.1, 41° (a)
1935	Cyanide solution, n.o.s.	60	6.1	6.1, 41° (b), (c)
1938	Bromoacetic acid	80	8	8, 31° (b)
1939	Phosphorus oxybromide	80	8	8, 11° (b)
1940	Thioglycolic acid	80	8	8, 32° (b)1.
1941	Dibromodifluoromethane	90	9	9, 33° (c)
1942	Ammonium nitrate	50	5.1	5.1, 21° (c)
1951	Argon, refrigerated liquid	22	2	2, 3°A
1952	Ethylene oxide and carbon dioxide mixture, with not more than 9% ethylene oxide	20	2	2, 2°A
1953	Compressed gas, toxic, flammable, n.o.s.	263	6.1 + 3	2, 1°TF
1954	Compressed gas, flammable, n.o.s.	23	3	2, 1°F
1955	Compressed gas, toxic, n.o.s.	26	6.1	2, 1°T
1956	Compressed gas, n.o.s.	20	2	2, 1°A
1957	Deuterium, compressed	23	3	2, 1°F
1958	1,2-Dichloro-1,1,2,2-tetrafluoroethane (R 114)	20	2	2, 2°A
1959	1,1-Difluoroethylene (R 1132a)	239	3	2, 2°F
1961	Ethane, refrigerated liquid	223	3	2, 3°F
1962	Ethylene, compressed	23	3	2, 1°F
1963	Helium, refrigerated liquid	22	2	2, 3°A
1964	Hydrocarbon gas mixture, compressed, n.o.s.	23	3	2, 1°F
1965	Butane (trade name): see Mixture A, A0	23	3	2, 2°F
1965	Mixture A, A0, A1, B, C: see Hydrocarbon gas mixture liquefied, n.o.s.	23	3	2, 2°F
1965	Propane (trade name): see Mixture C	23	3	2, 2°F

Substance Identification No. (Lower part) (a)	Name of substance (b)	Hazard Identification No. (Upper part) (c)	Label (d)	Class and item number (e)
1965	Hydrocarbon gas mixture, liquefied, n.o.s.	23	3	2, 2°F
1966	Hydrogen, refrigerated liquid	223	3	2, 3°F
1967	Insecticide gas, toxic, n.o.s.	26	6.1	2, 2°T
1968	Insecticide gas, n.o.s.	20	2	2, 2°A
1969	Isobutane	23	3	2, 2°F
1970	Krypton, refrigerated liquid	22	2	2, 3°A
1971	Methane, compressed	23	3	2, 1°F
1971	Natural gas, compressed	23	3	2, 1°F
1972	Methane, refrigerated liquid	223	3	2, 3°F
1972	Natural gas, refrigerated liquid	223	3	2, 3°F
1973	Chlorodifluoromethane and chloropentafluoroethane mixture (R 502)	20	2	2, 2°A
1974	Chlorodifluorobromomethane (R 12B1)	20	2	2, 2°A
1976	Octafluorocyclobutane (RC 318)	20	2	2, 2°A
1977	Nitrogen, refrigerated liquid	22	2	2, 3°A
1978	Propane	23	3	2, 2°F
1979	Rare gases mixture, compressed	20	2	2, 1°A
1980	Rare gases and oxygen mixture, compressed	20	2	2, 1°A
1981	Rare gases and nitrogen mixture, compressed	20	2	2, 1°A
1982	Tetrafluoromethane (R 14), compressed	20	2	2, 1°A
1983	1-Chloro-2,2,2-trifluoroethane (R 133a)	20	2	2, 2°A
1984	Trifluoromethane (R 23)	20	2	2, 2°A
1986	Alcohols, flammable, toxic, n.o.s.	336	3 + 6.1	3, 17° (a), (b)
1986	Alcohols, flammable, toxic, n.o.s.	36	3 + 6.1	3, 32° (c)
1987	Alcohols, flammable, n.o.s.	33	3	3, 2° (b), 3° (b)
1987	Alcohols, flammable, n.o.s.	30	3	3, 31° (c)
1988	Aldehydes, flammable, toxic, n.o.s.	336	3 + 6.1	3, 17° (a), (b)
1988	Aldehydes, flammable, toxic, n.o.s.	36	3 + 6.1	3, 32° (c)
1989	Aldehydes, flammable, n.o.s.	33	3	3, 2° (b), 3° (b)
1989	Aldehydes, flammable, n.o.s.	30	3	3, 31° (c)
1990	Benzaldehyde	90	9	9, 34° (c)
1991	Chloroprene, inhibited	336	3 + 6.1	3, 16° (a)
1992	Flammable liquid, toxic, n.o.s.	36	3 + 6.1	3, 32° (c)
1992	Flammable liquid, toxic, n.o.s.	336	3 + 6.1	3, 19° (a), (b)
1993	Flammable liquid, n.o.s.	33	3	3, 1° (a), 2° (a), (b), 3° (b), 5° (c)
1993	Flammable liquid, n.o.s.	30	3	3, 31° (c)
1994	Iron pentacarbonyl	663	6.1 + 3	6.1, 3°

Substance Identification No. (Lower part) (a)	Name of substance (b)	Hazard Identification No. (Upper part) (c)	Label (d)	Class and item number (e)
1999	Tars, liquid	33	3	3, 5° (b), (c)
1999	Tars, liquid	30	3	3, 31° (c)
2001	Cobalt naphthenates, powder	40	4.1	4.1, 12° (c)
2003	Metal alkyls, n.o.s. or metal aryls, n.o.s.	X333	4.2 + 4.3	4.2, 31° (a)
2004	Magnesium diamide	40	4.2	4.2, 16° (b)
2005	Magnesium diphenyl	X333	4.2 + 4.3	4.2, 31° (a)
2008	Zirconium powder, dry	40	4.2	4.2, 12° (b), (c)
2014	Hydrogen peroxide, aqueous solution	58	5.1 + 8	5.1, 1° (b)
2015	Hydrogen peroxide, aqueous solution, stabilized	559	5.1 + 8	5.1, 1° (a)
2015	Hydrogen peroxide, stabilized	559	5.1 + 8	5.1, 1° (a)
2018	Chloroanilines, solid	60	6.1	6.1, 12° (b)
2019	Chloroanilines, liquid	60	6.1	6.1, 12° (b)
2020	Chlorophenols, solid	60	6.1	6.1, 17° (c)
2021	Chlorophenols, liquid	60	6.1	6.1, 17° (c)
2022	Cresylic acid	68	6.1 + 8	6.1, 27° (b)
2023	Epichlorohydrin	63	6.1 + 3	6.1, 16° (b)
2024	Mercury compound, liquid, n.o.s.	66	6.1	6.1, 52° (a)
2024	Mercury compound, liquid, n.o.s.	60	6.1	6.1, 52° (b), (c)
2025	Mercury compound, solid, n.o.s.	66	6.1	6.1, 52° (a)
2025	Mercury compound, solid, n.o.s.	60	6.1	6.1, 52° (b), (c)
2026	Phenylmercuric compound, n.o.s.	66	6.1	6.1, 33° (a)
2026	Phenylmercuric compound, n.o.s.	60	6.1	6.1, 33° (b), (c)
2027	Sodium arsenite, solid	60	6.1	6.1, 51° (b)
2030	Hydrazine hydrate	86	8 + 6.1	8, 44° (b)
2030	Hydrazine, aqueous solution	86	8 + 6.1	8, 44° (b)
2031	Nitric acid containing more than 70% pure acid	885	8	8, 2° (a)1.
2031	Nitric acid containing less than 70% pure acid	80	8	8, 2° (b)
2032	Nitric acid, red fuming	856	8 + 05 + 6.1	8, 2° (a)2.
2033	Potassium monoxide	80	8	8, 41° (b)
2034	Hydrogen and methane mixture, compressed	23	3	2, 1°F
2035	1,1,1-Trifluoroethane (R 143a)	23	3	2, 2°F
2036	Xenon, compressed	20	2	2, 1°A
2038	Dinitrotoluenes	60	6.1	6.1, 12° (b)
2044	2,2-Dimethylpropane	23	3	2, 2°F
2045	Isobutyraldehyde	33	3	3, 3° (b)
2046	Cymenes (o-,m-,p-) (Methyl isopropyl benzenes)	30	3	3, 31° (c)
2047	Dichloropropenes	33	3	3, 3° (b)
2047	Dichloropropenes	30	3	3, 31° (c)

Substance Identification No. (Lower part) (a)	Name of substance (b)	Hazard Identification No. (Upper part) (c)	Label (d)	Class and item number (e)
2048	Dicyclopentadiene	30	3	3, 31° (c)
2049	Diethylbenzenes (o-,m-,p-)	30	3	3, 31° (c)
2050	Diisobutylene, isomeric compounds	33	3	3, 3° (b)
2051	2-Dimethylaminoethanol	83	8 + 3	8, 54° (b)
2052	Dipentene	30	3	3, 31° (c)
2053	Methyl isobutyl carbinol	30	3	3, 31° (c)
2054	Morpholine	30	3	3, 31° (c)
2055	Styrene monomer, inhibited (Vinylbenzene)	39	3	3, 31° (c)
2056	Tetrahydrofuran	33	3	3, 3° (b)
2057	Tripropylene	33	3	3, 3° (b)
2057	Tripropylene	30	3	3, 31° (c)
2058	Valeraldehyde	33	3	3, 3° (b)
2059	Nitrocellulose solution, flammable	33	3	3, 4° (a), (b)
2059	Nitrocellulose solution, flammable	30	3	3, 34° (c)
2067	Ammonium nitrate fertilizers, type A1	50	5.1	5.1, 21° (c)
2068	Ammonium nitrate fertilizers, type A2	50	5.1	5.1, 21° (c)
2069	Ammonium nitrate fertilizers, type A3	50	5.1	5.1, 21° (c)
2070	Ammonium nitrate fertilizers, type A4	50	5.1	5.1, 21° (c)
2073	Ammonia solution with more than 35% and not more than 40% ammonia	20	2	2, 4°A
2073	Ammonia solution with more than 40% and not more than 50% ammonia	20	2	2, 4°A
2074	Acrylamide	60	6.1	6.1, 12° (c)
2075	Chloral, anhydrous, inhibited	60	6.1	6.1, 17° (b)
2076	Cresols (o-,m-,p-)	68	6.1 + 8	6.1, 27° (b)
2077	alpha-Naphthylamine	60	6.1	6.1, 12° (c)
2078	Toluene diisocyanate	60	6.1	6.1, 19° (b)
2079	Diethylenetriamine	80	8	8, 53° (b)
2187	Carbon dioxide, refrigerated liquid	22	2	2, 3°A
2189	Dichlorosilane	263	6.1 + 05 + 8	2, 2°TFC
2191	Sulphuryl fluoride	26	6.1	2, 2°T
2193	Hexafluoroethane (R 116), compressed	20	2	2, 1°A
2197	Hydrogen iodide, anhydrous	268	6.1 + 8	2, 2°TC
2200	Propadiene, inhibited	239	3	2, 2°F
2201	Nitrous oxide, refrigerated liquid	225	2 + 05	2, 3°O
2203	Silane, compressed	23	3	2.1°F
2204	Carbonyl sulphide	263	6.1 + 3	2, 2°TF
2205	Adiponitrile	60	6.1	6.1, 12° (c)

Substance Identification No. (Lower part) (a)	Name of substance (b)	Hazard Identification No. (Upper part) (c)	Label (d)	Class and item number (e)
2206	Isocyanates, toxic, n.o.s.	60	6.1	6.1, 19° (b), (c)
2206	Isocyanate solution, toxic, n.o.s.	60	6.1	6.1, 19° (b), (c)
2208	Calcium hypochlorite mixture, dry	50	5.1	5.1, 15° (c)
2209	Formaldehyde solution	80	8	8, 63° (c)
2210	Maneb	40	4.2 + 4.3	4.2, 16° (c)
2210	Maneb preparation	40	4.2 + 4.3	4.2, 16° (c)
2211	Polymeric beads, expandable	90	9	9, 4° (c)
2212	Blue asbestos (Crocidolite)	90	9	9, 1° (b)
2212	Brown asbestos (Amosite or Mysorite)	90	9	9, 1° (b)
2213	Paraformaldehyde	40	4.1	4.1, 6° (c)
2214	Phthalic anhydride	80	8	8, 31° (c)
2215	Maleic anhydride	80	8	8, 31° (c)
2217	Seed cake	40	4.2	4.2, 2° (c)
2218	Acrylic acid, inhibited	839	8 + 3	8, 32° (b)2.
2219	Allyl glycidyl ether	30	3	3, 31° (c)
2222	Anisole (phenyl methyl ether)	30	3	3, 31° (c)
2224	Benzonitrile	60	6.1	6.1, 12° (b)
2225	Benzenesulphonyl chloride	80	8	8, 35° (c)
2226	Benzotrichloride	80	8	8, 66° (b)
2227	n-Butyl methacrylate, inhibited	39	3	3, 31° (c)
2232	Chloroacetaldehyde	66	6.1	6.1, 17° (a)
2233	Chloroanisidines	60	6.1	6.1, 17° (c)
2234	Chlorobenzotrifluorides (o-, m-, p-)	30	3	3, 31° (c)
2235	Chlorobenzyl chlorides	60	6.1	6.1, 17° (c)
2236	3-Chloro-4-methylphenyl isocyanate	60	6.1	6.1, 19° (b)
2237	Chloronitroanilines	60	6.1	6.1, 17° (c)
2238	Chlorotoluenes (o-,m-,p-)	30	3	3, 31° (c)
2239	Chlorotoluidines	60	6.1	6.1, 17° (c)
2240	Chromosulphuric acid	88	8	8, 1° (a)
2241	Cycloheptane	33	3	3, 3° (b)
2242	Cycloheptene	33	3	3, 3° (b)
2242	Cycloheptene	33	3	3, 3° (b)
2243	Cyclohexyl acetate	30	3	3, 31° (c)
2244	Cyclopentanol	30	3	3, 31° (c)
2245	Cyclopentanone	30	3	3, 31° (c)
2246	Cyclopentene	33	3	3, 2° (b)
2247	n-Decane	30	3	3, 31° (c)
2248	Di-n-butylamine	83	8 + 3	8, 54° (b)

Substance Identification No. (Lower part) (a)	Name of substance (b)	Hazard Identification No. (Upper part) (c)	Label (d)	Class and item number (e)
2250	Dichlorophenyl isocyanates	60	6.1	6.1, 19° (b)
2251	2,5-Norbornadiene (Dicycloheptadiene), inhibited	339	3	3, 3° (b)
2252	1,2-Dimethoxyethane	33	3	3, 3° (b)
2253	N,N-Dimethylaniline	60	6.1	6.1, 12° (b)
2256	Cyclohexene	33	3	3, 3° (b)
2257	Potassium	X423	4.3	4.3, 11° (a)
2258	1,2-Propylenediamine	83	8 + 3	8, 54° (b)
2259	Triethylenetetramine	80	8	8, 53° (b)
2260	Tripropylamine	38	3 + 8	3, 33° (c)
2261	Xylenols	60	6.1	6.1, 14° (b)
2262	Dimethylcarbamoyl chloride	80	8	8, 35° (b)1.
2263	Dimethylcyclohexanes	33	3	3, 3° (b)
2264	Dimethylcyclohexylamine	83	8 + 3	8, 54° (b)
2265	N,N-Dimethylformamide	30	3	3, 31° (c)
2266	Dimethyl-N-propylamine	338	3 + 8	3, 22° (b)
2267	Dimethyl thiophosphoryl chloride	68	6.1 + 8	6.1, 27° (b)
2269	3,3'-Iminodipropylamine	80	8	8, 53° (c)
2270	Ethylamine, aqueous solution	338	3 + 8	3, 22° (b)
2271	Ethyl amyl ketones	30	3	3, 31° (c)
2272	N-Ethylaniline	60	6.1	6.1, 12° (c)
2273	2-Ethylaniline	60	6.1	6.1, 12° (c)
2274	N-Ethyl-N-benzylaniline	60	6.1	6.1, 12° (c)
2275	2-Ethylbutanol	30	3	3, 31° (c)
2276	2-Ethylhexylamine	38	3 + 8	3, 33° (c)
2277	Ethyl methacrylate	339	3	3, 3° (b)
2278	n-Heptene	33	3	3, 3° (b)
2279	Hexachlorobutadiene	60	6.1	6.1, 15° (c)
2280	Hexamethylenediamine, solid	80	8	8, 52° (c)
2281	Hexamethylene diisocyanate	60	6.1	6.1, 19° (b)
2282	Hexanols	30	3	3, 31° (c)
2283	Isobutyl methacrylate, inhibited	39	3	3, 31° (c)
2284	Isobutyronitrile	336	3 + 6.1	3, 11° (b)
2285	Isocyanatobenzotrifluorides	63	6.1 + 3	6.1, 18° (b)
2286	Pentamethylheptane (Isododecane)	30	3	3, 31° (c)
2287	Isoheptene	33	3	3, 3° (b)
2288	Isohexene	33	3	3, 3° (b)
2289	Isophoronediamine	80	8	8, 53° (c)
2290	Isophorone diisocyanate	60	6.1	6.1, 19° (c)

Substance Identification No. (Lower part) (a)	Name of substance (b)	Hazard Identification No. (Upper part) (c)	Label (d)	Class and item number (e)
2291	Lead compound, soluble, n.o.s.	60	6.1	6.1, 62° (c)
2293	4-Methoxy-4-methylpentan-2-one	30	3	3, 31° (c)
2294	N-Methylaniline	60	6.1	6.1, 12° (c)
2295	Methyl chloroacetate	663	6.1 + 3	6.1, 16° (a)
2296	Methylcyclohexane	33	3	3, 3° (b)
2297	Methylcyclohexanones	30	3	3, 31° (c)
2298	Methylcyclopentane	33	3	3, 3° (b)
2299	Methyl dichloroacetate	60	6.1	6.1, 17° (c)
2300	2-Methyl-5-ethylpyridine	60	6.1	6.1, 12° (c)
2301	2-Methylfuran	33	3	3, 3° (b)
2302	5-Methylhexan-2-one	30	3	3, 31° (c)
2303	Isopropenylbenzene	30	3	3, 31° (c)
2304	Naphthalene, molten	44	4.1	4.1, 5°
2305	Nitrobenzenesulphonic acid	80	8	8, 34° (b)
2306	Nitrobenzotrifluorides	60	6.1	6.1, 12° (b)
2307	3-Nitro-4-chlorobenzotrifluoride	60	6.1	6.1, 12° (b)
2308	Nitrosylsulphuric acid	X80	8	8, 1° (b)
2309	Octadiene	33	3	3, 3° (b)
2310	Pentan-2,4-dione	36	3 + 6.1	3, 32° (c)
2311	Phenetidines	60	6.1	6.1, 12° (c)
2312	Phenol, molten	60	6.1	6.1, 24° (b)
2313	Picolines	30	3	3, 31° (c)
2315	Polychlorinated biphenyls	90	9	9, 2° (b)
2317	Sodium cuprocyanide solution	66	6.1	6.1, 41° (a)
2318	Sodium hydrosulphide hydrated	40	4.2	4.2, 13° (b)
2319	Terpene hydrocarbons, n.o.s.	30	3	3, 31° (c)
2320	Tetraethylenepentamine	80	8	8, 53° (c)
2321	Trichlorobenzenes, liquid	60	6.1	6.1, 15° (c)
2322	Trichlorobutene	60	6.1	6.1, 15° (b)
2323	Triethyl phosphite	30	3	3, 31° (c)
2324	Triisobutylene (Isobutylene trimer)	30	3	3, 31° (c)
2325	1,3,5-Trimethylbenzene	30	3	3, 31° (c)
2326	Trimethylcyclohexylamine	80	8	8, 53° (c)
2327	Trimethylhexamethylenediamine	80	8	8, 53° (c)
2328	Trimethylhexamethylene diisocyanate	60	6.1	6.1, 19° (c)
2329	Trimethyl phosphite	30	3	3, 31° (c)
2330	Undecane	30	3	3, 31° (c)
2331	Zinc chloride, anhydrous	80	8	8, 11° (c)

Substance Identification No. (Lower part) (a)	Name of substance (b)	Hazard Identification No. (Upper part) (c)	Label (d)	Class and item number (e)
2332	Acetaldehyde oxime	30	3	3, 31° (c)
2333	Allyl acetate	336	3 + 6.1	3, 17° (b)
2334	Allylamine	663	6.1 + 3	6.1, 7° (a)2.
2335	Allyl ethyl ether	336	3 + 6.1	3, 17° (b)
2336	Allyl formate	336	3 + 6.1	3. 17° (a)
2337	Phenyl mercaptan	663	6.1 + 3	6.1, 20° (a)
2338	Benzotrifluoride	33	3	3, 3° (b)
2339	2-Bromobutane	33	3	3, 3° (b)
2340	2-Bromoethyl ethyl ether	33	3	3, 3° (b)
2341	1-Bromo-3-methylbutane	30	3	3, 31° (c)
2342	Bromomethylpropanes	33	3	3, 3° (b)
2343	2-Bromopentane	33	3	3, 3° (b)
2344	Bromopropanes	33	3	3, 3° (b)
2345	3-Bromopropyne	33	3	3, 3° (b)
2346	Butanedione (diacetyl)	33	3	3, 3° (b)
2347	Butyl mercaptan	33	3	3, 3° (b)
2348	Butyl acrylates, inhibited	39	3	3, 31° (c)
2350	Butyl methyl ether	33	3	3, 3° (b)
2351	Butyl nitrites	33	3	3, 3° (b)
2351	Butyl nitrites	30	3	3, 31° (c)
2352	Butyl vinyl ether, inhibited	339	3	3, 3° (b)
2353	Butyryl chloride	338	3 + 8	3, 25° (b)
2354	Chloromethyl ethyl ether	336	3 + 6.1	3, 16° (b)
2356	2-Chloropropane	33	3	3, 2° (a)
2357	Cyclohexylamine	83	8 + 3	8, 54° (b)
2358	Cyclooctatetraene	33	3	3, 3° (b)
2359	Diallylamine	338	3 + 8 + 6.1	3, 27° (b)
2360	Diallyl ether	336	3 + 6.1	3, 17° (b)
2361	Diisobutylamine	38	3 + 8	3, 33° (c)
2362	1,1-Dichloroethane (Ethylidene chloride)	33	3	3, 3° (b)
2363	Ethyl mercaptan	33	3 + 6.1	3, 2° (a)
2364	n-Propylbenzene	30	3	3, 31° (c)
2366	Diethyl carbonate (Ethyl carbonate)	30	3	3, 31° (c)
2367	alpha-Methylvaleraldehyde	33	3	3, 3° (b)
2368	alpha-Pinene	30	3	3, 31° (c)
2370	1-Hexene	33	3	3, 3° (b)
2371	Isopentenes	33	3	3, 1° (a)
2372	1,2-Di-(dimethylamino) ethane	33	3	3, 3° (b)

Substance Identification No. (Lower part) (a)	Name of substance (b)	Hazard Identification No. (Upper part) (c)	Label (d)	Class and item number (e)
2373	Diethoxymethane	33	3	3, 3° (b)
2374	3,3-Diethoxypropene	33	3	3, 3° (b)
2375	Diethyl sulphide	33	3	3, 3° (b)
2376	2,3-Dihydropyran	33	3	3, 3° (b)
2377	1,1-Dimethoxyethane	33	3	3, 3° (b)
2378	2-Dimethylaminoacetonitrile	336	3 + 6.1	3, 11° (b)
2379	1,3-Dimethylbutylamine	338	3 + 8	3, 22° (b)
2380	Dimethyldiethoxysilane	33	3	3, 3° (b)
2381	Dimethyl disulphide	33	3	3, 3° (b)
2382	Dimethylhydrazine, symmetrical	663	6.1 + 3	6.1, 7° (a)2.
2383	Dipropylamine	338	3 + 8	3, 22° (b)
2384	Di-n-propyl ether	33	3	3, 3° (b)
2385	Ethyl isobutyrate	33	3	3, 3° (b)
2386	1-Ethylpiperidine	338	3 + 8	3, 23° (b)
2387	Fluorobenzene	33	3	3, 3° (b)
2388	Fluorotoluenes	33	3	3, 3° (b)
2389	Furan	33	3	3, 1°a)
2390	2-Iodobutane	33	3	3, 3° (b)
2391	Iodomethylpropanes	33	3	3, 3° (b)
2392	Iodopropanes	30	3	3, 31° (c)
2393	Isobutyl formate	33	3	3, 3° (b)
2394	Isobutyl propionate	33	3	3, 3° (b)
2395	Isobutyryl chloride	338	3 + 8	3, 25° (b)
2396	Methacrylaldehyde, inhibited	336	3 + 6.1	3, 17° (b)
2397	3-Methylbutan-2-one	33	3	3, 3° (b)
2398	Methyl tert-butyl ether	33	3	3, 3° (b)
2399	1-Methylpiperidine	338	3 + 8	3, 23° (b)
2400	Methyl isovalerate	33	3	3, 3° (b)
2401	Piperidine	338	3 + 8	3, 23° (b)
2402	Propanethiols (propyl mercaptans)	33	3	3, 3° (b)
2403	Isopropenyl acetate	33	3	3, 3° (b)
2404	Propionitrile	336	3 + 6.1	3, 11° (b)
2405	Isopropyl butyrate	30	3	3, 31° (c)
2406	Isopropyl isobutyrate	33	3	3, 3° (b)
2409	Isopropyl propionate	33	3	3, 3° (b)
2410	1,2,3,6-Tetrahydropyridine	33	3	3, 3° (b)
2411	Butyronitrile	336	3 + 6.1	3, 11° (b)
2412	Tetrahydrothiophene (thiolanne)	33	3	3, 3° (b)

Substance Identification No. (Lower part) (a)	Name of substance (b)	Hazard Identification No. (Upper part) (c)	Label (d)	Class and item number (e)
2413	Tetrapropyl orthotitanate	30	3	3, 31° (c)
2414	Thiophene	33	3	3, 3° (b)
2416	Trimethyl borate	33	3	3, 3° (b)
2417	Carbonyl fluoride, compressed	268	6.1 + 8	2, 1°TC
2419	Bromotrifluoroethylene	23	3	2, 2°F
2420	Hexafluoroacetone	268	6.1 + 8	2, 2°TC
2422	Octafluorobut-2-ene (R 1318)	20	2	2, 2°A
2424	Octafluoropropane (R 218)	20	2	2, 2°A
2426	Ammonium nitrate, liquid (hot concentrated solution)	59	5.1	5.1, 20°
2427	Potassium chlorate aqueous solution	50	5.1	5.1, 11° (b), (c)
2428	Sodium chlorate, aqueous solution	50	5.1	5.1, 11° (b), (c)
2429	Calcium chlorate, aqueous solution	50	5.1	5.1, 11° (b), (c)
2430	Alkylphenols, solid, n.o.s.	88	8	8, 39° (a)
2430	Alkylphenols, solid, n.o.s.	80	8	8, 39° (b), (c)
2431	Anisidines	60	6.1	6.1, 12° (c)
2432	N,N-Diethylaniline	60	6.1	6.1, 12° (c)
2433	Chloronitrotoluenes	60	6.1	6.1, 17° (c)
2434	Dibenzyldichlorosilane	X80	8	8, 36° (b)
2435	Ethylphenyldichlorosilane	X80	8	8, 36° (b)
2436	Thioacetic acid	33	3	3, 3° (b)
2437	Methylphenyldichlorosilane	X80	8	8, 36° (b)
2438	Trimethylacetyl chloride	663	6.1 + 3 + 8	6.1, 10° (a)
2439	Sodium hydrogendifluoride	80	8	8, 9° (b)
2440	Stannic chloride pentahydrate	80	8	8, 11° (c)
2442	Trichloroacetyl chloride	X80	8	8, 35° (b)1.
2443	Vanadium oxytrichloride	80	8	8, 12° (b)
2444	Vanadium tetrachloride	X88	8	8, 12° (a)
2445	Lithium alkyls	X333	4.2 + 4.3	4.2, 31° (a)
2446	Nitrocresols (o-,m-,p-)	60	6.1	6.1, 12° (c)
2447	Phosphorus, white or yellow, molten	446	4.2 + 6.1	4.2, 22°
2448	Sulphur, molten	44	4.1	4.1, 15°
2451	Nitrogen trifluoride, compressed	265	6.1 + 05	2, 1°TO
2452	Ethylacetylene, inhibited	239	3	2, 2°F
2453	Ethyl fluoride (R161)	23	3	2, 2°F
2454	Methyl fluoride (R41)	23	3	2, 2°F
2456	2-Chloropropene	33	3	3, 1° (a)
2457	2,3-Dimethylbutane	33	3	3, 3° (b)

Substance Identification No. (Lower part) (a)	Name of substance (b)	Hazard Identification No. (Upper part) (c)	Label (d)	Class and item number (e)
2458	Hexadiene	33	3	3, 3° (b)
2459	2-Methyl-1-butene	33	3	3, 1° (a)
2460	2-Methyl-2-butene	33	3	3, 2° (b)
2461	Methylpentadiene	33	3	3, 3° (b)
2464	Beryllium nitrate	56	5.1 + 6.1	5.1, 29° (b)
2465	Dichloroisocyanuric acid salts	50	5.1	5.1, 26° (b)
2465	Dichloroisocyanuric acid, dry	50	5.1	5.1, 26° (b)
2468	Trichloroisocyanuric acid, dry	50	5.1	5.1, 26° (b)
2469	Zinc bromate	50	5.1	5.1, 16° (c)
2470	Phenylacetonitrile, liquid	60	6.1	6.1, 12° (c)
2473	Sodium arsanilate	60	6.1	6.1, 34° (c)
2474	Thiophosgene	60	6.1	6.1, 21° (b)
2475	Vanadium trichloride	80	8	8, 11° (c)
2477	Methyl isothiocyanate	663	6.1 + 3	6.1, 20° (a)
2478	Isocyanates or isocyanate solution, flammable, toxic, n.o.s.	336	3 + 6.1	3, 14° (b)
2478	Isocyanates or isocyanate solution, flammable, toxic, n.o.s.	36	3 + 6.1	3, 32° (c)
2482	n-Propyl isocyanate	663	6.1 + 3	6.1, 6° (a)
2483	Isopropyl isocyanate	336	3 + 6.1	3, 14° (a)
2484	tert-Butyl isocyanate	663	6.1 + 3	6.1, 6° (a)
2485	n-Butyl isocyanate	663	6.1 + 3	6.1, 6° (a)
2486	Isobutyl isocyanate	336	3 + 6.1	3, 14° (b)
2487	Phenyl isocyanate	663	6.1 + 3	6.1, 18° (a)
2488	Cyclohexyl isocyanate	663	6.1 + 3	6.1, 18° (a)
2490	Dichloroisopropyl ether	60	6.1	6.1, 17° (b)
2491	Ethanolamine or ethanolamine solution	80	8	8, 53° (c)
2493	Hexamethyleneimine	338	3 + 8	3, 23° (b)
2495	Iodine pentafluoride	568	5.1 + 6.1 + 8	5.1, 5°
2496	Propionic anhydride	80	8	8, 32° (c)
2498	1,2,3,6-Tetrahydrobenzaldehyde	30	3	3, 31° (c)
2501	Tris-(1-aziridinyl) phosphine oxide solution	60	6.1	6.1, 23° (b), (c)
2502	Valeryl chloride	83	8 + 3	8, 35° (b)2.
2503	Zirconium tetrachloride	80	8	8, 11° (c)
2504	Tetrabromoethane	60	6.1	6.1, 15° (c)
2505	Ammonium fluoride	60	6.1	6.1, 63° (c)
2506	Ammonium hydrogen sulphate	80	8	8, 13° (b)
2507	Chloroplatinic acid, solid	80	8	8, 16° (c)

Substance Identification No. (Lower part) (a)	Name of substance (b)	Hazard Identification No. (Upper part) (c)	Label (d)	Class and item number (e)
2508	Molybdenum pentachloride	80	8	8, 11° (c)
2509	Potassium hydrogen sulphate	80	8	8, 13° (b)
2511	2-Chloropropionic acid	80	8	8, 32° (c)
2512	Aminophenols (o-,m-,p-)	60	6.1	6.1, 12° (c)
2513	Bromoacetyl bromide	X80	8	8, 35° (b)1.
2514	Bromobenzene	30	3	3, 31° (c)
2515	Bromoform	60	6.1	6.1, 15° (c)
2516	Carbon tetrabromide	60	6.1	6.1, 15° (c)
2517	1-Chloro-1, 1-difluoroethane (R 142b)	23	3	2, 2°F
2518	1,5,9-Cyclododecatriene	60	6.1	6.1, 25° (c)
2520	Cyclooctadienes	30	3	3, 31° (c)
2521	Diketene, inhibited	663	6.1 + 3	6.1, 13° (a)
2522	2-Dimethylaminoethyl methacrylate	69	6.1	6.1, 12° (b)
2524	Ethyl orthoformate	30	3	3, 31° (c)
2525	Ethyl oxalate	60	6.1	6.1, 14° (c)
2526	Furfurylamine	38	3 + 8	3, 33° (c)
2527	Isobutyl acrylate, inhibited	39	3	3, 31° (c)
2528	Isobutyl isobutyrate	30	3	3, 31° (c)
2529	Isobutyric acid	38	3 + 8	3, 33° (c)
2530	Isobutyric anhydride	38	3 + 8	3, 33° (c)
2531	Methacrylic acid, inhibited	89	8	8, 32° (c)
2533	Methyl trichloroacetate	60	6.1	6.1, 17° (c)
2535	4-Methylmorpholine	338	3 + 8	3, 23° (b)
2536	Methyltetrahydrofuran	33	3	3, 3° (b)
2538	Nitronaphthalene	40	4.1	4.1, 6° (c)
2541	Terpinolene	30	3	3, 31° (c)
2542	Tributylamine	60	6.1	6.1, 12° (b)
2545	Hafnium powder, dry	40	4.2	4.2, 12° (b), (c)
2546	Titanium powder, dry	40	4.2	4.2, 12° (b), (c)
2552	Hexafluoroacetone hydrate	60	6.1	6.1, 17° (b)
2554	Methylallyl chloride	33	3	3, 3° (b)
2558	Epibromohydrin	663	6.1 + 3	6.1, 16° (a)
2560	2-Methylpentan-2-ol	30	3	3, 31° (c)
2561	3-Methyl-1-butene (Isopropylethylene)	33	3	3, 1° (a)
2564	Trichloroacetic acid solution	80	8	8, 32° (b)1.
2564	Trichloroacetic acid solution	80	8	8, 32° (c)
2565	Dicyclohexylamine	80	8	8, 53° (c)
2567	Sodium pentachlorophenate	60	6.1	6.1, 17° (b)

Substance Identification No. (Lower part) (a)	Name of substance (b)	Hazard Identification No. (Upper part) (c)	Label (d)	Class and item number (e)
2570	Cadmium compound	66	6.1	6.1, 61° (a)
2570	Cadmium compound	60	6.1	6.1, 61° (b), (c)
2571	Alkylsulphuric acids	80	8	8, 34° (b)
2572	Phenylhydrazine	60	6.1	6.1, 12° (b)
2573	Thallium chlorate	56	5.1 + 6.1	5.1, 29° (b)
2574	Tricresyl phosphate	60	6.1	6.1, 23° (b)
2576	Phosphorus oxybromide, molten	80	8	8, 15°
2577	Phenylacetyl chloride	80	8	8, 35° (b)1.
2578	Phosphorus trioxide	80	8	8, 16° (c)
2579	Piperazine	80	8	8, 52° (c)
2580	Aluminium bromide solution	80	8	8, 5° (c)
2581	Aluminium chloride solution	80	8	8, 5° (c)
2582	Ferric chloride solution	80	8	8, 5° (c)
2583	Alkylsulphonic acids, solid	80	8	8, 1° (b)
2583	Arylsulphonic acids, solid	80	8	8, 1° (b)
2584	Alkylsulphonic acids, liquid	80	8	8, 1° (b)
2584	Arylsulphonic acids, liquid	80	8	8, 1° (b)
2585	Alkylsulphonic acids, solid	80	8	8, 34° (c)
2585	Arylsulphonic acids, solid	80	8	8, 34° (c)
2586	Alkylsulphonic acids, liquid	80	8	8, 34° (c)
2586	Arylsulphonic acids, liquid	80	8	8, 34° (c)
2587	Benzoquinone	60	6.1	6.1, 14° (b)
2588	Pesticide, solid, toxic, n.o.s.	66	6.1	6.1, 73° (a)
2588	Pesticide, solid, toxic, n.o.s.	60	6.1	6.1, 73° (b), (c)
2589	Vinyl chloroacetate	63	6.1 + 3	6.1, 16° (b)
2590	White asbestos (Actinolite, Anthophyllite, Chrysotile or Tremolite)	90	9	9, 1° (c)
2591	Xenon, refrigerated liquid	22	2	2, 3°A
2599	Chlorotrifluoromethane and trifluoromethane, azeotropic mixture (R 503)	20	2	2, 2°A
2600	Carbon monoxide and hydrogen mixture, compressed	263	6.1 + 3	2, 1°TF
2601	Cyclobutane	23	3	2, 2°F
2602	Dichlorodifluoromethane and 1,1-difluoroethane, azeotropic mixture (R 500)	20	2	2, 2°A
2603	Cycloheptatriene	336	3 + 6.1	3, 19° (b)
2604	Boron trifluoride diethyl etherate	883	8 + 3	8, 33° (a)
2605	Methoxymethyl isocyanate	336	3 + 6.1	3, 14° (a)
2606	Methyl orthosilicate (Tetramethoxysilane)	663	6.1 + 3	6.1, 8° (a)2.

Substance Identification No. (Lower part) (a)	Name of substance (b)	Hazard Identification No. (Upper part) (c)	Label (d)	Class and item number (e)
2607	Acrolein, dimer, stabilized	39	3	3, 31° (c)
2608	Nitropropanes	30	3	3, 31° (c)
2609	Triallyl borate	60	6.1	6.1, 14° (c)
2610	Triallylamine	38	3 + 8	3, 33° (c)
2611	Propylene chlorohydrin	63	6.1 + 3	6.1, 16° (b)
2612	Methyl propyl ether	33	3	3, 2° (b)
2614	Methallyl alcohol	30	3	3, 31° (c)
2615	Ethyl propyl ether	33	3	3, 3° (b)
2616	Triisopropyl borate	33	3	3, 3° (b)
2616	Triisopropyl borate	30	3	3, 31° (c)
2617	Methylcyclohexanols	30	3	3, 31° (c)
2618	Vinyltoluene, inhibited (o-,m-,p-)	39	3	3, 31° (c)
2619	Benzyldimethylamine	83	8 + 3	8, 54° (b)
2620	Amyl butyrates	30	3	3, 31° (c)
2621	Acetyl methyl carbinol	30	3	3, 31° (c)
2622	Glycidaldehyde	336	3 + 6.1	3, 17° (b)
2624	Magnesium silicide	423	4.3	4.3, 12° (b)
2626	Chloric acid, aqueous solution	50	5.1	5.1, 4° (b)
2627	Nitrites, inorganic, n.o.s.	50	5.1	5.1, 23° (b)
2628	Potassium fluoroacetate	66	6.1	6.1, 17° (a)
2629	Sodium fluoroacetate	66	6.1	6.1, 17° (a)
2642	Fluoroacetic acid	66	6.1	6.1, 17° (a)
2643	Methyl bromoacetate	60	6.1	6.1, 17° (b)
2644	Methyl iodide	66	6.1	6.1, 15° (a)
2645	Phenacyl bromide	60	6.1	6.1, 17° (b)
2646	Hexachlorocyclopentadiene	66	6.1	6.1, 15° (a)
2647	Malononitrile	60	6.1	6.1, 12° (b)
2648	1,2-Dibromobutan-3-one	60	6.1	6.1, 17° (b)
2649	1, 3-Dichloroacetone	60	6.1	6.1, 17° (b)
2650	1,1 -Dichloro-1-nitroethane	60	6.1	6.1, 17° (b)
2651	4,4'-Diaminodiphenylmethane	60	6.1	6.1, 12° (c)
2653	Benzyl iodide	60	6.1	6.1, 15° (b)
2655	Potassium fluorosilicate	60	6.1	6.1, 64° (c)
2656	Quinoline	60	6.1	6.1, 12° (c)
2657	Selenium disulphide	60	6.1	6.1, 55° (b)
2659	Sodium chloroacetate	60	6.1	6.1, 17° (c)
2660	Nitrotoluidines (mono)	60	6.1	6.1, 12° (c)
2661	Hexachloroacetone	60	6.1	6.1, 17° (c)

Substance Identification No. (Lower part) (a)	Name of substance (b)	Hazard Identification No. (Upper part) (c)	Label (d)	Class and item number (e)
2662	Hydroquinone	60	6.1	6.1, 14° (c)
2664	Dibromomethane	60	6.1	6.1, 15° (c)
2666	Ethyl cyanoacetate	60	6.1	6.1, 12° (c)
2667	Butyltoluenes	60	6.1	6.1, 25° (c)
2668	Chloroacetonitrile	63	6.1 + 3	6.1, 11° (b)2.
2669	Chlorocresols	60	6.1	6.1, 14° (b)
2670	Cyanuric chloride	80	8	8, 39° (b)
2671	Aminopyridines (o-, m-, p-)	60	6.1	6.1, 12° (b)
2672	Ammonia solution containing between 10 and 35% ammonia	80	8	8, 43° (c)
2673	2-Amino-4-chlorophenol	60	6.1	6.1, 12° (b)
2674	Sodium fluorosilicate	60	6.1	6.1, 64° (c)
2677	Rubidium hydroxide solution	80	8	8, 42° (b), (c)
2678	Rubidium hydroxide	80	8	8, 41° (b)
2679	Lithium hydroxide, solution	80	8	8, 42° (b), (c)
2680	Lithium hydroxide, monohydrate	80	8	8, 41° (b)
2681	Caesium hydroxide, solution	80	8	8, 42° (b), (c)
2682	Caesium hydroxide	80	8	8, 41° (b)
2683	Ammonium sulphide, solution	86	8 + 6.1 + 3	8, 45° (b)2.
2684	Diethylaminopropylamine	38	3 + 8	3, 33° (c)
2685	N,N-Diethylethylenediamine	83	8 + 3	8, 54° (b)
2686	2-Diethylaminoethanol	83	8 + 3	3, 54° (b)
2687	Dicyclohexylammonium nitrite	40	4.1	4.1, 11° (c)
2688	1-Bromo-3-chloropropane	60	6.1	6.1, 15° (c)
2689	Glycerol alpha-monochlorohydrin	60	6.1	6.1, 17° (c)
2690	N,n-Butylimidazole	60	6.1	6.1, 12° (b)
2691	Phosphorus pentabromide	80	8	8, 11° (b)
2692	Boron tribromide (boron bromide)	X88	8	8, 12° (a)
2693	Bisulphites, aqueous solution, n.o.s.	80	8	8, 17° (c)
2698	Tetrahydrophthalic anhydrides	80	8	8, 31° (c)
2699	Trifluoroacetic acid	88	8	8, 32° (a)
2705	1-Pentol	80	8	8, 66° (b)
2707	Dimethyldioxanes	33	3	3, 3° (b)
2707	Dimethyldioxanes	30	3	3, 31° (c)
2709	Butylbenzenes	30	3	3, 31° (c)
2710	Dipropyl ketone	30	3	3, 31° (c)
2713	Acridine	60	6.1	6.1, 12° (c)
2714	Zinc resinate	40	4.1	4.1, 12° (c)

Substance Identification No. (Lower part) (a)	Name of substance (b)	Hazard Identification No. (Upper part) (c)	Label (d)	Class and item number (e)
2715	Aluminium resinate	40	4.1	4.1, 12° (c)
2716	1,4-Butynediol	60	6.1	6.1, 14° (c)
2717	Camphor, synthetic	40	4.1	4.1, 6° (c)
2719	Barium bromate	56	5.1 + 6.1	5.1, 29° (b)
2720	Chromium nitrate	50	5.1	5.1, 22° (c)
2721	Copper chlorate	50	5.1	5.1, 11° (b)
2722	Lithium nitrate	50	5.1	5.1, 22° (c)
2723	Magnesium chlorate	50	5.1	5.1, 11° (b)
2724	Manganese nitrate	50	5.1	5.1, 22° (c)
2725	Nickel nitrate	50	5.1	5.1, 22° (c)
2726	Nickel nitrite	50	5.1	5.1, 23° (c)
2727	Thallium nitrate	65	6.1 + 05	6.1, 68° (b)
2728	Zirconium nitrate	50	5.1	5.1, 22° (c)
2729	Hexachlorobenzene	60	6.1	6.1, 15° (c)
2730	Nitroanisole	60	6.1	6.1, 12° (c)
2732	Nitrobromobenzene	60	6.1	6.1, 12° (c)
2733	Amines or polyamines, flammable, corrosive, n.o.s.	338	3 + 8	3, 22° (a), (b)
2733	Amines or polyamines, flammable, corrosive, n.o.s.	38	3 + 8	3, 33° (c)
2734	Amines or polyamines, liquid, corrosive, flammable, n.o.s.	883	8 + 3	8, 54° (a)
2734	Amines or polyamines, liquid, corrosive, flammable, n.o.s.	83	8 + 3	8, 54° (b)
2735	Amines or polyamines, liquid, corrosive, n.o.s.	88	8	8, 53° (a)
2735	Amines or polyamines, liquid, corrosive, n.o.s.	80	8	8, 53° (b), (c)
2738	N-Butylaniline	60	6.1	6.1, 12° (b)
2739	Butyric anhydride	80	8	8, 32° (c)
2740	n-Propyl chloroformate	668	6.1 + 8 + 3	6.1, 28° (a)
2741	Barium hypochlorite	56	5.1 + 6.1	5.1, 29° (b)
2742	Chloroformates, toxic, corrosive, flammable, n.o.s.	638	6.1 + 3 + 8	6.1, 28° (b)
2743	n-Butyl chloroformate	638	6.1 + 3 + 8	6.1, 28° (b)
2744	Cyclobutyl chloroformate	638	6.1 + 3 + 8	6.1, 28° (b)
2745	Chloromethyl chloroformate	68	6.1 + 8	6.1, 27° (b)
2746	Phenyl chloroformate	68	6.1 + 8	6.1, 27° (b)
2747	tert-Butylcyclohexyl chloroformate	60	6.1	6.1, 17° (c)
2748	2-Ethylhexyl chloroformate	68	6.1 + 8	6.1, 27° (b)
2749	Tetramethylsilane	33	3	3, 1° (a)
2750	1,3-Dichloropropanol-2	60	6.1	6.1, 17° (b)

Substance Identification No. (Lower part) (a)	Name of substance (b)	Hazard Identification No. (Upper part) (c)	Label (d)	Class and item number (e)
2751	Diethylthiophosphoryl chloride	80	8	8, 35° (b)1.
2752	1,2-Epoxy-3-ethoxypropane	30	3	3, 31° (c)
2753	N-Ethylbenzyltoluidines	60	6.1	6.1, 12° (c)
2754	N-Ethyltoluidines	60	6.1	6.1, 12° (b)
2757	Carbamate pesticide, solid, toxic	66	6.1	6.1, 73° (a)
2757	Carbamate pesticide, solid, toxic	60	6.1	6.1, 73° (b), (c)
2758	Carbamate pesticide, liquid, flammable, toxic	336	3 + 6.1	3, 41° (a), (b)
2759	Arsenical pesticide, solid, toxic	66	6.1	6.1, 73° (a)
2759	Arsenical pesticide, solid, toxic	60	6.1	6.1, 73° (b), (c)
2760	Arsenical pesticide, liquid, flammable, toxic	336	3 + 6.1	3, 41° (a), (b)
2761	Organochlorine pesticide, solid, toxic	66	6.1	6.1, 73° (a)
2761	Organochlorine pesticide, solid, toxic	60	6.1	6.1, 73° (b), (c)
2762	Organochlorine pesticide, liquid, flammable, toxic	336	3 + 6.1	3, 41° (a), (b)
2763	Triazine pesticide, solid, toxic	66	6.1	6.1, 73° (a)
2763	Triazine pesticide, solid, toxic	60	6.1	6.1, 73° (b), (c)
2764	Triazine pesticide, liquid, flammable, toxic	336	3 + 6.1	3, 41° (a), (b)
2765	Phenoxy pesticide, solid, toxic	66	6.1	6.1, 73° (a)
2765	Phenoxy pesticide, solid, toxic	60	6.1	6.1, 73° (b), (c)
2766	Phenoxy pesticide, liquid, flammable, toxic	336	3 + 6.1	3, 41° (a), (b)
2767	Phenyl urea pesticide, solid, toxic	66	6.1	6.1, 73° (a)
2767	Phenyl urea pesticide, solid, toxic	60	6.1	6.1, 73° (b), (c)
2768	Phenyl urea pesticide, liquid, flammable, toxic	336	3 + 6.1	3, 41° (a), (b)
2769	Benzoic derivative pesticide, solid, toxic	66	6.1	6.1, 73° (a)
2769	Benzoic derivative pesticide, solid, toxic	60	6.1	6.1, 73° (b), (c)
2770	Benzoic derivative pesticide, liquid, flammable, toxic	336	3 + 6.1	3, 41° (a), (b)
2771	Dithiocarbamate pesticide, solid, toxic	66	6.1	6.1, 73° (a)
2771	Dithiocarbamate pesticide, solid, toxic	60	6.1	6.1, 73° (b), (c)
2772	Dithiocarbamate pesticide, liquid, flammable, toxic	336	3 + 6.1	3, 41° (a), (b)
2773	Phthalimide derivative pesticide, solid, toxic	66	6.1	6.1, 73° (a)
2773	Phthalimide derivative pesticide, solid, toxic	60	6.1	6.1, 73° (b), (c)
2774	Phthalimide derivative pesticide, liquid, flammable, toxic	336	3 + 6.1	3, 41° (a), (b)
2775	Copper based pesticide, solid, toxic	66	6.1	6.1, 73° (a)
2775	Copper based pesticide, solid, toxic	60	6.1	6.1, 73° (b), (c)
2776	Copper based pesticide, liquid, flammable, toxic	336	3 + 6.1	3, 41° (a), (b)
2777	Mercury based pesticide, solid, toxic	66	6.1	6.1, 73° (a)
2777	Mercury based pesticide, solid, toxic	60	6.1	6.1, 73° (b), (c)

Substance Identification No. (Lower part) (a)	Name of substance (b)	Hazard Identification No. (Upper part) (c)	Label (d)	Class and item number (e)
2778	Mercury based pesticide, liquid, flammable, toxic	336	3 + 6.1	3, 41° (a), (b)
2779	Substituted nitrophenol pesticide, solid, toxic	66	6.1	6.1, 73° (a)
2779	Substituted nitrophenol pesticide, solid, toxic	60	6.1	6.1, 73° (b), (c)
2780	Substituted nitrophenol pesticide, liquid, flammable, toxic	336	3 + 6.1	3, 41° (a), (b)
2781	Bipyridilium pesticide, solid, toxic	66	6.1	6.1, 73° (a)
2781	Bipyridilium pesticide, solid, toxic	60	6.1	6.1, 73° (b), (c)
2782	Bipyridilium pesticide, liquid, flammable, toxic	336	3 + 6.1	3, 41° (a), (b)
2783	Organophosphorus pesticide, solid, toxic	66	6.1	6.1, 73° (a)
2783	Organophosphorus pesticide, solid, toxic	60	6.1	6.1, 73° (b), (c)
2784	Organophosphorous pesticide, liquid, flammable, toxic	336	3 + 6.1	3, 41° (a), (b)
2785	4-Thiapentanal	60	6.1	6.1, 21° (c)
2786	Organotin pesticide, solid, toxic	66	6.1	6.1, 73° (a)
2786	Organotin pesticide, solid, toxic	60	6.1	6.1, 73° (b), (c)
2787	Organotin pesticide, liquid, flammable, toxic	336	3 + 6.1	3, 41° (a), (b)
2788	Organotin compound, liquid, n.o.s.	66	6.1	6.1, 32° (a)
2788	Organotin compound, liquid, n.o.s.	60	6.1	6.1, 32° (b), (c)
2789	Acetic acid, glacial	83	8 + 3	8, 32° (b)2.
2789	Acetic acid, solution	83	8 + 3	8, 32° (b)2.
2790	Acetic acid, solution	80	8	8, 32° (b)1., (c)
2793	Ferrous metal borings, shavings, turnings or cuttings	40	4.2	4.2, 12° (c)
2794	Batteries, wet, filled with acid, electric storage	80	8	8, 81° (c)
2795	Batteries, wet, filled with alkali, electric storage	80	8	8, 81° (c)
2796	Battery fluid, acid	80	8	8, 1° (b)
2796	Sulphuric acid, with more than 51% acid	80	8	8, 1° (b)
2797	Battery fluid, alkali	80	8	8, 42° (b)
2798	Phenylphosphorus dichloride	80	8	8, 35° (b)1.
2799	Phenylphosphorus thiodichloride	80	8	8, 35° (b)1.
2800	Batteries, wet, non-spillable, electric storage	80	8	8, 81° (c)
2801	Dye or dye intermediate, liquid, corrosive, n.o.s	88	8	8, 66° (a)
2801	Dye or dye intermediate, liquid, corrosive, n.o.s.	80	8	8, 66° (b), (c)
2802	Copper chloride	80	8	8, 11° (c)
2803	Gallium	80	8	8, 65° (c)
2805	Lithium hydride, fused solid	423	4.3	4.3, 16° (b)
2809	Mercury	80	8	8, 66° (c)
2810	Toxic liquid, organic, n.o.s.	66	6.1	6.1, 25° (a)
2810	Toxic liquid, organic, n.o.s.	60	6.1	6.1, 25° (b), (c)

Substance Identification No. (Lower part) (a)	Name of substance (b)	Hazard Identification No. (Upper part) (c)	Label (d)	Class and item number (e)
2811	Toxic solid, organic, n.o.s.	66	6.1	6.1, 25° (a)
2811	Toxic solid, organic, n.o.s.	60	6.1	6.1, 25° (b), (c)
2813	Water-reactive solid, n.o.s.	423	4.3	4.3, 20° (b), (c)
2814	Infectious substance, affecting humans	606	6.2	6.2, 3° (b)
2815	N-Aminoethylpiperazine	80	8	8, 53° (c)
2817	Ammonium hydrogendifluoride solution	86	8 + 6.1	8, 7° (b), (c)
2818	Ammonium polysulphide solution	86	8 + 6.1	8, 45° (b)1.
2818	Ammonium polysulphide solution	86	8 + 6.1	8, 45° (c)
2819	Amyl acid phosphate	80	8	8, 38° (c)
2820	Butyric acid	80	8	8, 32° (c)
2821	Phenol solution	60	6.1	6.1, 14° (b), (c)
2822	2-Chloropyridine	60	6.1	6.1, 12° (b)
2823	Crotonic acid	80	8	8, 31° (c)
2826	Ethyl chlorothioformate	80	8	8, 64° (b)
2829	Caproic acid	80	8	8, 32° (c)
2830	Lithium ferrosilicon	423	4.3	4.3, 12° (b)
2831	1,1,1-Trichloroethane	60	6.1	6.1, 15° (c)
2834	Phosphorous acid	80	8	8, 16° (c)
2835	Sodium aluminium hydride	423	4.3	4.3, 16° (b)
2837	Bisulphates, aqueous solution	80	8	8, 1° (b), (c)
2838	Vinyl butyrate, inhibited	339	3	3, 3° (b)
2839	Aldol	60	6.1	6.1, 14° (b)
2840	Butyraldoxime	30	3	3, 31° (c)
2841	Di-n-amylamine	36	3 + 6.1	3, 32° (c)
2842	Nitroethane	30	3	3, 31° (c)
2844	Calcium manganese silicon	423	4.3	4.3, 12° (c)
2845	Pyrophoric liquid, organic, n.o.s.	333	4.2	4.2, 6° (a)
2849	3-Chloropropanol-1	60	6.1	6.1, 17° (c)
2850	Propylene tetramer	30	3	3, 31° (c)
2851	Boron trifluoride dihydrate	80	8	8, 10° (b)
2853	Magnesium fluorosilicate	60	6.1	6.1, 64° (c)
2854	Ammonium fluorosilicate	60	6.1	6.1, 64° (c)
2855	Zinc fluorosilicate	60	6.1	6.1, 64° (c)
2856	Fluorosilicates, n.o.s.	60	6.1	6.1, 64° (c)
2858	Zirconium, dry	40	4.1	4.1, 13° (c)
2859	Ammonium metavanadate	60	6.1	6.1, 58° (b)
2861	Ammonium polyvanadate	60	6.1	6.1, 58° (b)
2862	Vanadium pentoxide	60	6.1	6.1, 58° (b)

Substance Identification No. (Lower part) (a)	Name of substance (b)	Hazard Identification No. (Upper part) (c)	Label (d)	Class and item number (e)
2863	Sodium ammonium vanadate	60	6.1	6.1, 58° (b)
2864	Potassium metavanadate	60	6.1	6.1, 58° (b)
2865	Hydroxylamine sulphate	80	8	8, 16° (c)
2869	Titanium trichloride mixture	80	8	8, 11° (b), (c)
2870	Aluminium borohydride	X333	4.2 + 4.3	4.2, 17° (a)
2870	Aluminium borohydride in devices	X333	4.2 + 4.3	4.2, 17° (a)
2871	Antimony powder	60	6.1	6.1, 59° (c)
2872	Dibromochloropropanes	60	6.1	6.1, 15° (c)
2873	Dibutylaminoethanol	60	6.1	6.1, 12° (c)
2874	Furfuryl alcohol	60	6.1	6.1, 14°c)
2875	Hexachlorophene	60	6.1	6.1, 17° (c)
2876	Resorcinol	60	6.1	6.1, 14° (c)
2878	Titanium sponge, powder or granules	40	4.1	4.1, 13° (c)
2879	Selenium oxychloride	X886	8 + 6.1	8, 12° (a)
2880	Calcium hypochlorite, hydrated	50	5.1	5.1, 15° (b)
2880	Calcium hypochlorite, hydrated mixture	50	5.1	5.1, 15° (b)
2881	Metal catalyst, dry	40	4.2	4.2, 12° (b), (c)
2900	Infectious substance, affecting animals only	606	6.2	6.2, 3° (b)
2901	Bromine chloride	265	6.1 + 05 + 8	2, 2°TOC
2902	Pesticide, liquid, toxic, n.o.s.	66	6.1	6.1, 71° (a)
2902	Pesticide, liquid, toxic, n.o.s.	60	6.1	6.1, 71° (b), (c)
2903	Pesticide, liquid, toxic, flammable, n.o.s.	663	6.1 + 3	6.1, 72° (a)
2903	Pesticide, liquid, toxic, flammable, n.o.s.	63	6.1 + 3	6.1, 72° (b), (c)
2904	Chlorophenolates, liquid	80	8	8, 62° (c)
2904	Phenolates, liquid	80	8	8, 62° (c)
2905	Chlorophenolates, solid	80	8	8, 62° (c)
2905	Phenolates, solid	80	8	8, 62° (c)
2912	Radioactive material, low specific activity (LSA), n.o.s.	70	7A, 7B or 7C	7, Sch 5, 6 or 13
2912	Radioactive material, low specific activity (LSA), n.o.s., gas	72	7A, 7B or 7C	7, Sch 5, 6 or 13
2912	Radioactive material, low specific activity (LSA), n.o.s., gas, flammable	723	7A, 7B or 7C + 3	7, Sch 5, 6 or 13
2912	Radioactive material, low specific activity (LSA), n.o.s., liquid, flammable, with a flash-point not above 61 °C	73	7A, 7B or 7C + 3	7, Sch 5, 6 or 13
2912	Radioactive material, low specific activity (LSA), n.o.s., solid, flammable	74	7A, 7B or 7C + 4.1	7, Sch 5, 6 or 13
2912	Radioactive material, low specific activity (LSA), n.o.s., oxidizing	75	7A, 7B or 7C + 05	7, Sch 5, 6 or 13

Substance Identification No. (Lower part) (a)	Name of substance (b)	Hazard Identification No. (Upper part) (c)	Label (d)	Class and item number (e)
2912	Radioactive material, low specific activity (LSA), n.o.s., toxic	76	7A, 7B or 7C + 6.1	7, Sch 5, 6 or 13
2912	Radioactive material, low specific activity (LSA), n.o.s.,corrosive	78	7A, 7B or 7C + 8	7, Sch 5, 6 or 13
2920	Corrosive liquid, flammable, n.o.s.	883	8 + 3	8, 68° (a)
2920	Corrosive liquid, flammable, n.o.s.	83	8 + 3	8, 68° (b)
2921	Corrosive solid, flammable, n.o.s.	884	8 + 4.1	8, 67° (a)
2921	Corrosive solid, flammable, n.o.s.	84	8 + 4.1	8, 67° (b)
2922	Corrosive liquid, toxic, n.o.s.	886	8 + 6.1	8, 76° (a)
2922	Corrosive liquid, toxic, n.o.s.	86	8 + 6.1	8, 76° (b), (c)
2923	Corrosive solid, toxic, n.o.s.	886	8 + 6.1	8, 75° (a)
2923	Corrosive solid, toxic, n.o.s.	86	8 + 6.1	8, 75° (b), (c)
2924	Flammable liquid, corrosive, n.o.s.	338	3 + 8	3, 26° (a), (b)
2924	Flammable liquid, corrosive, n.o.s.	38	3 + 8	3, 33° (c)
2925	Flammable solid, corrosive, organic, n.o.s.	48	4.1 + 8	4.1, 8° (b), (c)
2926	Flammable solid, toxic, organic, n.o.s.	46	4.1 + 6.1	4.1, 7° (b), (c)
2927	Toxic liquid, corrosive, organic, n.o.s.	668	6.1 + 8	6.1, 27° (a)
2927	Toxic liquid, corrosive, organic, n.o.s.	68	6.1 + 8	6.1, 27° (b)
2928	Toxic solid, corrosive, organic, n.o.s.	668	6.1 + 8	6.1, 27° (a)
2928	Toxic solid, corrosive, organic, n.o.s.	68	6.1 + 8	6.1, 27° (b)
2929	Toxic liquid, flammable, organic, n.o.s.	663	6.1 + 3	6.1, 9° (a)
2929	Toxic liquid, flammable, organic, n.o.s.	663	6.1 + 3	6.1, 26° (a)1.
2929	Toxic liquid, flammable, organic, n.o.s.	63	6.1 + 3	6.1, 26° (b)1.
2930	Toxic solid, flammable, organic, n.o.s.	664	6.1 + 4.1	6.1, 26° (a)2.
2930	Toxic solid, flammable, organic, n.o.s.	64	6.1 + 4.1	6.1, 26° (b)2.
2931	Vanadyl sulphate	60	6.1	6.1, 58° (b)
2933	Methyl 2-chloropropionate	30	3	3, 31° (c)
2934	Isopropyl 2-chloropropionate	30	3	3, 31° (c)
2935	Ethyl 2-chloropropionate	30	3	3, 31° (c)
2936	Thiolactic acid	60	6.1	6.1, 21° (b)
2937	alpha-Methylbenzyl alcohol	60	6.1	6.1, 14° (c)
2940	9-Phosphabicyclononanes (cyclooctadiene phosphines)	40	4.2	4.2, 5° (b)
2941	Fluoroanilines	60	6.1	6.1, 12° (c)
2942	2-Trifluoromethylaniline	60	6.1	6.1, 12° (c)
2943	Tetrahydrofurfurylamine	30	3	3, 31° (c)
2945	N-Methylbutylamine	338	3 + 8	3, 22° (b)
2946	2-Amino-5-diethylaminopentane	60	6.1	6.1, 12° (c)
2947	Isopropyl chloroacetate	30	3	3, 31° (c)

Substance Identification No. (Lower part) (a)	Name of substance (b)	Hazard Identification No. (Upper part) (c)	Label (d)	Class and item number (e)
2948	3-Trifluoromethylaniline	60	6.1	6.1, 17° (b)
2949	Sodium hydrosulphide	80	8	8, 45° (b)1.
2950	Magnesium granules, coated	423	4.3	4.3, 11° (c)
2965	Boron trifluoride dimethyl etherate	382	4.3 + 3 + 8	4.3, 2° (a)
2966	Thioglycol	60	6.1	6.1, 21° (b)
2967	Sulphamic acid	80	8	8, 16° (c)
2968	Maneb preparation, stabilized	423	4.3	4.3, 20° (c)
2968	Maneb, stabilized	423	4.3	4.3, 20° (c)
2969	Castor beans	90	9	9, 35° (c)
2969	Castor flake	90	9	9, 35° (c)
2969	Castor meal	90	9	9, 35° (c)
2969	Castor pomace	90	9	9, 35° (c)
2980	Uranyl nitrate hexahydrate solution	78	7A, 7B or 7C + 8	7, Sch. 5, 6 or 13
2982	Radioactive material, n.o.s.	70	7A, 7B or 7C	7, Sch. 9, 10, 11 or 13
2982	Radioactive material, n.o.s., gas	72	7A, 7B or 7C	7, Sch. 9, 10, 11 or 13
2982	Radioactive material, n.o.s., gas, flammable	723	7A, 7B or 7C + 3	7, Sch. 9, 10, 11 or 13
2982	Radioactive material, n.o.s., liquid, flammable, with a flash-point not above 61 °C	73	7A, 7B or 7C + 3	7, Sch. 9, 10, 11 or 13
2982	Radioactive material, n.o.s., solid, flammable	74	7A, 7B or 7C + 4.1	7, Sch. 9, 10, 11 or 13
2982	Radioactive material, n.o.s., oxidizing	75	7A, 7B or 7C + 05	7, Sch. 9, 10, 11 or 13
2982	Radioactive material, n.o.s., toxic	76	7A, 7B or 7C + 6.1	7, Sch. 9, 10, 11 or 13
2982	Radioactive material, n.o.s., corrosive	78	7A, 7B or 7C + 8	7, Sch. 9, 10, 11 or 13
2983	Ethylene oxide and propylene oxide mixture	336	3 + 6.1	3, 17° (a)
2984	Hydrogen peroxide, aqueous solution	50	5.1	5.1, 1° (c)
2985	Chlorosilanes, flammable, corrosive, n.o.s.	338	3 + 8	3, 21° (b)
2986	Chlorosilanes, corrosive, flammable, n.o.s.	X83	8 + 3	8, 37° (b)
2987	Chlorosilanes, corrosive, n.o.s.	80	8	8, 36° (b)
2988	Chlorosilanes, water-reactive, flammable, corrosive, n.o.s.	X338	4.3 + 3 + 8	4.3, 1° (a)
2989	Lead phosphite, dibasic	40	4.1	4.1, 11° (b), (c)
2991	Carbamate pesticide, liquid, toxic, flammable	663	6.1 + 3	6.1, 72° (a)
2991	Carbamate pesticide, liquid, toxic, flammable	63	6.1 + 3	6.1, 72° (b), (c)
2992	Carbamate pesticide, liquid, toxic	66	6.1	6.1, 71° (a)
2992	Carbamate pesticide, liquid, toxic	60	6.1	6.1, 71° (b), (c)

Substance Identification No. (Lower part) (a)	Name of substance (b)	Hazard Identification No. (Upper part) (c)	Label (d)	Class and item number (e)
2993	Arsenical pesticide, liquid, toxic, flammable	663	6.1 + 3	6.1, 72° (a)
2993	Arsenical pesticide, liquid, toxic, flammable	63	6.1 + 3	6.1, 72° (b), (c)
2994	Arsenical pesticide, liquid, toxic	66	6.1	6.1, 71° (a)
2994	Arsenical pesticide, liquid, toxic	60	6.1	6.1, 71° (b), (c)
2995	Organochlorine pesticide, liquid, toxic, flammable	663	6.1 + 3	6.1, 72° (a)
2995	Organochlorine pesticide, liquid, toxic, flammable	63	6.1 + 3	6.1, 72° (b), (c)
2996	Organochlorine pesticide, liquid, toxic	66	6.1	6.1, 71° (a)
2996	Organochlorine pesticide, liquid, toxic	60	6.1	6.1, 71° (b), (c)
2997	Triazine pesticide, liquid, toxic, flammable	663	6.1 + 3	6.1, 72° (a)
2997	Triazine pesticide, liquid, toxic, flammable	63	6.1 + 3	6.1, 72° (b), (c)
2998	Triazine pesticide, liquid, toxic	66	6.1	6.1, 71° (a)
2998	Triazine pesticide, liquid, toxic	60	6.1	6.1, 71° (b), (c)
2999	Phenoxy pesticide, liquid, toxic, flammable	663	6.1 + 3	6.1, 72° (a)
2999	Phenoxy pesticide, liquid, toxic, flammable	63	6.1 + 3	6.1, 72° (b), (c)
3000	Phenoxy pesticide, liquid, toxic	66	6.1	6.1, 71° (a)
3000	Phenoxy pesticide, liquid, toxic	60	6.1	6.1, 71° (b), (c)
3001	Phenyl urea pesticide, liquid, toxic, flammable	663	6.1 + 3	6.1, 72° (a)
3001	Phenyl urea pesticide, liquid, toxic, flammable	63	6.1 + 3	6.1, 72° (b), (c)
3002	Phenyl urea pesticide, liquid, toxic	66	6.1	6.1, 71° (a)
3002	Phenyl urea pesticide, liquid, toxic	60	6.1	6.1, 71° (b), (c)
3003	Benzoic derivative pesticide, liquid, toxic, flammable	663	6.1 + 3	6.1, 72° (a)
3003	Benzoic derivative pesticide, liquid, toxic, flammable	63	6.1 + 3	6.1, 72° (b), (c)
3004	Benzoic derivative pesticide, liquid,toxic	66	6.1	6.1, 71° (a)
3004	Benzoic derivative pesticide, liquid,toxic	60	6.1	6.1, 71° (b), (c)
3005	Dithiocarbamate pesticide, liquid, toxic, flammable	663	6.1 + 3	6.1, 72° (a)
3005	Dithiocarbamate pesticide, liquid, toxic, flammable	63	6.1 + 3	6.1, 72° (b), (c)
3006	Dithiocarbamate pesticide, liquid, toxic	66	6.1	6.1, 71° (a)
3006	Dithiocarbamate pesticide, liquid, toxic	60	6.1	6.1, 71° (b), (c)
3007	Phthalimide derivative pesticide, liquid, toxic, flammable	663	6.1 + 3	6.1, 72° (a)
3007	Phthalimide derivative pesticide, liquid, toxic, flammable	63	6.1 + 3	6.1, 72° (b), (c)
3008	Phthalimide derivative pesticide, liquid, toxic	66	6.1	6.1, 71° (a)
3008	Phthalimide derivative pesticide, liquid, toxic	60	6.1	6.1, 71° (b), (c)
3009	Copper based pesticide, liquid, toxic, flammable	663	6.1 + 3	6.1, 72° (a)
3009	Copper based pesticide, liquid, toxic, flammable	63	6.1 + 3	6.1, 72° (b), (c)
3010	Copper based pesticide, liquid, toxic	66	6.1	6.1, 71° (a)

Substance Identification No. (Lower part) (a)	Name of substance (b)	Hazard Identification No. (Upper part) (c)	Label (d)	Class and item number (e)
3010	Copper based pesticide, liquid, toxic	60	6.1	6.1, 71° (b), (c)
3011	Mercury based pesticide, liquid, toxic, flammable	663	6.1 + 3	6.1, 72° (a)
3011	Mercury based pesticide, liquid, toxic, flammable	63	6.1 + 3	6.1, 72° (b), (c)
3012	Mercury based pesticide, liquid, toxic	66	6.1	6.1, 71° (a)
3012	Mercury based pesticide, liquid, toxic	60	6.1	6.1, 71° (b), (c)
3013	Substituted nitrophenol pesticide, liquid, toxic, flammable	663	6.1 + 3	6.1, 72° (a)
3013	Substituted nitrophenol pesticide, liquid, toxic, flammable	63	6.1 + 3	6.1, 72° (b), (c)
3014	Substituted nitrophenol pesticide, liquid, toxic	66	6.1	6.1, 71° (a)
3014	Substituted nitrophenol pesticide, liquid, toxic	60	6.1	6.1, 71° (b), (c)
3015	Bipyridilium pesticide, liquid, toxic, flammable	663	6.1 + 3	6.1, 72° (a)
3015	Bipyridilium pesticide, liquid, toxic, flammable	63	6.1 + 3	6.1, 72° (b), (c)
3016	Bipyridilium pesticide, liquid, toxic	66	6.1	6.1, 71° (a)
3016	Bipyridilium pesticide, liquid, toxic	60	6.1	6.1, 71° (b), (c)
3017	Organophosphorus pesticide, liquid, toxic, flammable	663	6.1 + 3	6.1, 72° (a)
3017	Organophosphorus pesticide, liquid, toxic, flammable	63	6.1 + 3	6.1, 72° (b), (c)
3018	Organophosphorus pesticide, liquid, toxic	66	6.1	6.1, 71° (a)
3018	Organophosphorus pesticide, liquid, toxic	60	6.1	6.1, 71° (b), (c)
3019	Organotin pesticide, liquid, toxic, flammable	663	6.1 + 3	6.1, 72° (a)
3019	Organotin pesticide, liquid, toxic, flammable	63	6.1 + 3	6.1, 72° (b), (c)
3020	Organotin pesticide, liquid, toxic	66	6.1	6.1, 71° (a)
3020	Organotin pesticide, liquid, toxic	60	6.1	6.1, 71° (b), (c)
3021	Pesticide, liquid, flammable, toxic, n.o.s.	336	3 + 6.1	3, 41° (a), (b)
3022	1,2-Butylene oxide, stabilized	339	3	3, 3° (b)
3023	2-Methyl-2-heptanethiol	663	6.1 + 3	6.1, 20° (a)
3024	Coumarin derivative pesticide, liquid, flammable, toxic	336	3 + 6.1	3, 41° (a), (b)
3025	Coumarin derivative pesticide, liquid, toxic, flammable	663	6.1 + 3	6.1, 72° (a)
3025	Coumarin derivative pesticide, liquid, toxic, flammable	63	6.1 + 3	6.1, 72° (b), (c)
3026	Coumarin derivative pesticide, liquid, toxic	66	6.1	6.1, 71° (a)
3026	Coumarin derivative pesticide, liquid, toxic	60	6.1	6.1, 71° (b), (c)
3027	Coumarin derivative pesticide, solid, toxic	66	6.1	6.1, 73° (a)
3027	Coumarin derivative pesticide, solid, toxic	60	6.1	6.1, 73° (b), (c)
3028	Batteries, dry containing potassium hydroxide solid, electric storage	80	8	8, 81° (c)

Substance Identification No. (Lower part) (a)	Name of substance (b)	Hazard Identification No. (Upper part) (c)	Label (d)	Class and item number (e)
3049	Metal alkyl halides, n.o.s. or metal aryl halides, n.o.s.	X333	4.2 + 4.3	4.2, 32° (a)
3050	Metal alkyl hydrides, n.o.s. or metal aryl hydrides, n.o.s.	X333	4.2 + 4.3	4.2, 32° (a)
3051	Aluminium alkyls	X333	4.2 + 4.3	4.2, 31° (a)
3052	Aluminium alkyl halides	X333	4.2 + 4.3	4.2, 32° (a)
3053	Magnesium alkyls	X333	4.2 + 4.3	4.2, 31° (a)
3054	Cyclohexyl mercaptan	30	3	3, 31° (c)
3055	2-(2-Aminoethoxy) ethanol	80	8	8, 53° (c)
3056	n-Heptaldehyde	30	3	3, 31° (c)
3057	Trifluoracetyl chloride	268	6.1 + 8	2, 2°TC
3065	Alcoholic beverages	33	3	3, 3° (b)
3065	Alcoholic beverages	30	3	3, 31° (c)
3066	Paint or paint related material	80	8	8, 66° (b), (c)
3070	Dichlorodifluoromethane and ethylene oxide mixture	20	2	2, 2°A
3071	Mercaptans, liquid, toxic, flammable, n.o.s.	63	6.1 + 3	6.1, 20° (b)
3071	Mercaptan mixture, liquid, toxic, flammable, n.o.s.	63	6.1 + 3	6.1, 20° (b)
3073	Vinylpyridines, inhibited	639	6.1 + 3 + 8	6.1, 11° (b)1.
3076	Aluminium alkyl hydrides	X333	4.2 + 4.3	4.2. 32° (a)
3077	Environmentally hazardous substance, solid, n.o.s.	90	9	9, 12° (c)
3078	Cerium	423	4.3	4.3, 13° (b)
3079	Methacrylonitrile, inhibited	336	3 + 6.1	3, 11° (a)
3080	Isocyanates, toxic, flammable, n.o.s.	63	6.1 + 3	6.1, 18° (b)
3080	Isocyanate solution, toxic, flammable, n.o.s.	63	6.1 + 3	6.1, 18° (b)
3082	Environmentally hazardous substance, liquid, n.o.s.	90	9	9, 11° (c)
3083	Perchloryl fluoride	265	6.1 + 05	2, 2°TO
3084	Corrosive solid, oxidizing, n.o.s.	885	8 + 05	8, 73° (a)
3084	Corrosive solid, oxidizing, n.o.s.	85	8 + 05	8, 73° (b)
3085	Oxidizing solid, corrosive, n.o.s.	58	5.1 + 8	5.1, 31° (b), (c)
3086	Toxic solid, oxidizing, n.o.s.	665	6.1 + 05	6.1, 68° (a)
3086	Toxic solid, oxidizing, n.o.s.	65	6.1 + 05	6.1, 68° (b)
3087	Oxidizing solid, toxic, n.o.s.	56	5.1 + 6.1	5.1, 29° (b), (c)
3088	Self-heating solid, organic, n.o.s.	40	4.2	4.2, 5° (b), (c)
3089	Metal powder, flammable, n.o.s.	40	4.1	4.1, 13° (b), (c)
3092	1-Methoxy-2-propanol	30	3	3, 31° (c)
3093	Corrosive liquid, oxidizing, n.o.s.	885	8 + 05	8, 74° (a)
3093	Corrosive liquid, oxidizing, n.o.s.	85	8 + 05	8, 74° (b)
3094	Corrosive liquid, water-reactive n.o.s.	823	8 + 4.3	8, 72° (a), (b)

Substance Identification No. (Lower part) (a)	Name of substance (b)	Hazard Identification No. (Upper part) (c)	Label (d)	Class and item number (e)
3095	Corrosive solid, self-heating, n.o.s.	84	8 + 4.2	8, 69° (b)
3096	Corrosive solid, water-reactive, n.o.s.	842	8 + 4.3	8, 71° (b)
3109	Organic peroxide, type F, liquid	539	5.2 + (8)	5.2, 9° (b)
3110	Organic peroxide, type F, solid	539	5.2	5.2, 10° (b)
3119	Organic peroxide, type F, liquid, temperature controlled	539	5.2	5.2, 19° (b)
3120	Organic peroxide, type F, solid, temperature controlled	539	5.2	5.2, 20° (b)
3122	Toxic liquid, oxidizing, n.o.s.	665	6.1 + 05	6.1, 68° (a)
3122	Toxic liquid, oxidizing, n.o.s.	65	6.1 + 05	6.1, 68° (b)
3123	Toxic liquid, water-reactive, n.o.s.	623	6.1 + 4.3	6.1, 44° (a), (b)
3124	Toxic solid, self-heating, n.o.s.	664	6.1 + 4.2	6.1, 66° (a)
3124	Toxic solid, self-heating, n.o.s.	64	6.1 + 4.2	6.1, 66° (b)
3125	Toxic solid, water-reactive, n.o.s.	642	6.1 + 4.3	6.1, 44° (b), (c)
3126	Self-heating solid, corrosive, organic, n.o.s.	48	4.2 + 8	4.2, 9° (b), (c)
3128	Self-heating solid, toxic, organic, n.o.s.	46	4.2 + 6.1	4.2, 7° (b), (c)
3129	Water-reactive liquid, corrosive, n.o.s.	X382	4.3 + 8	4.3, 25° (a)
3129	Water-reactive liquid, corrosive, n.o.s.	382	4.3 + 8	4.3, 25° (b), (c)
3130	Water-reactive liquid, toxic, n.o.s.	X362	4.3 + 6.1	4.3, 23° (a)
3130	Water-reactive liquid, toxic, n.o.s.	362	4.3 + 6.1	4.3, 23° (b), (c)
3131	Water-reactive solid, corrosive, n.o.s.	482	4.3 + 8	4.3, 24° (b), (c)
3134	Water-reactive solid, toxic, n.o.s.	462	4.3 + 6.1	4.3, 22° (b), (c)
3136	Trifluoromethane, refrigerated liquid	22	2	2, 3°A
3138	Ethylene, acetylene and propylene mixture, refrigerated liquid	223	3	2, 3°F
3140	Alkaloids or alcaloid salts, liquid, n.o.s.	66	6.1	6.1, 90° (a)
3140	Alkaloids or alcaloid salts, liquid, n.o.s.	60	6.1	6.1, 90° (b), (c)
3141	Antimony compound, inorganic, liquid, n.o.s.	60	6.1	6.1, 59° (c)
3142	Disinfectant, liquid, toxic, n.o.s.	66	6.1	6.1, 25° (a)
3142	Disinfectant, liquid, toxic, n.o.s.	60	6.1	6.1, 25° (b), (c)
3143	Dye, solid, toxic, n.o.s.	66	6.1	6.1, 25° (a)
3143	Dye, solid, toxic, n.o.s.	66	6.1	6.1, 25° (b)(c)
3143	Dye intermediate, solid, toxic, n.o.s.	66	6.1	6.1, 25° (a)
3143	Dye intermediate, solid, toxic, n.o.s.	60	6.1	6.1, 25° (b), (c)
3144	Nicotine compound or nicotine preparation, liquid, n.o.s.	66	6.1	6.1, 90° (a)
3144	Nicotine compound or nicotine preparation, liquid, n.o.s.	60	6.1	6.1, 90° (b), (c)
3145	Alkylphenols, liquid, n.o.s.	88	8	8, 40° (a)

Substance Identification No. (Lower part) (a)	Name of substance (b)	Hazard Identification No. (Upper part) (c)	Label (d)	Class and item number (e)
3145	Alkylphenols, liquid, n.o.s.	80	8	8, 40° (b), (c)
3146	Organotin compound, solid, n.o.s.	66	6.1	6.1, 32° (a)
3146	Organotin compound, solid, n.o.s.	60	6.1	6.1, 32° (b), (c)
3147	Dye or dye intermediate, solid, corrosive, n.o.s.	80	8	8, 65° (b), (c)
3148	Water-reactive liquid, n.o.s.	X323	4.3	4.3, 21° (a)
3148	Water-reactive liquid, n.o.s.	323	4.3	4.3, 21° (b), (c)
3149	Hydrogen peroxide and peroxyacetic acid mixture, stabilized	58	5.1 + 8	5.1, 1° (b)
3151	Polyhalogenated biphenyls, liquid	90	9	9, 2° (b)
3151	Polyhalogenated terphenyls, liquid	90	9	9, 2° (b)
3152	Polyhalogenated biphenyls, solid	90	9	9, 2° (b)
3152	Polyhalogenated terphenyls, solid	90	9	9, 2° (b)
3153	Perfluoromethylvinyl ether	23	3	2, 2°F
3154	Perfluoroethylvinyl ether	23	3	2, 2°F
3155	Pentachlorophenol	60	6.1	6.1, 17° (b)
3156	Compressed gas, oxidizing, n.o.s.	25	2 + 05	2, 1°O
3157	Liquefied gas, oxidizing, n.o.s.	25	2 + 05	2, 2°O
3158	Gas, refrigerated liquid, n.o.s.	22	2	2, 3°A
3159	1,1,1,2-Tetrafluoroethane (R 134a)	20	2	2, 2°A
3160	Liquefied gas, toxic, flammable, n.o.s.	263	6.1 + 3	2, 2°TF
3161	Liquefied gas, flammable, n.o.s.	23	3	2, 2°F
3162	Liquefied gas, toxic, n.o.s.	26	6.1	2, 2°T
3163	Liquefied gas, n.o.s.	20	2	2, 2°A
3170	Aluminium smelting by-products or aluminium remelting by-products	423	4.3	4.3, 13° (b), (c)
3172	Toxins, extracted from living sources, n.o.s.	66	6.1	6.1, 90° (a)
3172	Toxins, extracted from living sources, n.o.s.	60	6.1	6.1, 90° (b), (c)
3174	Titanium disulphide	40	4.2	4.2, 13° (c)
3175	Solids containing flammable liquid, n.o.s.	40	4.1	4.1, 4° (c)
3176	Flammable solid, organic, molten, n.o.s.	44	4.1	4.1, 5°
3178	Flammable solid, inorganic, n.o.s.	40	4.1	4.1, 11° (b), (c)
3179	Flammable solid, toxic, inorganic, n.o.s.	46	4.1 + 6.1	4.1, 16° (b), (c)
3180	Flammable solid, corrosive, inorganic, n.o.s.	48	4.1 + 8	4.1, 17° (b), (c)
3181	Metal salts of organic compounds, flammable, n.o.s.	40	4.1	4.1, 12° (b), (c)
3182	Metal hydrides, flammable, n.o.s.	40	4.1	4.1, 14° (b), (c)
3183	Self-heating liquid, organic, n.o.s.	30	4.2	4.2, 6° (b), (c)
3184	Self-heating liquid, toxic, organic, n.o.s.	36	4.2 + 6.1	4.2, 8° (b), (c)
3185	Self-heating liquid, corrosive, organic, n.o.s.	38	4.2 + 8	4.2, 10° (b), (c)

Substance Identification No. (Lower part) (a)	Name of substance (b)	Hazard Identification No. (Upper part) (c)	Label (d)	Class and item number (e)
3186	Self-heating liquid, inorganic, n.o.s.	30	4.2	4.2, 17° (b), (c)
3187	Self-heating liquid, toxic, inorganic, n.o.s.	36	4.2 + 6.1	4.2, 19° (b), (c)
3188	Self-heating liquid, corrosive, inorganic, n.o.s.	38	4.2 + 8	4.2, 21° (b), (c)
3189	Metal powder, self-heating, n.o.s.	40	4.2	4.2, 12° (b), (c)
3190	Self-heating solid, inorganic, n.o.s.	40	4.2	4.2, 16° (b), (c)
3191	Self-heating solid, toxic, inorganic, n.o.s.	46	4.2 + 6.1	4.2, 18° (b), (c)
3192	Self-heating solid, corrosive, inorganic, n.o.s.	48	4.2 + 8	4.2, 20° (b), (c)
3194	Pyrophoric liquid, inorganic, n.o.s.	333	4.2	4.2, 17° (a)
3203	Pyrophoric organometallic compound, n.o.s.	X333	4.2 + 4.3	4.2, 33° (a)
3205	Alkaline-earth metal alcoholates, n.o.s.	40	4.2	4.2, 14° (b), (c)
3206	Alkali metal alcoholates, n.o.s.	48	4.2 + 8	4.2, 15° (b), (c)
3207	Organometallic compound, or solution, or dispersion, water-reactive, flammable, n.o.s.	X323	4.3 + 3	4.3, 3° (a)
3207	Organometallic compound, or solution, or dispersion, water-reactive, flammable, n.o.s.	323	4.3 + 3	4.3, 3° (b), (c)
3208	Metallic substance, water-reactive, n.o.s.	423	4.3	4.3, 13° (b), (c)
3209	Metallic substance, water-reactive, self-heating, n.o.s.	423	4.3 + 4.2	4.3, 14° (b), (c)
3210	Chlorates, inorganic, aqueous solution, n.o.s.	50	5.1	5.1, 11° (b), (c)
3211	Perchlorates, inorganic, aqueous solution, n.o.s.	50	5.1	5.1, 13° (b), (c)
3212	Hypochlorites, inorganic, n.o.s.	50	5.1	5.1, 15° (b)
3213	Bromates, inorganic, aqueous solution n.o.s.	50	5.1	5.1, 16° (b), (c)
3214	Permanganates, inorganic, aqueous solution, n.o.s.	50	5.1	5.1, 17° (b)
3215	Persulphates, inorganic, n.o.s.	50	5.1	5.1, 18° (c)
3216	Persulphates, inorganic, aqueous solution, n.o.s.	50	5.1	5.1, 18° (c)
3218	Nitrates, inorganic, aqueous solution, n.o.s.	50	5.1	5.1, 22° (b), (c)
3219	Nitrites, inorganic, aqueous solution, n.o.s.	50	5.1	5.1, 23° (b), (c)
3220	Pentafluoroethane (R 125)	20	2	2, 2°A
3243	Solids containing toxic liquid, n.o.s.	60	6.1	6.1, 65° (b)
3244	Solids containing corrosive liquid, n.o.s.	80	8	8, 65° (b)
3246	Methanesulphonyl chloride	668	6.1 + 8	6.1, 27° (a)
3247	Sodium peroxoborate, anhydrous	50	5.1	5.1, 27° (b)
3248	Medicine, liquid, flammable, toxic, n.o.s.	336	3 + 6.1	3, 19° (b)
3248	Medicine, liquid, flammable, toxic, n.o.s.	36	3 + 6.1	3, 32° (c)
3249	Medicine, solid, toxic, n.o.s.	60	6.1	6.1, 90° (b), (c)
3250	Chloroacetic acid, molten	68	6.1 + 8	6.1, 24° (b)
3252	Difluoromethane	23	3	2, 2°F
3253	Disodium trioxosilicate	80	8	8, 41° (c)
3256	Elevated temperature liquid, flammable, n.o.s.	30	3	3, 61° (c)

Substance Identification No. (Lower part) (a)	Name of substance (b)	Hazard Identification No. (Upper part) (c)	Label (d)	Class and item number (e)
3257	Elevated temperature liquid, n.o.s	999	9	9, 20° (c)
3258	Elevated temperature solid, n.o.s.	999	9	9, 21° (c)
3259	Amines or polyamines, solid, corrosive, n.o.s.	88	8	8, 52° (a)
3259	Amines or polyamines, solid, corrosive, n.o.s.	80	8	8, 52° (b), (c)
3260	Corrosive solid, acidic, inorganic, n.o.s.	88	8	8, 16° (a)
3260	Corrosive solid, acidic, inorganic, n.o.s.	80	8	8, 16° (b), (c)
3261	Corrosive solid, acidic, organic, n.o.s.	88	8	8, 39° (a)
3261	Corrosive solid, acidic, organic, n.o.s.	80	8	8, 39° (b), (c)
3262	Corrosive solid, basic, inorganic, n.o.s.	88	8	8, 46° (a)
3262	Corrosive solid, basic, inorganic, n.o.s.	80	8	8, 46° (b), (c)
3263	Corrosive solid, basic, organic, n.o.s.	88	8	8, 55° (a)
3263	Corrosive solid, basic, organic, n.o.s.	80	8	8, 55° (b), (c)
3264	Corrosive liquid, acidic, inorganic, n.o.s.	88	8	8, 17° (a)
3264	Corrosive liquid, acidic, inorganic, n.o.s.	80	8	8, 17° (b), (c)
3265	Corrosive liquid, acidic, organic, n.o.s.	88	8	8, 40° (a)
3265	Corrosive liquid, acidic, organic, n.o.s.	80	8	8, 40° (b), (c)
3266	Corrosive liquid, basic, inorganic, n.o.s.	80	8	8, 47° (b), (c)
3266	Corrosive liquid, basic, inorganic, n.o.s.	88	8	8. 47° (a)
3267	Corrosive liquid, basic, organic, n.o.s.	88	8	8, 56° (a)
3267	Corrosive liquid, basic, organic, n.o.s.	80	8	8, 56° (b), (c)
3271	Ethers, n.o.s.	33	3	3, 3° (b)
3271	Ethers, n.o.s.	30	3	3, 31° (c)
3272	Esters, n.o.s.	33	3	3, 3° (b)
3272	Esters, n.o.s.	30	3	3, 31° (c)
3273	Nitriles, flammable, toxic, n.o.s.	336	3 + 6.1	3, 11° (a), (b)
3274	Alcoholates solution, n.o.s.	338	3 + 8	3, 24° (b)
3275	Nitriles, toxic, flammable, n.o.s.	663	6.1 + 3	6.1, 11° (a)
3275	Nitriles, toxic, flammable, n.o.s.	63	6.1 + 3	6.1, 11° (b)2.
3276	Nitriles, toxic, n.o.s.	66	6.1	6.1, 12° (a)
3276	Nitriles, toxic, n.o.s.	60	6.1	6.1, 12° (b), (c)
3277	Chloroformates, toxic, corrosive, n.o.s.	68	6.1 + 8	6.1, 27° (b)
3278	Organophosphorus compound, toxic, n.o.s.	66	6.1	6.1, 23° (a)
3278	Organophosphorus compound, toxic, n.o.s.	60	6.1	6.1, 23° (b), (c)
3279	Organophosphorus compound, toxic, flammable, n.o.s.	663	6.1 + 3	6.1, 9° (a)
3279	Organophosphorus compound, toxic, flammable, n.o.s.	663	6.1 + 3	6.1, 22° (a)
3279	Organophosphorus compound, toxic, flammable, n.o.s.	63	6.1 + 3	6.1, 22° (b)

Substance Identification No. (Lower part) (a)	Name of substance (b)	Hazard Identification No. (Upper part) (c)	Label (d)	Class and item number (e)
3280	Organoarsenic compound, n.o.s.	66	6.1	6.1, 34° (a)
3280	Organoarsenic compound, n.o.s.	60	6.1	6.1, 34° (b), (c)
3281	Metal carbonyls, n.o.s.	66	6.1	6.1, 36° (a)
3281	Metal carbonyls, n.o.s.	60	6.1	6.1, 36° (b), (c)
3282	Organometallic compound, toxic, n.o.s.	66	6.1	6.1, 35° (a)
3282	Organometallic compound, toxic, n.o.s.	60	6.1	6.1, 35° (b), (c)
3283	Selenium compound, n.o.s.	66	6.1	6.1, 55° (a)
3283	Selenium compound, n.o.s.	60	6.1	6.1, 55° (b), (c)
3284	Tellurium compound, n.o.s.	60	6.1	6.1, 57° (b), (c)
3285	Vanadium compound, n.o.s.	60	6.1	6.1, 58° (b), (c)
3286	Flammable liquid, toxic, corrosive, n.o.s.	368	3 + 6.1 + 8	3, 27° (a), (b)
3287	Toxic liquid, inorganic, n.o.s.	66	6.1	6.1, 65° (a)
3287	Toxic liquid, inorganic, n.o.s.	60	6.1	6.1, 65° (b), (c)
3288	Toxic solid, inorganic, n.o.s.	66	6.1	6.1, 65° (a)
3288	Toxic solid, inorganic, n.o.s.	60	6.1	6.1, 65° (b), (c)
3289	Toxic liquid, corrosive, inorganic, n.o.s.	668	6.1 + 8	6.1, 67° (a)
3289	Toxic liquid, corrosive, inorganic, n.o.s.	68	6.1 + 8	6.1, 67° (b)
3290	Toxic solid, corrosive, inorganic, n.o.s.	668	6.1 + 8	6.1, 67° (a)
3290	Toxic solid, corrosive, inorganic, n.o.s.	68	6.1 + 8	6.1, 67° (b)
3291	Clinical waste, unspecified, n.o.s.	606	6.2	6.2, 4° (b)
3293	Hydrazine, aqueous solution	60	6.1	6.1, 65° (c)
3294	Hydrogen cyanide, solution in alcohol	663	6.1 + 3	6.1, 2°
3295	Hydrocarbons, liquid, n.o.s.	33	3	3, 1° (a), 2° (a), (b), 3° (b)
3295	Hydrocarbons, liquid, n.o.s.	30	3	3, 31° (c)
3296	Heptafluoropropane (R 227)	20	2	2, 2°A
3297	Ethylene oxide and chlorotetrafluoroethane mixture	20	2	2, 2°A
3298	Ethylene oxide and pentafluoroethane mixture	20	2	2, 2°A
3299	Ethylene oxide and tetrafluoroethane mixture	20	2	2, 2°A
3300	Ethylene oxide and carbon dioxide mixture with more than 87 % ethylene oxide	263	6.1 + 3	2, 2°TF
3301	Corrosive liquid, self-heating, n.o.s.	884	8 + 4.2	8, 70° (a)
3301	Corrosive liquid, self-heating, n.o.s.	84	8 + 4.2	8, 70° (b)
3302	2-Dimethylaminoethyl acrylate	60	6.1	6.1, 12° (b)
3303	Compressed gas, toxic, oxidizing, n.o.s.	265	6.1 + 05	2, 1°TO
3304	Compressed gas, toxic, corrosive, n.o.s.	268	6.1 + 8	2, 1°TC
3305	Compressed gas, toxic, flammable, corrosive, n.o.s.	263	6.1 + 3 + 8	2, 1°TFC

Substance Identification No. (Lower part) (a)	Name of substance (b)	Hazard Identification No. (Upper part) (c)	Label (d)	Class and item number (e)
3306	Compressed gas, toxic, oxidizing, corrosive, n.o.s.	265	6.1 + 05 + 8	2, 1°TOC
3307	Liquefied gas, toxic, oxidizing, n.o.s.	265	6.1 + 05	2, 2°TO
3308	Liquefied gas, toxic, corrosive, n.o.s.	268	6.1 + 8	2, 2°TC
3309	Liquefied gas, toxic, flammable, corrosive, n.o.s.	263	6.1 + 3 + 8	2, 2TFC
3310	Liquefied gas, toxic, oxidizing, corrosive, n.o.s.	265	6.1 + 05 + 8	2, 2°TOC
3311	Gas, refrigerated liquid, oxidizing, n.o.s.	225	2 + 05	2, 3°O
3312	Gas, refrigerated liquid, flammable, n.o.s.	223	3	2, 3°F
3313	Organic pigments, self-heating	40	4.2	4.2, 5° (b), (c)
3314	Plastics moulding compound	90	9	9, 4° (c)
3318	Ammonia solution with more than 50% ammonia	268	6.1 + 8	2, 4°TC
3320	Sodium borohydride and sodium hydroxide solution, with not more than 12% sodium borohydride and not more than 40% sodium hydroxide by mass	80	8	8, 42° (b), (c)

250 001

Identification numbers shall be shown on the plate as indicated below

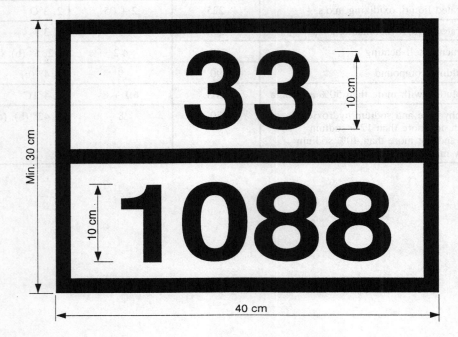

Identification number
of danger
(2 or 3 figures)

Identification number
of substance
(4 figures)

Background orange.
Border, horizontal line and figures black,
15 mm thickness.

250 002-
259 999

Editorial Note:
(This page is reproduced in colour at the end of this volume).

APPENDIX B.6

TRAINING CERTIFICATE FOR DRIVERS OF VEHICLES REQUIRED IN MARGINAL 10 315 (1)

(See marginal 10 381)

260 000 The certificate of competence for drivers of vehicles carrying dangerous goods issued in conformity with the prescription in marginal 10 315 shall have the layout as reproduced in the model below. It is recommended that the format shall be the same as the European national driving permit, namely A7 (7A x 105 mm) or a double sheet which can be folded to that format.

(For model certificate see over)

1

ADR - TRAINING CERTIFICATE FOR DRIVERS
OF VEHICLES CARRYING DANGEROUS GOODS

in tanks 1/ other than in tanks 1/

Certificat No . . . .

Distinguishing sign of issuing State . . . .

Valid for class(es) 1/ 2/

in tanks	other than in tanks
1	1
2	2 . . . .
3	3
4.1, 4.2, 4.3	4.1, 4.2, 4.3 . . . .
5.1, 5.2	5.1, 5.2
6.1, 6.2	6.1, 6.2
7	7
8	8 . . . .
9	9

until (date) 3/ . . . .

———

1/ Strike out what does not apply.
2/ For extension to other classes, see page 3.
3/ For renewal, see page 2.

2

Surname . . . .

First name(s) . . . .

Date of birth . . . . . . Nationality . . . . . .

Signature of holder . . . .

Issued by . . . .

Date . . . .

Signature 4/ . . . .

Renewed until . . . .

By . . . .

Date . . . .

Signature 4/ . . . .

———

4/ and/or seal (or stamp) of issuing
authority.

3

EXTENDED TO CLASS(ES) 5/
_____

in tanks

1
2
3   Date . . . .
4.1, 4.2, 4.3
5.1, 5.2   Signature and/or seal or stamp
6.1, 6.2   . . . .
7
8
9
_____

other than in tanks

1
2
3   Date . . . .
4.1, 4.2, 4.3
5.1, 5.2   Signature and/or seal or stamp
6.1, 6.2   . . . .
7
8
9
_____

5/ Strike out what does not apply.

4

For national regulations only

APPENDIX B.7

MARK FOR ELEVATED TEMPERATURE SUBSTANCES

270 000 The mark for elevated temperature substances required in marginals 91 500 (3), 211 960 and 212 960 is a triangular shaped mark with sides of at least 250 mm, to be shown in red, as reproduced below.

SUPPLEMENTS

SUPPLEMENT No. 1:   Alphabetical list of substances and articles of ADR

SUPPLEMENT No. 2:   Numerical list (per substance identification (UN) number) of substances and articles of ADR

SUPPLEMENT No. 3:   List of competent authorities

SUPPLEMENT No. 4:   Reproduction in colour of page 360 (marginal 250 001)

SUPPLEMENT No. 5:   Reproduction in colour of page 363 (marginal 270 000)

NOTE 1: Supplements Nos. 1 and 2 do not form an integral part of ADR. They have been submitted neither to the working Party on the Transport of Dangerous goods of the Inland Transport Committee for checking and approval nor to the Contracting Parties to ADR for formal acceptance. They have been prepared, with all necessary care, in order to facilitate the consultation of Annexes A and B, but they cannot be relied upon as a substitute for the careful study and observance of the actual provisions of those annexes which, in case of conflict, are deemed to be authoritative. ONLY ADR AND ITS ANNEXES A AND B HAVE LEGAL FORCE.

NOTE 2: Supplement No. 3 comprises a list of national competent authorities responsible for the application of ADR and in particular for the conclusion of bilateral and multilateral agreements under marginals 2010 and 10 602.

NOTE 3: Supplements Nos 4 and 5 are colour reproductions of page 360 (marginal 250 001) and page 363 (marginal 270 000), which for printing purposes, have been placed at the end of the publication.

SUPPLEMENT No. 1: Alphabetical list of substances and articles of ADR

Name of substance or article	Substance Identification No. (UN No.)	Class	Item number and letter
Acetal	1088	3	3 (b)
Acetaldehyde	1089	3	1 (a)
Acetaldehyde ammonia	1841	9	31 (c)
Acetaldehyde oxime	2332	3	31 (c)
Acetic acid, glacial or acetic acid solution, with more than 80% acid, by mass	2789	8	32 (b)2.
Acetic acid solution with not more than 25% pure acid, by mass: Not subject to ADR	2790	8	Note
Acetic acid solution, with more than 25% but less than 50% acid, by mass	2790	8	32 (c)
Acetic acid solution, with more than 50% but less than 80% acid, by mass	2790	8	32 (b)1.
Acetic anhydride	1715	8	32 (b)2.
Acetoin	2621	3	31 (c)
Acetone	1090	3	3 (b)
Acetone cyanohydrin, stabilized	1541	6.1	12 (a)
Acetone oils	1091	3	3 (b)
Acetonitrile	1648	3	3 (b)
Acetopolysilanes, see Corrosive liquid, acidic, organic, n.o.s.			
Acetoxysilanes, see Corrosive liquid, acidic, organic, n.o.s.			
Acetyl acetone	2310	3	32 (c)
Acetyl acetone peroxide, see Organic peroxide type D, liquid			
Acetyl acetone peroxide, see Organic peroxide type D, solid			
Acetyl benzoyl peroxide, see Organic peroxide type D, liquid			
Acetyl bromide	1716	8	35 (b)1.
Acetyl chloride	1717	3	25 (b)
Acetyl cyclohexanesulphonyl peroxide, see Organic peroxide type B, solid, temperature controlled			
Acetyl cyclohexanesulphonyl peroxide, see Organic peroxide type D, liquid, temperature controlled			
Acetylene, dissolved	1001	2	4F
Acetylene tetrabromide	2504	6.1	15 (c)
Acetylene tetrachloride	1702	6.1	15 (b)
Acetyl iodide	1898	8	35 (b)1.
Acetyl methyl carbinol	2621	3	31 (c)
2-Acetylthiophene, see Toxic liquid, organic, n.o.s.			
Acid mixture, hydrofluoric and sulphuric	1786	8	7 (a)
Acid mixture, nitrating	1796	8	3 (a), (b)
Acridine	2713	6.1	12 (c)
Acrolein dimer, stabilized	2607	3	31 (c)
Acrolein, inhibited	1092	6.1	8 (a)

Name of substance or article	Substance Identification No. (UN No.)	Class	Item number and letter
Acrylamide	2074	6.1	12 (c)
Acrylic acid, inhibited	2218	8	32 (b)2.
Acrylonitrile, inhibited	1093	3	11 (a)
Actinolite	2590	9	1 (c)
Adhesives containing flammable liquid	1133	3	5 (a), (b), (c), 31 (c)
Adiponitrile	2205	6.1	12 (c)
Adrenalin, see Toxic solid, organic, n.o.s.			
Aerosol dispensers	1950	2	5 A
Aerosol dispensers	1950	2	5 O
Aerosol dispensers	1950	2	5 F
Aerosol dispensers	1950	2	5 T
Aerosol dispensers	1950	2	5 TF
Aerosol dispensers	1950	2	5 TC
Aerosol dispensers	1950	2	5 TO
Aerosol dispensers	1950	2	5 TFC
Aerosol dispensers	1950	2	5 TOC
Air bag inflators	3268	9	8 (c)
Air bag modules	3268	9	8 (c)
Air, compressed	1002	2	1 A
Aircraft hydraulic power unit fuel tank (containing a mixture of anhydrous hydrazine and methylhydrazine) (M86 fuel)	3165	3	28
Air, refrigerated liquid	1003	2	3 O
Alcoholates solution, n.o.s., in alcohol	3274	3	24 (b)
Alcoholic beverages	3065	3	3 (b), 31 (c)
Alcohols, flammable, toxic, n.o.s.	1986	3	17 (a), (b), 32 (c)
Alcohols, n.o.s.	1987	3	2 (b), 3 (b), 31 (c)
Aldehydes, flammable, toxic, n.o.s.	1988	3	17 (a), (b), 32 (c)
Aldehydes, n.o.s.	1989	3	2 (a), (b), 3 (b), 31 (c)
Aldicarb (pesticide), see Carbamate pesticides			
Aldol	2839	6.1	14 (b)
Aldrin (pesticide), see Organochlorine pesticides			
Alkali metal alcoholates, self-heating, corrosive, n.o.s.	3206	4.2	15 (b), (c)
Alkali metal alloy, liquid, n.o.s.	1421	4.3	11 (a)
Alkali metal amalgam	1389	4.3	11 (a)
Alkali metal amides	1390	4.3	19 (b)

Name of substance or article	Substance Identification No. (UN No.)	Class	Item number and letter
Alkali metal dispersion	1391	4.3	11 (a)
Alkaline earth metal alcoholates, n.o.s.	3205	4.2	14 (b), (c)
Alkaline earth metal alloy, n.o.s.	1393	4.3	11 (b)
Alkaline earth metal amalgam	1392	4.3	11 (a)
Alkaline earth metal dispersion	1391	4.3	11 (a)
Alkaline residues, see Caustic alkali liquid, n.o.s.			
Alkaloid pesticides, see under Pesticide etc.			
Alkaloids, liquid, n.o.s. or alkaloid salts, liquid, n.o.s.	3140	6.1	90 (a), (b), (c)
Alkaloids, solid, n.o.s. or alkaloid salts, solid, n.o.s.	1544	6.1	90 (a), (b), (c)
Alkyloxyphenols, liquid, see Toxic liquid, organic, n.o.s.			
Alkyloxyphenols, solid, see Toxic solid, organic, n.o.s.			
Alkylphenols, with C2 -C12 homologues, liquid	3145	8	40 (a), (b), (c)
Alkylphenols, with C2 -C12 homologues, solid	2430	8	39 (a), (b, (c)
Alkylsulphonic acids, liquid, with more than 5% free sulphuric acid	2584	8	1 (b)
Alkylsulphonic acids, liquid, with not more than 5% free sulphuric	2586	8	34 (c)
Alkylsulphonic acids, solid, with more than 5% free sulphuric acid	2583	8	1 (b)
Alkylsulphonic acids, solid, with not more than 5% free sulphuric	2585	8	34 (c)
Alkylsulphuric acids	2571	8	34 (b)
Allidochlor (pesticide), see Organochlorine pesticides			
Allyl acetate	2333	3	17 (b)
Allyl alcohol	1098	6.1	8 (a)
Allylamine	2334	6.1	7 (a)2.
Allyl bromide	1099	3	16 (a)
Allyl chloride	1100	3	16 (a)
Allyl chloroformate	1722	6.1	28 (a)
Allyl ethyl ether	2335	3	17 (b)
Allyl formate	2336	3	17 (a)
Allyl glycidyl ether	2219	3	31 (c)
Allyl iodide	1723	3	25 (b)
Allyl isothiocyanate, inhibited	1545	6.1	20 (b)
Allyltrichlorosilane, stabilized	1724	8	37 (b)
Aluminium alkyl halides	3052	4.2	32 (a)
Aluminium alkyl hydrides	3076	4.2	32 (a)
Aluminium alkyls	3051	4.2	31 (a)
Aluminium borohydride	2870	4.2	17 (a)
Aluminium borohydride in devices	2870	4.2	17 (a)
Aluminium bromide, anhydrous	1725	8	11 (b)
Aluminium bromide hexahydrate: Not subject to ADR		8	11 (b), Note
Aluminium bromide solution	2580	8	5 (c)

Name of substance or article	Substance Identification No. (UN No.)	Class	Item number and letter
Aluminium carbide	1394	4.3	17 (b)
Aluminium chloride, anhydrous	1726	8	11 (b)
Aluminium chloride, hexahydrate: Not subject to ADR		8	11 (b), Note
Aluminium chloride monohydrate: Not subject to ADR		8	11 (b), Note
Aluminium chloride solution	2581	8	5 (c)
Aluminium ferrosilicon powder	1395	4.3	15 (b)
Aluminium hydride	2463	4.3	16 (a)
Aluminium nitrate	1438	5.1	22 (c)
Aluminium phosphide	1397	4.3	18 (a)
Aluminium phosphide pesticide	3048	6.1	43 (a)
Aluminium powder, coated	1309	4.1	13 (b), (c)
Aluminium powder, uncoated	1396	4.3	13 (b)
Aluminium remelting by-products	3170	4.3	13 (b), (c)
Aluminium resinate	2715	4.1	12 (c)
Aluminium silicon powder, uncoated	1398	4.3	13 (c)
Aluminium smelting by-products	3170	4.3	13 (b), (c)
Aluminium telluride, see Tellurium compound, n.o.s.			
Amines, flammable, corrosive, n.o.s.	2733	3	22 (a), (b), 33 (c)
Amines, liquid, corrosive, flammable, n.o.s.	2734	8	54 (a), (b)
Amines, liquid, corrosive, n.o.s.	2735	8	53 (a), (b), (c)
Amines, solid, corrosive, n.o.s.	3259	8	52 (a), (b), (c)
2-Aminobenzonitrile, see Toxic solid, organic, n.o.s.			
Aminocarb (pesticide), see Carbamate pesticides			
2-Amino-4-chlorophenol	2673	6.1	12 (b)
2-Amino-5-diethylaminopentane	2946	6.1	12 (c)
2-Amino-4,6-dinitrophenol, wetted with not less than 20% water, by mass	3317	4.1	22 (a)1.
2-(2-Aminoethoxy)ethanol	3055	8	53 (c)
N-Aminoethylpiperazine	2815	8	53 (c)
Aminonitrobenzonitrile, see Toxic solid, organic, n.o.s.			
Aminophenols (o-, m-, p-)	2512	6.1	12 (c)
bis-Aminopropylamine	2269	8	53 (c)
Aminopyridines (o-, m-, p-)	2671	6.1	12 (b)
Aminothiophenol, see Toxic liquid, organic, n.o.s.			
Ammonia, anhydrous	1005	2	2 TC
Ammonia solution, relative density between 0.880 and 0.957 at 15 °C in water, with more than 10% but not more than 35% ammonia	2672	8	43 (c)
Ammonia solution, relative density less than 0.880 at 15 °C in water, with more than 50% ammonia	3318	2	4 TC

Supplement No.1

Name of substance or article	Substance Identification No. (UN No.)	Class	Item number and letter
Ammonia solution, relative density less than 0.880 at 15 °C in water, with more than 35% but not more than 50% ammonia	2073	2	4 A
Ammonium arsenate	1546	6.1	51 (b)
Ammonium bifluoride solution	2817	8	7 (b), (c)
Ammonium bisulphate	2506	8	13 (b)
Ammonium dichromate	1439	5.1	27 (b)
Ammonium dinitro-o-cresolate	1843	6.1	12 (b)
Ammonium fluoride	2505	6.1	63 (c)
Ammonium fluorosilicate	2854	6.1	64 (c)
Ammonium hydrogendifluoride, solid	1727	8	9 (b)
Ammonium hydrogendifluoride, solution	2817	8	7 (b), (c)
Ammonium hydrogen sulphate	2506	8	13 (b)
Ammonium metavanadate	2859	6.1	58 (b)
Ammonium nitrate	1942	5.1	21 (c)
Ammonium nitrate fertilizer, n.o.s.: Not to be accepted for carriage	2072	5.1	Note (1)
Ammonium nitrate fertilizers: Not subject to ADR	2071	9	Note (1) above
Ammonium nitrate fertilizers, type A1	2067	5.1	21 (c)
Ammonium nitrate fertilizers, type A2	2068	5.1	21 (c)
Ammonium nitrate fertilizers, type A3	2069	5.1	21 (c)
Ammonium nitrate fertilizers, type A4	2070	5.1	21 (c)
Ammonium nitrate fertilizer, which is more liable to explode than ammonium nitrate with 0.2% combustible substances, including any organic substance calculated as carbon, to the exclusion of any other added substance	0223	1.1D	4
Ammonium nitrate, liquid	2426	5.1	20
Ammonium nitrate with more than 0.2% combustible substances, including any organic substance calculated as carbon, to the exclusion of any other added substance	0222	1.1D	4
Ammonium perchlorate	0402	1.1D	4
Ammonium perchlorate	1442	5.1	12 (b)
Ammonium persulphate	1444	5.1	18 (c)
Ammonium picrate dry or wetted with less than 10% water, by mass	0004	1.1D	4
Ammonium picrate, wetted with not less than 10% water, by mass	1310	4.1	21 (a)1.
Ammonium polysulphide solution	2818	8	45 (b)1., (c)
Ammonium polyvanadate	2861	6.1	58 (b)
Ammonium sulphide solution	2683	8	45 (b)2.
Ammonium thiocyanate: Not subject to ADR		6.1	41, Note 1
Ammunition, illuminating with or without burster, expelling charge or propelling charge	0171	1.2G	21
Ammunition, illuminating with or without burster, expelling charge or propelling charge	0254	1.3G	30

Name of substance or article	Substance Identification No. (UN No.)	Class	Item number and letter
Ammunition, illuminating with or without burster, expelling charge or propelling charge	0297	1.4G	43
Ammunition, incendiary, liquid or gel, with burster, expelling charge or propelling charge	0247	1.3J	32
Ammunition, incendiary, white phosphorus with burster, expelling charge or propelling charge	0243	1.2H	22
Ammunition, incendiary, white phosphorus with burster, expelling charge or propelling charge	0244	1.3H	31
Ammunition, incendiary with or without burster, expelling charge or propelling charge	0009	1.2G	21
Ammunition, incendiary with or without burster, expelling charge or propelling charge	0010	1.3G	30
Ammunition, incendiary, with or without burster, expelling charge or propelling charge	0300	1.4G	43
Ammunition, practice	0362	1.4G	43
Ammunition, practice	0488	1.3G	30
Ammunition, proof	0363	1.4G	43
Ammunition, smoke, white phosphorus with burster, expelling charge or propelling charge	0245	1.2H	22
Ammunition, smoke, white phosphorus with burster, expelling charge or propelling charge	0246	1.3H	31
Ammunition, smoke with or without burster, expelling charge or propelling charge	0015	1.2G	21
Ammunition, smoke with or without burster, expelling charge or propelling charge	0016	1.3G	30
Ammunition, smoke with or without burster, expelling charge or propelling charge	0303	1.4G	43
Ammunition, tear-producing, non-explosive without burster or expelling charge, non-fuzed	2017	6.1	27 (b)
Ammunition, tear-producing with burster, expelling charge or propelling charge	0018	1.2G	21
Ammunition, tear-producing with burster, expelling charge or propelling charge	0019	1.3G	30
Ammunition, tear-producing with burster, expelling charge or propelling charge	0301	1.4G	43
Ammunition, toxic, non-explosive without burster or expelling charge, non-fuzed	2016	6.1	25 (b)
Ammunition, toxic with burster, expelling charge or propelling charge: Not to be accepted for carriage	0020	1.2K	See marginal 2100 (8)
Ammunition, toxic with burster, expelling charge or propelling charge: Not to be accepted for carriage	0021	1.3K	See marginal 2100 (8)
Amosite	2212	9	1 (b)
Amyl acetates	1104	3	31 (c)
Amyl acid phosphate	2819	8	38 (c)
Amyl alcohols	1105	3	3 (b), 31 (c)

Name of substance or article	Substance Identification No. (UN No.)	Class	Item number and letter
sec-Amyl alcohol, see Amyl alcohols			
tert-Amyl alcohol, see Amyl alcohols			
Amylamine	1106	3	22 (b), 33 (c)
Amyl butyrates	2620	3	31 (c)
Amyl chloride	1107	3	3 (b)
n-Amylene	1108	3	1 (a)
Amyl formates	1109	3	31 (c)
tert-Amyl hydroperoxide, see Organic peroxide type E, liquid			
Amyl mercaptan	1111	3	3 (b)
n-Amyl methyl ketone	1110	3	31 (c)
Amyl nitrate	1112	3	31 (c)
Amyl nitrite	1113	3	3 (b)
tert-Amyl peroxyacetate, see Organic peroxide type E, liquid			
tert-Amyl peroxybenzoate, see Organic peroxide type D, liquid			
tert-Amyl peroxy-2-ethylhexanoate, see Organic peroxide type D, liquid, temperature controlled			
tert-Amyl peroxy-2-ethylhexyl carbonate, see Organic peroxide type D, liquid			
tert-Amyl peroxyneodecanoate, see Organic peroxide type D, liquid, temperature controlled			
tert-Amyl peroxypivalate, see Organic peroxide type C, liquid, temperature controlled			
tert-Amyl peroxy-3,5,5-trimethylhexanoate, see Organic peroxide type B, liquid			
Amyltrichlorosilane	1728	8	36 (b)
Aniline	1547	6.1	12 (b)
Aniline hydrochloride	1548	6.1	12 (c)
Anisidines	2431	6.1	12 (c)
Anisole	2222	3	31 (c)
Anisoyl chloride	1729	8	35 (b)1.
Anthophyllite	2590	9	1 (c)
Anti-knock additive	1649	6.1	31 (a)
Antimony and lead, ashes of, see Toxic solid, inorganic, n.o.s.			
Antimony, ashes of, see Antimony compound, inorganic, solid, n.o.s.			
Antimony compound, inorganic, liquid, n.o.s	3141	6.1	59 (c)
Antimony compound, inorganic, solid, n.o.s.	1549	6.1	59 (c)
Antimony compound, organic, liquid, see Organo- metallic compond, toxic, n.o.s.			
Antimony compound, organic, solid, see Organo- metallic compound, n.o.s			

Name of substance or article	Substance Identification No. (UN No.)	Class	Item number and letter
Antimony compound, residues and wastes, liquid, see Antimony compound, inorganic, liquid, n.o.s.			
Antimony compound, residues and wastes, solid, see Antimony compound, inorganic, solid, n.o.s.			
Antimony lactate	1550	6.1	59 (c)
Antimony oxides, see Antimony compound, inorganic, solid, n.o.s.			
Antimony pentachloride, liquid	1730	8	12 (b)
Antimony pentachloride solution	1731	8	12 (b), (c)
Antimony pentafluoride	1732	8	10 (b)
Antimony potassium tartrate	1551	6.1	59 (c)
Antimony powder	2871	6.1	59 (c)
Antimony salts, see Antimony compound, inorganic, solid, n.o.s.			
Antimony trichloride	1733	8	11 (b)
ANTU (pesticide), see under Pesticide, etc.			
Apparatus such as transformers, condensers and hydraulic apparatus containing PCBs or PCTs or mixtures thereof		9	3
Argon, compressed	1006	2	1 A
Argon, refrigerated liquid	1951	2	3 A
Arsenates, liquid, see Arsenic compound, liquid, n.o.s.			
Arsenates, solid, see Arsenic compound, solid, n.o.s.			
Arsenic	1558	6.1	51 (b)
Arsenic acid, liquid	1553	6.1	51 (a)
Arsenic acid, solid	1554	6.1	51 (b)
Arsenical compound, liquid, n.o.s., inorganic	1556	6.1	51 (a), (b), (c)
Arsenical compound, solid, n.o.s., inorganic	1557	6.1	51 (a), (b), (c)
Arsenical dust	1562	6.1	51 (b)
Arsenical pesticide, liquid, flammable, toxic, flash-point less than 23 °C	2760	3	41 (a), (b)
Arsenical pesticide, liquid, toxic	2994	6.1	71 (a), (b), (c)
Arsenical pesticide, liquid, toxic, flammable, flash point not less than 23 °C	2993	6.1	72 (a), (b), (c)
Arsenical pesticide, solid, toxic	2759	6.1	73 (a), (b), (c)
Arsenic bromide	1555	6.1	51 (b)
Arsenic compound, liquid, n.o.s.	1556	6.1	51 (a), (b), (c)
Arsenic compound, solid, n.o.s.	1557	6.1	51 (a), (b), (c)
Arsenic pentoxide	1559	6.1	51 (b)
Arsenic sulphides, liquid, see Arsenic compound, liquid, n.o.s.			
Arsenic sulphides, solid, see Arsenic compound, solid, n.o.s.			
Arsenic trichloride	1560	6.1	51 (a)
Arsenic trioxide	1561	6.1	51 (b)
Arsenic trioxide (pesticide), see Arsenical pesticides			

Name of substance or article	Substance Identification No. (UN No.)	Class	Item number and letter
Arsenites, liquid, see Arsenic compound, liquid, n.o.s.			
Arsenites, solid, see Arsenic compound, solid, n.o.s.			
Arsine	2188	2	2 TF
Articles, explosive, extremely insensitive (Articles, EEI)	0486	1.6N	50
Articles, explosive, n.o.s.	0349	1.4S	47
Articles, explosive, n.o.s.	0350	1.4B	35
Articles, explosive, n.o.s.	0351	1.4C	37
Articles, explosive, n.o.s.	0353	1.4G	43
Articles, explosive, n.o.s.	0354	1.1L	12
Articles, explosive, n.o.s.	0355	1.2L	25
Articles, explosive, n.o.s.	0356	1.3L	34
Articles, explosive, n.o.s.	0462	1.1C	3
Articles, explosive, n.o.s.	0463	1.1D	5
Articles, explosive, n.o.s.	0464	1.1E	6
Articles, explosive, n.o.s.	0465	1.1F	7
Articles, explosive, n.o.s.	0466	1.2C	15
Articles, explosive, n.o.s.	0467	1.2D	17
Articles, explosive, n.o.s.	0468	1.2E	18
Articles, explosive, n.o.s.	0469	1.2F	19
Articles, explosive, n.o.s.	0470	1.3C	27
Articles, explosive, n.o.s.	0471	1.4E	40
Articles, explosive, n.o.s.	0472	1.4F	41
Articles, explosive, n.o.s.	0352	1.4D	39
Articles impregnated with pesticides: Not subject to ADR		6.1	Section F, Note 2 (a)
Articles, pressurized, pneumatic or hydraulic (containing non-flammable gas)	3164	2	6 A
Articles, pyrophoric	0380	1.2L	25
Articles, pyrotechnic for technical purposes	0428	1.1G	9
Articles, pyrotechnic for technical purposes	0429	1.2G	21
Articles, pyrotechnic for technical purposes	0430	1.3G	30
Articles, pyrotechnic for technical purposes	0431	1.4G	43
Articles, pyrotechnic for technical purposes	0432	1.4S	47
Aryl sulphonic acids liquid, with more than 5% free sulphuric acid	2584	8	1 (b)
Aryl sulphonic acids liquid, with not more than 5% free sulphuric acid	2586	8	34 (c)
Aryl sulphonic acids solid, with more than 5% free sulphuric acid	2583	8	1 (b)
Aryl sulphonic acids, solid, with not more than 5% free sulphuric acid	2585	8	34 (c)
Azinphos-ethyl (pesticide), see Organophosphorus pesticides			
Azinphos-methyl (pesticide), see Organophosphorus pesticides			

Name of substance or article	Substance Identification No. (UN No.)	Class	Item number and letter
Azodicarbonamide	3242	4.1	26 (b)
Azodicarbonamide formulation type B, temperature controlled, see Self-reactive solid, type B, temperature controlled			
Azodicarbonamide formulation type C, see Self-reactive solid type C			
Azodicarbonamide formulation type C, temperature controlled, see Self-reactive solid type C, temperature controlled			
Azodicarbonamide formulation type D, see Self-reactive solid, type D			
Azodicarbonamide formulation type D, temperature controlled, see Self-reactive solid, type D, temperature controlled			
2,2'-Azodi(2,4-dimethyl-4-methoxyvaleronitrile), see Self-reactive solid type D, temperature controlled			
2,2'-Azodi(2,4-dimethylvaleronitrile), see Self-reactive solid type D, temperature controlled			
2,2-Azodi(ethyl 2-methylpropionate), see Self-reactive liquid, type D, temperature controlled			
1,1-Azodi(hexahydrobenzonitrile), see Self-reactive solid type D			
2,2'-Azodi(isobutyronitrile), see Self-reactive substance type C, temperature controlled			
2,2'-Azodi(2-methylbutyronitrile), see Self-reactive solid type D, temperature controlled			
Barium	1400	4.3	11 (b)
Barium alloys, pyrophoric	1854	4.2	12 (a)
Barium azide, dry or wetted with less than 50% water, by mass	0224	1.1A+6.1	01
Barium azide, wetted with not less than 50% water, by mass	1571	4.1	25 (a)
Barium bromate	2719	5.1	29 (b)
Barium carbonate, see Barium compound, n.o.s.			
Barium chlorate	1445	5.1	29 (b)
Barium chloride, see Barium compound, n.o.s.			
Barium compound, n.o.s.	1564	6.1	60 (b), (c)
Barium cyanide	1565	6.1	41 (a)
Barium fluoride, see Barium compound, n.o.s.			
Barium hydroxide, see Barium compound, n.o.s.			
Barium hypochlorite with more than 22% available chlorine	2741	5.1	29 (b)
Barium nitrate	1446	5.1	29 (b)
Barium oxide	1884	6.1	60 (c)
Barium perchlorate	1447	5.1	29 (b)
Barium permanganate	1448	5.1	29 (b)
Barium peroxide	1449	5.1	29 (b)
Barium selenate, see Selenates			
Barium selenite, see Selenites			
Barium silicofluoride, see under Pesticide, etc.			

Name of substance or article	Substance Identification No. (UN No.)	Class	Item number and letter
Barium stearate: Not subject to ADR		6.1	60 (c), Note 3
Barium sulphate: Not subject to ADR		6.1	60 (c), Note 3
Barium sulphide, see Barium compound, n.o.s.			
Barium titanate: Not subject to ADR		6.1	60 (c), Note 3
Batteries, containing sodium	3292	4.3	31 (b)
Batteries, dry, containing potassium hydroxide solid, electric storage	3028	8	81 (c)
Batteries, wet, filled with acid, electric storage	2794	8	81 (c)
Batteries, wet, filled with alkali, electric storage	2795	8	81 (c)
Batteries, wet, non-spillable, electric storage	2800	8	81 (c)
Battery fluid, acid	2796	8	1 (b)
Battery fluid, alkali	2797	8	42 (b)
Battery-powered equipment (wet battery): Not subject to ADR	3171	9	Exempt
Battery-powered vehicle (wet battery): Not subject to ADR	3171	9	Exempt
Bendiocarb (pesticide), see Carbamate pesticides			
Benfuracarb (pesticide), see Carbamate pesticides			
Benquinox (pesticide), see under Pesticide, etc.			
Benzaldehyde	1990	9	34 (c)
Benzene	1114	3	3 (b)
Benzene-1,3-disulphonylhydrazide, see Self-reactive solid, type D			
Benzene sulphonyl chloride	2225	8	35 (c)
Benzene sulphonylhydrazide, see Self-reactive solid, type D			
Benzidine	1885	6.1	12 (b)
Benzidine dihydrochloride, see Toxic solid, organic, n.o.s.			
Benzidine sulphate, see Toxic solid, organic, n.o.s.			
3-Benzidine sulphonic acid, see Aryl sulphonic acids			
Benzoic derivative pesticide, liquid, flammable, toxic, flash-point less than 23 °C	2770	3	41 (a), (b)
Benzoic derivative pesticide, liquid,toxic	3004	6.1	71 (a), (b), (c)
Benzoic derivative pesticide, liquid, toxic, flammable, flash point not less than 23 °C	3003	6.1	72 (a), (b), (c)
Benzoic derivative pesticide, solid, toxic	2769	6.1	73 (a), (b), (c)
Benzonitrile	2224	6.1	12 (b)
Benzoquinone	2587	6.1	14 (b)
Benzotrichloride	2226	8	66 (b)
Benzotrifluoride	2338	3	3 (b)
Benzoyl chloride	1736	8	35 (b)1.
Benzoyl cyanide, see Toxic liquid, organic, n.o.s.			
Benzylamine, see Corrosive liquid, basic, organic, n.o.s.			
Benzyl bromide	1737	6.1	27 (b)

Name of substance or article	Substance Identification No. (UN No.)	Class	Item number and letter
Benzyl chloride	1738	6.1	27 (b)
Benzyl chloroformate	1739	8	64 (a)
Benzyl dimethylamine	2619	8	54 (b)
[4-Benzyl(ethyl)amino]-3-ethoxybenzenediazonium zinc chloride, see Self-reactive solid, type D			
Benzylidene chloride	1886	6.1	15 (b)
Benzyl iodide	2653	6.1	15 (b)
[4-Benzyl(methyl)amino]-3-ethoxybenzenediazonium zinc chloride, see Self-reactive solid type D, temperature controlled			
Beryllium compound, n.o.s.	1566	6.1	54 (b)2., (c)
Beryllium nitrate	2464	5.1	29 (b)
Beryllium powder	1567	6.1	54 (b)1.
Bicyclo-(2.2.1)-hepta-2,5-diene inhibited	2251	3	3 (b)
Bifluorides, see Hydrogendifluorides, n.o.s.			
Binapicryl (pesticide), see Substituted nitrophenol pesticides			
Bipyridilium pesticide, liquid, flammable, toxic, flash-point less than 23 °C	2782	3	41 (a), (b)
Bipyridilium pesticide, liquid, toxic	3016	6.1	71 (a), (b), (c)
Bipyridilium pesticide, liquid, toxic, flammable, flash point not less than 23 °C	3015	6.1	72 (a), (b), (c)
Bipyridilium pesticide, solid, toxic	2781	6.1	73 (a), (b), (c)
Bisulphates, aqueous solution, n.o.s.	2837	8	1 (b), (c)
Bisulphites, aqueous solution, n.o.s.	2693	8	17 (c)
Black powder, compressed	0028	1.1D	4
Black powder, granular or as a meal	0027	1.1D	4
Black powder, in pellets	0028	1.1D	4
Blasticidine-S-3 (pesticide), see under Pesticide, etc.			
Blue asbestos (crocidolite)	2212	9	1 (b)
Bombs, photoflash	0037	1.1F	7
Bombs, photoflash	0038	1.1D	5
Bombs, photoflash	0039	1.2G	21
Bombs, photoflash	0299	1.3G	30
Bombs, smoke, non-explosive with corrosive liquid, without initiating device	2028	8	82 (b)
Bombs with bursting charge	0033	1.1F	7
Bombs with bursting charge	0034	1.1D	5
Bombs with bursting charge	0035	1.2D	17
Bombs with bursting charge	0291	1.2F	19
Bombs with flammable liquid with bursting charge	0399	1.1J	10
Bombs with flammable liquid with bursting charge	0400	1.2J	23

Name of substance or article	Substance Identification No. (UN No.)	Class	Item number and letter
Boosters with detonator	0225	1.1B	1
Boosters with detonator	0268	1.2B	13
Boosters without detonator	0042	1.1D	5
Boosters without detonator	0283	1.2D	17
Borneol	1312	4.1	6 (c)
Boron bromide	2692	8	12 (a)
Boron tribromide	2692	8	12 (a)
Boron trichloride	1741	2	2 TC
Boron trifluoride acetic acid complex	1742	8	33 (b)
Boron trifluoride, compressed	1008	2	1 TC
Boron trifluoride diethyl etherate	2604	8	33 (a)
Boron trifluoride dihydrate	2851	8	10 (b)
Boron trifluoride dimethyletherate	2965	4.3	2 (a)
Boron trifluoride ether complex	2604	8	33 (a)
Boron trifluoride phenol complex, see Corrosive liquid, acidic, organic, n.o.s.			
Boron trifluoride propionic acid complex	1743	8	33 (b)
Brodifacoum (pesticide), see Coumarin derivative pesticides			
Bromates, inorganic, aqueous solution, n.o.s.	3213	5.1	16 (b), (c)
Bromates, inorganic, n.o.s.	1450	5.1	16 (b)
Bromine chloride	2901	2	2 TOC
Bromine or Bromine solutions	1744	8	14
Bromine pentafluoride	1745	5.1	5
Bromine trifluoride	1746	5.1	5
Bromoacetic acid	1938	8	31 (b)
Bromoacetone	1569	6.1	16 (b)
Bromoacetyl bromide	2513	8	35 (b)1.
Bromoanilines, liquid, see Toxic liquid, organic, n.o.s.			
Bromoanilines, solid, see Toxic solid, organic, n.o.s.			
Bromobenzene	2514	3	31 (c)
Bromobenzyl chloride, see Toxic liquid, organic, n.o.s.			
Bromobenzyl cyanides	1694	6.1	17 (a)
1-Bromobutane	1126	3	3 (b)
2-Bromobutane	2339	3	3 (b)
Bromochloromethane	1887	6.1	15 (c)
1-Bromo-3-chloropropane	2688	6.1	15 (c)
2-Bromoethyl ethyl ether	2340	3	3 (b)
Bromoform	2515	6.1	15 (c)
1-Bromo-3-methylbutane	2341	3	31 (c)

Supplement No.1

Name of substance or article	Substance Identification No. (UN No.)	Class	Item number and letter
Bromomethylpropanes	2342	3	3 (b)
2-Bromo-2-nitropropane-1,3-diol	3241	4.1	26 (c)
2-Bromopentane	2343	3	3 (b)
Bromophos-ethyl (pesticide), see Organophosphorus pesticides			
1-Bromopropane, see Bromopropanes			
2-Bromopropane, see Bromopropanes			
Bromopropanes	2344	3	3 (b)
3-Bromopropyne	2345	3	3 (b)
Bromotrifluoroethylene	2419	2	2 F
Bromotrifluoromethane	1009	2	2 A
Bromoxynil (pesticide), see under Pesticide, etc.			
Brown asbestos (amosite or mysorite)	2212	9	1 (b)
Brucine	1570	6.1	90 (a)
Bursters, explosive	0043	1.1D	5
1,2-Butadiene, inhibited	1010	2	2 F
1,3-Butadiene, inhibited	1010	2	2 F
1,3-Butadiene mixture with hydrocarbons, inhibited.	1010	2	2 F
Butadienes, inhibited	1010	2	2 F
Butane	1011	2	2 F
Butanedione	2346	3	3 (b)
Butanols	1120	3	3 (b), 31 (c)
Butanol, secondary, see Butanols			
n-Butanol-2, see Butanols			
Butanol, tertiary, see Butanols			
1-Butene	1012	2	2 F
cis-2-Butene	1012	2	2 F
trans-2-Butene	1012	2	2 F
Butocarboxim pesticide, see Carbamate pesticides			
Butyl acetates	1123	3	3 (b), 31 (c)
n-Butyl acetate, see Butyl acetates			
Butyl acid phosphate	1718	8	38 (c)
Butyl acrylates, inhibited	2348	3	31 (c)
Butyl alcohol, normal, see Butyl alcohols			
Butyl alcohol, secondary, see Butyl alcohols			
Butyl alcohol, tertiary, see Butyl alcohols			
n-Butylamine	1125	3	22 (b)
N-Butylaniline	2738	6.1	12 (b)
Butylbenzenes	2709	3	31 (c)
n-Butyl bromide	1126	3	3 (b)

- 380 -

Name of substance or article	Substance Identification No. (UN No.)	Class	Item number and letter
Butyl chlorides	1127	3	3 (b)
n-Butyl chloroformate	2743	6.1	28 (b)
tert-Butyl cumyl peroxide, see Organic peroxide type D, liquid and solid			
tert-Butylcyclohexyl chloroformate	2747	6.1	17 (c)
n-Butyl-4,4-di-(tert-butylperoxy)valerate, see Organic peroxide type C, liquid			
n-Butyl-4,4-di-(tert-butylperoxy)valerate, see Organic peroxide type D, solid			
n-Butyl-4,4-di-(tert-butylperoxy)valerate, see Organic peroxide type E, solid			
1-Butylene	1012	2	2 F
cis-2-Butylene	1012	2	2 F
trans-2-Butylene	1012	2	2 F
1,2-Butylene oxide, stabilized	3022	3	3 (b)
Butylenes mixture	1012	2	2 F
n-Butyl ether, see Dibutyl ethers			
Butyl ethyl ether, see Ethyl butyl ether			
n-Butyl formate	1128	3	3 (b)
tert-Butyl hydroperoxide + di-tert-butylperoxide, see Organic peroxide type C, liquid			
tert-Butyl hydroperoxide, see Organic peroxide type C, liquid			
tert-Butyl hydroperoxide, see Organic peroxide type D, liquid			
tert-Butyl hydroperoxide, see Organic peroxide type F, liquid			
tert-Butyl hypochlorite	3255	4.2	10 (a)
N,n-Butylimidazole	2690	6.1	12 (b)
n-Butyl isocyanate	2485	6.1	6 (a)
tert-Butyl isocyanate	2484	6.1	6 (a)
tert-Butyl isocyanide, see Flammable liquid toxic, n.o.s.			
Butyl mercaptan	2347	3	3 (b)
n-Butyl methacrylate inhibited	2227	3	31 (c)
Butyl methyl ether	2350	3	3 (b)
tert-Butyl monoperoxymaleate, see Organic peroxide type B, solid			
tert-Butyl monoperoxymaleate, see Organic peroxide type C, liquid			
tert-Butyl monoperoxymaleate, see Organic peroxide type E, solid			
tert-Butyl monoperoxyphthalate, see Organic peroxide type B, solid			
Butyl nitrites	2351	3	3 (b), 31 (c)
tert-Butyl peroxyacetate, see Organic peroxide type B, liquid			
tert-Butyl peroxyacetate, see Organic peroxide type C, liquid			
tert-Butyl peroxyacetate, see Organic peroxide type F, liquid			

Name of substance or article	Substance Identification No. (UN No.)	Class	Item number and letter
tert-Butyl peroxybenzoate, see Organic peroxide type C, liquid			
tert-Butyl peroxybenzoate, see Organic peroxide type D, liquid and solid			
tert-Butyl peroxybutyl fumerate, see Organic peroxide type D, liquid			
tert-Butyl peroxycrotonate, see Organic peroxide type D, liquid			
tert-Butyl peroxydiethylacetate, see Organic peroxide type C, liquid, temperature controlled			
tert-Butyl peroxydiethylacetate + tert-butyl peroxybenzoate, see Organic peroxide type D, liquid			
tert-Butyl peroxy-2-ethylhexanoate, see Organic peroxide type C, liquid, temperature controlled			
tert-Butyl peroxy-2-ethylhexanoate, see Organic peroxide type E, liquid, temperature controlled			
tert-Butyl peroxy-2-ethylhexanoate, see Organic peroxide type E, solid, temperature controlled			
tert-Butyl peroxy-2-ethylhexanoate, see Organic peroxide type F, liquid, temperature controlled			
tert-Butyl peroxy-2-ethylhexanoate + 2,2-di-(tert-butylperoxy)butane, see Organic peroxide type D, liquid, temperature controlled			
tert-Butyl peroxy-2-ethylhexanoate + 2,2-di-(tert-butylperoxy)butane, see Organic peroxide type D, solid			
tert-Butyl peroxy-2-ethylhexylcarbonate, see Organic peroxide type D, liquid			
tert-Butyl peroxyisobutyrate, see Organic peroxide type B, liquid, temperature controlled			
tert-Butyl peroxyisobutyrate, see Organic peroxide type D, liquid, temperature controlled			
tert-Butyl peroxy isopropylcarbonate, see Organic peroxide type C, liquid			
1-(2-tert-Butylperoxy isopropyl)-3-isopropenylbenzene, see Organic peroxide type D, liquid			
1-(2-tert-Butylperoxy isopropyl)-3-isopropenylbenzene, see Organic peroxide type E, solid			
tert-Butyl peroxy-2-methylbenzoate, see Organic peroxide type C, liquid			
tert-Butyl peroxyneodeconate, see Organic peroxide type D, liquid, temperature controlled			
tert-Butyl peroxyneodeconate, see Organic peroxide type E, liquid, temperature controlled			
tert-Butyl peroxyneodeconate, see Organic peroxide type E, solid, temperature controlled			
tert-Butyl peroxyneoheptanoate, see Organic peroxide type D, liquid, temperature controlled			
3-tert-Butylperoxy-3-phenylphthalide, see Organic peroxide type D, solid			

Name of substance or article	Substance Identification No. (UN No.)	Class	Item number and letter
tert-Butyl peroxypivalate, see Organic peroxide type C, liquid, temperature controlled			
tert-Butyl peroxypivalate, see Organic peroxide type D, liquid, temperature controlled			
tert-Butyl peroxypivalate, see Organic peroxide type F, liquid, temperature controlled			
tert-Butylperoxy stearylcarbonate, see Organic peroxide type D, solid			
tert-Butyl peroxy-3,5,5-trimethylhexanoate, see Organic peroxide type D, liquid			
tert-Butyl peroxy-3,5,5-trimethylhexanoate, see Organic peroxide type F, liquid			
Butyl propionates	1914	3	31 (c)
Butyltin trichloride, see Corrosive liquid, n.o.s.			
Butyltoluenes	2667	6.1	25 (c)
Butyltrichlorosilane	1747	8	37 (b)
5-tert-Butyl-2,4,6-trinitro-m-xylene(musk-xylene)	2956	4.1	26 (c)
Butyl vinyl ether, inhibited	2352	3	3 (b)
2-Butyne	1144	3	1 (a)
1,4-Butynediol	2716	6.1	14 (c)
Butyraldehyde	1129	3	3 (b)
Butyraldoxime	2840	3	31 (c)
Butyric acid	2820	8	32 (c)
Butyric anhydride	2739	8	32 (c)
Butyronitrile	2411	3	11 (b)
Butyryl chloride	2353	3	25 (b)
Cacodylic acid	1572	6.1	51 (b)
Cadmium acetate, see Cadmium compound			
Cadmium carbonate, see Cadmium compound			
Cadmium compound	2570	6.1	61 (a), (b), (c)
Cadmium nitrate, see Cadmium compound			
Cadmium pigments : Not subject to ADR		6.1	61 (c), Note
Cadmium salts of higher fatty acids (e.g. cadmium stearate): Not subject to ADR		6.1	61 (c), Note
Cadmium sulphate, see Cadmium compound			
Cadmium sulphide: Not subject to ADR		6.1	61 (c), Note
Cadmium sulphoselenides: Not subject to ADR		6.1	61 (c), Note
Cadmium telluride, see Cadmium compound			
Caesium	1407	4.3	11 (a)
Caesium hydroxide	2682	8	41 (b)
Caesium hydroxide solution	2681	8	42 (b), (c)

Name of substance or article	Substance Identification No. (UN No.)	Class	Item number and letter
Caesium nitrate	1451	5.1	22 (c)
Calcium	1401	4.3	11 (b)
Calcium alloys, pyrophoric	1855	4.2	12 (a)
Calcium arsenate	1573	6.1	51 (b)
Calcium arsenate and calcium arsenite mixture, solid	1574	6.1	51 (b)
Calcium arsenate (pesticide), see Arsenical pesticides			
Calcium carbide	1402	4.3	17 (b)
Calcium chlorate	1452	5.1	11 (b)
Calcium chlorate, aqueous solution	2429	5.1	11 (b), (c)
Calcium chlorite	1453	5.1	14 (b)
Calcium cyanamide with more than 0.1% calcium carbide	1403	4.3	19 (c)
Calcium cyanide	1575	6.1	41 (a)
Calcium dithionite	1923	4.2	13 (b)
Calcium hydride	1404	4.3	16 (a)
Calcium hydrosulphite, see Calcium dithionite			
Calcium hypochlorite, dry	1748	5.1	15 (b)
Calcium hypochlorite, hydrated	2880	5.1	15 (b)
Calcium hypochlorite, hydrated mixture with not less than 5.5% but not more than 10% water	2880	5.1	15 (b)
Calcium hypochlorite mixture, dry with more than 10% but not more than 39% available chlorine	2208	5.1	15 (c)
Calcium hypochlorite mixture, dry with more than 39% available chlorine (8.8% available oxygen)	1748	5.1	15 (b)
Calcium manganese silicon	2844	4.3	12 (c)
Calcium nitrate	1454	5.1	22 (c)
Calcium oxide	1910	8	Exempt
Calcium perchlorate	1455	5.1	13 (b)
Calcium permanganate	1456	5.1	17 (b)
Calcium peroxide	1457	5.1	25 (b)
Calcium phosphide	1360	4.3	18 (a)
Calcium, pyrophoric	1855	4.2	12 (a)
Calcium resinate	1313	4.1	12 (c)
Calcium resinate, fused	1314	4.1	12 (c)
Calcium selenate	2630	6.1	55 (a)
Calcium silicide	1405	4.3	12 (b), (c)
Calomel, see Environmentally hazardous substance, solid, n.o.s.			
Camphechlor (pesticide), see Organochlorine pesticides			
Camphor oil	1130	3	31 (c)
Camphor, synthetic	2717	4.1	6 (c)
Caproic acid	2829	8	32 (c)

Name of substance or article	Substance Identification No. (UN No.)	Class	Item number and letter
Carbamate pesticide, liquid, flammable, toxic, flash-point less than 23 °C	2758	3	41 (a), (b)
Carbamate pesticide, liquid, toxic	2992	6.1	71 (a), (b), (c)
Carbamate pesticide, liquid, toxic, flammable, flash point not less than 23 °C	2991	6.1	72 (a), (b), (c)
Carbamate pesticide, solid, toxic	2757	6.1	73 (a), (b), (c)
Carbaryl (pesticide), see Carbamate pesticides			
Carbofuran (pesticide), see Carbamate pesticides			
Carbon, activated	1362	4.2	1 (c)
Carbon, animal or vegetable origin	1361	4.2	1 (b), (c)
Carbon dioxide	1013	2	2 A
Carbon dioxide and ethylene oxide mixture with more than 9% but not more than 87% ethylene oxide	1041	2	2 F
Carbon dioxide and nitrous oxide mixture	1015	2	2 A
Carbon dioxide and oxygen mixture, compressed	1014	2	1 O
Carbon dioxide, refrigerated liquid	2187	2	3 A
Carbon dioxide, solid (dry ice): Not subject to ADR	1845	9	-
Carbon disulphide	1131	3	18 (a)
Carbon monoxide and hydrogen mixture, compressed	2600	2	1 TF
Carbon monoxide, compressed	1016	2	1 TF
Carbon tetrabromide	2516	6.1	15 (c)
Carbon tetrachloride	1846	6.1	15 (b)
Carbonyl fluoride, compressed	2417	2	1 TC
Carbonyl sulphide	2204	2	2 TF
Carbophenothion (pesticides), see Organophosphorus pesticides			
Cartap hydrochloride (pesticide), see Carbamate pesticides			
Cartridges, flash	0049	1.1G	9
Cartridges, flash	0050	1.3G	30
Cartridges for weapons, blank	0014	1.4S	47
Cartridges for weapons, blank	0326	1.1C	3
Cartridges for weapons, blank	0327	1.3C	27
Cartridges for weapons, blank	0338	1.4C	37
Cartridges for weapons, blank	0413	1.2C	15
Cartridges for weapons, inert projectile	0012	1.4S	47
Cartridges for weapons, inert projectile	0328	1.2C	15
Cartridges for weapons, inert projectile	0339	1.4C	37
Cartridges for weapons, inert projectile	0417	1.3C	27
Cartridges for weapons with bursting charge	0005	1.1F	7
Cartridges for weapons with bursting charge	0006	1.1E	6
Cartridges for weapons with bursting charge	0007	1.2F	19

Name of substance or article	Substance Identification No. (UN No.)	Class	Item number and letter
Cartridges for weapons with bursting charge	0321	1.2E	18
Cartridges for weapons with bursting charge	0348	1.4F	41
Cartridges for weapons with bursting charge	0412	1.4E	40
Cartridges, oil well	0277	1.3C	27
Cartridges, oil well	0278	1.4C	37
Cartridges, power device	0275	1.3C	27
Cartridges, power device	0276	1.4C	37
Cartridges, power device	0323	1.4S	47
Cartridges, power device	0381	1.2C	15
Cartridges, signal	0054	1.3G	30
Cartridges, signal	0312	1.4G	43
Cartridges, signal	0405	1.4S	47
Cartridges, small arms	0012	1.4S	47
Cartridges, small arms	0339	1.4C	37
Cartridges, small arms	0417	1.3C	27
Cartridges, small arms, blank	0014	1.4S	47
Cartridges, small arms, blank	0327	1.3C	27
Cartridges, small arms, blank	0338	1.4C	37
Cases, cartridge, empty, with primer	0055	1.4S	47
Cases, cartridge, empty, with primer	0379	1.4C	37
Cases, combustible, empty, without primer	0446	1.4C	37
Cases, combustible, empty, without primer	0447	1.3C	27
Castor beans or castor meal or castor pomace or castor flake	2969	9	35 (b)
Caustic alkali liquid, n.o.s.	1719	8	42 (b), (c)
Caustic potash	1814	8	42 (b), (c)
Caustic soda	1824	8	42 (b), (c)
Cells, containing sodium	3292	4.3	31 (b)
Celluloid, in blocks, rods, rolls, sheets, tubes, etc., except scrap	2000	4.1	3 (c)
Celluloid, scrap	2002	4.2	4 (c)
Cereal grains, impregnated with pesticide or other toxic substance		6.1	See Note 2 (b) to section F
Cerium, slabs, ingots or rods	1333	4.1	13 (b)
Cerium, turnings or gritty powder	3078	4.3	13 (b)
Charges, bursting, plastics bonded	0457	1.1D	5
Charges, bursting, plastics bonded	0458	1.2D	17
Charges, bursting, plastics bonded	0459	1.4D	39
Charges, bursting, plastics bonded	0460	1.4S	47
Charges, demolition	0048	1.1D	5
Charges, depth	0056	1.1D	5

Name of substance or article	Substance Identification No. (UN No.)	Class	Item number and letter
Charges, explosive, commercial without detonator	0442	1.1D	5
Charges, explosive, commercial without detonator	0443	1.2D	17
Charges, explosive, commercial without detonator	0444	1.4D	39
Charges, explosive, commercial without detonator	0445	1.4S	47
Charges, propelling	0271	1.1C	3
Charges, propelling	0272	1.3C	27
Charges, propelling	0415	1.2C	15
Charges, propelling	0491	1.4C	39
Charges, propelling, for cannon	0242	1.3C	27
Charges, propelling, for cannon	0279	1.1C	3
Charges, propelling, for cannon	0414	1.2C	15
Charges, shaped, commercial without detonator	0059	1.1D	5
Charges, shaped, commercial without detonator	0439	1.2D	17
Charges, shaped, commercial without detonator	0440	1.4D	39
Charges, shaped, commercial without detonator	0441	1.4S	47
Charges, shaped, flexible, linear	0237	1.4D	39
Charges, shaped, flexible, linear	0288	1.1D	5
Charges, supplementary, explosive	0060	1.1D	5
Chemical kit	3316	9	36 (b), (c)
Chemical sample, toxic, liquid or solid	3315	6.1	90 (a)
Chinomethionate (pesticide), see under Pesticide, etc.			
Chloral, anhydrous, inhibited	2075	6.1	17 (b)
Chlorate and borate mixture	1458	5.1	11 (b)
Chlorate and magnesium chloride mixture	1459	5.1	11 (b)
Chlorates, inorganic, aqueous solution, n.o.s.	3210	5.1	11 (b), (c)
Chlorates, inorganic, n.o.s.	1461	5.1	11 (b)
Chlordane (pesticide), see Organochlorine pesticides			
Chlordimeform hydrochloride (pesticide), see Organochlorine pesticides			
Chlordimeform (pesticide), see Organochlorine pesticides			
Chlorfenvinphos (pesticide), see Organophosphorus pesticides			
Chloric acid, aqueous solution with not more than 10% chloric acid	2626	5.1	4 (b)
Chlorine	1017	2	2 TC
Chlorine pentafluoride	2548	2	2 TOC
Chlorine trifluoride	1749	2	2 TOC
Chlorite solution	1908	8	61 (b), (c)
Chlorites, inorganic, n.o.s.	1462	5.1	14 (b)
Chlormephos (pesticide), see Organophosphorus pesticides			
Chloroacetaldehyde	2232	6.1	17 (a)
Chloroacetic acid mixture, see Corrosive liquid, acidic, organic, n.o.s.			

Supplement No.1

Name of substance or article	Substance Identification No. (UN No.)	Class	Item number and letter
Chloroacetic acid, molten	3250	6.1	24 (b)2.
Chloroacetic acid, solid	1751	6.1	27 (b)
Chloroacetic acid solution	1750	6.1	27 (b)
Chloroacetone, stabilized	1695	6.1	10 (a)
Chloroacetonitrile	2668	6.1	11 (b)
Chloroacetophenone	1697	6.1	17 (b)
Chloroacetyl chloride	1752	6.1	27 (a)
2-Chloroacrylonitrile, see Flammable liquid, toxic, n.o.s.			
Chloroanilines, liquid	2019	6.1	12 (b)
Chloroanilines, solid	2018	6.1	12 (b)
Chloroanisidines	2233	6.1	17 (c)
Chlorobenzaldehyde, liquid, see Toxic liquid, organic, n.o.s.			
o-Chlorobenzaldehyde, see Toxic liquid, organic, n.o.s.			
Chlorobenzaldehyde, solid, see Toxic solid, organic, n.o.s.			
Chlorobenzene	1134	3	31 (c)
Chlorobenzotrifluorides	2234	3	31 (c)
o-Chlorobenzoyl chloride. see Corrosive liquid, acidic, organic, n.o.s.			
p-Chlorobenzoyl chloride, see Corrosive liquid, acidic, organic, n.o.s.			
Chlorobenzyl chlorides	2235	6.1	17 (c)
1-Chloro-3-bromopropane	2688	6.1	15 (c)
Chlorobutanes	1127	3	3 (b)
Chlorocresols	2669	6.1	14 (b)
3-Chloro-4-diethylaminobenzenediazonium zinc chloride, see Self-reactive solid, type D			
Chlorodifluorobromomethane	1974	2	2 A
1-Chloro-1,1-difluoroethane	2517	2	2 F
Chlorodifluoromethane	1018	2	2 A
Chlorodifluoromethane and chloropentafluoroethane mixture with fixed boiling point, with approximately 49% chlorodifluoromethane	1973	2	2 A
Chlorodimethyl sulphate, see Toxic liquid, organic, n.o.s.			
Chlorodinitrobenzenes	1577	6.1	12 (b)
Chloroethyl isocyanate, see Isocyanates, toxic, flammable, n.o.s.			
Chloroform	1888	6.1	15 (c)
Chloroformates, toxic, corrosive, flammable, n.o.s.	2742	6.1	28 (b)
Chloroformates, toxic, corrosive, n.o.s.	3277	6.1	27 (b)
Chloro-methoxyethyl mercury (pesticide), see Mercury-based pesticides			
Chloromethyl chloroformate	2745	6.1	27 (b)
Chloromethyl ethyl ether	2354	3	16 (b)
3-Chloro-4-methylphenyl isocyanate	2236	6.1	19 (b)

Name of substance or article	Substance Identification No. (UN No.)	Class	Item number and letter
Chloronitroanilines	2237	6.1	17 (c)
Chloronitrobenzenes	1578	6.1	12 (b)
1-Chloro-1-nitropropane, see Toxic liquid, organic, n.o.s.			
Chloronitrotoluenes	2433	6.1	17 (c)
Chloropentafluoroethane	1020	2	2 A
3-Chloroperoxybenzoic acid, see Organic peroxide type B, solid			
3-Chloroperoxybenzoic acid, see Organic peroxide type D, solid			
Chlorophacinone (pesticide), see Organochlorine pesticides			
2-Chlorophenol, see Chlorophenols, liquid			
3-Chlorophenol, see Chlorophenols, liquid			
4-Chlorophenol, see Chlorophenols, liquid			
Chlorophenolates, liquid	2904	8	62 (c)
Chlorophenolates, solid	2905	8	62 (c)
Chlorophenols, liquid	2021	6.1	17 (c)
Chlorophenols, solid	2020	6.1	17 (c)
Chloro-phenoxyacetic pesticides, see Phenoxy pesticides			
3-Chlorophenyl isocyanate, see Isocyanates, toxic, n.o.s.			
4-Chlorophenyl isocyanate, see Isocyanates, toxic, n.o.s.			
Chlorophenyl trichlorosilane	1753	8	36 (b)
Chloropicrin	1580	6.1	17 (a)
Chloropicrin and methyl bromide mixture	1581	2	2 T
Chloropicrin and methyl chloride mixture	1582	2	2 T
Chloropicrin mixture, n.o.s.	1583	6.1	17 (a), (b), (c)
Chloroplatinic acid, solid	2507	8	16 (c)
Chloroprene, inhibited	1991	3	16 (a)
1-Chloropropane	1278	3	2 (b)
2-Chloropropane	2356	3	2 (a)
3-Chloropropanol-1	2849	6.1	17 (c)
2-Chloropropene	2456	3	1 (a)
2-Chloropropionic acid	2511	8	32 (c)
2-Chloropyridine	2822	6.1	12 (b)
Chloropyriphos (pesticide), see Organophosphorus pesticides			
Chlorosilanes, corrosive, flammable, n.o.s.	2986	8	37 (b)
Chlorosilanes, corrosive, n.o.s.	2987	8	36 (b)
Chlorosilanes, flammable, corrosive, n.o.s.	2985	3	21 (b)
Chlorosilanes, water-reactive, flammable, corrosive, n.o.s.	2988	4.3	1 (a)
Chlorosulphonic acid	1754	8	12 (a)
1-Chloro-1,2,2,2-tetrafluoroethane	1021	2	2 A
Chlorothiophos (pesticide), see Organophosphorus pesticides			

Name of substance or article	Substance Identification No. (UN No.)	Class	Item number and letter
Chlorotoluenes	2238	3	31 (c)
4-Chloro-o-toluidine hydrochloride	1579	6.1	17 (c)
Chlorotoluidines	2239	6.1	17 (c)
1-Chloro-1,1,2-trifluoroethane		2	2 A Note
1-Chloro-1,2,2-trifluoroethane		2	2 A Note
1-Chloro-2,2,2-trifluoroethane	1983	2	2 A
Chlorotrifluoroethylene, inhibited	1082	2	2 TF
Chlorotrifluoromethane and trifluoromethane azeotropic mixture, with approximately 60% chlorotrifluoromethane	2599	2	2 A
Chlorotrifluoromethane .	1022	2	2 A
Chlorotrifluoropyrimidine, see Toxic liquid organic, n.o.s.,			
5-Chlorovaleric acid, see Corrosive liquid, acidic, organic, n.o.s.			
Chromic acid, solid, see Chromium trioxide, anhydrous			
Chromic acid solution	1755	8	17 (b), (c)
Chromic fluoride, solid	1756	8	9 (b)
Chromic fluoride solution	1757	8	8 (b), (c)
Chromium carbonyl, see Metal carbonyls, n.o.s.			
Chromium nitrate	2720	5.1	22 (c)
Chromium oxychloride	1758	8	12 (a)
Chromium trioxide, anhydrous	1463	5.1	31 (b)
Chromosulphuric acid	2240	8	1 (a)
Chromyl chloride	1758	8	12 (a)
Chrysotile	2590	9	1 (c)
Cinnabar: Not subject to ADR		6.1	52, Note 2
Clinical waste, unspecified, n.o.s.	3291	6.2	4 (b)
Coal gas, compressed	1023	2	1 TF
Coal tar distillates, flammable	1136	3	3 (b), 31 (c)
Coal tar naphtha, see Petroleum distillates, n.o.s.			
Coal tar oil, flammable, see Coal tar distillates			
Coating solution (includes surface treatments or coatings used for industrial or other purposes such as vehicle undercoating, drum or barrel lining)	1139	3	5 (a), (b), (c), 31 (c)
Cobalt carbonyl, see Metal carbonyls, n.o.s.			
Cobalt catalyst, dry, see Metal catalyst, dry			
Cobalt catalyst, wetted, see Metal catalyst, wetted			
Cobalt chloride, see Toxic solid, inorganic, n.o.s.			
Cobalt naphthenates, powder	2001	4.1	12 (c)
Cobalt resinate, precipitated	1318	4.1	12 (c)
Colchicine, see Alkaloids, solid, n.o.s.			
Collodion solutions, see Nitrocellulose solution, flammable			

Name of substance or article	Substance Identification No. (UN No.)	Class	Item number and letter
Colours for leathers, flammable	1263	3	5 (a), (b), (c), 31 (c) (See Note to Section E)
Colours for rotogravures, flammable	1210	3	5 (a), (b), (c), 31 (c) (See Note to Section E)
Components, explosive train, n.o.s.	0382	1.2B	13
Components, explosive train, n.o.s.	0383	1.4B	35
Components, explosive train, n.o.s.	0384	1.4S	47
Components, explosive train, n.o.s.	0461	1.1B	1
Compressed gas, flammable, n.o.s.	1954	2	1 F
Compressed gas, n.o.s.	1956	2	1 A
Compressed gas, oxidizing, n.o.s.	3156	2	1 O
Compressed gas, toxic, corrosive, n.o.s.	3304	2	1 TC
Compressed gas, toxic, flammable, n.o.s.	1953	2	1 TF
Compressed gas, toxic, flammable, corrosive, n.o.s.	3305	2	1 TFC
Compressed gas, toxic, n.o.s.	1955	2	1 T
Compressed gas, toxic, oxidizing, corrosive, n.o.s.	3306	2	1 TOC
Compressed gas, toxic, oxidizing, n.o.s.	3303	2	1 TO
Contrivances, water-activated with burster, expelling charge or propelling charge	0248	1.2L	25
Contrivances, water-activated with burster, expelling charge or propelling charge	0249	1.3L	34
Copper acetoarsenite	1585	6.1	51 (b)
Copper arsenite	1586	6.1	51 (b)
Copper based pesticide, liquid, flammable, toxic, flash-point less than 23 °C	2776	3	41 (a), (b)
Copper based pesticide, liquid, toxic	3010	6.1	71 (a), (b), (c)
Copper based pesticide, liquid, toxic, flammable, flash point not less than 23 °C	3009	6.1	72 (a), (b), (c)
Copper based pesticide, solid, toxic	2775	6.1	73 (a), (b), (c)
Copper catalyst, dry, see Metal catalyst, dry			
Copper catalyst, wetted, see Metal catalyst, wetted			
Copper chlorate	2721	5.1	11 (b)
Copper chloride	2802	8	11 (c)
Copper cyanide	1587	6.1	41 (b)
Copper oxychloride (pesticide), see Copper-based pesticides			
Copper selenate, see Selenates			
Copper selenite, see Selenites			
Copper sulphate (pesticide), see Copper-based pesticides			
Copra	1363	4.2	2 (c)

Name of substance or article	Substance Identification No. (UN No.)	Class	Item number and letter
Cord, detonating, flexible	0065	1.1D	5
Cord, detonating, flexible	0289	1.4D	39
Cord (fuse), detonating, metal clad	0102	1.2D	17
Cord (fuse), detonating, metal clad	0290	1.1D	5
Cord (fuse), detonating, mild effect, metal clad	0104	1.4D	39
Cord, igniter	0066	1.4G	43
Corrosive liquid, acidic, inorganic, n.o.s.	3264	8	17 (a), (b), (c)
Corrosive liquid, acidic, organic, n.o.s.	3265	8	40 (a), (b), (c)
Corrosive liquid, basic, inorganic, n.o.s.	3266	8	47 (a), (b), (c)`
Corrosive liquid, basic, organic, n.o.s.	3267	8	56 (a), (b), (c)
Corrosive liquid, flammable, n.o.s.	2920	8	68 (a), (b)
Corrosive liquid, n.o.s.	1760	8	66 (a), (b), (c)
Corrosive liquid, oxidizing, n.o.s.	3093	8	74 (a), (b)
Corrosive liquid, self-heating, n.o.s.	3301	8	70 (a), (b)
Corrosive liquid, toxic, n.o.s.	2922	8	76 (a), (b), (c)
Corrosive liquid, water-reactive, n.o.s.	3094	8	72 (a), (b)
Corrosive solid, acidic, inorganic, n.o.s.	3260	8	16 (a), (b), (c)
Corrosive solid, acidic, organic, n.o.s.	3261	8	39 (a), (b), (c)
Corrosive solid, basic, inorganic, n.o.s.	3262	8	46 (a), (b), (c)
Corrosive solid, basic, organic, n.o.s.	3263	8	55 (a), (b), (c)
Corrosive solid, flammable, n.o.s.	2921	8	67 (a), (b)
Corrosive solid, n.o.s.	1759	8	65 (a), (b), (c)
Corrosive solid, oxidizing, n.o.s.	3084	8	73 (a), (b)
Corrosive solid, self-heating, n.o.s.	3095	8	69 (a), (b)
Corrosive solid, toxic, n.o.s.	2923	8	75 (a), (b), (c)
Corrosive solid, water-reactive, n.o.s.	3096	8	71 (a), (b)
Cotton waste, oily	1364	4.2	3 (c)
Cotton, wet	1365	4.2	3 (c)
Coumachlor (pesticide), see Coumarin derivative pesticides			
Coumafuryl (pesticide), see Coumarin derivative pesticides			
Coumaphos (pesticide), see Coumarin derivative pesticides			
Coumarin derivative pesticide, liquid, flammable, toxic, flash point less than 23 °C	3024	3	41 (a), (b)
Coumarin derivative pesticide, liquid, toxic	3026	6.1	71 (a), (b), (c)
Coumarin derivative pesticide, liquid, toxic, flammable, flash point not less than 23 °C	3025	6.1	72 (a), (b), (c)
Coumarin derivative pesticide, solid, toxic	3027	6.1	73 (a), (b), (c)
Coumatetralyl (Racumin) (pesticide), see Coumarin derivative pesticides			
Cresols	2076	6.1	27 (b)

Name of substance or article	Substance Identification No. (UN No.)	Class	Item number and letter
Cresols, alkaline solutions, see Corrosive liquid, n.o.s.			
Cresylic acid	2022	6.1	27 (b)
Crimidin (pesticide), see Organochlorine pesticides			
Crocidolite	2212	9	1 (b)
Crotonaldehyde, stabilized	1143	6.1	8 (a)
Crotonic acid	2823	8	31 (c)
Crotonylene	1144	3	1 (a)
Crotoxyphos (pesticide), see Organophosphorus pesticides			
Crufomate (pesticide), see Organophosphorus pesticides			
Cumene	1918	3	31 (c)
Cumyl hydroperoxide, see Organic peroxide type E, liquid			
Cumyl hydroperoxide, see Organic peroxide type F, liquid			
Cumyl peroxyneodecanoate, see Organic peroxide type D, liquid, temperature controlled			
Cumyl peroxyneodecanoate, see Organic peroxide type F, liquid, temperature controlled			
Cumyl peroxyneoheptanoate, see Organic peroxide type D, liquid, temperature controlled			
Cumyl peroxypivalate, see Organic peroxide type D, liquid, temperature controlled			
Cupriethylenediamine solution	1761	8	53 (b), (c)
Cutters, cable, explosive	0070	1.4S	47
Cyanazine (pesticide), see Triazine pesticides			
Cyanide solution, n.o.s.	1935	6.1	41 (a), (b), (c)
Cyanides, inorganic, solid, n.o.s.	1588	6.1	41 (a), (b), (c)
Cyanogen	1026	2	2 TF
Cyanogen bromide	1889	6.1	27 (a)
Cyanogen chloride, inhibited	1589	2	2 TC
Cyanophos (pesticide), see Organophosphorus pesticides			
Cyanuric chloride	2670	8	39 (b)
Cyclobutane	2601	2	2 F
Cyclobutyl chloroformate	2744	6.1	28 (b)
1,5,9-Cyclododecatriene	2518	6.1	25 (c)
Cycloheptane	2241	3	3 (b)
1,3,5-Cycloheptatriene	2603	3	19 (b)
Cycloheptene	2242	3	3 (b)
Cyclohexane	1145	3	3 (b)
Cyclohexanone	1915	3	31 (c)
Cyclohexanone peroxide(s), see Organic peroxide type C, solid			
Cyclohexanone peroxide(s), see Organic peroxide type D, liquid			

Name of substance or article	Substance Identification No. (UN No.)	Class	Item number and letter
Cyclohexanone peroxide(s), see Organic peroxide type D, solid			
Cyclohexene	2256	3	3 (b)
Cyclohexenyltrichlorosilane	1762	8	36 (b)
Cycloheximide (pesticide), see under Pesticide, etc.			
Cyclohexyl acetate	2243	3	31 (c)
Cyclohexylamine	2357	8	54 (b)
Cyclohexyl chloroformate, see Chloroformates, toxic, corrosive, flammable, n.o.s.			
Cyclohexyl isocyanate	2488	6.1	18 (a)
Cyclohexyl mercaptan	3054	3	31 (c)
Cyclohexyltrichlorosilane	1763	8	36 (b)
Cyclonite, see Cyclotrimethylenetrinitramine			
Cyclooctadiene phosphines, see 9-Phosphabicyclononanes			
Cyclooctadienes	2520	3	31 (c)
Cyclooctatetraene	2358	3	3 (b)
Cyclopentane	1146	3	3 (b)
Cyclopentanol	2244	3	31 (c)
Cyclopentanone	2245	3	31 (c)
Cyclopentene	2246	3	2 (b)
Cyclopropane	1027	2	2 F
Cyclotetramethylenetetranitramine, wetted with not less than 15% water, by mass	0226	1.1D	4
Cyclotetramethylenetetranitramine, desensitized	0484	1.1D	4
Cyclotrimethylenetrinitramine, desensitized	0483	1.1D	4
Cyclotrimethylenetrinitramine and cyclotetramethylenetetranitramine mixture, desensitized with not less than 10% phlegmatizer, by mass	0391	1.1D	4
Cyclotrimethylenetrinitramine and cyclotetramethylenetetranitramine mixture, wetted with not less than 15% water, by mass	0391	1.1D	4
Cyclotrimethylenetrinitramine, wetted with not less than 15% water, by mass	0072	1.1D	4
Cyhexatin (Tricyclohexyl-tin hydroxide) (pesticide), see Organotin pesticides			
Cymenes	2046	3	31 (c)
Cypermethrin (pesticide), see under Pesticide, etc.			
2,4-D (pesticide), see Phenoxy pesticides			
Dazomet (pesticide), see under Pesticide, etc.			
2,4-DB (pesticide), see Phenoxy pesticides			
DDT (pesticide), see Organochlorine pesticides pesticides			
Decaborane	1868	4.1	16 (b)
Decahydronaphthalene	1147	3	31 (c)

Name of substance or article	Substance Identification No. (UN No.)	Class	Item number and letter
Decalin	1147	3	31 (c)
n-Decane	2247	3	31 (c)
Deflagrating metal salts of aromatic nitro-derivatives, n.o.s.	0132	1.3C	26
DEF (pesticide), see Organophosphorus pesticides			
Demephion (pesticide), see Organophosphorus pesticides			
Demeton (pesticide), see Organophosphorus pesticides			
Demeton-O (Systox) (pesticide), see Organophosphorus pesticides			
Demeton-O-methyl (pesticide), see Organophosphorus pesticides			
Demeton-S-methyl (pesticide), see Organophosphorus pesticides			
Demeton-S-methyl-sulfone (pesticide), see Organophosphorus pesticides			
Detonator assemblies, non-electric for blasting	0360	1.1B	1
Detonator assemblies, non-electric for blasting	0361	1.4B	35
Detonator assemblies, non-electric for blasting	0500	1.4S	47
Detonators, electric for blasting	0030	1.1B	1
Detonators, electric for blasting	0255	1.4B	35
Detonators, electric for blasting	0456	1.4S	47
Detonators for ammunition	0364	1.2B	13
Detonators for ammunition	0365	1.4B	35
Detonators for ammunition	0366	1.4S	47
Detonators for ammunition	0073	1.1B	1
Detonators, non-electric for blasting	0029	1.1B	1
Detonators, non-electric for blasting	0267	1.4B	35
Detonators, non-electric for blasting	0455	1.4S	47
Deuterium, compressed	1957	2	1 F
Devices, small, hydrocarbon gas powered	3150	2	6F
Diacetone alcohol, chemically pure	1148	3	31 (c)
Diacetone alcohol peroxides, see Organic peroxide type D, liquid, temperature controlled			
Diacetone alcohol, technically pure	1148	3	3 (b)
Diacetyl	2346	3	3 (b)
Diacetyl peroxide, see Organic peroxide type D, liquid, temperature controlled			
Dialifos (pesticide), see Organophosphorus pesticides			
Di-allate (pesticide), see Carbamate pesticides			
Diallylamine	2359	3	27 (b)
Diallyl ether	2360	3	17 (b)
4,4'-Diaminodiphenylmethane	2651	6.1	12 (c)
Di-n-amylamine	2841	3	32 (c)
Di-tert-amyl peroxide, see Organic peroxide type E, liquid			

Name of substance or article	Substance Identification No. (UN No.)	Class	Item number and letter
1,1-Di-(tert-amylperoxy)cyclohexane, see Organic peroxide type C, liquid			
Diazinon (pesticide), see Organophosphorus pesticides			
2-Diazo-1-naphthol-4-sulphochloride	3222	4.1	32 (b)
2-Diazo-1-naphthol-5-sulphochloride	3222	4.1	32 (b)
Diazonitrophenol, wetted with not less than 40% water, or mixture of alcohol and water, by mass	0074	1.1A	01
Dibenzoyl peroxide, see Benzoyl peroxide			
Dibenzoyl peroxide, see Organic peroxide type B, solid			
Dibenzoyl peroxide, see Organic peroxide type C, solid			
Dibenzoyl peroxide, see Organic peroxide type D, solid			
Dibenzoyl peroxide, see Organic peroxide type E, liquid			
Dibenzoyl peroxide, see Organic peroxide type E, solid			
Dibenzoyl peroxide, see Organic peroxide type F, liquid			
Dibenzyldichlorosilane	2434	8	36 (b)
Dibenzyl peroxydicarbonate, see Organic peroxide type B, solid, temperature controlled			
Diborane	1911	2	1 TF
1,2-Dibromobutan-3-one	2648	6.1	17 (b)
1,2-Dibromo-3-chloropropane (pesticide), see Organochlorine pesticides			
Dibromochloropropanes	2872	6.1	15 (b), (c)
1,2-Dibromo-3-chloropropane, see Dibromochloropropanes			
Dibromodifluoromethane	1941	9	33 (c)
Dibromomethane	2664	6.1	15 (c)
Di-n-butylamine	2248	8	54 (b)
Dibutylaminoethanol	2873	6.1	12 (c)
Di-(4-tert-butylcyclohexyl) peroxydicarbonate, see Organic peroxide, type C, solid temperature controlled			
Di-(4-tert-butylcyclohexyl) peroxydicarbonate, see Organic peroxide type F, liquid, temperature controlled			
Dibutyl ethers	1149	3	31 (c)
Di-n-butyl ether, see Dibutyl ethers			
Di-tert-butyl peroxide, see Organic peroxide type E, liquid			
Di-tert-butyl peroxide, see Organic peroxide type F, liquid			
Di-tert-butyl peroxyazelate, see Organic peroxide type D, liquid			
2,2-Di-(tert-butylperoxy)butane, see Organic peroxide type C, liquid			
1,1-Di-(tert-butylperoxy)cyclohexane, see Organic peroxide type B, liquid			
1,1-Di-(tert-butylperoxy)cyclohexane, see Organic peroxide type C, liquid			

Name of substance or article	Substance Identification No. (UN No.)	Class	Item number and letter
1,1-Di-(tert-butylperoxy)cyclohexane, see Organic peroxide type D, liquid			
1,1-Di-(tert-butylperoxy)cyclohexane, see Organic peroxide type E, liquid			
1,1-Di-(tert-butylperoxy)cyclohexane, see Organic peroxide type F, liquid			
Di-n-butyl peroxydicarbonate, see Organic peroxide type D, liquid, temperature controlled			
Di-n-butyl peroxydicarbonate, see Organic peroxide type E, liquid, temperature controlled			
Di-n-butyl peroxydicarbonate, see Organic peroxide type E, solid, temperature controlled			
Di-sec-butyl peroxydicarbonate, see Organic peroxide type C, liquid, temperature controlled			
Di-sec-butyl peroxydicarbonate, see Organic peroxide type D, liquid, temperature controlled			
Di-(2-tert-butylperoxyisopropyl)benzene(s), see Organic peroxide type D, solid			
Di-(tert-butylperoxy)phthalate, see Organic peroxide type D, liquid			
Di-(tert-butylperoxy)phthalate, see Organic peroxide type D, solid			
Di-(tert-butylperoxy)phthalate, see Organic peroxide type E, liquid			
2,2-Di-(tert-butylperoxy)propane, see Organic peroxide type D, liquid			
2,2-Di-(tert-butylperoxy)propane, see Organic peroxide type D, solid			
1,1-Di-(tert-butylperoxy)-3,3,5-trimethylcyclohexane, see Organic peroxide type B, liquid			
1,1-Di-(tert-butylperoxy)-3,3,5-trimethylcyclohexane, see Organic peroxide type D, solid			
1,1-Di-(tert-butylperoxy)-3,3,5-trimethylcyclohexane, see Organic peroxide type E, liquid			
1,1-Di-(tert-butylperoxy)-3,3,5-trimethylcyclohexane, see Organic peroxide type C, liquid			
Dibutyl tin chloride, see Organotin compound, solid, n.o.s.			
Dibutyl tin compounds (other than dibutyl tin chloride), see Organotin compound, solid, n.o.s.			
Dicetyl peroxydicarbonate, see Organic peroxide type D, solid, temperature controlled			
Dicetyl peroxydicarbonate, see Organic peroxide type F, liquid, temperature controlled			
Dichlofenthion (pesticide), see Organophosphorus pesticides			
Dichloroacetic acid	1764	8	32 (b)1.
1,3-Dichloroacetone	2649	6.1	17 (b)
Dichloroacetyl chloride	1765	8	35 (b)1.
Dichloroanilines	1590	6.1	12 (b)
o-Dichlorobenzene	1591	6.1	15 (c)

Name of substance or article	Substance Identification No. (UN No.)	Class	Item number and letter
Di-4-chlorobenzoyl peroxide, see Organic peroxide type B, solid			
Di-4-chlorobenzoyl peroxide, see Organic peroxide type D, solid			
2-2'-Dichlorodiethyl ether	1916	6.1	16 (b)
Dichlorodifluoromethane	1028	2	2 A
Dichlorodifluoromethane and 1,1-difluoroethane, azeotropic mixture, with approximately 74% dichlorodifluoromethane	2602	2	2 A
Dichlorodifluoromethane and ethylene oxide mixture with not more than 12.5% ethylene oxide	3070	2	2 A
Dichlorodimethyl ether, symmetrical: Not to be accepted for carriage	2249	6.1	26 (a), Note
1,1-Dichloroethane	2362	3	3 (b)
1,2-Dichloroethane	1184	3	16 (b)
1,2-Dichloroethylene	1150	3	3 (b)
2,2'-Dichloroethyl ether	1916	6.1	16 (b)
Dichlorofluoromethane	1029	2	2 A
Dichloroisocyanuric acid, dry	2465	5.1	26 (b)
Dichloroisocyanuric acid salts	2465	5.1	26 (b)
Dichloroisopropyl ether	2490	6.1	17 (b)
Dichloromethane	1593	6.1	15 (c)
1,1-Dichloro-1-nitroethane	2650	6.1	17 (b)
Dichloropentanes	1152	3	31 (c)
Dichlorophenols, liquid, see Chlorophenols, liquid			
Dichlorophenols, solid, see Chlorophenols, solid			
Dichlorophenyl isocyanates	2250	6.1	19 (b)
Dichlorophenyltrichlorosilane	1766	8	36 (b)
1,2-Dichloropropane	1279	3	3 (b)
1,3-Dichloropropanol-2	2750	6.1	17 (b)
Dichloropropenes	2047	3	3 (b), 31 (c)
Dichloroquinoxaline-carbonyl chloride, see Corrosive solid, acidic, organic, n.o.s.			
Dichlorosilane	2189	2	2 TFC
1,2-Dichloro-1,1,2,2-tetrafluoroethane	1958	2	2 A
Dichlorotoluidines, see Toxic solid, organic, n.o.s.			
Dichlorvos (pesticide), see Organophosphorus pesticides			
Dicoumarol (pesticide), see Coumarin derivative pesticides			
Dicrotophos (pesticide) see Organophosphorus pesticides			
Dicumyl peroxide, see Organic peroxide type F, solid			
Dicycloheptadiene	2251	3	3 (b)
Dicyclohexyl peroxydicarbonate, see Organic peroxide type B, solid, temperature controlled			

Name of substance or article	Substance Identification No. (UN No.)	Class	Item number and letter
Dicyclohexyl peroxydicarbonate, see Organic peroxide type C, solid, temperature controlled			
Dicyclohexylamine	2565	8	53 (c)
Dicyclohexylammonium nitrite	2687	4.1	11 (c)
Dicyclopentadiene	2048	3	31 (c)
Didecanoyl peroxide, see Organic peroxide type C, solid, temperature controlled			
2,2-Di-(4,4-di(tert-butylperoxy)cyclohexyl)-propane, see Organic peroxide type D, solid			
Di-2,4-dichlorobenzoyl peroxide, see Organic peroxide type B, solid			
Di-2,4-dichlorobenzoyl peroxide, see Organic peroxide type D, solid			
1,2-Di-(dimethylamino) ethane	2372	3	3 (b)
Didymium nitrate	1465	5.1	22 (c)
Dieldrin (pesticide), see Organochlorine pesticides			
Diesel fuel	1202	3	31 (c)
1,1-Diethoxyethane	1088	3	3 (b)
1,2-Diethoxyethane	1153	3	31 (c)
Diethoxymethane	2373	3	3 (b)
2,5-Diethoxy-4-morpholinobenzenediazonium tetrafluoroborate, see Self-reactive solid, type D, temperature controlled			
2,5-Diethoxy-4-morpholinobenzenediazonium zinc chloride, see Self-reactive solid, type D, temperature controlled			
2,5-Diethoxy-4-(phenylsulphonyl) benzenediazonium chloride, see Self-reactive solid, type D, temperature controlled			
3,3-Diethoxypropene	2374	3	3 (b)
Diethylamine	1154	3	22 (b)
Diethylaminoacetonitrile, see Toxic liquid, organic, n.o.s.			
Diethylaminoethanol	2686	8	54 (b)
Diethylaminopropylamine	2684	3	33 (c)
N,N-Diethylaniline	2432	6.1	12 (c)
Diethylbenzene	2049	3	31 (c)
Diethyl carbonate	2366	3	31 (c)
Diethyldichlorosilane	1767	8	37 (b)
Diethylenediamine	2579	8	52 (c)
Diethyleneglycol bis (allyl carbonate) + diisopropyl peroxydicarbonate, see Self-reactive liquid type E, temperature controlled			
Diethyleneglycol dinitrate, desensitized with not less than 25% non-volatile, water-insoluble phlegmatizer, by mass	0075	1.1D	4
Diethylenetriamine	2079	8	53 (b)
Diethyl ether	1155	3	2 (a)
N,N-Diethylethylenediamine	2685	8	54 (b)

Name of substance or article	Substance Identification No. (UN No.)	Class	Item number and letter
Di-(2-ethylhexyl) peroxydicarbonate, see Organic peroxide type C, liquid, temperature controlled			
Di-(2-ethylhexyl) peroxydicarbonate, see Organic peroxide type D, liquid, temperature controlled			
Di-(2-ethylhexyl) peroxydicarbonate, see Organic peroxide type E, solid, temperature controlled			
Di-(2-ethylhexyl) peroxydicarbonate, see Organic peroxide type E, liquid, temperature controlled			
Di-(2-ethylhexyl) peroxydicarbonate, see Organic peroxide type F, liquid, temperature controlled			
Diethyl ketone	1156	3	3 (b)
Diethyl peroxydicarbonate,, see Organic peroxide type D, liquid, temperature controlled			
Diethyl sulphate	1594	6.1	14 (b)
Diethyl sulphide	2375	3	3 (b)
Diethylthiophosphoryl chloride	2751	8	35 (b)1.
Diethylzinc	1366	4.2	31 (a)
Difenacoum (pesticide), see Coumarin derivative pesticides			
Difenzoquat (pesticide), see under Pesticide, etc.			
1,1-Difluoro-1-chloroethane	2517	2	2 F
1,1-Difluoroethane	1030	2	2 F
1,1-Difluoroethylene	1959	2	2 F
Difluoromethane	3252	2	2 F
Difluorophosphoric acid, anhydrous	1768	8	8 (b)
2,2-Dihydroperoxypropane, see Organic peroxide type B, solid			
2,3-Dihydropyran	2376	3	3 (b)
Di-(1-hydroxycyclohexyl) peroxide, see Organic peroxide type D, solid			
Diisoamyl ether, see Flammable liquid, n.o.s.			
Diisobutylamine	2361	3	33 (c)
Diisobutylene, isomeric compounds	2050	3	3 (b)
Diisobutyl ketone	1157	3	31 (c)
Diisobutyryl peroxide, see Organic peroxide type B, liquid, temperature controlled			
Diisobutyryl peroxide, see Organic peroxide type D, liquid, temperature controlled			
Diisooctyl acid phosphate	1902	8	38 (c)
Diisopropylamine	1158	3	22 (b)
Di-isopropylbenzene dihydroperoxide, see Organic peroxide type D, solid			
Diisopropyl ether	1159	3	3 (b)
Diisopropyl peroxydicarbonate + diethyleneglycol bis (allyl carbonate), see Self-reactive liquid type E, temperature controlled			

Name of substance or article	Substance Identification No. (UN No.)	Class	Item number and letter
Diisopropyl peroxydicarbonate, see Organic peroxide type B, solid, temperature controlled			
Diisopropyl peroxydicarbonate, see Organic peroxide type D, liquid, temperature controlled			
Diisotridecyl peroxydicarbonate, see Organic peroxide type D, liquid, temperature controlled			
Diketene, inhibited	2521	6.1	13 (a)
Dilauroyl peroxide, see Organic peroxide type D, solid			
Dilauroyl peroxide, see Organic peroxide type F, liquid			
Dimefox (pesticide), see Organophosphorus pesticides			
Dimetan (pesticide), see Carbamate pesticides			
Dimethoate (pesticide), see Organophosphorus pesticides			
1,1-Dimethoxyethane	2377	3	3 (b)
1,2-Dimethoxyethane	2252	3	3 (b)
Dimethoxymethane	1234	3	2 (b)
2,5-Dimethoxy-4-(4-methylphenylsulphonyl)benzenediazonium zinc chloride, see Self-reactive solid, type D, temperature controlled			
Dimethylamine, anhydrous	1032	2	2 F
Dimethylamine aqueous solution	1160	3	22 (b)
2-Dimethylaminoacetonitrile	2378	3	11 (b)
4-Dimethylamino-6-(2-dimethylaminoethoxy)-toluene-2-diazonium zinc chloride, see Self-reactive solid, type D, temperature controlled			
2-Dimethylaminoethanol	2051	8	54 (b)
2-Dimethylaminoethyl acrylate	3302	6.1	12 (b)
2-Dimethylaminoethyl methacrylate	2522	6.1	12 (b)
N,N-Dimethylaniline	2253	6.1	12 (b)
Dimethylbenzenes	1307	3	3 (b), 31 (c)
Di-(2-methylbenzoyl) peroxide, see Organic peroxide type B, solid, temperature controlled			
Di-(4-methylbenzoyl) peroxide, see Organic peroxide type D, solid			
2,3-Dimethylbutane	2457	3	3 (b)
1,3-Dimethylbutylamine	2379	3	22 (b)
Dimethylcarbamoyl chloride	2262	8	35 (b)1.
Dimethyl carbonate	1161	3	3 (b)
Dimethylcyclohexanes	2263	3	3 (b)
Dimethylcyclohexylamine	2264	8	54 (b)
2,5-Dimethyl-2,5-di-(benzoylperoxy)hexane, see Organic peroxide type B, solid			
2,5-Dimethyl-2,5-di-(benzoylperoxy)hexane, see Organic peroxide type C, solid			

Name of substance or article	Substance Identification No. (UN No.)	Class	Item number and letter
2,5-Dimethyl-2,5-di-(benzoylperoxy)hexane, see Organic peroxide type D, solid			
2,5-Dimethyl-2,5-di-(tert-butylperoxy)hexane, see Organic peroxide type D, liquid			
2,5-Dimethyl-2,5-di-(tert-butylperoxy)hexane, see Organic peroxide type E, solid			
2,5-Dimethyl-2,5-di-(tert-butylperoxy)hexane, see Organic peroxide type F, liquid			
2,5-Dimethyl-2,5-di-(tert-butylperoxy)hexane, see Organic peroxide type D, liquid			
2,5-Dimethyl-2,5-di-(tert-butylperoxy)hexyne-3, see Organic peroxide type C, liquid			
2,5-Dimethyl-2,5-di-(tert-butylperoxy)hexyne-3, see Organic peroxide type D, solid			
Dimethyldichlorosilane	1162	3	21 (b)
Dimethyldiethoxysilane	2380	3	3 (b)
2,5-Dimethyl-2,5-di-(2-ethylhexanoylperoxy)hexane, see Organic peroxide type D, liquid, temperature controlled			
2,5-Dimethyl-2,5-dihydroperoxyhexane, see Organic peroxide type C, solid			
Dimethyldioxanes	2707	3	3 (b), 31 (c)
Dimethyl disulphide	2381	3	3 (b)
2,5-Dimethyl-2,5-di-(3,5,5-trimethylhexanoylperoxy)hexane, see Organic peroxide type D, liquid			
Dimethyl ether	1033	2	2 F
N,N-Dimethylformamide	2265	3	31 (c)
1,1-dimethylhydrazine, see Dimethylhydrazine, symmetrical			
1,2-dimethylhydrazine, see Dimethylhydrazine, unsymmetrical			
Dimethylhydrazine, symmetrical	2382	6.1	7 (a)2.
Dimethylhydrazine, unsymmetrical	1163	6.1	7 (a)1.
1,1-Dimethyl-3-hydroxybutyl peroxyneoheptanoate, see Organic peroxide type E, liquid, temperature controlled			
2,2-Dimethylpropane	2044	2	2 F
Dimethyl-N-propylamine	2266	3	22 (b)
Dimethylpyridine, see Toxic liquid, flammable, organic, n.o.s.			
Dimethylsilane	1953	2	1 TF
Dimethyl sulphate	1595	6.1	27 (a)
Dimethyl sulphide	1164	3	2 (b)
Dimethylthiophosphoryl chloride	2267	6.1	27 (b)
Dimethyl tin chloride, see Organotin compound, liquid, n.o.s.			
Dimethylzinc	1370	4.2	31 (a)
Dimetilan (pesticide), see Carbamate pesticides			

Name of substance or article	Substance Identification No. (UN No.)	Class	Item number and letter
Dimexano (pesticide), see under Pesticide, etc.			
Dimyristyl peroxydicarbomate, see Organic peroxide type F, liquid, temperature controlled			
Di-(2-neodecanoylperoxyisopropyl)benzene, see Organic peroxide type D, liquid, temperature controlled			
DINGU, see Dinitroglycoluril			
Dinitroanilines	1596	6.1	12 (b)
Dinitrobenzenes	1597	6.1	12 (b)
Dinitro-o-cresol	1598	6.1	12 (b)
Dinitro-o-cresol (pesticide), see Substituted nitrophenol pesticides			
Dinitrogen tetroxide	1067	2	2 TOC
Dinitroglycoluril	0489	1.1D	4
Dinitrophenolates, alkali metals, dry or wetted with less than 15% water, by mass	0077	1.3C	26
Dinitrophenolates, wetted with not less than 15% water, by mass	1321	4.1	22 (a)1.
Dinitrophenol, dry or wetted with less than 15% water, by mass	0076	1.1D	4
Dinitrophenol solution	1599	6.1	12 (b), (c)
Dinitrophenol, wetted with not less than 15% water, by mass	1320	4.1	22 (a)1.
Dinitroresorcinol, dry or wetted with less than 15% water, by mass	0078	1.1D	4
Dinitroresorcinol, wetted with not less than 15% water, by mass	1322	4.1	21 (a)1.
Dinitrosobenzene	0406	1.3C	26
N,N'-Dinitroso-N,N'-dimethylterephthalamide, see Self-reactive solid, type C			
N,N'-Dinitrosopentamethylenetetramine, see Self-reactive solid, type C			
Dinitrotoluenes	2038	6.1	12 (b)
Dinitrotoluenes, molten	1600	6.1	24 (b)1.
Dinobuton (pesticide), see Substituted nitrophenol pesticides			
Di-n-nonanoyl peroxide, see Organic peroxide type D, solid, temperature controlled			
Dinoseb acetate (pesticide), see Substituted nitrophenol pesticides			
Dinoseb (pesticide), see Substituted nitrophenol pesticides			
Dinoterb acetate (pesticide), see Substituted nitrophenol pesticides			
Dinoterb (pesticide), see Substituted nitrophenol pesticides			
Di-n-octanoyl peroxide, see Organic peroxide type C, solid, temperature controlled			
Dioxacarb (pesticide), see Carbamate pesticides			
Dioxane	1165	3	3 (b)
Dioxathion (pesticide), see Organophosphorus pesticides			
Dioxolane	1166	3	3 (b)
Dipentene	2052	3	31 (c)

Name of substance or article	Substance Identification No. (UN No.)	Class	Item number and letter
Diperoxy azelaic acid, see Organic peroxide type D, solid, temperature controlled			
Diperoxy dodecane diacid, see Organic peroxide type D, solid, temperature controlled			
Diphacinone (pesticide), see under Pesticide, etc.			
Di-(2-phenoxyethyl) peroxydicarbonate, see Organic peroxide type B, solid			
Di-(2-phenoxyethyl) peroxydicarbonate, see Organic peroxide type D, solid			
Diphenylamine chloroarsine	1698	6.1	34 (a)
Diphenylchloroarsine	1699	6.1	34 (a)
Diphenyldichlorosilane	1769	8	36 (b)
Diphenylmethyl bromide	1770	8	65 (b)
Diphenyloxide-4,4'-disulphonylhydrazide, see Self-reactive solid, type D			
Dipicrylamine, see Hexanitrodiphenylamine			
Dipicryl sulphide, dry or wetted with less than 10% water, by mass	0401	1.1D	4
Dipicryl sulphide, wetted with not less than 10% water, by mass	2852	4.1	21 (a)2.
Dipropionyl peroxide, see Organic peroxide type E, liquid, temperature controlled			
Dipropyl acid phosphate, see Corrosive liquid, acidic, organic, n.o.s.			
Dipropylamine	2383	3	22 (b)
4-Dipropylaminobenzenediazonium zinc chloride, see Self-reactive solid, type D			
Dipropylenetriamine	2269	8	53 (c)
Di-n-propyl ether	2384	3	3 (b)
Dipropyl ketone	2710	3	31 (c)
Di-n-propyl peroxydicarbonate, see Organic peroxide type C, liquid, temperature controlled			
Diquat (pesticide), see Bipyridilium pesticides			
Disinfectant, liquid, corrosive, n.o.s.	1903	8	66 (a), (b), (c)
Disinfectant, liquid, toxic, n.o.s.	3142	6.1	25 (a), (b), (c)
Disinfectant, solid, toxic, n.o.s.	1601	6.1	25 (a), (b), (c)
Disodium trioxosilicate	3253	8	41 (c)
Distearyl peroxydicarbonate, see Organic peroxide type D, solid			
Disuccinic acid peroxide, see Organic peroxide type B, solid			
Disuccinic acid peroxide, see Organic peroxide type D, solid, temperature controlled			
Disulfoton (pesticide), see Organophosphorus pesticides			
Disulphur dichloride, see Sulphur chlorides			
Dithiocarbamate pesticide, liquid, flammable, toxic, flash-point less than 23 °C	2772	3	41 (a), (b)

Name of substance or article	Substance Identification No. (UN No.)	Class	Item number and letter
Dithiocarbamate pesticide, liquid, toxic	3006	6.1	71 (a), (b), (c)
Dithiocarbamate pesticide, liquid, toxic, flammable, flash point not less than 23 °C	3005	6.1	72 (a), (b), (c)
Dithiocarbamate pesticide, solid, toxic	2771	6.1	73 (a), (b), (c)
Di-(3,5,5-trimethyl-1,2-dioxolanyl-3) peroxide, see Organic peroxide type D, solid, temperature controlled			
Di-(3,5,5-trimethylhexanoyl) peroxide, see Organic peroxide type D, liquid, temperature controlled			
Di-(3,5,5-trimethylhexanoyl) peroxide, see Organic peroxide type E, liquid, temperature controlled			
Di-(3,5,5-trimethylhexanoyl) peroxide, see Organic peroxide type F, liquid, temperature controlled			
Divinyl ether, inhibited	1167	3	2 (a)
DNOC (pesticide), see Substituted nitrophenol pesticides			
Dodecyltrichlorosilane	1771	8	36 (b)
Drazoxolon (pesticide), see under Pesticide, etc.			
Dye intermediate, liquid, corrosive, n.o.s	2801	8	66 (a), (b), (c)
Dye intermediate, liquid, toxic, n.o.s.	1602	6.1	25 (a), (b), (c)
Dye intermediate, solid, corrosive, n.o.s.	3147	8	65 (b), (c)
Dye intermediate, solid, toxic, n.o.s.	3143	6.1	25 (a), (b), (c)
Dye, liquid, corrosive, n.o.s.	2801	8	66 (a), (b), (c)
Dye, liquid, toxic, n.o.s	1602	6.1	25 (a), (b), (c)
Dye, solid, corrosive, n.o.s.	3147	8	65 (b), (c)
Dye, solid, toxic, n.o.s.	3143	6.1	25 (a), (b), (c)
Edifenphos (pesticide), see Organophosphorus pesticides			
Elevated temperature liquid, flammable, n.o.s. with flash point above 61 °C at or above its flash point (including molten metals and molten salts)	3256	3	61 (c)
Elevated temperature liquid, n.o.s., at or above 100 °C substance with a flash point, below its flash point (including molten metals and molten salts)	3257	9	20 (c)
Elevated temperature solid, n.o.s., at or above 240 °C	3258	9	21 (c)
Empty demountable tanks, uncleaned		2	8
Empty demountable tanks, uncleaned		3	71
Empty demountable tanks, uncleaned		4.1	51
Empty demountable tanks, uncleaned		4.2	41
Empty demountable tanks, uncleaned		4.3	41
Empty demountable tanks, uncleaned		5.1	41
Empty demountable tanks, uncleaned		5.2	31
Empty demountable tanks, uncleaned		6.1	91
Empty demountable tanks, uncleaned		8	91

Item number and letter	Name of substance or article			Substance Identification No. (UN No.)	Class	Item number and letter
	Empty demountable tanks, uncleaned				9	71
	Empty intermediate bulk containers, uncleaned				3	71
	Empty intermediate bulk containers, uncleaned				4.1	51
	Empty intermediate bulk containers, uncleaned				4.2	41
	Empty intermediate bulk containers, uncleaned				4.3	41
	Empty intermediate bulk containers, uncleaned				5.1	41
	Empty intermediate bulk containers, uncleaned				5.2	31
	Empty intermediate bulk containers, uncleaned				6.1	91
	Empty intermediate bulk containers, uncleaned				6.2	11
	Empty intermediate bulk containers, uncleaned				8	91
	Empty intermediate bulk containers, uncleaned				9	71
	Empty packagings, uncleaned				1	91
	Empty packagings, uncleaned				3	71
	Empty packagings, uncleaned				4.1	51
	Empty packagings, uncleaned				4.2	41
	Empty packagings, uncleaned				4.3	41
	Empty packagings, uncleaned				5.1	41
	Empty packagings, uncleaned				5.2	31
	Empty packagings, uncleaned				6.1	91
	Empty packagings, uncleaned				6.2	11
	Empty packagings, uncleaned				8	91
	Empty packagings, uncleaned				9	71
	Empty receptacles				2	8
	Empty small, bulk, containers, uncleaned				4.1	51
	Empty small, bulk, containers, uncleaned				4.2	41
	Empty small, bulk, containers, uncleaned				4.3	41
	Empty small, bulk, containers, uncleaned				5.1	41
	Empty small, bulk, containers, uncleaned				6.1	91
	Empty small, bulk, containers, uncleaned				8	91
	Empty tank-containers, uncleaned				2	8
	Empty tank-containers, uncleaned				3	71
	Empty tank-containers, uncleaned				4.1	51
	Empty tank-containers, uncleaned				4.2	41
	Empty tank-containers, uncleaned				4.3	41
	Empty tank-containers, uncleaned				5.1	41
	Empty tank-containers, uncleaned				6.1	91
	Empty tank-containers, uncleaned				5.2	31
	Empty tank-containers, uncleaned				6.2	11
	Empty tank-containers, uncleaned				8	91

Name of substance or article	Substance Identification No. (UN No.)	Class	Item number and letter
Empty tank-containers, uncleaned		9	71
Empty tank vehicles, uncleaned		2	8
Empty tank vehicles, uncleaned		3	71
Empty tank vehicles, uncleaned		4.1	51
Empty tank vehicles, uncleaned		4.2	41
Empty tank vehicles, uncleaned		4.3	41
Empty tank vehicles, uncleaned		5.1	41
Empty tank vehicles, uncleaned		5.2	31
Empty tank vehicles, uncleaned		6.1	91
Empty tank vehicles, uncleaned		6.2	11
Empty tank vehicles, uncleaned		8	91
Empty tank vehicles, uncleaned		9	71
Empty tanks, uncleaned		4.1	51
Empty tanks, uncleaned		4.2	41
Empty tanks, uncleaned		4.3	41
Empty tanks, uncleaned		5.1	41
Empty tanks, uncleaned		6.1	91
Empty tanks, uncleaned		6.2	11
Empty tanks, uncleaned		8	91
Enamels	1263	3	5 (a), (b), (c), 31 (c) (See Note to Section E)
Endosulfan (pesticide), see Organochlorine pesticides			
Endothal-sodium (pesticide) see under Pesticide, etc.			
Endothion (pesticide), see Organophosphorus pesticides			
Endrin (pesticide), see Organochlorine pesticides			
Engines, internal combustion, including when fitted in machinery or vehicles: Not subject to ADR	3166	9	-
Environmentally hazardous substance, liquid, n.o.s.	3082	9	11 (c)
Environmentally hazardous substance, solid, n.o.s.	3077	9	12 (c)
Epibromohydrin	2558	6.1	16 (a)
Epichlorohydrin	2023	6.1	16 (b)
EPN (pesticide), see Organophosphorus pesticides			
1,2-Epoxy-3-ethoxypropane	2752	3	31 (c)
Esters, n.o.s.	3272	3	3 (b), 31 (c)
Ethanal	1089	3	1 (a)
Ethane	1035	2	2 F
Ethane, refrigerated liquid	1961	2	3 F
Ethanolamine or Ethanolamine solution	2491	8	53 (c)
Ethanol or Ethanol solution	1170	3	3 (b), 31 (c)

Name of substance or article	Substance Identification No. (UN No.)	Class	Item number and letter
Ethers, n.o.s.	3271	3	3 (b), 31 (c)
Ethion (pesticide), see Organophosphorus pesticides			
Ethoate-methyl (pesticide), see Organophosphorus pesticides			
Ethoprophos (pesticide), see Organophosphorus pesticides			
2-(n,n-Ethoxycarbonylphenylamino)-3-methoxy-4-(N-methyl-N-cyclohexylamino)-benzene diazonium zinc chloride, see Self-reactive solid, type D			
2-Ethoxyethanol	1171	3	31 (c)
2-Ethoxyethyl acetate	1172	3	31 (c)
Ethyl acetate	1173	3	3 (b)
Ethylacetylene, inhibited	2452	2	2 F
Ethyl acrylate, inhibited	1917	3	3 (b)
Ethyl alcohol	1170	3	3 (b), 31 (c)
Ethyl alcohol solution	1170	3	3 (b), 31 (c)
Ethylamine	1036	2	2 F
Ethylamine, aqueous solution with not less than 50% but not more than 70% ethylamine	2270	3	22 (b)
Ethyl amyl ketones	2271	3	31 (c)
N-Ethylaniline	2272	6.1	12 (c)
2-Ethylaniline	2273	6.1	12 (c)
Ethylbenzene	1175	3	3 (b)
N-Ethyl-N-benzylaniline	2274	6.1	12 (c)
N-Ethylbenzyltoluidines	2753	6.1	12 (c)
Ethyl borate	1176	3	3 (b)
Ethyl bromide	1891	6.1	15 (b)
Ethyl bromoacetate	1603	6.1	16 (b)
2-Ethylbutanol	2275	3	31 (c)
Ethylbutyl acetate	1177	3	31 (c)
N-Ethylbutylamine, see Flammable liquid, n.o.s.			
Ethyl butyl ether	1179	3	3 (b)
2-Ethylbutyraldehyde	1178	3	3 (b)
Ethyl butyrate	1180	3	31 (c)
Ethyl chloride	1037	2	2 F
Ethyl chloroacetate	1181	6.1	16 (b)
Ethyl chloroformate	1182	6.1	10 (a)
Ethyl 2-chloropropionate	2935	3	31 (c)
Ethyl chlorothioformate	2826	8	64 (b)
Ethyl crotonate	1862	3	3 (b)
Ethyl cyanoacetate	2666	6.1	12 (c)

Name of substance or article	Substance Identification No. (UN No.)	Class	Item number and letter
Ethyl 3,3-di-(tert-amylperoxy)butyrate, see Organic peroxide type D, liquid			
Ethyl 3,3-di-(tert-butylperoxy)butyrate, see Organic peroxide type D, solid			
Ethyl 3,3-di-(tert-butylperoxy)butyrate, see Organic peroxide type C, liquid			
Ethyldichloroarsine	1892	6.1	34 (a)
Ethyldichlorosilane	1183	4.3	1 (a)
Ethyldiphenylphosphine, see Toxic liquid organic, n.o.s.,			
Ethylene, acetylene and propylene mixture, refrigerated liquid containing at least 71.5% ethylene with not more than 22.5% acetylene and not more than 6% propylene	3138	2	3 F
Ethylene chlorohydrin	1135	6.1	16 (a)
Ethylene, compressed	1962	2	1 F
Ethylenediamine	1604	8	54 (b)
Ethylene dibromide	1605	6.1	15 (a)
Ethylene dibromide and methyl bromide mixture, liquid	1647	6.1	15 (a)
Ethylene dichloride	1184	3	16 (b)
Ethylene glycol diethyl ether	1153	3	31 (c)
Ethylene glycol monoethyl ether	1171	3	31 (c)
Ethylene glycol monoethyl ether acetate	1172	3	31 (c)
Ethylene glycol monomethyl ether	1188	3	31 (c)
Ethylene glycol monomethyl ether acetate	1189	3	31 (c)
Ethyleneimine, inhibited	1185	6.1	4
Ethylene oxide	1040	2	2 TF
Ethylene oxide and carbon dioxide mixture with not more than 9% ethylene oxide	1952	2	2 A
Ethylene oxide and carbon dioxide mixture with more than 87% ethylene oxide	3300	2	2 TF
Ethylene oxide and carbon dioxide mixture with more than 9% but not more than 87% ethylene oxide	1041	2	2 F
Ethylene oxide and chlorotetrafluoroethane mixture with not more than 8.8% ethylene oxide	3297	2	2 A
Ethylene oxide and dichlorodifluoromethane mixture with not more than 12.5% ethylene oxide	3070	2	2 A
Ethylene oxide and methyl formate mixtures	1953	2	1 TF
Ethylene oxide and pentafluoroethane mixture with not more than 7.9% ethylene oxide	3298	2	2 A
Ethylene oxide and propylene oxide mixture, with not more than 30% ethylene oxide	2983	3	17 (a)
Ethylene oxide and tetrafluoroethane mixture with not more than 5.6% ethylene oxide	3299	2	2 A

Name of substance or article	Substance Identification No. (UN No.)	Class	Item number and letter
Ethylene oxide with nitrogen up to a total pressure of 1 Mpa (10 bar) at 50 °C	1040	2	2 TF
Ethylene, refrigerated liquid	1038	2	3 F
Ethyl ether	1155	3	2 (a)
Ethyl fluid, see Motor fuel anti-knock mixture	1649	6.1	31 (a)
Ethyl fluoride	2453	2	2 F
Ethyl formate	1190	3	3 (b)
2-Ethyl hexaldehyde, see Octyl aldehydes, flammable			
2-Ethylhexylamine	2276	3	33 (c)
2-Ethylhexyl chloride, see Flammable liquid, n.o.s.			
2-Ethylhexyl chloroformate	2748	6.1	27 (b)
Ethylidene chloride	2362	3	3 (b)
Ethyl isobutyrate	2385	3	3 (b)
Ethyl isocyanate	2481	3	13
Ethyl isothiocyanate, see Toxic liquid, flammable, organic, n.o.s.			
Ethyl lactate	1192	3	31 (c)
Ethyl mercaptan	2363	3	2 (a)
Ethyl methacrylate	2277	3	3 (b)
Ethyl methyl ether	1039	2	2 F
Ethyl methyl ketone	1193	3	3 (b)
Ethyl nitrite solution	1194	3	15 (a)
Ethyl orthoformate	2524	3	31 (c)
Ethyl oxalate	2525	6.1	14 (c)
Ethylphenyldichlorosilane	2435	8	36 (b)
1-Ethylpiperidine	2386	3	23 (b)
Ethyl propionate	1195	3	3 (b)
Ethyl propyl ether	2615	3	3 (b)
2-Ethylthiophene, see Toxic liquid, flammable, organic, n.o.s.			
N-Ethyltoluidines	2754	6.1	12 (b)
Ethyltriacetoxysilane, see Corrosive liquid, acidic, organic, n.o.s.			
Ethyltrichlorosilane	1196	3	21 (b)
Explosive, blasting, type A	0081	1.1D	4
Explosive, blasting, type B	0082	1.1D	4
Explosive, blasting, type B	0331	1.5D	48
Explosive, blasting, type C	0083	1.1D	4
Explosive, blasting, type D	0084	1.1D	4
Explosive, blasting, type E	0241	1.1D	4
Explosive, blasting, type E	0332	1.5D	48

Name of substance or article	Substance Identification No. (UN No.)	Class	Item number and letter
Extracts, aromatic, liquid	1169	3	5 (a), (b), (c), 31 (c)
Extracts, flavouring, liquid	1197	3	5 (a), (b), (c), 31 (c)
Fenaminosulph (pesticide), see under Pesticide, etc.			
Fenaminphos (pesticide), see Organophosphorus pesticides			
Fenitrothion (pesticide), see Organophosphorus pesticides			
Fenpropathrin (pesticide), see under Pesticide, etc.			
Fensulfothion (pesticide), see Organophosphorus pesticides			
Fenthion (pesticide), see Organophosphorus pesticides			
Fentin acetate (pesticide), see Organotin pesticides			
Fentin hydroxide (pesticide), see Organotin pesticides			
Ferric arsenate	1606	6.1	51 (b)
Ferric arsenite	1607	6.1	51 (b)
Ferric chloride, anhydrous	1773	8	11 (c)
Ferric chloride hexahydrate: Not subject to ADR		8	11 (c), Note
Ferric chloride solution	2582	8	5 (c)
Ferric nitrate	1466	5.1	22 (c)
Ferricyanides: Not subject to ADR		6.1	41, Note
Ferrocerium	1323	4.1	13 (b)
Ferrocerium, stabilized against corrosion, with a minimum iron content of 10%: Not subject to ADR		4.1	13 (b) Note 1
Ferrocyanides: Not subject to ADR		6.1	41, Note
Ferrosilicon	1408	4.3	15 (c)
Ferrous arsenate	1608	6.1	51 (b)
Ferrous metal borings, shavings, turnings or cuttings	2793	4.2	12 (c)
Fertilizer ammoniating solution with free ammonia	1043	2	4 A
Fibres or fabrics animal or vegetable or synthetic, n.o.s., with oil	1373	4.2	3 (c)
Fibres or fabrics impregnated with weakly nitrated nitrocellulose, n.o.s.	1353	4.1	3 (c)
Films, nitrocellulose base, gelatin coated, except scrap	1324	4.1	3 (c)
Fire extinguisher charges, corrosive liquid	1774	8	82 (b)
Fire extinguishers, with compressed or liquefied gas	1044	2	6 A
Firelighters, solid with flammable liquid	2623	4.1	2 (c)
Fireworks	0333	1.1G	9
Fireworks	0334	1.2G	21
Fireworks	0335	1.3G	30
Fireworks	0336	1.4G	43
Fireworks	0337	1.4S	47
First aid kit	3316	9	36 (b), (c)
Fischer Tropsch gas	2600	2	1 TF

Name of substance or article	Substance Identification No. (UN No.)	Class	Item number and letter
Fish meal (fish scrap), stabilized: Not subject to ADR	2216	9	-
Fish meal (fish scrap), unstabilized	1374	4.2	2 (b)
Flammable liquid, corrosive, n.o.s.	2924	3	26 (a), (b), 33 (c)
Flammable liquid, n.o.s.	1993	3	1 (a), 2 (a), 2 (b), 3 (b), 5 (c), 31 (c)
Flammable liquid, toxic, corrosive, n.o.s.	3286	3	27 (a), (b)
Flammable liquid, toxic, n.o.s.	1992	3	19 (a), (b), 32 (c)
Flammable solid, corrosive, inorganic, n.o.s.	3180	4.1	17 (b), (c)
Flammable solid, corrosive, organic, n.o.s.	2925	4.1	8 (b), (c)
Flammable solid, inorganic, n.o.s.	3178	4.1	11 (b), (c)
Flammable solid, organic, molten, n.o.s.	3176	4.1	5
Flammable solid, organic, n.o.s.	1325	4.1	6 (b), (c)
Flammable solid, oxidizing, n.o.s.: Not to be accepted for carriage	3097	4.1	See marginal 2400 (11)
Flammable solid, toxic, inorganic, n.o.s.	3179	4.1	16 (b), (c)
Flammable solid, toxic, organic, n.o.s.	2926	4.1	7 (b), (c)
Flares, aerial	0093	1.3G	30
Flares, aerial	0403	1.4G	43
Flares, aerial	0404	1.4S	47
Flares, aerial	0420	1.1G	9
Flares, aerial	0421	1.2G	21
Flares, surface	0092	1.3G	30
Flares, surface	0418	1.1G	9
Flares, surface	0419	1.2G	21
Flash powder	0094	1.1G	8
Flash powder	0305	1.3G	29
Flowers of sulphur, see Sulphur			
Fluoracetamide (pesticide), see under Pesticide, etc.			
Fluorides, soluble in water, see Toxic solid, inorganic, n.o.s.			
Fluorine, compressed	1045	2	1 TOC
Fluoroacetic acid	2642	6.1	17 (a)
Fluoroanilines	2941	6.1	12 (c)
Fluorobenzene	2387	3	3 (b)
Fluoroboric acid	1775	8	8 (b)
Fluoroboric acid, aqueous solutions over 78% acid: Not to be accepted for carriage	1775	8	8 (b), Note
Fluorophosphoric acid, anhydrous	1776	8	8 (b)

Name of substance or article	Substance Identification No. (UN No.)	Class	Item number and letter
Fluorosilicates, n.o.s.	2856	6.1	64 (c)
Fluorosilicic acid	1778	8	8 (b)
Fluorosulphonic acid	1777	8	8 (a)
Fluorotoluenes	2388	3	3 (b)
Fonofos (pesticide), see Organophosphorus pesticides			
Formaldehyde, aqueous solutions with less than 5% formaldehyde: Not subject to ADR		8	63 (c), Note
Formaldehyde solution, flammable	1198	3	33 (c)
Formaldehyde solution with not less than 25% formaldehyde	2209	8	63 (c)
Formic acid	1779	8	32 (b)1.
Formothion (pesticide), see Organophosphorus pesticides			
N-Formyl-2-(nitromethylene) 1,3-perhydrothiazine', see Self-reactive solid, type D, temperature controlled			
Fracturing devices, explosive without detonator, for oil wells	0099	1.1D	5
Fuel, aviation, turbine engine	1863	3	1 (a), 2 (a), 2 (b), 3 (b), 31 (c)
Fulminates of mercury: Not to be accepted for carriage		6.1	52, Note 3
Fumaryl chloride	1780	8	35 (b)1.
Furan	2389	3	1 (a)
Furfural	1199	6.1	13 (b)
Furfuraldehydes	1199	6.1	13 (b)
Furfuryl alcohol	2874	6.1	14 (c)
Furfurylamine	2526	3	33 (c)
Furfuryl mercaptan, see Toxic liquid, flammable, organic, n.o.s.			
Fuse, igniter, tubular, metal clad	0103	1.4G	43
Fusel oil	1201	3	3 (b), 31 (c)
Fuse, non-detonating	0101	1.3G	30
Fuse, safety	0105	1.4S	47
Fuzes, detonating	0106	1.1B	1
Fuzes, detonating	0107	1.2B	13
Fuzes, detonating	0257	1.4B	35
Fuzes, detonating	0367	1.4S	47
Fuzes, detonating with protective features	0408	1.1D	5
Fuzes, detonating with protective features	0409	1.2D	17
Fuzes, detonating with protective features	0410	1.4D	39
Fuzes, igniting	0368	1.4S	47

Name of substance or article	Substance Identification No. (UN No.)	Class	Item number and letter
Fuzes, igniting	0316	1.3G	30
Fuzes, igniting	0317	1.4G	43
Gallium	2803	8	65 (c)
Gas cartridges, without a release device, non-refillable	2037	2	5
Gas drips, hydrocarbon, see Hydrocarbons, liquid			
Gas oil	1202	3	31 (c)
Gasoline	1203	3	3 (b)
Gas sample, non-pressurized, flammable, n.o.s., not refrigerated liquid	3167	2	7 F
Gas sample, non-pressurized, toxic, flammable, n.o.s., not refrigerated liquid	3168	2	7 TF
Gas sample, non-pressurized, toxic, n.o.s., not refrigerated liquid	3169	2	7 T
Gas, refrigerated liquid, flammable, n.o.s.	3312	2	3 F
Gas, refrigerated liquid, n.o.s.	3158	2	3 A
Gas, refrigerated liquid, oxidizing, n.o.s.	3311	2	3 O
Genetically modified micro-organisms	3245	9	13 (b)
Genetically modified organisms		9	14
Germane	2192	2	2 TF
Glycerol alpha-monochlorohydrin	2689	6.1	17 (c)
Glycidaldehyde	2622	3	17 (b)
Grenades, hand or rifle, with bursting charge	0284	1.1D	5
Grenades, hand or rifle, with bursting charge	0285	1.2D	17
Grenades, hand or rifle, with bursting charge	0292	1.1F	7
Grenades, hand or rifle, with bursting charge	0293	1.2F	19
Grenades, practice, hand or rifle	0110	1.4S	47
Grenades, practice, hand or rifle	0318	1.3G	30
Grenades, practice, hand or rifle	0372	1.2G	21
Grenades, practice, hand or rifle	0452	1.4G	43
Guanidine nitrate	1467	5.1	22 (c)
Guanyl nitrosaminoguanylidene hydrazine, wetted with not less than 30% water, by mass	0113	1.1A	01
Guanyl nitrosaminoguanyltetrazene (tetrazene), wetted with not less than 30% water, or mixture of alcohol and water, by mass	0114	1.1A	01
Gunpowder, see Black powder			
Hafnium powder, dry	2545	4.2	12 (a), (b), (c)
Hafnium powder, wetted with not less than 25% water	1326	4.1	13 (b)
Hay, straw or bhusa, wet, damp or contaminated with oil	1327	4.1	-
Heating oil, light	1202	3	31 (c)
Heavy hydrogen	1957	2	1 F
Helium, compressed	1046	2	1 A
Helium, refrigerated liquid,	1963	2	3 A

Name of substance or article	Substance Identification No. (UN No.)	Class	Item number and letter
Heptachlor (pesticide), see Organochlorine pesticides			
Heptafluorobutyric acid, see Corrosive liquid, acidic, organic, n.o.s.			
Heptafluoropropane	3296	2	2 A
n-Heptaldehyde	3056	3	31 (c)
Heptanes	1206	3	3 (b)
n-Heptene	2278	3	3 (b)
Heptenophos (pesticide), see Organophosphorus pesticides			
Hexachloroacetone	2661	6.1	17 (c)
Hexachlorobenzene	2729	6.1	15 (c)
Hexachlorobutadiene	2279	6.1	15 (c)
Hexachlorocyclopentadiene	2646	6.1	15 (a)
Hexachlorophene	2875	6.1	15 (c)
Hexadecyltrichlorosilane	1781	8	36 (b)
Hexadiene	2458	3	3 (b)
Hexaethyl tetraphosphate	1611	6.1	23 (b)
Hexaethyl tetraphosphate and compressed gas mixture	1612	2	1 T
Hexafluoroacetone	2420	2	2 TC
Hexafluoroacetone hydrate	2552	6.1	17 (b)
Hexafluoroethane, compressed	2193	2	1 A
Hexafluorophosphoric acid	1782	8	8 (b)
Hexafluoropropylene	1858	2	2 A
Hexaldehyde	1207	3	31 (c)
Hexamethylenediamine, solid	2280	8	52 (c)
Hexamethylenediamine, solution	1783	8	53 (b), (c)
Hexamethylene diisocyanate	2281	6.1	19 (b)
Hexamethyleneimine	2493	3	23 (b)
Hexamethylenetetramine	1328	4.1	6 (c)
3,3,6,6,9,9-Hexamethyl-1,2,4,5-tetraoxacyclononane, see Organic peroxide type B, solid			
3,3,6,6,9,9-Hexamethyl-1,2,4,5-tetraoxacyclononane, see Organic peroxide type D, liquid			
3,3,6,6,9,9-Hexamethyl-1,2,4,5-tetraoxacyclononane, see Organic peroxide type D, solid			
Hexanes	1208	3	3 (b)
Hexanitrodiphenylamine	0079	1.1D	4
Hexanitrostilbene	0392	1.1D	4
Hexanols	2282	3	31 (c)
1-Hexene	2370	3	3 (b)
Hexogen, see Cyclotrimethylenetrinitramine			
Hexolite (hexolite), dry or wetted with less than 15% water, by mass	0118	1.1D	4

Name of substance or article	Substance Identification No. (UN No.)	Class	Item number and letter
Hexotol, see Hexolite			
Hexotonal	0393	1.1D	4
Hexyl, see Hexanitrodiphenylamine			
Hexyltrichlorosilane	1784	8	36 (b)
HMX, see Cyclotetramethylenetetranitramine			
Hydrazine, anhydrous	2029	8	44 (a)
Hydrazine, aqueous solution with not more than 37% hydrazine by mass	3293	6.1	65 (c)
Hydrazine, aqueous solution with not less than 37% but not more than 64% hydrazine, by mass	2030	8	44 (b)
Hydrazine dihydrobromide, see Toxic solid, inorganic, n.o.s.			
Hydrazine dihydrochloride, see Toxic solid, inorganic, n.o.s.			
Hydrazine hydrate	2030	8	44 (b)
Hydrazine monohydrobromide, see Toxic solid, inorganic, n.o.s.			
Hydrazine monohydrochloride, see Toxic solid, inorganic, n.o.s.			
Hydrazine sulphate, see Toxic solid, inorganic, n.o.s.			
Hydriodic acid	1787	8	5 (b), (c)
Hydrobromic acid	1788	8	5 (b), (c)
Hydrocarbon gas mixture, compressed, n.o.s.	1964	2	1 F
Hydrocarbon gas mixture, liquefied, n.o.s.	1965	2	2 F
Hydrocarbon gas refills for small devices with release device	3150	2	6 F
Hydrocarbons, liquid, n.o.s.	3295	3	1 (a), 2 (a), (b), 3 (b), 31 (c)
Hydrochloric acid	1789	8	5 (b), (c)
Hydrocyanic acid and solutions, see Hydrogen cyanide and solutions			
Hydrofluoric acid solution	1790	8	
Hydrofluoric acid, anhydrous, see Hydrogen fluoride, anhydrous			
Hydrofluoric acid, aqueous solution, mixtures, with inorganic acids, see Corrosive liquid, acidic, inorganic, n.o.s.			
Hydrofluoric and sulphuric acid mixture	1786	8	7 (a)
Hydrogen and methane mixtures, compressed	2034	2	1 F
Hydrogen bromide, anhydrous	1048	2	2 TC
Hydrogen chloride, anhydrous	1050	2	2 TC
Hydrogen chloride, refrigerated liquid: Not to be accepted for carriage	2186	2	Note
Hydrogen, compressed	1049	2	1 F
Hydrogen cyanide, aqueous solution with not more than 20% hydrogen cyanide	1613	6.1	2
Hydrogen cyanide, solution in alcohol with not more than 45% hydrogen cyanide	3294	6.1	2
Hydrogen cyanide, stabilized containing less than 3% water	1051	6.1	1

Name of substance or article	Substance Identification No. (UN No.)	Class	Item number and letter
Hydrogen cyanide, stabilized, containing less than 3% water and absorbed in a porous inert material	1614	6.1	1
Hydrogendifluorides, n.o.s.	1740	8	9 (b), (c)
Hydrogen fluoride	1052	8	6
Hydrogen iodide, anhydrous	2197	2	2 TC
Hydrogen peroxide and peroxyacetic acid mixture, stabilized	3149	5.1	1 (b)
Hydrogen peroxide, aqueous solution with less than 8% hydrogen peroxide: Not subject to ADR		5.1	1 (c) Note
Hydrogen peroxide, aqueous solution with not less than 20% but not more than 60% hydrogen peroxide	2014	5.1	1 (b)
Hydrogen peroxide, aqueous solution with not less than 8% but less than 20% hydrogen peroxide	2984	5.1	1 (c)
Hydrogen peroxide, aqueous solution, stabilized with more than 60% hydrogen peroxide	2015	5.1	1 (a)
Hydrogen peroxide, stabilized	2015	5.1	1 (a)
Hydrogen, refrigerated liquid	1966	2	3 F
Hydrogen selenide, anhydrous	2202	2	2 TF
Hydrogen sulphates, aqueous solution	2837	8	1 (b), (c)
Hydrogen sulphide	1053	2	2 TF
Hydrogen sulphides, aqueous solutions, see Caustic alkali liquid, n.o.s.			
Hydroquinone	2662	6.1	14 (c)
2-(2-Hydroxyethoxy)-1-(pyrrolidin-1-yl)benzene-4-diazonium zinc chloride, see Self-reactive solid, type D, temperature controlled			
3-(2-Hydroxyethoxy)-4-pyrrolidin-1-yl-benzenediazonium zinc chloride, see Self-reactive solid, type D, temperature controlled			
Hydroxylamine sulphate	2865	8	16 (c)
Hypochlorites, inorganic, n.o.s.	3212	5.1	15 (b)
Hypochlorite solution containing not more than 5% available chlorine: Not subject to ADR		8	61 (c), Note
Hypochlorite solution	1791	8	61 (b), (c)
Igniters	0121	1.1G.	9
Igniters	0314	1.2G	21
Igniters	0315	1.3G	30
Igniters	0325	1.4G	43
Igniters	0454	1.4S	47
Imazalil (pesticide), see under Pesticide, etc.			
3,3'-Iminodipropylamine	2269	8	53 (c)
Infectious substance, affecting animals	2900	6.2	1, 2, 3 (b)
Infectious substance, affecting humans	2814	6.2	1, 2 or 3 (b)
Ink, printing, flammable	1210	3	5 (a), (b), (c), 31 (c) (See Note to Section E)

Name of substance or article	Substance Identification No. (UN No.)	Class	Item number and letter
Insecticide gas, n.o.s.	1968	2	2 A
Insecticide gas, toxic, n.o.s.	1967	2	2 T
Iodine monochloride	1792	8	12 (b)
Iodine pentafluoride	2495	5.1	5
2-Iodobutane	2390	3	3 (b)
Iodomethylpropanes	2391	3	3 (b)
Iodopropanes	2392	3	31 (c)
Ioxynil (pesticide), see under Pesticide, etc.			
Iprobenfos (pesticide), see Organophosphorus pesticides			
Iron (III) chloride, anhydrous	1773	8	11 (c)
Iron chloride solution	2582	8	5 (c)
Iron oxide, spent	1376	4.2	16 (c)
Iron pentacarbonyl	1994	6.1	3
Iron sponge, spent	1376	4.2	16 (c)
2-Isoamylene	2561	3	1 (a)
Isoamyl formate, see Amyl formates			
Isobenzane (pesticide), see Organochlorine pesticides			
Isobutane	1969	2	2 F
Isobutanol	1212	3	31 (c)
Isobutene	1055	2	2 F
Isobutyl acetate	1213	3	3 (b)
Isobutyl acrylate, inhibited	2527	3	31 (c)
Isobutyl alcohol	1212	3	31 (c)
Isobutyl aldehyde	2045	3	3 (b)
Isobutylamine	1214	3	22 (b)
Isobutylene	1055	2	2 F
Isobutyl formate	2393	3	3 (b)
Isobutyl isobutyrate	2528	3	31 (c)
Isobutyl isocyanate	2486	3	14 (b)
Isobutyl methacrylate inhibited	2283	3	31 (c)
Isobutyl propionate	2394	3	3 (b)
Isobutyraldehyde	2045	3	3 (b)
Isobutyric acid	2529	3	33 (c)
Isobutyric anhydride	2530	3	33 (c)
Isobutyronitrile	2284	3	11 (b)
Isobutyryl chloride	2395	3	25 (b)
Isocyanates, flammable, toxic, n.o.s. or Isocyanate solution, flammable, toxic, n.o.s	2478	3	14 (b), 32 (c)

Name of substance or article	Substance Identification No. (UN No.)	Class	Item number and letter
Isocyanates, toxic, flammable, n.o.s. or Isocyanate solution, toxic, flammable, n.o.s.	3080	6.1	18 (b)
Isocyanates, toxic, n.o.s. or Isocyanate solution, toxic, n.o.s.	2206	6.1	19 (b), (c)
Isocyanatobenzotrifluorides	2285	6.1	18 (b)
Isododecane	2286	3	31 (c)
Isodrin (pesticide), see Organochlorine pesticides			
Isofenphos (pesticide), see Organophosphorus pesticides			
Isoheptene	2287	3	3 (b)
Isohexene	2288	3	3 (b)
Isolan (pesticide), see Carbamate pesticides			
Isooctane, see Octanes	1262	3	3 (b)
Isooctene	1216	3	3 (b)
Isooctyl acid phosphate, see Corrosive liquid, acidic, organic, n.o.s.			
Isopentane	1265	3	1 (a)
Isopentenes	2371	3	1 (a)
Isophoronediamine	2289	8	53 (c)
Isophorone diisocyanate	2290	6.1	19 (c)
Isophthaloyl chloride, see Corrosive solid, acidic, organic, n.o.s.			
Isoprene, inhibited	1218	3	2 (a)
Isoprocarb (pesticide), see Carbamate pesticides			
Isopropanol	1219	3	3 (b)
Isopropenyl acetate	2403	3	3 (b)
Isopropenylbenzene	2303	3	31 (c)
Isopropyl acetate	1220	3	3 (b)
Isopropyl acid phosphate	1793	8	38 (c)
Isopropyl alcohol	1219	3	3 (b)
Isopropylamine	1221	3	22 (a)
Isopropylbenzene	1918	3	31 (c)
Isopropyl butyrate	2405	3	31 (c)
Isopropyl chloride, see 2-Chloropropane			
Isopropyl chloroacetate	2947	3	31 (c)
Isopropyl chloroformate	2407	6.1	10 (a)
Isopropyl 2-chloropropionate	2934	3	31 (c)
Isopropylcumyl hydroperoxide, see Organic peroxide type F, liquid			
Isopropylethylene	2561	3	1 (a)
Isopropyl isobutyrate	2406	3	3 (b)
Isopropyl isocyanate	2483	3	14 (a)
Isopropyl isothiocyanate, see Flammable liquid, toxic, n.o.s.			
Isopropyl nitrate	1222	3	3 (b)

Name of substance or article	Substance Identification No. (UN No.)	Class	Item number and letter
Isopropyl propionate	2409	3	3 (b)
Isosorbide dinitrate mixture	2907	4.1	23 (b)
Isosorbide-5-mononitrate	3251	4.1	26 (c)
Isothioate (pesticide), see Organophosphorus pesticides			
Isothiocyanate solutions, flash-point below 23 °C, see Flammable liquid, toxic, n.o.s.			
Isoxathion (pesticide), see Organophosphorus pesticides			
Jet perforating guns, charged, oil well, without detonator	0124	1.1D	5
Jet perforating guns, charged, oil well, without detonator	0494	1.4D	39
Kelevan (pesticide), see under Pesticide, etc.			
Kerosene	1223	3	31 (c)
Ketones, liquid, n.o.s.	1224	3	2 (b), 3 (b), 31 (c)
Krypton, compressed	1056	2	1 A
Krypton, refrigerated liquid	1970	2	3 A
Lacquer, nitrocellulose, see Nitrocellulose solution			
Lactonitrile, see Toxic liquid, organic, n.o.s.			
Lead acetate	1616	6.1	62 (c)
Lead alkyls, mixtures, see Motor fuel anti-knock mixture			
Lead arsenates	1617	6.1	51 (b)
Lead arsenites	1618	6.1	51 (b)
Lead, ashes of, see Lead compound, soluble, n.o.s.			
Lead azide, wetted with not less than 20% water, or mixture of alcohol and water, by mass	0129	1.1A	01
Lead chloride, see Lead compound, soluble, n.o.s.			
Lead chromate, see Lead compound, soluble, n.o.s.			
Lead compound, soluble, n.o.s.	2291	6.1	62 (c)
Lead compounds, residues, see Lead compound, soluble, n.o.s.			
Lead cyanide	1620	6.1	41 (b)
Lead dioxide	1872	5.1	29 (c)
Lead nitrate	1469	5.1	29 (b)
Lead perchlorate	1470	5.1	29 (b)
Lead phosphite dibasic	2989	4.1	11 (b), (c)
Lead salts, see Lead compound, soluble, n.o.s.			
Lead sludge, with less than 3% free sulphuric acid, see Lead compound, soluble, n.o.s.			
Lead styphnate, wetted with not less than 20% water, or mixture of alcohol and water, by mass	0130	1.1A	01
Lead sulphate with 3% or more free acid	1794	8	1 (b)
Lead tetraethyl, see Motor fuel anti-knock mixture			

Name of substance or article	Substance Identification No. (UN No.)	Class	Item number and letter
Lead tetramethyl, see Motor fuel anti-knock mixture			
Lead trinitroresorcinate, see Lead styphnate			
Life-saving appliances, not self-inflating,	3072	9	7
Life-saving appliances, self-inflating, such as aircraft evacuation chutes and aircraft survival kits	2990	9	6
Lighter refills (cigarettes) containing flammable gas	1057	2	6 F
Lighters containing flammable gas	1057	2	6 F
Lighters, fuse	0131	1.4S	47
Lignite tar oil, see Tars, liquid			
Limonene, inactive	2052	3	31 (c)
Lindane (pesticide), see Organochlorine pesticides			
Liquefied gas, flammable, n.o.s.	3161	2	2 F
Liquefied gas, n.o.s.	3163	2	2 A
Liquefied gas, oxidizing, n.o.s.	3157	2	2 O
Liquefied gas, toxic, corrosive, n.o.s.	3308	2	2 TC
Liquefied gas, toxic, flammable, corrosive, n.o.s.	3309	2	2 TFC
Liquefied gas, toxic, flammable, n.o.s.	3160	2	2 TF
Liquefied gas, toxic, n.o.s.	3162	2	2 T
Liquefied gas, toxic, oxidizing, corrosive, n.o.s.	3310	2	2 TOC
Liquefied gas, toxic, oxidizing, n.o.s.	3307	2	2 TO
Liquefied gases, non-flammable, charged with nitrogen, carbon dioxide or air	1058	2	2 A
Liquefied natural gas	1972	2	3 F
Liquefied petroleum gases	1075	2	2 F
Lithium	1415	4.3	11 (a)
Lithium alkyls	2445	4.2	31 (a)
Lithium aluminium hydride	1410	4.3	16 (a)
Lithium aluminium hydride, ethereal	1411	4.3	16 (a)
Lithium batteries	3090	9	5
Lithium batteries contained in or packed with equipment	3091	9	5
Lithium borohydride	1413	4.3	16 (a)
Lithium ferrosilicon	2830	4.3	12 (b)
Lithium hydride	1414	4.3	16 (a)
Lithium hydride, fused, solid	2805	4.3	16 (b)
Lithium hydroxide monohydrate	2680	8	41 (b)
Lithium hydroxide solution	2679	8	42 (b), (c)
Lithium hypochlorite, dry	1471	5.1	15 (b)
Lithium hypochlorite, mixture	1471	5.1	15 (b)
Lithium nitrate	2722	5.1	22 (c)

Name of substance or article	Substance Identification No. (UN No.)	Class	Item number and letter
Lithium nitride	2806	4.3	17 (a)
Lithium peroxide	1472	5.1	25 (b)
Lithium silicon	1417	4.3	12 (b)
LNG	1972	2	3 F
London purple	1621	6.1	51 (b)
London purple (pesticide), see Arsenical pesticides			
LPG	1075	2	2 F
Lye	1823	8	41 (b)
Magnesium alkyls	3053	4.2	31 (a)
Magnesium alloys, powder	1418	4.3	14 (b)
Magnesium alloys with more than 50% magnesium pellets, turnings or ribbons	1869	4.1	13 (c)
Magnesium aluminium phosphide	1419	4.3	18 (a)
Magnesium arsenate	1622	6.1	51 (b)
Magnesium bromate	1473	5.1	16 (b)
Magnesium chlorate	2723	5.1	11 (b)
Magnesium diamide	2004	4.2	16 (b)
Magnesium diphenyl	2005	4.2	31 (a)
Magnesium fluorosilicate	2853	6.1	64 (c)
Magnesium granules, coated	2950	4.3	11 (c)
Magnesium hydride	2010	4.3	16 (a)
Magnesium in pellets, turnings or ribbons	1869	4.1	13 (c)
Magnesium nitrate	1474	5.1	22 (c)
Magnesium perchlorate	1475	5.1	13 (b)
Magnesium peroxide	1476	5.1	25 (b)
Magnesium phosphide	2011	4.3	18 (a)
Magnesium powder	1418	4.3	14 (a), (b), (c)
Magnesium silicide	2624	4.3	12 (b)
Magnetized material: Not subject to ADR	2807	9	-
Maleic anhydride	2215	8	31 (c)
Malononitrile	2647	6.1	12 (b)
Maneb	2210	4.2	16 (c)
Maneb preparation	2210	4.2	16 (c)
Maneb preparation, stabilized	2968	4.3	20 (c)
Maneb, stabilized	2968	4.3	20 (c)
Manganese catalyst, dry, see Metal catalyst, dry			
Manganese catalyst, wetted, see Metal catalyst, wetted			
Manganese ethylene 1,2-bis(dithiocarbamate), see Maneb and Maneb, stabilized			

Name of substance or article	Substance Identification No. (UN No.)	Class	Item number and letter
Manganese nitrate	2724	5.1	22 (c)
Manganese resinate	1330	4.1	12 (c)
Mannitol hexanitrate, wetted with not less than 40% water, or mixture of alcohol and water, by mass	0133	1.1D	4
Matches, fusee	2254	4.1	2 (c)
Matches, safety	1944	4.1	2 (c)
Matches, 'strike anywhere'	1331	4.1	2 (c)
Matches, wax, 'vesta'	1945	4.1	2 (c)
Medicine, liquid, flammable, toxic, n.o.s.	3248	3	19 (b), 32 (c)
Medicine, liquid, toxic, n.o.s.	1851	6.1	90 (b), (c)
Medicine, solid, toxic, n.o.s.	3249	6.1	90 (b), (c)
Medinoterb, see Substituted nitrophenol pesticides			
p-Menthyl hydroperoxide, see Organic peroxide type D, liquid			
p-Menthyl hydroperoxide, see Organic peroxide type F, liquid			
Mephosfolan (pesticide), see Organophosphorus pesticides			
Mercaptan mixture, liquid, flammable toxic, n.o.s.	1228	3	18 (b), 32 (c)
Mercaptans, liquid, flammable, toxic, n.o.s.	1228	3	18 (b), 32 (c)
Mercaptans, liquid, toxic, flammable, n.o.s. or Mercaptan mixture, liquid, toxic, flammable, n.o.s.	3071	6.1	20 (b)
Mercapto-dimethur (pesticide), see Carbamate pesticides			
5-Mercaptotetrazol-1-acetic acid	0448	1.4C	36
Mercuric arsenate	1623	6.1	51 (b)
Mercuric chloride	1624	6.1	52 (b)
Mercuric chloride (pesticide), see Mercury based pesticides			
Mercuric nitrate	1625	6.1	52 (b)
Mercuric potassium cyanide	1626	6.1	41 (a)
Mercurous chloride, see Environmentally hazardous, solid, n.o.s.			
Mercurous nitrate	1627	6.1	52 (b)
Mercury	2809	8	66 (c)
Mercury acetate	1629	6.1	52 (b)
Mercury ammonium chloride	1630	6.1	52 (b)
Mercury based pesticide, liquid, flammable, toxic, flash-point less than 23 °C	2778	3	41 (a), (b)
Mercury based pesticide, liquid, toxic	3012	6.1	71 (a), (b), (c)
Mercury based pesticide, liquid, toxic, flammable, flash point not less than 23 °C	3011	6.1	72 (a), (b), (c)
Mercury based pesticide, solid, toxic	2777	6.1	73 (a), (b), (c)
Mercury benzoate	1631	6.1	52 (b)
Mercury bromides	1634	6.1	52 (b)
Mercury compound, liquid, n.o.s.	2024	6.1	52 (a), (b), (c)

Name of substance or article	Substance Identification No. (UN No.)	Class	Item number and letter
Mercury compound, solid, n.o.s.	2025	6.1	52 (a), (b), (c)
Mercury cyanide	1636	6.1	41 (b)
Mercury fulminate, wetted with not less than 20% water, or mixture of alcohol and water, by mass	0135	1.1A	01
Mercury gluconate	1637	6.1	52 (b)
Mercury iodide	1638	6.1	52 (b)
Mercury nucleate	1639	6.1	52 (b)
Mercury oleate	1640	6.1	52 (b)
Mercury oxide	1641	6.1	52 (b)
Mercury oxide (pesticide), see Mercury based pesticides			
Mercury oxycyanide, desensitized	1642	6.1	41 (b)
Mercury potassium iodide	1643	6.1	52 (b)
Mercury salicylate	1644	6.1	52 (b)
Mercury sulphate	1645	6.1	52 (b)
Mercury thiocyanate	1646	6.1	52 (b)
Mesitylene	2325	3	31 (c)
Mesityl oxide	1229	3	31 (c)
Metal alkyl halides, n.o.s. or metal aryl halides, n.o.s.	3049	4.2	32 (a)
Metal alkyl hydrides, n.o.s. or metal aryl hydrides, n.o.s.	3050	4.2	32 (a)
Metal alkyls, n.o.s. or metal aryls, n.o.s.	2003	4.2	31 (a)
Metal carbonyls, n.o.s.	3281	6.1	36 (a), (b), (c)
Metal catalyst, dry	2881	4.2	12 (a), (b), (c)
Metal catalyst, wetted	1378	4.2	12 (b)
Metaldehyde	1332	4.1	6 (c)
Metal hydrides, flammable, n.o.s.	3182	4.1	14 (b), (c)
Metal hydrides, water-reactive, n.o.s.	1409	4.3	16 (a), (b)
Metal powder, flammable, n.o.s.	3089	4.1	13 (b), (c)
Metal powder, self-heating, n.o.s.	3189	4.2	16 (b), (c)
Metal salts of organic compounds, flammable, n.o.s.	3181	4.1	12 (b), (c)
Metallic substance, water-reactive, n.o.s.	3208	4.3	13 (a), (b), (c)
Metallic substance, water-reactive, self-heating, n.o.s.	3209	4.3	14 (a), (b), (c)
Metam-sodium (pesticide), see Dithiocarbamate pesticides			
Methacrylaldehyde, inhibited	2396	3	17 (b)
Methacrylic acid, inhibited	2531	8	32 (c)
Methacrylonitrile, inhibited	3079	3	11 (a)
Methallyl alcohol	2614	3	31 (c)
Methamidophos (pesticide), see Organophosphorus pesticides			
Methane and hydrogen mixture	2034	2	1 F
Methane, compressed	1971	2	1 F

Name of substance or article	Substance Identification No. (UN No.)	Class	Item number and letter
Methane, refrigerated liquid	1972	2	3 F
Methanesulphonic acid, see Alkyl sulphonic acids			
Methanesulphonyl chloride	3246	6.1	27 (a)
Methanol	1230	3	17 (b)
Methasulfocarb (pesticide), see Carbamate pesticides			
Methidathion (pesticide), see Organophosphorus pesticides			
Methomyl (pesticide), see Carbamate pesticides			
2-Methoxyethanol	1188	3	31 (c)
Methoxymethyl isocyanate	2605	3	14 (a)
4-Methoxy-4-methylpentan-2-one	2293	3	31 (c)
1-Methoxy-2-propanol	3092	3	31 (c)
Methoxypropionitrile, see Toxic liquid, organic, n.o.s.			
Methyl acetate	1231	3	3 (b)
Methyl acetylene and propadiene mixture, stabilized	1060	2	2 F
Methyl acrylate inhibited	1919	3	3 (b)
Methylal	1234	3	2 (b)
Methyl alcohol	1230	3	17 (b)
Methylallyl alcohol	2614	3	31 (c)
Methylallyl chloride	2554	3	3 (b)
Methylamine, anhydrous	1061	2	2 F
Methylamine, aqueous solution	1235	3	22 (b)
2-(n,n-Methylaminoethylcarbonyl)-4-(3,4-dimethylphenylsulphonyl) benzene diazonium hydrogen sulphate, see Self-reactive solid, type D, temperature controlled			
Methylamyl acetate	1233	3	31 (c)
Methylamyl alcohol	2053	3	31 (c)
N-Methylaniline	2294	6.1	12 (c)
4-Methylbenzenesulphonylhydrazide, see Self-reactive solid, type D			
alpha-Methylbenzyl alcohol	2937	6.1	14 (c)
Methyl bromide	1062	2	2 T
Methyl bromide and chloropicrin mixture	1581	2	2 T
Methyl bromide and ethylene dibromide, gas mixtures	1953	2	1 TF
Methyl bromide and ethylene dibromide, liquid mixtures	1647	6.1	15 (a)
Methyl bromoacetate	2643	6.1	17 (b)
3-Methylbutan-2-one	2397	3	3 (b)
2-Methyl-1-butene	2459	3	1 (a)
3-Methyl-1-butene	2561	3	1 (a)
2-Methyl-2-butene	2460	3	2 (b)
N-Methylbutylamine	2945	3	22 (b)

Name of substance or article	Substance Identification No. (UN No.)	Class	Item number and letter
Methyl tert-butyl ether	2398	3	3 (b)
Methyl butyrate	1237	3	3 (b)
Methyl chloride and chloropicrin mixture	1582	2	2 T
Methyl chloride and methylene chloride mixture	1912	2	2 F
Methyl chloride	1063	2	2 F
Methyl chloroacetate	2295	6.1	16 (a)
Methyl chloroformate	1238	6.1	10 (a)
Methyl chloromethyl ether	1239	6.1	9 (a)
Methyl 2-chloropropionate	2933	3	31 (c)
Methylchlorosilane	2534	2	2 TFC
Methyl chlorothioformate, see Flammable liquid, toxic, n.o.s.			
Methyl cyanide	1648	3	3 (b)
Methylcyclohexane	2296	3	3 (b)
Methylcyclohexanols	2617	3	31 (c)
Methylcyclohexanone	2297	3	31 (c)
Methylcyclohexanone peroxide(s), see Organic peroxide type D, liquid, temperature controlled			
Methylcyclopentane	2298	3	3 (b)
Methyl dichloroacetate	2299	6.1	17 (c)
Methyldichlorosilane	1242	4.3	1 (a)
Methylene chloride	1593	6.1	15 (c)
Methylene chloride and methyl chloride mixture	1912	2	2 F
Methyl ethyl ketone	1193	3	3 (b)
Methyl ethyl ketone peroxide(s), see Organic peroxide type B, liquid			
Methyl ethyl ketone peroxide(s), see Organic peroxide type D, liquid			
Methyl ethyl ketone peroxide(s), see Organic peroxide type E, liquid			
2-Methyl-5-ethylpyridine	2300	6.1	12 (c)
Methyl fluoride	2454	2	2 F
Methyl formate	1243	3	1 (a)
2-Methylfuran	2301	3	3 (b)
2-Methyl-2-heptanethiol	3023	6.1	20 (a)
5-Methylhexan-2-one	2302	3	31 (c)
Methylhydrazine	1244	6.1	7 (a)1.
Methyl iodide	2644	6.1	15 (a)
Methyl isobutyl carbinol	2053	3	31 (c)
Methyl isobutyl ketone	1245	3	3 (b)
Methyl isobutyl ketone peroxide(s), see Organic peroxide type D, liquid			
Methyl isocyanate	2480	6.1	5
Methyl isopropenyl ketone, inhibited	1246	3	3 (b)

Name of substance or article	Substance Identification No. (UN No.)	Class	Item number and letter
Methyl isopropyl benzenes	2046	3	31 (c)
Methyl isopropyl ether, see Flammable liquid, n.o.s.			
Methyl isothiocyanate	2477	6.1	20 (a)
Methyl isovalerate	2400	3	3 (b)
Methyl magnesium bromide in ethyl ether	1928	4.3	3 (a)
Methyl mercaptan	1064	2	2 TF
Methyl methacrylate monomer, inhibited	1247	3	3 (b)
Methylmorpholine	2535	3	23 (b)
Methyl nitrite: Not to be accepted for carriage	2455	2	Note
Methyl orthosilicate	2606	6.1	8 (a)
Methylpentadiene	2461	3	3 (b)
2-Methylpentan-2-ol	2560	3	31 (c)
3-Methyl-2-pentene-4-yne-1-ol	2705	8	66 (b)
Methylphenyldichlorosilane	2437	8	36 (b)
1-Methylpiperidine	2399	3	23 (b)
Methyl propionate	1248	3	3 (b)
Methyl propyl ether	2612	3	2 (b)
Methyl propyl ketone	1249	3	3 (b)
Methylpyridines	2313	3	31 (c)
3-Methyl-4(pyrrolidin-1-yl)benzenediazonium tetrafluoroborate, see Self-reactive solid, type C, temperature controlled			
Methylsilane	1954	2	1 F
Methyltetrahydrofuran	2536	3	3 (b)
Methyl trichloroacetate	2533	6.1	17 (c)
Methyltrichlorosilane	1250	3	21 (a)
Methyltrithion (pesticide), see Organophosphorus pesticides			
alpha-Methylvaleraldehyde	2367	3	3 (b)
Methyl vinyl ether, inhibited	1087	2	2 F
Methyl vinyl ketone, stabilized	1251	6.1	8 (a)1.
Mevinphos (pesticide), see Organophosphorus pesticides			
Mexacarbate (pesticide), see Carbamate pesticides			
Mines with bursting charge	0136	1.1F	7
Mines with bursting charge	0137	1.1D	5
Mines with bursting charge	0138	1.2D	17
Mines with bursting charge	0294	1.2F	19
Mirex (pesticide), see Organochlorine pesticides			
Mixtures of 1,3-butadiene and hydrocarbons, inhibited	1010	2	2 F
Mobam (pesticide), see Carbamate pesticides			
Molybdenum pentachloride	2508	8	11 (c)

Name of substance or article	Substance Identification No. (UN No.)	Class	Item number and letter
Molybdenum trioxide, see Toxic solid, inorganic, n.o.s.			
Monoalkyl tin chlorides, see Organotin compound, liquid, n.o.s.			
Monocrotophos (pesticide), see Organophosphorus pesticides			
Mononitroanilines, see Nitroanilines (o-,m-,p-)			
Mononitrotoluenes, see Nitrotoluenes (o-,m-,p-)			
Morpholine	2054	3	31 (c)
Motor fuel anti-knock mixture	1649	6.1	31 (a)
Motor fuel, in tanks of vehicles: Not subject to ADR		3	See marginal 2301a
Motor spirit	1203	3	3 (b)
Muritan (pesticide), see Carbamate pesticides			
Mysorite	2212	9	1 (b)
Nabam (pesticide), see Dithiocarbamate pesticides			
Naled (pesticide), see Organophosphorus pesticides			
Naphthalene, molten	2304	4.1	5
Naphthalene, refined	1334	4.1	6 (c)
Naphtha, petroleum, see Petroleum distillates, n.o.s.			
Naphtha, see Petroleum distillates, n.o.s.			
Naphtha, solvent, see Petroleum distillates, n.o.s.			
alpha-Naphthylamine	2077	6.1	12 (c)
beta-Naphthylamine	1650	6.1	12 (b)
alpha-Naphthyl isocyanate, see Isocyanates, toxic, n.o.s. or Isocyanate solution, toxic, n.o.s.			
Naphthylthiourea	1651	6.1	21 (b)
Naphthylurea	1652	6.1	12 (b)
Natural gas, compressed	1971	2	1 F
Natural gas, condensation products, see Petroleum products			
Natural gasoline, see Motor spirit			
Natural gas, refrigerated liquid	1972	2	3 F
Neon, compressed	1065	2	1 A
Neon, refrigerated liquid	1913	2	3 A
Nickel carbonyl	1259	6.1	3
Nickel catalyst, dry, see Metal catalyst, dry			
Nickel catalyst, wetted, see Metal catalyst, wetted			
Nickel cyanide	1653	6.1	41 (b)
Nickel nitrate	2725	5.1	22 (c)
Nickel nitrite	2726	5.1	23 (c)
Nickel tetracarbonyl	1259	6.1	3
Nicotine	1654	6.1	90 (b)

Name of substance or article	Substance Identification No. (UN No.)	Class	Item number and letter
Nicotine compound, liquid, n.o.s. or Nicotine preparation, liquid, n.o.s.	3144	6.1	90 (a), (b), (c)
Nicotine compound, solid, n.o.s. or Nicotine preparation, solid, n.o.s.	1655	6.1	90 (a), (b), (c)
Nicotine hydrochloride or nicotine hydrochloride solution	1656	6.1	90 (b)
Nicotine preparations (pesticide), see under Pesticide, etc			
Nicotine salicylate	1657	6.1	90 (b)
Nicotine sulphate, solid or solution	1658	6.1	90 (b)
Nicotine tartrate	1659	6.1	90 (b)
Nitrates, inorganic, aqueous solution, n.o.s.	3218	5.1	22 (b), (c)
Nitrates, inorganic, n.o.s.	1477	5.1	22 (b), (c)
Nitrating acid mixture	1796	8	3 (a), (b)
Nitrating acid mixture, spent	1826	8	3 (a), (b)
Nitric acid, mixtures, with acetic acid and phosphoric acid, see Corrosive liquid, acidic, inorganic, n.o.s			
Nitric acid, mixtures with hydrochloric acid: Not to be accepted for carriage		8	3, Note 1
Nitric acid, other than red fuming	2031	8	2 (a)1., (b)
Nitric acid, red fuming	2032	8	2 (a)2.
Nitric oxide and dinitrogen tetroxide mixture (nitric oxide and nitrogen dioxide mixture)	1975	2	2 TOC
Nitric oxide, compressed	1660	2	1 TOC
Nitriles, flammable, toxic, n.o.s.	3273	3	11 (a), (b)
Nitriles, toxic, flammable, n.o.s.	3275	6.1	11 (a), (b)
Nitriles, toxic, n.o.s.	3276	6.1	12 (a), (b), (c)
Nitrites, inorganic, aqueous solution, n.o.s.	3219	5.1	23 (b), (c)
Nitrites, inorganic, n.o.s.	2627	5.1	23 (b)
Nitro urea	0147	1.1D	4
3-Nitro-4-chlorobenzotrifluoride	2307	6.1	12 (b)
Nitroanilines (o-, m-, p-)	1661	6.1	12 (b)
Nitroanisole	2730	6.1	12 (c)
Nitrobenzene	1662	6.1	12 (b)
Nitrobenzenesulphonic acid	2305	8	34 (b)
Nitrobenzenesulphonyl chloride, see Corrosive solid, acidic, organic, n.o.s.			
5-Nitrobenzotriazol	0385	1.1D	4
Nitrobenzotrifluorides	2306	6.1	12 (b)
p-Nitrobenzoyl chloride, see Corrosive solid, acidic, organic, n.o.s.			
Nitrobenzyl bromide, see Toxic solid, organic, n.o.s.			
Nitrobromobenzene	2732	6.1	12 (c)
Nitrocellulose, dry or wetted with less than 25% water (or alcohol), by mass	0340	1.1D	4

Name of substance or article	Substance Identification No. (UN No.)	Class	Item number and letter
Nitrocellulose membrane filters	3270	4.1	3 (b)
Nitrocellulose, plasticized with not less than 18% plasticizer, by mass	0343	1.3C	26
Nitrocellulose solution, flammable, with not more than 12.6% nitrogen, by mass, and not more than 55% nitrocellulose	2059	3	4 (a), (b), 34 (c)
Nitrocellulose, wetted with not less than 25% alcohol, by mass	0342	1.3C	26
Nitrocellulose with alcohol not less than 25% alcohol, by mass, not more than 12.6% nitrogen, by dry mass	2556	4.1	24 (b)
Nitrocellulose with or without plasticizer and with or without pigment	2557	4.1	24 (b)
Nitrocellulose with water (not less than 25% water, by mass)	2555	4.1	24 (b)
Nitrocellulose, unmodified or plasticized with less than 18% plasticizing substance, by mass	0341	1.1D	4
Nitrocresols	2446	6.1	12 (c)
Nitroethane	2842	3	31 (c)
Nitrogen, compressed	1066	2	1 A
Nitrogen dioxide	1067	2	2 TOC
Nitrogen mixture with rare gases	1981	2	1 A
Nitrogen monoxide	1660	2	1 TOC
Nitrogen peroxide	1067	2	2 TOC
Nitrogen, refrigerated liquid	1977	2	3 A
Nitrogen tetroxide	1067	2	2 TOC
Nitrogen trifluoride, compressed	2451	2	1 TO
Nitrogen trioxide: Not to be accepted for carriage	2421	2	Note
Nitroglycerin, desensitized with not less than 40% non-volatile water-insoluble phlegmatizer, by mass	0143	1.1D	4
Nitroglycerin mixture with more than 2% but not more than 10% nitroglycerin, by mass, desensitized	3319	4.1	13 (b) Note 2
Nitroglycerin solution in alcohol with more than 1% but not more than 5% nitroglycerin	3064	3	6
Nitroglycerine solution in alcohol with more than 1% not more than 10% nitroglycerin	0144	1.1D	4
Nitroglycerine solution in alcohol with not more than 1% nitroglycerin	1204	3	7 (b)
Nitroguanidine, dry or wetted with less than 20% water, by mass	0282	1.1D	4
Nitroguanidine, wetted with not less than 20% water, by mass	1336	4.1	21 (a)1.
Nitrohydrochloric acid: Not to be accepted for carriage	1798	8	3, Note 1
Nitromannite, see Mannitol hexanitrate			
Nitromethane	1261	3	3 (b)
Nitronaphthalene	2538	4.1	6 (c)
Nitrophenols (o-,m-,p-)	1663	6.1	12 (c)
Nitropropanes	2608	3	31 (c)
p-Nitrosodimethylaniline	1369	4.2	5 (b)
4-Nitrosophenol, see Self-reactive solid, type D, temperature controlled			

Name of substance or article	Substance Identification No. (UN No.)	Class	Item number and letter
Nitrostarch, dry or wetted with less than 20% water, by mass	0146	1.1D	4
Nitrostarch, wetted with not less than 20% water, by mass	1337	4.1	21 (a)1.
Nitrosyl chloride	1069	2	2 TC
Nitrosylsulphuric acid	2308	8	1 (b)
Nitrotoluenes (o-,m-,p-)	1664	6.1	12 (b)
Nitrotoluidines	2660	6.1	12 (c)
Nitrotriazolone	0490	1.1D	4
Nitrous oxide	1070	2	2 O
Nitrous oxide, refrigerated liquid	2201	2	3 O
Nitroxylenes (o-,m-,p-)	1665	6.1	12 (b)
Nonanes	1920	3	31 (c)
Nonyltrichlorosilane	1799	8	36 (b)
Norbormide (pesticide), see under Pesticide, n.o.s.			
2,5-Norbornadiene (dicycloheptadiene), inhibited	2251	3	3 (b)
NTO, see Nitrotoluidines			
Octadecyltrichlorosilane	1800	8	36 (b)
Octadiene	2309	3	3 (b)
Octafluorobut-2-ene	2422	2	2 A
Octafluorocyclobutane	1976	2	2 A
Octafluoropropane	2424	2	2 A
Octanes	1262	3	3 (b)
Octenes, see Flammable liquid, n.o.s.			
Octogen, see Cyclotetramethylenetetranitramine			
Octolite, dry or wetted with less than 15% water, by mass	0266	1.1D	4
Octol, see Octolite			
Octonal	0496	1.1D	4
Octyl aldehydes, flammable	1191	3	31 (c)
tert-Octyl mercaptan	3023	6.1	20 (a)
Octyltrichlorosilane	1801	8	36 (b)
Oil gas, compressed	1071	2	1 TF
Oil, petroleum crude, see Petroleum crude oil			
Oleum	1831	8	1 (a)
Omethoate (pesticide), see Organophosphorus pesticides			
Organoarsenic compound, n.o.s.	3280	6.1	34 (a), (b), (c)
Organic peroxide type B, liquid	3101	5.2	1 (b)
Organic peroxide type B, liquid, temperature controlled	3111	5.2	11 (b)
Organic peroxide type B, solid	3102	5.2	2 (b)
Organic peroxide type B, solid, temperature controlled	3112	5.2	12 (b)
Organic peroxide type C, liquid	3103	5.2	3 (b)

Name of substance or article	Substance Identification No. (UN No.)	Class	Item number and letter
Organic peroxide type C, liquid, temperature controlled	3113	5.2	13 (b)
Organic peroxide type C, solid	3104	5.2	4 (b)
Organic peroxide type C, solid, temperature controlled	3114	5.2	14 (b)
Organic peroxide type D, liquid	3105	5.2	5 (b)
Organic peroxide type D, liquid, temperature controlled	3115	5.2	15 (b)
Organic peroxide type D, solid	3106	5.2	6 (b)
Organic peroxide type D, solid, temperature controlled	3116	5.2	16 (b)
Organic peroxide type E, liquid	3107	5.2	7 (b)
Organic peroxide type E, liquid, temperature controlled	3117	5.2	17 (b)
Organic peroxide type E, solid	3108	5.2	8 (b)
Organic peroxide type E, solid, temperature controlled	3118	5.2	18 (b)
Organic peroxide type F, liquid	3109	5.2	9 (b)
Organic peroxide type F, liquid, temperature controlled	3119	5.2	19 (b)
Organic peroxide type F, solid	3110	5.2	10 (b)
Organic peroxide type F, solid, temperature controlled	3120	5.2	20 (b)
Organic pigments, self-heating	3313	4.2	5 (b), (c)
Organochlorine pesticide, liquid, flammable, toxic, flash-point less than 23 °C	2762	3	41 (a), (b)
Organochlorine pesticide, liquid, toxic	2996	6.1	71 (a), (b), (c)
Organochlorine pesticide, liquid, toxic, flammable, flash-point not less than 23 °C	2995	6.1	72 (a), (b), (c)
Organochlorine pesticide, solid, toxic	2761	6.1	73 (a), (b), (c)
Organomercury pesticides, see Mercury based pesticides			
Organometallic compound or compound solution or compound dispersion, water-reactive, flammable, n.o.s.	3207	4.3	3 (a), (b), (c)
Organometallic compound, toxic, n.o.s.	3282	6.1	35 (a), (b), (c)
Organophosphorus compound, toxic, flammable, n.o.s.	3279	6.1	22 (a), (b)
Organophosphorus compound, toxic, n.o.s.	3278	6.1	23 (a), (b), (c)
Organophosphorus pesticide, liquid, flammable, toxic, flash-point less than 23 °C	2784	3	41 (a), (b)
Organophosphorus pesticide, liquid, toxic	3018	6.1	71 (a), (b), (c)
Organophosphorus pesticide, liquid, toxic, flammable, flash point not less than 23 °C	3017	6.1	72 (a), (b), (c)
Organophosphorus pesticide, solid, toxic	2783	6.1	73 (a), (b), (c)
Organotin compound, liquid, n.o.s.	2788	6.1	32 (a), (b), (c)
Organotin compound, solid, n.o.s.	3146	6.1	32 (a), (b), (c)
Organotin pesticide, liquid, flammable, toxic, flash-point less than 23 °C	2787	3	41 (a), (b)
Organotin pesticide, liquid, toxic	3020	6.1	71 (a), (b), (c)
Organotin pesticide, liquid, toxic, flammable, flash point not less than 23 °C	3019	6.1	72 (a), (b), (c)

Name of substance or article	Substance Identification No. (UN No.)	Class	Item number and letter
Organotin pesticide, solid, toxic	2786	6.1	73 (a), (b), (c)
Osmium compounds, liquid, see Toxic liquid, inorganic, n.o.s.			
Osmium compounds, solid, see Toxic solid, inorganic, n.o.s.			
Osmium tetroxide	2471	6.1	56 (a)
Oxamyl (pesticide), see Carbamate pesticides			
Oxidizing liquid, corrosive, n.o.s.	3098	5.1	32 (a), (b), (c)
Oxidizing liquid, n.o.s.	3139	5.1	28 (a), (b), (c)
Oxidizing liquid, toxic, n.o.s.	3099	5.1	30 (a), (b), (c)
Oxidizing solid, corrosive, n.o.s.	3085	5.1	31 (a), (b), (c)
Oxidizing solid, flammable, n.o.s.: Not to be accepted for carriage	3137	5.1	See marginal 2500 (12)
Oxidizing solid, n.o.s.	1479	5.1	27 (a), (b), (c)
Oxidizing solid, self-heating, n.o.s. .: Not to be accepted for carriage	3100	5.1	See marginal 2500 (12)
Oxidizing solid, toxic, n.o.s.	3087	5.1	29 (a), (b), (c)
Oxidizing solid, water-reactive, n.o.s.: Not to be accepted for carriage	3121	5.1	See marginal 2500 (12)
Oxydemeton-methyl (pesticide), see Organophosphorus pesticides			
Oxydisulfoton (pesticide), see Organophosphorus pesticides			
Oxygen, compressed	1072	2	1 O
Oxygen difluoride, compressed	2190	2	1 TOC
Oxygen, refrigerated liquid	1073	2	3 O
Paint	1263	3	5 (a), (b), (c), 31 (c) (See Note to Section E)
Paint	3066	8	66 (b), (c)
Paint, nitrocellulose, see Nitrocellulose solution, flammable			
Paint related material	3066	8	66 (b), (c)
Paper, unsaturated, oil treated	1379	4.2	3 (c)
Paraformaldehyde	2213	4.1	6 (c)
Paraldehyde	1264	3	31 (c)
Paraoxon (pesticide), see Organophosphorus pesticides			
Paraquat (pesticide), see Bipyridilium pesticides			
Parathion-methyl (pesticide), see Organophosphorus pesticides			
Parathion (pesticide), see Organophosphorus pesticides			
PCBs, see Polychlorinated biphenyls			
PCTs, see Polyhalogenated terphenyls			
Peat tar oil, see Tars, liquid			
Pentaborane	1380	4.2	19 (a)
Pentachloroethane	1669	6.1	15 (b)

Name of substance or article	Substance Identification No. (UN No.)	Class	Item number and letter
Pentachlorophenol	3155	6.1	17 (b)
1,4-Pentadiene, see Flammable liquid, n.o.s.			
Pentaerythrite tetranitrate with not less than 7% wax, by mass	0411	1.1D	4
Pentaerythrite tetranitrate, desensitized with not less than 15% phlegmatizer, by mass	0150	1.1D	4
Pentaerythrite tetranitrate, wetted with not less than 25% water, by mass	0150	1.1D	4
Pentaerythritol tetranitrate, see Pentaerythrite tetranitrate			
Pentaethylenehexamine, see Amines, liquid, corrosive, n.o.s.			
Pentafluorobenzaldehyde, see Toxic liquid, organic, n.o.s.			
Pentafluoroethane	3220	2	2 A
Pentamethylheptane	2286	3	31 (c)
Pentane-2,4-dione	2310	3	32 (c)
n-Pentane	1265	3	2 (b)
Pentanes, liquid	1265	3	1 (a), 2 (b)
2-Pentene, see Flammable liquid, n.o.s.			
1-Pentene	1108	3	1 (a)
1-Pentol	2705	8	66 (b)
Pentolite, dry or wetted with less than 15% water, by mass	0151	1.1D	4
Perchlorates, inorganic, aqueous solution, n.o.s.	3211	5.1	13 (b), (c)
Perchlorates, inorganic, n.o.s.	1481	5.1	13 (b)
Perchloric acid in aqueous solution with more than 50% but not more than 72% acid	1873	5.1	3 (a)
Perchloric acid, not more than 50% acid, by mass in aqueous solution	1802	8	4 (b)
Perchloric acid, with more than 72% acid: Not to be accepted for carriage		8	4, Note
Perchloromethyl mercaptan	1670	6.1	17 (a)
Perchloryl fluoride	3083	2	2 TO
Perfluoro(ethyl vinyl ether)	3154	2	2 F
Perfluoro(methyl vinyl ether)	3153	2	2 F
Perfumery products with flammable solvents	1266	3	5 (a), (b), (c), 31 (c)
Permanganates, inorganic, aqueous solution, n.o.s.	3214	5.1	17 (b)
Permanganates, inorganic, n.o.s.	1482	5.1	17 (b)
Peroxides, inorganic, n.o.s.	1483	5.1	25 (b)
Peroxyacetic acid, type D, stabilized, see Organic peroxide type D, liquid			
Peroxyacetic acid, type E, stabilized, see Organic peroxide type E, liquid			
Peroxyacetic acid, type F, stabilized, see Organic peroxide type F, liquid			

Name of substance or article	Substance Identification No. (UN No.)	Class	Item number and letter
Persulphates, inorganic, aqueous solutions, n.o.s.	3216	5.1	18 (c)
Persulphates, inorganic, n.o.s.	3215	5.1	18 (c)
Pesticide, liquid, flammable, toxic, n.o.s., flash point less than 23 °C	3021	3	41 (a), (b)
Pesticide, liquid, toxic, n.o.s.	2902	6.1	71 (a), (b), (c)
Pesticide, liquid, toxic, flammable, n.o.s., flash point not less than 23 °C	2903	6.1	72 (a), (b), (c)
Pesticide, solid, toxic, n.o.s.	2588	6.1	73 (a), (b), (c)
Pesticides, halogenated organic compounds, see Organochlorine pesticides			
PETN, see Pentaerythrite tetranitrate			
Petrol	1203	3	3 (b)
Petroleum crude oil	1267	3	1 (a), 2 (a), (b), 3 (b), 31 (c)
Petroleum distillates, n.o.s.	1268	3	1 (a), 2 (a), (b), 3 (b), 31 (c)
Petroleum ether, see Petroleum distillates, n.o.s.			
Petroleum gases, liquefied	1075	2	2 F
Petroleum oil, see Petroleum distillates, n.o.s.			
Petroleum products, n.o.s.	1268	3	1 (a), 2 (a), (b), 3 (b), 31 (c)
Petroleum spirit, see Petroleum distillates, n.o.s			
Phenacyl bromide	2645	6.1	17 (b)
Phenetidines	2311	6.1	12 (c)
Phenkapton (pesticide), see Organophosphorus pesticides			
Phenobarbital, see Toxic solid, organic, n.o.s.			
Phenol, alkaline solutions, see Corrosive liquid, n.o.s			
Phenolates, liquid	2904	8	62 (c)
Phenolates, solid	2905	8	62 (c)
Phenol, molten	2312	6.1	24 (b)1.
Phenol, solid	1671	6.1	14 (b)
Phenol solution	2821	6.1	14 (b), (c)
Phenolsulphonic acid, liquid	1803	8	34 (b)
Phenoxy pesticide, liquid, flammable, toxic, flash-point less than 23 °C	2766	3	41 (a), (b)
Phenoxy pesticide, liquid, toxic	3000	6.1	71 (a), (b), (c)
Phenoxy pesticide, liquid, toxic, flammable, flash-point not less than 23 °C	2999	6.1	72 (a), (b), (c)
Phenoxy pesticide, solid, toxic	2765	6.1	73 (a), (b), (c)
Phenthoat (pesticide), see Organophosphorus pesticides			
Phenylacetonitrile, liquid	2470	6.1	12 (c)
Phenylacetyl chloride	2577	8	35 (b)1.

Name of substance or article	Substance Identification No. (UN No.)	Class	Item number and letter
Phenylcarbylamine chloride	1672	6.1	17 (a)
Phenyl chloride	1134	3	31 (c)
Phenyl chloroformate	2746	6.1	27 (b)
Phenylenediamines (o-, m-, p-)	1673	6.1	12 (c)
Phenylhydrazine	2572	6.1	12 (b)
Phenyl isocyanate	2487	6.1	18 (a)
Phenyl mercaptan	2337	6.1	20 (a)
Phenylmercuric acetate	1674	6.1	33 (b)
Phenylmercuric acetate (pesticide), see Mercury based pesticides			
Phenylmercuric compound, n.o.s.	2026	6.1	33 (a), (b), (c)
Phenylmercuric hydroxide	1894	6.1	33 (b)
Phenylmercuric nitrate	1895	6.1	33 (b)
Phenylmercuric pyrocatechin (pesticide), see Mercury based pesticides			
Phenyl methyl ether	2222	3	31 (c)
Phenylphosphorus dichloride	2798	8	35 (b)1.
Phenylphosphorus thiodichloride	2799	8	35 (b)1.
Phenyltrichlorosilane	1804	8	36 (b)
Phenyl urea pesticide, liquid, flammable, toxic, flash-point less than 23 °C	2768	3	41 (a), (b)
Phenyl urea pesticide, liquid, toxic, flammable, flash point not less than 23 °C	3001	6.1	72 (a), (b), (c)
Phenyl urea pesticide, liquid,toxic	3002	6.1	71 (a), (b), (c)
Phenyl urea pesticide, solid, toxic	2767	6.1	73 (a), (b), (c)
Phorate (pesticide), see Organophosphorus pesticides			
Phosalone (pesticide), see Organophosphorus pesticides			
Phosfolan (pesticide), see Organophosphorus pesticides			
Phosgene	1076	2	2 TC
Phosmet (pesticide), see Organophosphorus pesticides			
9-Phosphabicyclononanes	2940	4.2	5 (b)
Phosphamidon (pesticide), see Organophosphorus pesticides			
Phosphine	2199	2	2 TF
Phosphoric acid	1805	8	17 (c)
Phosphoric acid, anhydrous	1807	8	16 (b)
Phosphorous acid	2834	8	16 (c)
Phosphorus, amorphous	1338	4.1	11 (c)
Phosphorus heptasulphide	1339	4.1	11 (b)
Phosphorus oxybromide	1939	8	11 (b)
Phosphorus oxybromide, molten	2576	8	15
Phosphorus oxychloride	1810	8	12 (b)

Name of substance or article	Substance Identification No. (UN No.)	Class	Item number and letter
Phosphorus pentabromide	2691	8	11 (b)
Phosphorus pentachloride	1806	8	11 (b)
Phosphorus pentafluoride, compressed	2198	2	1 TC
Phosphorus pentasulphide	1340	4.3	20 (b)
Phosphorus pentoxide	1807	8	16 (b)
Phosphorus sesquisulphide	1341	4.1	11 (b)
Phosphorus tribromide	1808	8	12 (b)
Phosphorus trichloride	1809	6.1	67 (a)
Phosphorus trioxide	2578	8	16 (c)
Phosphorus trisulphide	1343	4.1	11 (b)
Phosphorus, white, molten	2447	4.2	22
Phosphorus, white or yellow, dry or under water or in solution	1381	4.2	11 (a)
Phosphoryl chloride	1810	8	12 (b)
Phthalic anhydride	2214	8	31 (c)
Phthalimide derivative pesticide, liquid, flammable, toxic, flash-point less than 23 °C	2774	3	41 (a), (b)
Phthalimide derivative pesticide, liquid, toxic	3008	6.1	71 (a), (b), (c)
Phthalimide derivative pesticide, liquid, toxic, flash point not less than 23 °C	3007	6.1	72 (a), (b), (c)
Phthalimide derivative pesticide, solid, toxic	2773	6.1	73 (a), (b), (c)
Phthalophos (pesticide), see Organophosphorus pesticides			
Picolines	2313	3	31 (c)
Picramide, see Trinitroaniline			
Picric acid, see Trinitrophenol			
Picrite, see Nitroguanidine			
Picryl chloride, see Trinitrochlorobenzene			
Pinanyl hydroperoxide, see Organic peroxide type D, liquid			
Pinanyl hydroperoxide, see Organic peroxide type F, liquid			
Pindone (and salts of) (pesticide), see under Pesticide, etc.			
Pine oil	1272	3	31 (c)
alpha-Pinene	2368	3	31 (c)
Piperazine	2579	8	52 (c)
Piperidine	2401	3	23 (b)
Pirimicarb (pesticide), see Carbamate pesticides			
Pirimiphos-ethyl (pesticide), see Organophosphorus pesticides			
Plastics moulding compound in dough, sheet or extruded rope form evolving flammable vapour	3314	9	4 (c)
Plastics, nitrocellulose-based, self-heating, n.o.s	2006	4.2	4 (c)
PMA (pesticide), see Mercury based pesticides			
PMB (pesticide), see Mercury based pesticides			

Name of substance or article	Substance Identification No. (UN No.)	Class	Item number and letter
Polishes	1263	3	5 (a), (b), (c), 31 (c) (See Note to Section E)
Polyamines, flammable, corrosive, n.o.s.	2733	3	22 (a), (b), 33 (c)
Polyamines, liquid, corrosive,flammable,n.o.s.,see Amines, etc., n.o.s.			
Polyamines, liquid, corrosive, n.o.s., see Amines, etc., n.o.s.			
Polyamines, solid, corrosive, n.o.s., see Amines, etc., n.o.s.			
Polychlorinated biphenyls	2315	9	2 (b)
Polyester resin kits	3269	3	5 (b), (c), 31 (c)
Polyhalogenated biphenyls, liquid	3151	9	2 (b)
Polyhalogenated biphenyls, solid	3152	9	2 (b)
Polyhalogenated terphenyls, liquid	3151	9	2 (b)
Polyhalogenated terphenyls, solid	3252	9	2 (b)
Polymeric beads, expandable	2211	9	4 (c)
Potash lye	1814	8	42 (b), (c)
Potassium	2257	4.3	11 (a)
Potassium arsenate	1677	6.1	51 (b)
Potassium arsenite	1678	6.1	51 (b)
Potassium bifluoride	1811	8	9 (b)
Potassium bisulphate, aqueous solutions, see Potassium hydrogen sulphate			
Potassium borohydride	1870	4.3	16 (a)
Potassium bromate	1484	5.1	16 (b)
Potassium chlorate	1485	5.1	11 (b)
Potassium chlorate, aqueous solution	2427	5.1	11 (b), (c)
Potassium cuprocyanide	1679	6.1	41 (b)
Potassium cyanide	1680	6.1	41 (a)
Potassium dithionite	1929	4.2	13 (b)
Potassium fluoride	1812	6.1	63 (c)
Potassium fluoroacetate	2628	6.1	17 (a)
Potassium fluorosilicate	2655	6.1	64 (c)
Potassium hydrogendifluoride	1811	8	9 (b)
Potassium hydrogen sulphate	2509	8	13 (b)
Potassium hydrosulphite, see Potassium dithionite			
Potassium hydroxide, solid	1813	8	41 (b)
Potassium hydroxide solution	1814	8	42 (b), (c)
Potassium hypochlorite, solution, see Hypochlorite solution			
Potassium metal alloys	1420	4.3	11 (a)
Potassium metavanadate	2864	6.1	58 (b)

Name of substance or article	Substance Identification No. (UN No.)	Class	Item number and letter
Potassium monoxide	2033	8	41 (b)
Potassium nitrate	1486	5.1	22 (c)
Potassium nitrate and sodium nitrite mixtures	1487	5.1	24 (b)
Potassium nitrite	1488	5.1	23 (b)
Potassium oxide, see Potassium monoxide			
Potassium perchlorate	1489	5.1	13 (b)
Potassium permanganate	1490	5.1	17 (b)
Potassium peroxide	1491	5.1	25 (a)
Potassium persulphate	1492	5.1	18 (c)
Potassium phosphide	2012	4.3	18 (a)
Potassium selenate, see Selenates			
Potassium selenite, see Selenites			
Potassium sodium alloys	1422	4.3	11 (a)
Potassium sulphide	1382	4.2	13 (b)
Potassium sulphide, anhydrous	1382	4.2	13 (b)
Potassium sulphide, aqueous solutions, see Potassium sulphide, hydrated			
Potassium sulphide, hydrated, containing not less than 30% water of crystallization	1847	8	45 (b)1.
Potassium sulphide with less than 30% water of crystallization	1382	4.2	13 (b)
Potassium superoxide	2466	5.1	25 (a)
Powder cake, wetted with not less than 25% water, by mass	0159	1.3C	26
Powder cake, wetted, with not less than 17% alcohol, by mass	0433	1.1C	2
Powder paste, see Powder cake			
Powder, smokeless	0160	1.1C	2
Powder, smokeless	0161	1.3C	26
Primers, cap type	0044	1.4S	47
Primers, cap type	0377	1.1B	1
Primers, cap type	0378	1.4B	35
Primers, tubular	0319	1.3G	30
Primers, tubular	0320	1.4G	43
Primers, tubular	0376	1.4S	47
Printing ink, flammable	1210	3	5 (a), (b), (c), 31 (c) (See Note to Section E)
Projectiles, inert with tracer	0345	1.4S	47
Projectiles, inert with tracer	0424	1.3G	30
Projectiles, inert with tracer	0425	1.4G	43
Projectiles with burster or expelling charge	0346	1.2D	17
Projectiles with burster or expelling charge	0347	1.4D	39
Projectiles with burster or expelling charge	0426	1.2F	19

Name of substance or article	Substance Identification No. (UN No.)	Class	Item number and letter
Projectiles with burster or expelling charge	0427	1.4F	41
Projectiles with burster or expelling charge	0434	1.2G	21
Projectiles with burster or expelling charge	0435	1.4G	43
Projectiles with bursting charge	0167	1.1F	7
Projectiles with bursting charge	0168	1.1D	5
Projectiles with bursting charge	0169	1.2D	17
Projectiles with bursting charge	0324	1.2F	19
Projectiles with bursting charge	0344	1.4D	39
Promecarb (pesticide), see Carbamate pesticides			
Promorit (pesticide), see Carbamate pesticides			
Propadiene, inhibited	2200	2	2 F
Propadiene with 1% to 4% methyl acetylene, stabilized, see Methyl acetylene and propadiene mixtures, stabilized			
Propane, mixture of gases	1965	2	2 F
Propane, technically pure	1978	2	2 F
Propanethiols	2402	3	3 (b)
n-Propanol	1274	3	3 (b), 31 (c)
Propaphos (pesticide), see Organophosphorus pesticides			
Propellant, liquid	0495	1.3C	26
Propellant, liquid	0497	1.1C	2
Propellant, solid	0498	1.1C	2
Propellant, solid	0499	1.3C	26
Propene	1077	2	2 F
Propionaldehyde	1275	3	3 (b)
Propionic acid	1848	8	32 (c)
Propionic acid with less than 50% acid: Not subject to ADR		8	32 (c), Note
Propionic anhydride	2496	8	32 (c)
Propionitrile	2404	3	11 (b)
Propionyl chloride	1815	3	25 (b)
Propoxur (pesticide), see Carbamate pesticides			
n-Propyl acetate	1276	3	3 (b)
Propyl alcohol, normal	1274	3	3 (b), 31 (c)
Propylamine	1277	3	22 (b)
n-Propylbenzene	2364	3	31 (c)
Propyl chloride	1278	3	2 (b)
n-Propyl chloroformate	2740	6.1	28 (a)
Propylene	1077	2	2 F
Propylene chlorohydrin	2611	6.1	16 (b)
1,2-Propylenediamine	2258	8	54 (b)

Name of substance or article	Substance Identification No. (UN No.)	Class	Item number and letter
Propylene dichloride	1279	3	3 (b)
Propyleneimine, inhibited	1921	3	12
Propylene oxide	1280	3	2 (a)
Propylene tetramer	2850	3	31 (c)
Propylene trimer	2057	3	31 (c)
Propyl formates	1281	3	3 (b)
n-Propyl isocyanate	2482	6.1	6 (a)
Propyl mercaptan	2402	3	3 (b)
n-Propyl nitrate	1865	3	3 (b)
Propyltrichlorosilane	1816	8	37 (b)
Prothoate (pesticide), see Organophosphorus pesticides			
Pyrazophos (pesticide) see Organophosphorus pesticides			
Pyrazoxon (pesticide) see Organophosphorus pesticides			
Pyridine	1282	3	3 (b)
Pyrocatechol, see Toxic solid, organic, n.o.s.			
Pyrophoric alloy, n.o.s.	1383	4.2	12 (a)
Pyrophoric liquid, inorganic, n.o.s.	3194	4.2	17 (a)
Pyrophoric liquid, organic, n.o.s.	2845	4.2	6 (a)
Pyrophoric metal, n.o.s.	1383	4.2	12 (a)
Pyrophoric organometallic compound, n.o.s.	3203	4.2	33 (a)
Pyrophoric solid, inorganic, n.o.s.	3200	4.2	16 (a)
Pyrophoric solid, organic, n.o.s.	2846	4.2	5 (a)
Pyrosulphuryl chloride	1817	8	12 (b)
Pyrrolidine	1922	3	23 (b)
Quickmatch, see Fuse instantaneous non-detonating			
Quinalphos (pesticide), see Organophosphorus pesticides			
Quinhydrone, see Toxic solid, organic, n.o.s.			
Quinoline	2656	6.1	12 (c)
Refrigerant gas R 11		2	2 A Note
Refrigerant gas R 12	1028	2	2 A
Refrigerant gas R 12B1	1974	2	2 A
Refrigerant gas R 13	1022	2	2 A
Refrigerant gas R 13B1	1009	2	2 A
Refrigerant gas R 14	1982	2	1 A
Refrigerant gas R 21	1029	2	2 A
Refrigerant gas R 22	1018	2	2 A
Refrigerant gas R 23	1984	2	2 A
Refrigerant gas R 32	3252	2	2 F
Refrigerant gas R 40	1063	2	2 F

Name of substance or article	Substance Identification No. (UN No.)	Class	Item number and letter
Refrigerant gas R 41	2454	2	2 F
Refrigerant gas R 113		2	2 A Note
Refrigerant gas R 113a		2	2 A Note
Refrigerant gas R 114	1958	2	2 A
Refrigerant gas R 115	1020	2	2 A
Refrigerant gas R 116	2193	2	1 A
Refrigerant gas R 124	1021	2	2 A
Refrigerant gas R 125	3220	2	2 A
Refrigerant gas R 133		2	2 A Note
Refrigerant gas R 133a	1983	2	2 A
Refrigerant gas R 133b		2	2 A Note
Refrigerant gas R 134a	3159	2	2 A
Refrigerant gas R 142b	2517	2	2 F
Refrigerant gas R 143a	2035	2	2 F
Refrigerant gas R 152a	1030	2	2 F
Refrigerant gas R 161	2453	2	2 F
Refrigerant gas R 218	2424	2	2 A
Refrigerant gas R 227	3296	2	2 A
Refrigerant gas R 500	2602	2	2 A
Refrigerant gas R 502	1973	2	2 A
Refrigerant gas R 503	2599	2	2 A
Refrigerant gas R 1132a	1959	2	2 F
Refrigerant gas R 1216	1858	2	2 A
Refrigerant gas R 1318	2422	2	2 A
Racumin (pesticide), see Coumarin derivative pesticides			
Radioactive material, n.o.s.	2982	7	Sch. 9, 10, 11, 13
- under special arrangement	2982		Sch. 13
Radioactive material, fissile, n.o.s.	2818	7	Sch. 12, 13
Radioactive material, limited quantities in excepted package	2910	7	
- articles manufactured from natural or depleted uranium or natural thorium	2910	7	Sch. 3
- empty packaging	2910	7	Sch. 4
- instruments or articles	2910	7	Sch. 2
- limited quantity of material	2910	7	Sch. 1

Name of substance or article	Substance Identification No. (UN No.)	Class	Item number and letter
Radioactive material, low specific activity (LSA), not otherwise specified	2912	7	
- LSA-I	2912	7	Sch. 5
- LSA-II	2912		Sch. 6
- LSA-III	2912		Sch. 7
- under special arrangement	2912		Sch. 13
Radioactive material, special form, n.o.s.	2974	7	Sch. 9, 10, 11, 13
- under special arrangement	2974		Sch. 13
Radioactive material, surface contaminated objects (SCO)	2913	7	
- SCO-I and SCO-II	2913	7	Sch. 8
- under special arrangement	2913		Sch. 13
Rare gases and carbon dioxide mixtures	1979	2	1 A
Rare gases and nitrogen mixtures	1981	2	1 A
Rare gases and oxygen mixtures	1980	2	1 A
Rare gases in mixtures	1979	2	1 A
RC 318	1976	2	2 A
RDX, see Cyclotrimethylenetrinitramine			
Receptacles, small, containing gas without release device, non-refillable	2037	2	5 A
Receptacles, small, containing gas without release device, non-refillable	2037	2	5 O
Receptacles, small, containing gas without release device, non-refillable	2037	2	5 F
Receptacles, small, containing gas without release device, non-refillable	2037	2	5 T
Receptacles, small, containing gas without release device, non-refillable	2037	2	5 TF
Receptacles, small, containing gas without release device, non-refillable	2037	2	5 TC
Receptacles, small, containing gas without release device, non-refillable	2037	2	5 TO
Receptacles, small, containing gas without release device, non-refillable	2037	2	5 TFC
Receptacles, small, containing gas without release device, non-refillable	2037	2	5 TOC
Refrigerant gas, n.o.s.	1078	2	2 A
Refrigerating machines containing non-flammable, non-toxic, liquefied gas or ammonia solutions (UN 2672)	2857	2	6 A
Release devices, explosive	0173	1.4S	47

Supplement No.1

Name of substance or article	Substance Identification No. (UN No.)	Class	Item number and letter
Resins in solution in flammable liquids	1866	3	5 (a), (b), (c), 31 (c)
Resorcinol	2876	6.1	14 (c)
Rivets, explosive	0174	1.4S	47
Rockets, line-throwing	0238	1.2G	21
Rockets, line-throwing	0240	1.3G	30
Rockets, line-throwing	0453	1.4G	43
Rockets, liquid fuelled with bursting charge	0397	1.1J	10
Rockets, liquid fuelled with bursting charge	0398	1.2J	23
Rocket motors	0186	1.3C	27
Rocket motors	0280	1.1C	3
Rocket motors	0281	1.2C	15
Rocket motors with hypergolic liquids with or without expelling charge	0250	1.3L	34
Rocket motors with hypergolic liquids with or without expelling charge	0322	1.2L	25
Rocket motors, liquid fuelled	0395	1.2J	23
Rocket motors, liquid fuelled	0396	1.3J	32
Rockets with bursting charge	0180	1.1F	7
Rockets with bursting charge	0181	1.1E	6
Rockets with bursting charge	0182	1.2E	18
Rockets with bursting charge	0295	1.2F	19
Rockets with expelling charge	0436	1.2C	15
Rockets with expelling charge	0437	1.3C	27
Rockets with expelling charge	0438	1.4C	37
Rockets with inert head	0183	1.3C	27
Rosin oil	1286	3	5 (a), (b), (c), 31 (c)
Rotenone (pesticide), see under Pesticide, etc.			
Rubber scrap	1345	4.1	1 (b)
Rubber shoddy	1345	4.1	1 (b)
Rubber solution	1287	3	5 (a), (b), (c), 31 (c)
Rubidium	1423	4.3	11 (a)
Rubidium hydroxide	2678	8	41 (b)
Rubidium hydroxide solution	2677	8	42 (b), (c)
Salithion (pesticide), see Organophosphorus pesticides			
Samples, explosive, other than initiating explosive	0190	1	51
Schradan (pesticide), see Organophosphorus pesticides			
Seat-belt pre-tensioners	3268	9	8 (c)
Seed cake with more than 1.5% oil and not more than 11% moisture	1386	4.2	2 (c)

Name of substance or article	Substance Identification No. (UN No.)	Class	Item number and letter
Seed cake with not more than 1.5% oil and not more than 11% moisture	2217	4.2	2 (c)
Seed, dressed impregnated with pesticide or other toxic substance		6.1	See Note 2b to section F
Selenates	2630	6.1	55 (a)
Selenic acid	1905	8	16 (a)
Selenites	2630	6.1	55 (a)
Selenium compound, n.o.s.	3283	6.1	55 (a), (b), (c)
Selenium dioxide, see Selenium compound, n.o.s.			
Selenium disulphide	2657	6.1	55 (b)
Selenium hexafluoride	2194	2	2 TC
Selenium oxychloride	2879	8	12 (a)
Self-heating liquid, corrosive, inorganic, n.o.s.	3188	4.2	21 (b), (c)
Self-heating liquid, corrosive, organic, n.o.s.	3185	4.2	10 (b), (c)
Self-heating liquid, inorganic, n.o.s.	3186	4.2	17 (b), (c)
Self-heating liquid, organic, n.o.s.	3183	4.2	6 (b), (c)
Self-heating liquid, toxic, inorganic, n.o.s.	3187	4.2	19 (b), (c)
Self-heating liquid, toxic, organic, n.o.s.	3184	4.2	8 (b), (c)
Self-heating metal powder, n.o.s.	3189	4.2	12 (b), (c)
Self-heating solid, corrosive, inorganic, n.o.s.	3192	4.2	20 (b), (c)
Self-heating solid, corrosive, organic, n.o.s.	3126	4.2	9 (b), (c)
Self-heating solid, inorganic, n.o.s.	3190	4.2	16 (b), (c)
Self-heating solid, organic, n.o.s.	3088	4.2	5 (b), (c)
Self-heating solid, oxidizing, n.o.s.	3127	4.2	See marginal 2430 (11)
Self-heating solid, toxic, inorganic, n.o.s.	3191	4.2	18 (b), (c)
Self-heating solid, toxic, organic, n.o.s.	3128	4.2	7 (b), (c)
Self-reactive liquid, sample, see Self-reactive liquid, type C			
Self-reactive liquid, sample, temperature controlled, see Self-reactive liquid, type C, temperature controlled			
Self-reactive liquid, type B	3221	4.1	31 (b)
Self-reactive liquid, type B, temperature controlled	3231	4.1	41 (b)
Self-reactive liquid, type C	3223	4.1	33 (b)
Self-reactive liquid, type C, temperature controlled	3233	4.1	43 (b)
Self-reactive liquid, type D	3225	4.1	35 (b)
Self-reactive liquid, type D, temperature controlled	3235	4.1	45 (b)
Self-reactive liquid, type E	3227	4.1	37 (b)
Self-reactive liquid, type E, temperature controlled	3237	4.1	47 (b)
Self-reactive liquid, type F	3229	4.1	39 (b)
Self-reactive liquid, type F, temperature controlled	3239	4.1	49 (b)

Name of substance or article	Substance Identification No. (UN No.)	Class	Item number and letter
Self-reactive solid, sample, see Self-reactive solid, type C			
Self-reactive solid, sample, temperature controlled, see Self-reactive solid, type C, temperature controlled			
Self-reactive solid, type B	3222	4.1	32 (b)
Self-reactive solid, type B, temperature controlled	3232	4.1	42 (b)
Self-reactive solid, type C	3224	4.1	34 (b)
Self-reactive solid, type C, temperature controlled	3234	4.1	44 (b)
Self-reactive solid, type D	3226	4.1	36 (b)
Self-reactive solid, type D, temperature controlled	3236	4.1	46 (b)
Self-reactive solid, type E	3228	4.1	38 (b)
Self-reactive solid, type E, temperature controlled	3238	4.1	48 (b)
Self-reactive solid, type F	3230	4.1	40 (b)
Self-reactive solid, type F, temperature controlled	3240	4.1	50 (b)
Shale oil	1288	3	3 (b), 31 (c)
Signal devices, hand	0191	1.4G	43
Signal devices, hand	0373	1.4S	47
Signals, distress, ship	0194	1.1G	9
Signals, distress, ship	0195	1.3G	30
Signals, railway track, explosive	0192	1.1G	9
Signals, railway track, explosive	0193	1.4S	47
Signals, railway track, explosive	0492	1.3G	30
Signals, railway track, explosive	0493	1.4G	43
Signals, smoke	0196	1.1G	9
Signals, smoke	0197	1.4G	43
Signals, smoke	0313	1.2G	21
Signals, smoke	0487	1.3G	30
Silane, compressed	2203	2	1 F
Silicofluorides, see Fluorosilicates, n.o.s.			
Silicon powder, amorphous	1346	4.1	13 (c)
Silicon tetrachloride	1818	8	12 (b)
Silicon tetrafluoride, compressed	1859	2	1 TC
Silver arsenite	1683	6.1	51 (b)
Silver cyanide	1684	6.1	41 (b)
Silver nitrate	1493	5.1	22 (b)
Silver picrate, wetted with not less than 30% water, by mass	1347	4.1	21 (a)1.
Sludge acid	1906	8	1 (b)
Soda lime	1907	8	41 (c)
Soda lye	1824	8	42 (b), (c)
Sodium	1428	4.3	11 (a)

Name of substance or article	Substance Identification No. (UN No.)	Class	Item number and letter
Sodium 2-diazo-1-naphthol-4-sulphonate, see Self-reactive solid, type D			
Sodium 2-diazo-1-naphthol-5-sulphonate, see Self-reactive solid, type D			
Sodium aluminate solution	1819	8	42 (b), (c)
Sodium aluminate, solid: Not subject to ADR	2812	8	See marginal 2800 (9)
Sodium aluminium hydride	2835	4.3	16 (b)
Sodium ammonium vanadate	2863	6.1	58 (b)
Sodium arsanilate	2473	6.1	34 (c)
Sodium arsenate	1685	6.1	51 (b)
Sodium arsenite (pesticide), see Arsenical pesticides			
Sodium arsenite, aqueous solution	1686	6.1	51 (b), (c)
Sodium arsenite, solid	2027	6.1	51 (b)
Sodium azide	1687	6.1	42 (b)
Sodium bifluoride	2439	8	9 (b)
Sodium bisulphate, aqueous solutions, see Bisulphates, aqueous solution			
Sodium borohydride	1426	4.3	16 (a)
Sodium borohydride and sodium hydroxide solution with not more than 12% sodium borohydride and not more than 40% sodium hydroxide, by mass	3320	8	42 (b), (c)
Sodium bromate	1494	5.1	16 (b)
Sodium cacodylate	1688	6.1	51 (b)
Sodium chlorate	1495	5.1	11 (b)
Sodium chlorate, aqueous solution	2428	5.1	11 (b), (c)
Sodium chlorite	1496	5.1	14 (b)
Sodium chloroacetate	2659	6.1	17 (c)
Sodium cuprocyanide, solid	2316	6.1	41 (a)
Sodium cuprocyanide solution	2317	6.1	41 (a)
Sodium cyanide	1689	6.1	41 (a)
Sodium dimethylarsenate, see Sodium cacodylate			
Sodium dinitro-o-cresolate, dry or wetted with less than 15% water, by mass	0234	1.3C	26
Sodium dinitro-o-cresolate, wetted with not less than 15% water, by mass	1348	4.1	22 (a)1.
Sodium dinitro-o-cresolate, wetted with not less than 10% water, by mass	0234	4.1	22 (a)2.
Sodium dithionite	1384	4.2	13 (b)
Sodium fluoride	1690	6.1	63 (c)
Sodium fluoroacetate	2629	6.1	17 (a)
Sodium fluorosilicate	2674	6.1	64 (c)
Sodium hydride	1427	4.3	16 (a)

Name of substance or article	Substance Identification No. (UN No.)	Class	Item number and letter
Sodium hydrogen sulphate, aqueous solutions, see Bisulphates, aqueous solution			
Sodium hydrogendifluoride	2439	8	9 (b)
Sodium hydrosulphide with less than 25% water of crystallization	2318	4.2	13 (b)
Sodium hydrosulphide with not less than 25% water of crystallization	2949	8	45 (b)1.
Sodium hydrosulphite, see Sodium dithionite			
Sodium hydroxide solution	1824	8	42 (b), (c)
Sodium hydroxide, solid	1823	8	41 (b)
Sodium hypochlorite, solution, see Hypochlorite solution			
Sodium metasilicate pentahydrate, see Disodium trioxosilicate pentahydrate			
Sodium methylate	1431	4.2	15 (b)
Sodium methylate solution in alcohol	1289	3	24 (b), 33 (c)
Sodium monoxide	1825	8	41 (b)
Sodium nitrate	1498	5.1	22 (c)
Sodium nitrate and potassium nitrate mixture	1499	5.1	22 (c)
Sodium nitrite	1500	5.1	23 (c)
Sodium oxide	1825	8	41 (b)
Sodium pentachlorophenate	2567	6.1	17 (b)
Sodium percarbonates	2467	5.1	19 (c)
Sodium perchlorate	1502	5.1	13 (b)
Sodium permanganate	1503	5.1	17 (b)
Sodium peroxide	1504	5.1	25 (a)
Sodium peroxoborate, anhydrous	3247	5.1	27 (b)
Sodium persulphate	1505	5.1	18 (c)
Sodium phosphide	1432	4.3	18 (a)
Sodium picramate, dry or wetted with less than 20% water, by mass	0235	1.3C	26
Sodium picramate, wetted with not less than 20% water, by mass	1349	4.1	21 (a)1.
Sodium selenate, see Selenates			
Sodium selenite, see Selenites			
Sodium silicofluoride, see under Pesticide, etc.			
Sodium sulphide, anhydrous	1385	4.2	13 (b)
Sodium sulphide, hydrated, not less than 30% water of crystallization	1849	8	45 (b)1.
Sodium sulphide with less than 30% water of crystallization	1385	4.2	13 (b)
Sodium superoxide	2547	5.1	25 (a)
Solids containing corrosive liquid, n.o.s.	3244	8	65 (b)
Solids containing flammable liquid, n.o.s.	3175	4.1	4 (c)
Solids containing toxic liquid, n.o.s.	3243	6.1	65 (b)
Sounding devices, explosive	0204	1.2F	19

Supplement No.1

Name of substance or article	Substance Identification No. (UN No.)	Class	Item number and letter
Sounding devices, explosive	0296	1.1F	7
Sounding devices, explosive	0374	1.1D	5
Sounding devices, explosive	0375	1.2D	17
Stannic chloride, anhydrous	1827	8	12 (b)
Stannic chloride, pentahydrate	2440	8	11 (c)
Stannic phosphides	1433	4.3	18 (a)
Stibine	2676	2	2 TF
Strontium arsenite	1691	6.1	51 (b)
Strontium chlorate	1506	5.1	11 (b)
Strontium nitrate	1507	5.1	22 (c)
Strontium perchlorate	1508	5.1	13 (b)
Strontium peroxide	1509	5.1	25 (b)
Strontium phosphide	2013	4.3	18 (a)
Strychnine	1692	6.1	90 (a)
Strychnine (pesticide), see under Pesticide, etc.			
Strychnine salts	1692	6.1	90 (a)
Styphnic acid, see Trinitroresorcinol			
Styrene monomer, inhibited	2055	3	31 (c)
Substances, explosive, n.o.s.	0485	1.4G	42
Substances, explosive, n.o.s.	0357	1.1L	11
Substances, explosive, n.o.s.	0358	1.2L	24
Substances, explosive, n.o.s.	0359	1.3L	33
Substances, explosive, n.o.s.	0474	1.1C	2
Substances, explosive, n.o.s.	0475	1.1D	4
Substances, explosive, n.o.s.	0476	1.1G	8
Substances, explosive, n.o.s.	0477	1.3C	26
Substances, explosive, n.o.s.	0478	1.3G	29
Substances, explosive, n.o.s.	0479	1.4C	36
Substances, explosive, n.o.s.	0480	1.4D	38
Substances, explosive, n.o.s.	0481	1.4S	46
Substances, explosive, n.o.s.	0473	1.1A	01
Substances, explosive, very insensitive (substances, EVI), n.o.s.	0482	1.5D	48
Substituted nitrophenol pesticide, liquid, flammable, toxic, flash-point less than 23 °C	2780	3	41 (a), (b)
Substituted nitrophenol pesticide, liquid, toxic	3014	6.1	71 (a), (b), (c)
Substituted nitrophenol pesticide, liquid, toxic, flammable, flash point not less than 23 °C	3013	6.1	72 (a), (b), (c)
Substituted nitrophenol pesticide, solid, toxic	2779	6.1	73 (a), (b), (c)
Sulfotep (pesticide), see Organophosphorus pesticides			

Supplement No.1

Name of substance or article	Substance Identification No. (UN No.)	Class	Item number and letter
Sulphamic acid	2967	8	16 (c)
Sulphides, aqueous solutions, see Corrosive liquid, basic, inorganic, n.o.s			
Sulphur	1350	4.1	11 (c)
Sulphur chlorides	1828	8	12 (a)
Sulphur dioxide	1079	2	2 TC
Sulphur hexafluoride	1080	2	2 A
Sulphuric acid, fuming	1831	8	1 (a)
Sulphuric acid, mixtures with hydrochloric acid, see Corrosive liquid, acidic, inorganic, n.o.s.			
Sulphuric acid, residual mixtures with nitric acid: Not to be accepted for carriage		8	3 Note 2
Sulphuric acid, spent	1832	8	1 (b)
Sulphuric acid with more than 51% acid	1830	8	1 (b)
Sulphuric acid with not more than 51% acid	2796	8	1 (b)
Sulphuric and hydrofluoric acid mixture	1786	8	7 (a)
Sulphuric anhydride, inhibited, see Sulphur trioxide, inhibited			
Sulphur, molten	2448	4.1	15
Sulphurous acid	1833	8	1 (b)
Sulphur tetrafluoride	2418	2	2 TC
Sulphur trioxide, inhibited	1829	8	1 (a)
Sulphur trioxide, stabilized	1829	8	1 (a)
Sulphuryl chloride	1834	8	12 (a)
Sulphuryl fluoride	2191	2	2 T
Sulprofos (pesticide), see Organophosphorus pesticides			
Synthesis gas	2600	2	1 TF
Systox (pesticide), see Organophosphorus pesticides			
2,4,5-T (pesticide), see Phenoxy pesticides			
Talc		9	1 Note 1
Tars, liquid	1999	3	5 (b), (c), 31 (c)
Tear gas candles	1700	6.1	26 (b)2.
Tear gas substance, liquid or solid, n.o.s.	1693	6.1	25 (a), (b)
Tellurium compound, n.o.s.	3284	6.1	57 (a), (b), (c)
Tellurium dioxide, see Tellurium compound, n.o.s.			
Tellurium hexafluoride	2195	2	2 TC
Temephos (pesticide), see Organophosphorus pesticides			
TEPP (pesticide), see Organophosphorus pesticides			
Terbufos (pesticide), see Organophosphorus pesticides			
Terbumeton (pesticide), see Triazine pesticides			
Terpene hydrocarbons, n.o.s.	2319	3	31 (c)

Name of substance or article	Substance Identification No. (UN No.)	Class	Item number and letter
Terpinolene	2541	3	31 (c)
Tetrabromoethane	2504	6.1	15 (c)
Tetrachlorobenzenes, see Toxic solid, organic, n.o.s.			
Tetrachloroethane	1702	6.1	15 (b)
Tetrachloroethylene	1897	6.1	15 (c)
Tetrachlorophenols, see Chlorophenols, liquid			
Tetraethyl dithiopyrophosphate	1704	6.1	23 (b)
Tetraethylenepentamine	2320	8	53 (c)
Tetraethyl lead	1649	6.1	31 (a)
Tetraethyl silicate	1292	3	31 (c)
1,1,1,2-Tetrafluoroethane	3159	2	2 A
Tetrafluoroethylene, inhibited	1081	2	2 F
Tetrafluoromethane, compressed	1982	2	1 A
1,2,3,6-Tetrahydrobenzaldehyde	2498	3	31 (c)
Tetrahydrofuran	2056	3	3 (b)
Tetrahydrofurfurylamine	2943	3	31 (c)
Tetrahydronaphthyl hydroperoxide, see Organic peroxide type D, solid			
Tetrahydrophthalic anhydrides	2698	8	31 (c)
1,2,3,6-Tetrahydropyridine	2410	3	3 (b)
Tetrahydrothiophene	2412	3	3 (b)
Tetramethyl lead, see Motor fuel, anti-knock mixture			
Tetramethylammonium hydroxide	1835	8	51 (b)
1,1,3,3-Tetramethylbutyl hydroperoxide, see Organic peroxide type D, liquid			
1,1,3,3-Tetramethylbutyl peroxy-2-ethylhexanoate, see Organic peroxide type D, liquid temperature controlled			
Tetramethylethylenediamine	2372	3	3 (b)
Tetramethylsilane	2749	3	1 (a)
Tetramine palladium (II) nitrate, see Self-reactive solid, type C, temperature controlled			
Tetranitroaniline	0207	1.1D	4
Tetranitromethane	1510	5.1	2 (a)
Tetrapropyl orthotitanate	2413	3	31 (c)
Tetrapropylene	2850	3	31 (c)
Tetrazol-1-acetic acid	0407	1.4C	36
Tetryl, see Trinitrophenylmethylnitramine			
Thallium chlorate	2573	5.1	29 (b)
Thallium compound, n.o.s	1707	6.1	53 (b)
Thallium nitrate	2727	6.1	68 (b)
Thallium sulphate (pesticide), see under Pesticide, etc.			

Name of substance or article	Substance Identification No. (UN No.)	Class	Item number and letter
4-Thiapentanal	2785	6.1	20 (c)
Thioacetic acid	2436	3	3 (b)
Thiocyanates, alkaline: Not subject to ADR		6.1	41, Note 1
Thioglycol	2966	6.1	21 (b)
Thioglycolic acid	1940	8	32 (b)1.
Thiolactic acid	2936	6.1	21 (b)
Thiolanne, see Tetrahydrothiophene			
Thiomethon (pesticide), see Organophosphorus pesticides			
Thionazin (pesticide), see Organophosphorus pesticides			
Thionyl chloride	1836	8	12 (a)
Thiophene	2414	3	3 (b)
Thiophosgene	2474	6.1	21 (b)
Thiophosphoryl chloride	1837	8	12 (b)
Thorium metal, pyrophoric	2975	7	Sch 9, 10, 11, 13
- under special arrangement	2975		Sch. 13
Thorium nitrate, solid	2976	7	Sch 5,6,9,10, 11,13
- LSA-I	2976		Sch 5
- LSA-II	2976		Sch. 6
- under special arrangement	2976		Sch. 13
Tinctures, medicinal	1293	3	3 (b), 31 (c)
Titanium disulphide	3174	4.2	13 (c)
Titanium hydride	1871	4.1	14 (b)
Titanium powder, dry	2546	4.2	12 (a), (b), (c)
Titanium powder, wetted	1352	4.1	13 (b)
Titanium sponge granules	2878	4.1	13 (c)
Titanium sponge powders	2878	4.1	13 (c)
Titanium tetrachloride	1838	8	12 (b)
Titanium trichloride mixture	2869	8	11 (b), (c)
Titanium trichloride, pyrophoric	2441	4.2	15 (a)
TNT, see Trinitrotoluene			
Tolite, see Trinitrotoluene			
Toluene	1294	3	3 (b)
Toluene diisocyanate	2078	6.1	19 (b)
Toluene sulphonic acid, see Aryl sulphonic acids			
Toluidines	1708	6.1	12 (b)
2,4-Toluylenediamine	1709	6.1	12 (c)

Name of substance or article	Substance Identification No. (UN No.)	Class	Item number and letter
Tolyl isocyanates, see Isocyanates, toxic, n.o.s. or Isocyanate solution, toxic, n.o.s			
Torpedoes, liquid fuelled with inert head	0450	1.3J	32
Torpedoes, liquid fuelled with or without bursting charge	0449	1.1J	10
Torpedoes with bursting charge	0329	1.1E	6
Torpedoes with bursting charge	0330	1.1F	7
Torpedoes with bursting charge	0451	1.1D	5
Tosyl isocyanate, see Isocyanates, toxic, n.o.s. or Isocyanate solution, toxic, n.o.s			
Town gas	1023	2	1 TF
Toxic liquid, corrosive, inorganic, n.o.s.	3289	6.1	67 (a), (b)
Toxic liquid, corrosive, organic, n.o.s.	2927	6.1	27 (a), (b)
Toxic liquid, flammable, organic, n.o.s.	2929	6.1	26 (a)1., (b)1.
Toxic liquid, inorganic, n.o.s.	3287	6.1	65 (a), (b), (c)
Toxic liquid, organic, n.o.s.	2810	6.1	25 (a), (b), (c)
Toxic liquid, oxidizing, n.o.s.	3122	6.1	68 (a), (b)
Toxic liquid, water-reactive, n.o.s.	3123	6.1	44 (a), (b)
Toxic solid, corrosive, inorganic, n.o.s.	3290	6.1	67 (a), (b)
Toxic solid, corrosive, organic, n.o.s.	2928	6.1	27 (a), (b)
Toxic solid, flammable, organic, n.o.s.	2930	6.1	26 (a)2., (b)2.
Toxic solid, inorganic, n.o.s.	3288	6.1	65 (a), (b), (c)
Toxic solid, organic, n.o.s.	2811	6.1	25 (a), (b), (c)
Toxic solid, oxidizing, n.o.s.	3086	6.1	68 (a), (b), (c)
Toxic solid, self-heating, n.o.s.	3124	6.1	66 (b), (c)
Toxic solid, water-reactive, n.o.s.	3125	6.1	44 (a), (b)
Toxins, extracted from living sources, n.o.s.	3172	6.1	90 (a), (b), (c)
Tracers for ammunition	0212	1.3G	30
Tracers for ammunition	0306	1.4G	43
Tremolite	2590	9	1 (c)
Triadimefon (pesticide), see Phenoxy pesticides			
Triallylamine	2610	3	33 (c)
Triallyl borate	2609	6.1	14 (c)
Triamiphos (pesticide), see Organophosphorus pesticides			
Triazine pesticide, liquid, flammable, toxic, flash-point less than 23 °C	2764	3	41 (a), (b)
Triazine pesticide, liquid, toxic	2998	6.1	71 (a), (b), (c)
Triazine pesticide, liquid, toxic, flammable, flash point not less than 23 °C	2997	6.1	72 (a), (b), (c)
Triazine pesticide, solid, toxic	2763	6.1	73 (a), (b), (c)
Triazophos (pesticide), see Organophosphorus pesticides			
Tributylamine	2542	6.1	12 (b)

Name of substance or article	Substance Identification No. (UN No.)	Class	Item number and letter
Tributylphosphane	3254	4.2	6 (a)
Tricamba (pesticide), see Benzoic derivative pesticides			
Trichlorfon (pesticide), see Organophosphorus pesticides			
Trichloroacetic acid	1839	8	31 (b)
Trichloroacetic acid solution	2564	8	32 (b)1., (c)
Trichloroacetic anhydride, see Corrosive solid, acidic, organic, n.o.s			
Trichloroacetonitrile, see Toxic liquid, organic, n.o.s.			
Trichloroacetyl chloride	2442	8	35 (b)1.
Trichlorobenzenes, liquid	2321	6.1	15 (c)
Trichlorobutene	2322	6.1	15 (b)
1,1,1-Trichloroethane	2831	6.1	15 (c)
Trichloroethylene	1710	6.1	15 (c)
Trichlorofluoromethane		2	2 A Note
Trichloroisocyanuric acid, dry	2468	5.1	26 (b)
Trichloromethylbenzene	2226	8	66 (b)
Trichloronat (pesticide), see Organophosphorus pesticides			
Trichloronitroethane, see Toxic liquid, flammable, organic, n.o.s			
Trichlorophenols, see Chlorophenols, solid			
Trichloropropane, see Toxic liquid, organic, n.o.s			
Trichlorosilane	1295	4.3	1 (a)
1,1,2-Trichloro-1,2,2-trifluoroethane		2	2 A Note
1,1,1-Trichloro-2,2,2-trifluoroethane		2	2 A Note
Tricresyl phosphate with more than 3% ortho isomer	2574	6.1	23 (b)
Triethylamine	1296	3	22 (b)
Triethylenetetramine	2259	8	53 (b)
Triethyl phosphine, see Toxic liquid, flammable, organic, n.o.s.			
Triethyl phosphite	2323	3	31 (c)
Trifluoroacetic acid	2699	8	32 (a)
Trifluoroacetyl chloride	3057	2	2 TC
Trifluorochloroethylene, inhibited	1082	2	2 TF
1,1,1-Trifluoroethane	2035	2	2 F
Trifluoromethane	1984	2	2 A
Trifluoromethane, refrigerated liquid	3136	2	3 A
2-Trifluoromethylaniline	2942	6.1	12 (c)
3-Trifluoromethylaniline	2948	6.1	17 (b)
Triisobutylene	2324	3	31 (c)
Triisopropyl borate	2616	3	3 (b)
Triisopropyl borate, chemically pure	2616	3	31 (c)
Trimethylacetyl chloride	2438	6.1	10 (a)

Name of substance or article	Substance Identification No. (UN No.)	Class	Item number and letter
Trimethylamine, anhydrous	1083	2	2 F
Trimethylamine, aqueous solution, not more than 50% trimethylamine, by mass	1297	3	22 (a), (b), 33 (c)
1,3,5-Trimethylbenzene	2325	3	31 (c)
Trimethyl borate	2416	3	3 (b)
2,4,4-Trimethylpentyl-2-peroxyneodecanoate, see Organic peroxide type F, liquid, temperature controlled			
2,4,4-Trimethylpentyl-2-peroxy phenoxyacetate, see Organic peroxide type D, liquid, temperature controlled			
Trimethyl phosphite	2329	3	31 (c)
Trimethylchlorosilane	1298	3	21 (b)
Trimethylcyclohexylamine	2326	8	53 (c)
Trimethylhexamethylene diisocyanate	2328	6.1	19 (c)
Trimethylhexamethylenediamines	2327	8	53 (c)
Trimethylsilane	1953	2	1 TF
Trinitroaniline	0153	1.1D	4
Trinitroanisole	0213	1.1D	4
Trinitrobenzene, dry or wetted with less than 30% water, by mass	0214	1.1D	4
Trinitrobenzene, wetted with not less than 10% water, by mass	0214	4.1	21 (a)2.
Trinitrobenzenesulphonic acid	0386	1.1D	4
Trinitrobenzene, wetted with not less than 30% water, by mass	1354	4.1	21 (a)1.
Trinitrobenzoic acid, dry or wetted with less than 30% water, by mass	0215	1.1D	4
Trinitrobenzoic acid, wetted with not less than 30% water, by mass	1355	4.1	21 (a)1.
Trinitrobenzoic acid, wetted with not less than 10% water, by mass	0215	4.1	21 (a)2.
Trinitrochlorobenzene	0155	1.1D	4
Trinitrochlorobenzene, wetted with not less than 10% water, by mass	0155	4.1	21 (a)2.
Trinitro-m-cresol	0216	1.1D	4
Trinitrofluorenone	0387	1.1D	4
Trinitronaphthalene	0217	1.1D	4
Trinitrophenetole	0218	1.1D	4
Trinitrophenol, dry or wetted with less than 30% water, by mass	0154	1.1D	4
Trinitrophenol, wetted with not less than 30% water, by mass	1344	4.1	21 (a)1.
Trinitrophenol, wetted with not less than 10% water, by mass	0154	4.1	21 (a)2.
Trinitrophenylmethylnitramine	0208	1.1D	4
Trinitroresorcinol, dry or wetted with less than 20% water, or mixture of alcohol and water, by mass	0219	1.1D	4
Trinitroresorcinol, wetted with not less than 20% water, or mixture of alcohol and water, by mass	0394	1.1D	4
Trinitrotoluene and hexanitrostilbene mixture	0388	1.1D	4
Trinitrotoluene and trinitrobenzene mixture	0388	1.1D	4

Name of substance or article	Substance Identification No. (UN No.)	Class	Item number and letter
Trinitrotoluene mixture containing trinitrobenzene and hexanitrostilbene	0389	1.1D	4
Trinitrotoluene, dry or wetted with less than 30% water, by mass	0209	1.1D	4
Trinitrotoluene, wetted with not less than 30% water, by mass	1356	4.1	21 (a)1.
Trinitrotoluene, wetted with not less than 10% water, by mass	0209	4.1	21 (a)2.
Triphenylphosphine oxide, see Toxic solid, organic, n.o.s.			
Tripropylamine	2260	3	33 (c)
Tripropylene	2057	3	3 (b), 31 (c)
Tris-(1-aziridinyl) phosphine oxide solution	2501	6.1	23 (b), (c)
Tritonal	0390	1.1D	4
Tungsten hexafluoride	2196	2	2 TC
Turpentine	1299	3	31 (c)
Turpentine substitute	1300	3	3 (b), 31 (c)
Undecane	2330	3	31 (c)
Uranium hexafluoride, fissile	2977	7	
- in approved packages	2977	7	Sch. 12
- under special arrangement	2977		Sch. 13
Uranium hexafluoride, non fissile or fissile-excepted	2978	7	
- LSA-I	2978	7	Sch. 5
- LSA-II	2978		Sch. 6
- under special arrangement	2978		Sch. 13
Uranyl nitrate, solid	2981	7	
- LSA-I	2981		Sch. 5
- LSA-II	2981		Sch. 6
- under special arrangement	2981		Sch. 13
Urea hydrogen peroxide	1511	5.1	31 (c)
Urea nitrate, dry or wetted with less than 20% water, by mass	0220	1.1D	4
Urea nitrate, wetted with not less than 20% water, by mass	1357	4.1	21 (a)1.
Urea nitrate, wetted with not less than 10% water, by mass	0220	4.1	21 (a)3.
Valeraldehyde	2058	3	3 (b)
Valeryl chloride	2502	8	35 (b)2.
Vamidothion (pesticide), see Organophosphorus pesticides			
Vanadium compound, n.o.s.	3285	6.1	58 (a), (b), (c)
Vanadium oxytrichloride	2443	8	12 (b)
Vanadium pentoxide, fuzed: Not subject to ADR		6.1	58 (b), Note
Vanadium pentoxide, non-fuzed form	2862	6.1	58 (b)
Vanadium tetrachloride	2444	8	12 (a)

Name of substance or article	Substance Identification No. (UN No.)	Class	Item number and letter
Vanadium trichloride	2475	8	11 (c)
Vanadyl sulphate	2931	6.1	58 (b)
Varnish	1263	3	5 (a), (b), (c), 31 (c) (See Note to Section E)
Varnish, nitrocellulose, see Nitrocellulose solution, flammable			
Vinyl acetate, inhibited	1301	3	3 (b)
Vinylbenzene	2055	3	31 (c)
Vinyl bromide, inhibited	1085	2	2 F
Vinyl butyrate, inhibited	2838.	3	3 (b)
Vinyl chloride, inhibited	1086	2	2 F
Vinyl chloride, stabilized	1086	2	2 F
Vinyl chloroacetate	2589	6.1	16 (b)
Vinyl ethyl ether inhibited	1302	3	2 (a)
Vinyl fluoride, inhibited	1860	2	2 F
Vinylidene chloride, inhibited	1303	3	1 (a)
Vinylidene fluoride	1959	2	2 F
Vinyl isobutyl ether, inhibited	1304	3	3 (b)
Vinyl methyl ether, inhibited	1087	2	2 F
Vinylpyridines, inhibited	3073	6.1	11 (b)1.
Vinyltoluenes, inhibited	2618	3	31 (c)
Vinyltrichlorosilane, inhibited	1305	3	21 (a)
Warfarin (and salts of) (pesticide) see Coumarin derivative pesticides			
Warheads, rocket with burster or expelling charge	0370	1.4D	39
Warheads, rocket with burster or expelling charge	0371	1.4F	41
Warheads, rocket with bursting charge	0286	1.1D	5
Warheads, rocket with bursting charge	0287	1.2D	17
Warheads, rocket with bursting charge	0369	1.1F	7
Warheads, torpedo with bursting charge	0221	1.1D	5
Water gas	2600	2	1 TF
Water-reactive liquid, corrosive, n.o.s.	3129	4.3	25 (a), (b), (c)
Water-reactive liquid, n.o.s.	3148	4.3	21 (a), (b), (c)
Water-reactive liquid, toxic, n.o.s.	3130	4.3	23 (a), (b), (c)
Water-reactive solid, corrosive, n.o.s.	3131	4.3	24 (a), (b), (c)
Water-reactive solid, flammable, n.o.s.	3132		
Water-reactive solid, n.o.s.	2813	4.3	20 (a), (b), (c)
Water-reactive solid, oxidizing, n.o.s.	3133		
Water-reactive solid, self-heating, n.o.s.	3135		
Water-reactive solid, toxic, n.o.s.	3134	4.3	22 (a), (b), (c)

Supplement No.1

Name of substance or article	Substance Identification No. (UN No.)	Class	Item number and letter
White asbestos	2590	9	1 (c)
White lead, see Lead compound, soluble, n.o.s.			
White or yellow phosphorus, dry or under water or in solution	1381	4.2	11 (a)
White spirit	1300	3	3 (b), 31 (c)
Wood preservatives, liquid	1306	3	5 (b), (c), 31 (c)
Wood tar oil, see Tars, liquid			
Xenon, compressed	2036	2	1 A
Xenon, refrigerated liquid	2591	2	3 A
Xylenes	1307	3	3 (b), 31 (c)
o-Xylene, see Xylenes			
Xylenols	2261	6.1	14 (b)
Xylenols, alkaline solutions, see Corrosive liquid, n.o.s.			
Xylidines	1711	6.1	12 (b)
Xylyl bromide	1701	6.1	15 (b)
Zinc ammonium nitrite	1512	5.1	23 (b)
Zinc arsenate, zinc arsenite, or zinc arsenate and zinc arsenite mixtures	1712	6.1	51 (b)
Zinc ashes	1435	4.3	13 (c)
Zinc bromate	2469	5.1	16 (c)
Zinc chlorate	1513	5.1	11 (b)
Zinc chloride, anhydrous	2331	8	11 (c)
Zinc chloride, solution	1840	8	5 (c)
Zinc cyanide	1713	6.1	41 (a)
Zinc dithionite	1931	9	32 (c)
Zinc dust	1436	4.3	14 (a), (b), (c)
Zinc fluorosilicate	2855	6.1	64 (c)
Zinc hydrosulphite, see Zinc dithionite			
Zinc nitrate	1514	5.1	22 (b)
Zinc permanganate	1515	5.1	17 (b)
Zinc peroxide	1516	5.1	25 (b)
Zinc phosphide	1714	4.3	18 (a)
Zinc powder	1436	4.3	14 (a), (b), (c)
Zinc resinate	2714	4.1	12 (c)
Zinc selenate, see Selenates			
Zinc selenite, see Selenites			
Zinc telluride, see Tellurium compound, n.o.s.			
Zirconium, dry, coiled wire, finished metal sheets, strip (thinner than 254 microns but not thinner than 18 microns)	2858	4.1	13 (c)
Zirconium, dry, finished sheets, strip or coiled wire	2009	4.2	12 (c)
Zirconium hydride	1437	4.1	14 (b)

Supplement No.1

Name of substance or article	Substance Identification No. (UN No.)	Class	Item number and letter
Zirconium nitrate	2728	5.1	22 (c)
Zirconium picramate, dry or wetted with less than 20% water, by mass	0236	1.3C	26
Zirconium picramate, wetted with not less than 20% water, by mass	1517	4.1	21 (a)1.
Zirconium powder, dry	2008	4.2	12 (a), (b), (c)
Zirconium powder, wetted	1358	4.1	13 (b)
Zirconium scrap	1932	4.2	12 (c)
Zirconium suspended in a flammable liquid	1308	3	1 (a), 2 (a), (b), 3 (b), 31 (c)
Zirconium tetrachloride	2503	8	11 (c)

SUPPLEMENT No.2 : Numerical list (per substance identification (UN) number) of substances and articles of ADR

Index of UN numbers with their ADR class and items. In some instances the following terms are used under the heading ADR item(s):

Prohibited   indicating that a substance with this UN number is not accepted for carriage under ADR;

Exempt   indicating that, normally, a substance with this UN number is not subject to the requirements of ADR;

-    indicating that no ADR item provides for a corresponding entry.

a space indicates that an assimilation has not been determined.

UN No.	Class	ADR item(s)	UN No.	Class	ADR item(s)	UN No.	Class	ADR item(s)
0004	1.1D	4	0074	1.1A	Prohibited	0150	1.1D	4
0005	1.1F	7	0075	1.1D	4	0151	1.1D	4
0006	1.1E	6	0076	1.1D	4	0153	1.1D	4
0007	1.2F	19	0077	1.3C	26	0154	1.1D	4
0009	1.2G	21	0078	1.1D	4		4.1	21 (a)2.
0010	1.3G	30	0079	1.1D	4	0155	1.1D	4
0012	1.4S	47	0081	1.1D	4		4.1	21 (a)2.
0014	1.4S	47	0082	1.1D	4	0159	1.3C	26
0015	1.2G	21	0083	1.1D	4	0160	1.1C	2
0016	1.3G	30	0084	1.1D	4	0161	1.3C	26
0018	1.2G	21	0092	1.3G	30	0167	1.1F	7
0019	1.3G	30	0093	1.3G	30	0168	1.1D	5
0020	1.2K	Prohibited	0094	1.1G	8	0169	1.2D	17
0021	1.3K	Prohibited	0099	1.1D	5	0171	1.2G	21
0027	1.1D	4	0101	1.3G	30	0173	1.4S	47
0028	1.1D	4	0102	1.2D	17	0174	1.4S	47
0029	1.1B	1	0103	1.4G	43	0180	1.1F	7
0030	1.1B	1	0104	1.4D	39	0181	1.1E	6
0033	1.1F	7	0105	1.4S	47	0182	1.2E	18
0034	1.1D	5	0106	1.1B	1	0183	1.3C	27
0035	1.2D	17	0107	1.2B	13	0186	1.3C	27
0037	1.1F	7	0110	1.4S	47	0190	1	51
0038	1.1D	5	0113	1.1A	Prohibited	0191	1.4G	43
0039	1.2G	21	0114	1.1A	Prohibited	0192	1.1G	9
0042	1.1D	5	0118	1.1D	4	0193	1.4S	47
0043	1.1D	5	0121	1.1G	9	0194	1.1G	9
0044	1.4S	47	0124	1.1D	5	0195	1.3G	30
0048	1.1D	5	0129	1.1A	Prohibited	0196	1.1G	9
0049	1.1G	9	0130	1.1A	Prohibited	0197	1.4G	43
0050	1.3G	30	0131	1.4S	47	0204	1.2F	19
0054	1.3G	30	0132	1.3C	26	0207	1.1D	4
0055	1.4S	47	0133	1.1D	4	0208	1.1D	4
0056	1.1D	5	0135	1.1A	Prohibited	0209	1.1D	4
0059	1.1D	5	0136	1.1F	7		4.1	21 (a)2.
0060	1.1D	5	0137	1.1D	5	0212	1.3G	30
0065	1.1D	5	0138	1.2D	17	0213	1.1D	4
0066	1.4G	43	0143	1.1D	4	0214	1.1D	4
0070	1.4S	47	0144	1.1D	4		4.1	21 (a)2.
0072	1.1D	4	0146	1.1D	4	0215	1.1D	4
0073	1.1B	1	0147	1.1D	4		4.1	21 (a)2.

UN No.	Class	ADR item(s)	UN No.	Class	ADR item(s)	UN No.	Class	ADR item(s)
0216	1.1D	4	0295	1.2F	19	0358	1.2L	24
0217	1.1D	4	0296	1.1F	7	0359	1.3L	33
0218	1.1D	4	0297	1.4G	43	0360	1.1B	1
0219	1.1D	4	0299	1.3G	30	0361	1.4B	35
0220	1.1D	4	0300	1.4G	43	0362	1.4G	43
0221	1.1D	5	0301	1.4G	43	0363	1.4G	43
0222	1.1D	4	0303	1.4G	43	0364	1.2B	13
0223	1.1D	4	0305	1.3G	29	0365	1.4B	35
0224	1.1A	Prohibited	0306	1.4G	43	0366	1.4S	47
0225	1.1B	1	0312	1.4G	43	0367	1.4S	47
0226	1.1D	4	0313	1.2G	21	0368	1.4S	47
0234	1.3C	26	0314	1.2G	21	0369	1.1F	7
0235	1.3C	26	0315	1.3G	30	0370	1.4D	39
0236	1.3C	26	0316	1.3G	30	0371	1.4F	41
0237	1.4D	39	0317	1.4G	43	0372	1.2G	21
0238	1.2G	21	0318	1.3G	30	0373	1.4S	47
0240	1.3G	30	0319	1.3G	30	0374	1.1D	5
0241	1.1D	4	0320	1.4G	43	0375	1.2D	17
0242	1.3C	27	0321	1.2E	18	0376	1.4S	47
0243	1.2H	22	0322	1.2L	25	0377	1.1B	1
0244	1.3H	31	0323	1.4S	47	0378	1.4B	35
0245	1.2H	22	0324	1.2F	19	0379	1.4C	37
0246	1.3H	31	0325	1.4G	43	0380	1.2L	25
0247	1.3J	32	0326	1.1C	3	0381	1.2C	15
0248	1.2L	25	0327	1.3C	27	0382	1.2B	13
0249	1.3L	34	0328	1.2C	15	0383	1.4B	35
0250	1.3L	34	0329	1.1E	6	0384	1.4S	47
0254	1.3G	30	0330	1.1F	7	0385	1.1D	4
0255	1.4B	35	0331	1.5D	48	0386	1.1D	4
0257	1.4B	35	0332	1.5D	48	0387	1.1D	4
0266	1.1D	4	0333	1.1G	9	0388	1.1D	4
0267	1.4B	35	0334	1.2G	21	0389	1.1D	4
0268	1.2B	13	0335	1.3G	30	0390	1.1D	4
0271	1.1C	3	0336	1.4G	43	0391	1.1D	4
0272	1.3C	27	0337	1.4S	47	0392	1.1D	4
0275	1.3C	27	0338	1.4C	37	0393	1.1D	4
0276	1.4C	37	0339	1.4C	37	0394	1.1D	4
0277	1.3C	27	0340	1.1D	4	0395	1.2J	23
0278	1.4C	37	0341	1.1D	4	0396	1.3J	32
0279	1.1C	3	0342	1.3C	26	0397	1.1J	10
0280	1.1C	3	0343	1.3C	26	0398	1.2J	23
0281	1.2C	15	0344	1.4D	39	0399	1.1J	10
0282	1.1D	4	0345	1.4S	47	0400	1.2J	23
0283	1.2D	17	0346	1.2D	17	0401	1.1D	4
0284	1.1D	5	0347	1.4D	39	0402	1.1D	4
0285	1.2D	17	0348	1.4F	41	0403	1.4G	43
0286	1.1D	5	0349	1.4S	47	0404	1.4S	47
0287	1.2D	17	0350	1.4B	35	0405	1.4S	47
0288	1.1D	5	0351	1.4C	37	0406	1.3C	26
0289	1.4D	39	0352	1.4D	39	0407	1.4C	36
0290	1.1D	5	0353	1.4G	43	0408	1.1D	5
0291	1.2F	19	0354	1.1L	12	0409	1.2D	17
0292	1.1F	7	0355	1.2L	25	0410	1.4D	39
0293	1.2F	19	0356	1.3L	34	0411	1.1D	4
0294	1.2F	19	0357	1.1L	11	0412	1.4E	40

UN No.	Class	ADR item(s)	UN No.	Class	ADR item(s)	UN No.	Class	ADR item(s)
0413	1.2C	15	0471	1.4E	40	1032	2	2F
0414	1.2C	15	0472	1.4F	41	1033	2	2F
0415	1.2C	15	0473	1.1A	Prohibited	1035	2	2F
0417	1.3C	27	0474	1.1C	2	1036	2	2F
0418	1.1G	9	0475	1.1D	4	1037	2	2F
0419	1.2G	21	0476	1.1G	8	1038	2	3F
0420	1.1G	9	0477	1.3C	26	1039	2	2F
0421	1.2G	21	0478	1.3G	29	1040	2	2TF
0424	1.3G	30	0479	1.4C	36	1041	2	2F
0425	1.4G	43	0480	1.4D	38	1043	2	4A
0426	1.2F	19	0481	1.4S	46	1044	2	6A
0427	1.4F	41	0482	1.5D	48	1045	2	1TOC
0428	1.1G	9	0483	1.1D	4	1046	2	1A
0429	1.2G	21	0484	1.1D	4	1048	2	2TC
0430	1.3G	30	0485	1.4G	42	1049	2	1F
0431	1.4G	43	0486	1.6N	50	1050	2	2TC
0432	1.4S	47	0487	1.3G	30	1051	6.1	1
0433	1.1C	2	0488	1.3G	30	1052	8	6
0434	1.2G	21	0489	1.1D	4	1053	2	2TF
0435	1.4G	43	0490	1.1D	4	1055	2	2F
0436	1.2C	15	0491	1.4C	37	1056	2	1A
0437	1.3C	27	0492	1.3G	30	1057	2	6F
0438	1.4C	37	0493	1.4G	43	1058	2	2A
0439	1.2D	17	0494	1.4D	39	1060	2	2F
0440	1.4D	39	0495	1.3C	26	1061	2	2F
0441	1.4S	47	0496	1.1D	4	1062	2	2T
0442	1.1D	5	0497	1.1C	2	1063	2	2F
0443	1.2D	17	0498	1.1C	2	1064	2	2TF
0444	1.4D	39	0499	1.3C	26	1065	2	1A
0445	1.4S	47	0500	1.4S	47	1066	2	1A
0446	1.4C	37	1001	2	4F	1067	2	2TOC
0447	1.3C	27	1002	2	1A	1069	2	2TC
0448	1.4C	36	1003	2	3O	1070	2	2O
0449	1.1J	10	1005	2	2TC	1071	2	1TF
0450	1.3J	32	1006	2	1A	1072	2	1O
0451	1.1D	5	1008	2	1TC	1073	2	3O
0453	1.4G	43	1009	2	2A	1075	2	2F
0452	1.4G	43	1010	2	2F	1076	2	2TC
0454	1.4S	47	1011	2	2F	1077	2	2F
0455	1.4S	47	1012	2	2F	1078	2	2A
0456	1.4S	47	1013	2	2A	1079	2	2TC
0457	1.1D	5	1014	2	1O	1080	2	2A
0458	1.2D	17	1015	2	2A	1081	2	2F
0459	1.4D	39	1016	2	1TF	1082	2	2TF
0460	1.4S	47	1017	2	2TC	1083	2	2F
0461	1.1B	1	1018	2	2A	1085	2	2F
0462	1.1C	3	1020	2	2A	1086	2	2F
0463	1.1D	5	1021	2	2A	1087	2	2F
0464	1.1E	6	1022	2	2A	1088	3	3 (b)
0465	1.1F	7	1023	2	1TF	1089	3	1 (a)
0466	1.2C	15	1026	2	2TF	1090	3	3 (b)
0467	1.2D	17	1027	2	2F	1091	3	3 (b)
0468	1.2E	18	1028	2	2A	1092	6.1	8 (a)
0469	1.2F	19	1029	2	2A	1093	3	11 (a)
0470	1.3C	27	1030	2	2F	1098	6.1	8 (a)

UN No.	Class	ADR item(s)	UN No.	Class	ADR item(s)	UN No.	Class	ADR item(s)
1099	3	16 (a)	1169	3	5 (a), (b), (c)	1233	3	31 (c)
1100	3	16 (a)			or 31 (c)	1234	3	2 (b)
1104	3	31 (c)	1170	3	3 (b) or 31 (c)	1235	3	22 (b)
1105	3	3 (b) or 31 (c)	1171	3	31 (c)	1237	3	3 (b)
1106	3	22 (b)	1172	3	31 (c)	1238	6.1	10 (a)
		or 33 (c)	1173	3	3 (b)	1239	6.1	9 (a)
1107	3	3 (b)	1175	3	3 (b)	1242	4.3	1 (a)
1108	3	1 (a)	1176	3	3 (b)	1243	3	1 (a)
1109	3	31 (c)	1177	3	31 (c)	1244	6.1	7 (a)1.
1110	3	31 (c)	1178	3	3 (b)	1245	3	3 (b)
1111	3	3 (b)	1179	3	3 (b)	1246	3	3 (b)
1112	3	31 (c)	1180	3	31 (c)	1247	3	3 (b)
1113	3	3 (b)	1181	6.1	16 (b)	1248	3	3 (b)
1114	3	3 (b)	1182	6.1	10 (a)	1249	3	3 (b)
1120	3	3 (b) or 31 (c)	1183	4.3	1 (a)	1250	3	21 (a)
1123	3	3 (b) or 31 (c)	1184	3	16 (b)	1251	6.1	8 (a)1.
1125	3	22 (b)	1185	6.1	4	1259	6.1	3
1126	3	3 (b)	1188	3	31 (c)	1261	3	3 (b)
1127	3	3 (b)	1189	3	31 (c)	1262	3	3 (b)
1128	3	3 (b)	1190	3	3 (b)	1263	3	5 (a), (b), (c)
1129	3	3 (b)	1191	3	31 (c)			or 31 (c)
1130	3	31 (c)	1192	3	31 (c)	1264	3	31 (c)
1131	3	18 (a)	1193	3	3 (b)	1265	3	1 (a) or 2 (b)
1133	3	5 (a), (b), (c)	1194	3	15 (a)	1266	3	5 (a), (b), (c)
		or 31 (c)	1195	3	3 (b)			or 31 (c)
1134	3	31 (c)	1196	3	21 (b)	1267	3	1 (a), 2 (a), (b),
1135	6.1	16 (a)	1197	3	5 (a), (b), (c)			3 (b) or 31 (c)
1136	3	3 (b) or 31 (c)			or 31 (c)	1268	3	1 (a), 2 (a), (b),
1139	3	5 (a) (b), (c)	1198	3	33 (c)			3 (b) or 31 (c)
		or 31 (c)	1199	6.1	13 (b)	1272	3	31 (c)
1143	6.1	8 (a)	1201	3	3 (b) or 31 (c)	1274	3	3 (b) or 31 (c)
1144	3	1 (a)	1202	3	31 (c)	1275	3	3 (b)
1145	3	3 (b)	1203	3	3 (b)	1276	3	3 (b)
1146	3	3 (b)	1204	3	7 (b)	1277	3	22 (b)
1147	3	31 (c)	1206	3	3 (b)	1278	3	2 (b)
1148	3	3 (b) or 31 (c)	1207	3	31 (c)	1279	3	3 (b)
1149	3	31 (c)	1208	3	3 (b)	1280	3	2 (a)
1150	3	3 (b)	1210	3	5 (a), (b), (c)	1281	3	3 (b)
1152	3	31 (c)			or 31 (c)	1282	3	3 (b)
1153	3	31 (c)	1212	3	31 (c)	1286	3	5 (a), (b), (c)
1154	3	22 (b)	1213	3	3 (b)			or 31 (c)
1155	3	2 (a)	1214	3	22 (b)	1287	3	5 (a), (b), (c)
1156	3	3 (b)	1216	3	3 (b)			or 31 (c)
1157	3	31 (c)	1218	3	2 (a)	1288	3	3 (b) or 31 (c)
1158	3	22 (b)	1219	3	3 (b)	1289	3	24 (b) or 33 (c)
1159	3	3 (b)	1220	3	3 (b)	1292	3	31 (c)
1160	3	22 (b)	1221	3	22 (a)	1293	3	3 (b) or 31 (c)
1161	3	3 (b)	1222	3	3 (b)	1294	3	3 (b)
1162	3	21 (b)	1223	3	31 (c)	1295	4.3	1 (a)
1163	6.1	7 (a)1.	1224	3	2 (b), 3 (b)	1296	3	22 (b)
1164	3	2 (b)			or 31 (c)	1297	3	22 (a), (b)
1165	3	3 (b)	1228	3	18 (b) or 32 (c)			or 33 (c)
1166	3	3 (b)	1229	3	31 (c)	1298	3	21 (b)
1167	3	2 (a)	1230	3	17 (b)	1299	3	31 (c)
			1231	3	3 (b)	1300	3	3 (b) or 31 (c)

UN No.	Class	ADR item(s)	UN No.	Class	ADR item(s)	UN No.	Class	ADR item(s)
1301	3	3 (b)	1363	4.2	2 (c)	1435	4.3	13 (c)
1302	3	2 (a)	1364	4.2	3 (c)	1436	4.3	14 (a), (b)
1303	3	1 (a)	1365	4.2	3 (c)			or (c)
1304	3	3 (b)	1366	4.2	31 (a)	1437	4.1	14 (b)
1305	3	21 (a)	1369	4.2	5 (b)	1438	5.1	22 (c)
1306	3	5 (b), (c)	1370	4.2	31 (a)	1439	5.1	27 (b)
		or 31 (c)	1373	4.2	3 (c)	1442	5.1	12 (b)
1307	3	3 (b) or 31 (c)	1374	4.2	2 (b)	1444	5.1	18 (c)
1308	3	1 (a), 2 (a),	1376	4.2	16 (c)	1445	5.1	29 (b)
		(b), 3 (b)	1378	4.2	12 (b)	1446	5.1	29 (b)
		or 31 (c)	1379	4.2	3 (c)	1447	5.1	29 (b)
1309	4.1	13 (b) or (c)	1380	4.2	19 (a)	1448	5.1	29 (b)
1310	4.1	21 (a)1.	1381	4.2	11 (a)	1449	5.1	29 (b)
1312	4.1	6 (c)	1382	4.2	13 (b)	1450	5.1	16 (b)
1313	4.1	12 (c)	1383	4.2	12 (a)	1451	5.1	22 (c)
1314	4.1	12 (c)	1384	4.2	13 (b)	1452	5.1	11 (b)
1318	4.1	12 (c)	1385	4.2	13 (b)	1453	5.1	14 (b)
1320	4.1	22 (a)1.	1386	4.2	2 (c)	1454	5.1	22 (c)
1321	4.1	22 (a)1.	1389	4.3	11 (a)	1455	5.1	13 (b)
1322	4.1	21 (a)1.	1390	4.3	19 (b)	1456	5.1	17 (b)
1323	4.1	13 (b)	1391	4.3	11 (a)	1457	5.1	25 (b)
1324	4.1	3 (c)	1392	4.3	11 (a)	1458	5.1	11 (b)
1325	4.1	6 (b) or (c)	1393	4.3	11 (b)	1459	5.1	11 (b)
1326	4.1	13 (b)	1394	4.3	17 (b)	1461	5.1	11 (b)
1327	4.1	-	1395	4.3	15 (b)	1462	5.1	14 (b)
1328	4.1	6 (c)	1396	4.3	13 (b)	1463	5.1	31 (b)
1330	4.1	12 (c)	1397	4.3	18 (a)	1465	5.1	22 (c)
1331	4.1	2 (c)	1398	4.3	13 (c)	1466	5.1	22 (c)
1332	4.1	6 (c)	1400	4.3	11 (b)	1467	5.1	22 (c)
1333	4.1	13 (b)	1401	4.3	11 (b)	1469	5.1	29 (b)
1334	4.1	6 (c)	1402	4.3	17 (b)	1470	5.1	29 (b)
1336	4.1	21 (a)1.	1403	4.3	19 (c)	1471	5.1	15 (b)
1337	4.1	21 (a)1.	1404	4.3	16 (a)	1472	5.1	25 (b)
1338	4.1	11 (c)	1405	4.3	12 (b) or (c)	1473	5.1	16 (b)
1339	4.1	11 (b)	1407	4.3	11 (a)	1474	5.1	22 (c)
1340	4.3	20 (b)	1408	4.3	15 (c)	1475	5.1	13 (b)
1341	4.1	11 (b)	1409	4.3	16 (a) or (b)	1476	5.1	25 (b)
1343	4.1	11 (b)	1410	4.3	16 (a)	1477	5.1	22 (b) or (c)
1344	4.1	21 (a)1.	1411	4.3	16 (a)	1479	5.1	27 (a), (b)
1345	4.1	1 (b)	1413	4.3	16 (a)			or (c)
1346	4.1	13 (c)	1414	4.3	16 (a)	1481	5.1	13 (b)
1347	4.1	21 (a)1.	1415	4.3	11 (a)	1482	5.1	17 (b)
1348	4.1	22 (a)1.	1417	4.3	12 (b)	1483	5.1	25 (b)
1349	4.1	21 (a)1.	1418	4.3	14 (b)	1484	5.1	16 (b)
1350	4.1	11 (c)	1419	4.3	18 (a)	1485	5.1	11 (b)
1352	4.1	13 (b)	1420	4.3	11 (a)	1486	5.1	22 (c)
1353	4.1	3 (c)	1421	4.3	11 (a)	1487	5.1	24 (b)
1354	4.1	21 (a)1.	1422	4.3	11 (a)	1488	5.1	23 (b)
1355	4.1	21 (a)1.	1423	4.3	11 (a)	1489	5.1	13 (b)
1356	4.1	21 (a)1.	1426	4.3	16 (a)	1490	5.1	17 (b)
1357	4.1	21 (a)1.	1427	4.3	16 (a)	1491	5.1	25 (a)
1358	4.1	13 (b)	1428	4.3	11 (a)	1492	5.1	18 (c)
1360	4.3	18 (a)	1431	4.2	15 (b)	1493	5.1	22 (b)
1361	4.2	1 (b) or (c)	1432	4.3	18 (a)	1494	5.1	16 (b)
1362	4.2	1 (c)	1433	4.3	18 (a)	1495	5.1	11 (b)

UN No.	Class	ADR item(s)	UN No.	Class	ADR item(s)	UN No.	Class	ADR item(s)
1496	5.1	14 (b)	1579	6.1	17 (c)	1640	6.1	52 (b)
1498	5.1	22 (c)	1580	6.1	17 (a)	1641	6.1	52 (b)
1499	5.1	22 (c)	1581	2	2T	1642	6.1	41 (b)
1500	5.1	23 (c)	1582	2	2T	1643	6.1	52 (b)
1502	5.1	13 (b)	1583	6.1	17 (a), (b)	1644	6.1	52 (b)
1503	5.1	17 (b)			or (c)	1645	6.1	52 (b)
1504	5.1	25 (a)	1585	6.1	51 (b)	1646	6.1	52 (b)
1505	5.1	18 (c)	1586	6.1	51 (b)	1647	6.1	15 (a)
1506	5.1	11 (b)	1587	6.1	41 (b)	1648	3	3 (b)
1507	5.1	22 (c)	1588	6.1	41 (a), (b)	1649	6.1	31 (a)
1508	5.1	13 (b)			or (c)	1650	6.1	12 (b)
1509	5.1	25 (b)	1589	2	2TC	1651	6.1	21 (b)
1510	5.1	2 (a)	1590	6.1	12 (b)	1652	6.1	12 (b)
1511	5.1	31 (c)	1591	6.1	15 (c)	1653	6.1	41 (b)
1512	5.1	23 (b)	1593	6.1	15 (c)	1654	6.1	90 (b)
1513	5.1	11 (b)	1594	6.1	14 (b)	1655	6.1	90 (a), (b)
1514	5.1	22 (b)	1595	6.1	27 (a)			or (c)
1515	5.1	17 (b)	1596	6.1	12 (b)	1656	6.1	90 (b)
1516	5.1	25 (b)	1597	6.1	12 (b)	1657	6.1	90 (b)
1517	4.1	21 (a)1.	1598	6.1	12 (b)	1658	6.1	90 (b)
1541	6.1	12 (a)	1599	6.1	12 (b) or (c)	1659	6.1	90 (b)
1544	6.1	90 (a), (b)	1600	6.1	24 (b)1.	1660	2	1TOC
		or (c)	1601	6.1	25 (a), (b)	1661	6.1	12 (b)
1545	6.1	20 (b)			or (c)	1662	6.1	12 (b)
1546	6.1	51 (b)	1602	6.1	25 (a), (b)	1663	6.1	12 (c)
1547	6.1	12 (b)			or (c)	1664	6.1	12 (b)
1548	6.1	12 (c)	1603	6.1	16 (b)	1665	6.1	12 (b)
1549	6.1	59 (c)	1604	8	54 (b)	1669	6.1	15 (b)
1550	6.1	59 (c)	1605	6.1	15 (a)	1670	6.1	17 (a)
1551	6.1	59 (c)	1606	6.1	51 (b)	1671	6.1	14 (b)
1553	6.1	51 (a)	1607	6.1	51 (b)	1672	6.1	17 (a)
1554	6.1	51 (b)	1608	6.1	51 (b)	1673	6.1	12 (c)
1555	6.1	51 (b)	1611	6.1	23 (b)	1674	6.1	33 (b)
1556	6.1	51 (a), (b)	1612	2	1T	1677	6.1	51 (b)
		or (c)	1613	6.1	2	1678	6.1	51 (b)
1557	6.1	51 (a), (b)	1614	6.1	1	1679	6.1	41 (b)
		or (c)	1616	6.1	62 (c)	1680	6.1	41 (a)
1558	6.1	51 (b)	1617	6.1	51 (b)	1683	6.1	51 (b)
1559	6.1	51 (b)	1618	6.1	51 (b)	1684	6.1	41 (b)
1560	6.1	51 (a)	1620	6.1	41 (b)	1685	6.1	51 (b)
1561	6.1	51 (b)	1621	6.1	51 (b)	1686	6.1	51 (b) or (c)
1562	6.1	51 (b)	1622	6.1	51 (b)	1687	6.1	42 (b)
1564	6.1	60 (b) or (c)	1623	6.1	51 (b)	1688	6.1	51 (b)
1565	6.1	41 (a)	1624	6.1	52 (b)	1689	6.1	41 (a)
1566	6.1	54 (b)2. or (c)	1625	6.1	52 (b)	1690	6.1	63 (c)
1567	6.1	54 (b)1.	1626	6.1	41 (a)	1691	6.1	51 (b)
1569	6.1	16 (b)	1627	6.1	52 (b)	1692	6.1	90 (a)
1570	6.1	90 (a)	1629	6.1	52 (b)	1693	6.1	25 (a) or (b)
1571	4.1	25 (a)	1630	6.1	52 (b)	1694	6.1	17 (a)
1572	6.1	51 (b)	1631	6.1	52 (b)	1695	6.1	10 (a)
1573	6.1	51 (b)	1634	6.1	52 (b)	1697	6.1	17 (b)
1574	6.1	51 (b)	1636	6.1	41 (b)	1698	6.1	34 (a)
1575	6.1	41 (a)	1637	6.1	52 (b)	1699	6.1	34 (a)
1577	6.1	12 (b)	1638	6.1	52 (b)	1700	6.1	26 (b)2.
1578	6.1	12 (b)	1639	6.1	52 (b)	1701	6.1	15 (b)

Supplement No.2

UN No.	Class	ADR item(s)	UN No.	Class	ADR item(s)	UN No.	Class	ADR item(s)
1702	6.1	15 (b)	1762	8	36 (b)	1824	8	42 (b) or (c)
1704	6.1	23 (b)	1763	8	36 (b)	1825	8	41 (b)
1707	6.1	53 (b)	1764	8	32 (b)1.	1826	8	3 (a) or (b)
1708	6.1	12 (b)	1765	8	35 (b)1.	1827	8	12 (b)
1709	6.1	12 (c)	1766	8	36 (b)	1828	8	12 (a)
1710	6.1	15 (c)	1767	8	37 (b)	1829	8	1 (a)
1711	6.1	12 (b)	1768	8	8 (b)	1830	8	1 (b)
1712	6.1	51 (b)	1769	8	36 (b)	1831	8	1 (a)
1713	6.1	41 (a)	1770	8	65 (b)	1832	8	1 (b)
1714	4.3	18 (a)	1771	8	36 (b)	1833	8	1 (b)
1715	8	32 (b)2.	1773	8	11 (c)	1834	8	12 (a)
1716	8	35 (b)1.	1774	8	82 (b)	1835	8	51 (b)
1717	3	25 (b)	1775	8	8 (b)	1836	8	12 (a)
1718	8	38 (c)	1776	8	8 (b)	1837	8	12 (b)
1719	8	42 (b) or (c)	1777	8	8 (a)	1838	8	12 (b)
1722	6.1	28 (a)	1778	8	8 (b)	1839	8	31 (b)
1723	3	25 (b)	1779	8	32 (b)1.	1840	8	5 (c)
1724	8	37 (b)	1780	8	35 (b)1.	1841	9	31 (c)
1725	8	11 (b)	1781	8	36 (b)	1843	6.1	12 (b)
1726	8	11 (b)	1782	8	8 (b)	1845	9	Exempt
1727	8	9 (b)	1783	8	53 (b) or (c)	1846	6.1	15 (b)
1728	8	36 (b)	1784	8	36 (b)	1847	8	45 (b)1.
1729	8	35 (b)1.	1786	8	7 (a)	1848	8	32 (c)
1730	8	12 (b)	1787	8	5 (b) or (c)	1849	8	45 (b)1.
1731	8	12 (b) or (c)	1788	8	5 (b) or (c)	1851	6.1	90 (b) or (c)
1732	8	10 (b)	1789	8	5 (b) or (c)	1854	4.2	12 (a)
1733	8	11 (b)	1790	8	6 or 7	1855	4.2	12 (a)
1736	8	35 (b)1.	1791	8	61 (b) or (c)	1858	2	2A
1737	6.1	27 (b)	1792	8	12 (b)	1859	2	1TC
1738	6.1	27 (b)	1793	8	38 (c)	1860	2	2F
1739	8	64 (a)	1794	8	1 (b)	1862	3	3 (b)
1740	8	9 (b) or (c)	1796	8	3 (a) or (b)	1863	3	1 (a), 2 (a), (b),
1741	2	2TC	1798	8	3 Prohibited			3 (b) or 31 (c)
1742	8	33 (b)	1799	8	36 (b)	1865	3	3 (b)
1743	8	33 (b)	1800	8	36 (b)	1866	3	5 (a), (b), (c)
1744	8	14	1801	8	36 (b)			or 31 (c)
1745	5.1	5	1802	8	4 (b)	1868	4.1	16 (b)
1746	5.1	5	1803	8	34 (b)	1869	4.1	13 (c)
1747	8	37 (b)	1804	8	36 (b)	1870	4.3	16 (a)
1748	5.1	15 (b)	1805	8	17 (c)	1871	4.1	14 (b)
1749	2	2TOC	1806	8	11 (b)	1872	5.1	29 (c)
1750	6.1	27 (b)	1807	8	16 (b)	1873	5.1	3 (a)
1751	6.1	27 (b)	1808	8	12 (b)	1884	6.1	60 (c)
1752	6.1	27 (a)	1809	6.1	67 (a)	1885	6.1	12 (b)
1753	8	36 (b)	1810	8	12 (b)	1886	6.1	15 (b)
1754	8	12 (a)	1811	8	9 (b)	1887	6.1	15 (c)
1755	8	17 (b) or (c)	1812	6.1	63 (c)	1888	6.1	15 (c)
1756	8	9 (b)	1813	8	41 (b)	1889	6.1	27 (a)
1757	8	8 (b) or (c)	1814	8	42 (b) or (c)	1891	6.1	15 (b)
1758	8	12 (a)	1815	3	25 (b)	1892	6.1	34 (a)
1759	8	65 (a), (b)	1816	8	37 (b)	1894	6.1	33 (b)
		or (c)	1817	8	12 (b)	1895	6.1	33 (b)
1760	8	66 (a), (b)	1818	8	12 (b)	1897	6.1	15 (c)
		or (c)	1819	8	42 (b) or (c)	1898	8	35 (b)1.
1761	8	53 (b) or (c)	1823	8	41 (b)	1902	8	38 (c)

UN No.	Class	ADR item(s)	UN No.	Class	ADR item(s)	UN No.	Class	ADR item(s)
1903	8	66 (a), (b) or (c)	1973	2	2A	2024	6.1	52 (a), (b) or (c)
1905	8	16 (a)	1974	2	2A	2025	6.1	52 (a), (b) or (c)
1906	8	1 (b)	1975	2	2TOC			
1907	8	41 (c)	1976	2	2A	2026	6.1	33 (a), (b) or (c)
1908	8	61 (b) or (c)	1977	2	3A			
1910	8	Exempt	1978	2	2F	2027	6.1	51 (b)
1911	2	1TF	1979	2	1A	2028	8	82 (b)
1912	2	2F	1980	2	1A	2029	8	44 (a)
1913	2	3A	1981	2	1A	2030	8	44 (b)
1914	3	31 (c)	1982	2	1A	2031	8	2 (a)1. or (b)
1915	3	31 (c)	1983	2	2A	2032	8	2 (a)2.
1916	6.1	16 (b)	1984	2	2A	2033	8	41 (b)
1917	3	3 (b)	1986	3	17 (a), (b) or 32 (c)	2034	2	1F
1918	3	31 (c)				2035	2	2F
1919	3	3 (b)	1987	3	2 (b), 3 (b) or 31 (c)	2036	2	1A
1920	3	31 (c)				2037	2	5
1921	3	12	1988	3	17 (a), (b) or 32 (c)	2038	6.1	12 (b)
1922	3	23 (b)				2044	2	2F
1923	4.2	13 (b)	1989	3	2 (a),(b), 3 (b) or 31 (c)	2045	3	3 (b)
1928	4.3	3 (a)				2046	3	31 (c)
1929	4.2	13 (b)	1990	9	34 (c)	2047	3	3 (b) or 31 (c)
1931	9	32 (c)	1991	3	16 (a)	2048	3	31 (c)
1932	4.2	12 (c)	1992	3	19 (a), (b) or 32 (c)	2049	3	31 (c)
1935	6.1	41 (a), (b) or (c)				2050	3	3 (b)
			1993	3	1 (a), 2 (a), (b), 3 (b), 5 (c) or 31 (c)	2051	8	54 (b)
1938	8	31 (b)				2052	3	31 (c)
1939	8	11 (b)	1994	6.1	3	2053	3	31 (c)
1940	8	32 (b)1.	1999	3	5 (b), (c) or 31 (c)	2054	3	31 (c)
1941	9	32 (c)				2055	3	31 (c)
1942	5.1	21 (c)	2000	4.1	3 (c)	2056	3	3 (b)
1944	4.1	2 (c)	2001	4.1	12 (c)	2057	3	3 (b) or 31 (c)
1945	4.1	2 (c)	2002	4.2	4 (c)	2058	3	3 (b)
1950	2	5	2003	4.2	31 (a)	2059	3	4 (a), (b) or 34 (c)
1951	2	3A	2004	4.2	16 (b)			
1952	2	2A	2005	4.2	31 (a)	2067	5.1	21 (c)
1953	2	1TF	2006	4.2	4 (c)	2068	5.1	21 (c)
1954	2	1F	2008	4.2	12 (a), (b) or (c)	2069	5.1	21 (c)
1955	2	1T				2070	5.1	21 (c)
1956	2	1A	2009	4.2	12 (c)	2071	9	Exempt
1957	2	1F	2010	4.3	16 (a)	2072	5.1	Prohibited
1958	2	2A	2011	4.3	18 (a)	2073	2	4A
1959	2	2F	2012	4.3	18 (a)	2074	6.1	12 (c)
1961	2	3F	2013	4.3	18 (a)	2075	6.1	17 (b)
1962	2	1F	2014	5.1	1 (b)	2076	6.1	27 (b)
1963	2	3A	2015	5.1	1 (a)	2077	6.1	12 (c)
1964	2	1F	2016	6.1	25 (b)	2078	6.1	19 (b)
1965	2	2F	2017	6.1	27 (b)	2079	8	53 (b)
1966	2	3F	2018	6.1	12 (b)	2186	2	Prohibited
1967	2	2T	2019	6.1	12 (b)	2187	2	3A
1968	2	2A	2020	6.1	17 (c)	2188	2	2TF
1969	2	2F	2021	6.1	17 (c)	2189	2	2TFC
1970	2	3A	2022	6.1	27 (b)	2190	2	1TOC
1971	2	1F	2023	6.1	16 (b)	2191	2	2T
1972	2	3F				2192	2	2TF

UN No.	Class	ADR item(s)	UN No.	Class	ADR item(s)	UN No.	Class	ADR item(s)
2193	2	1A	2256	3	3 (b)	2313	3	31 (c)
2194	2	2TC	2257	4.3	11 (a)	2315	9	2 (b)
2195	2	2TC	2258	8	54 (b)	2316	6.1	41 (a)
2196	2	2TC	2259	8	53 (b)	2317	6.1	41 (a)
2197	2	2TC	2260	3	33 (c)	2318	4.2	13 (b)
2198	2	1TC	2261	6.1	14 (b)	2319	3	31 (c)
2199	2	2TF	2262	8	35 (b)1.	2320	8	53 (c)
2200	2	2F	2263	3	3 (b)	2321	6.1	15 (c)
2201	2	3O	2264	8	54 (b)	2322	6.1	15 (b)
2202	2	2TF	2265	3	31 (c)	2323	3	31 (c)
2203	2	1F	2266	3	22 (b)	2324	3	31 (c)
2204	2	2TF	2267	6.1	27 (b)	2325	3	31 (c)
2205	6.1	12 (c)	2269	8	53 (c)	2326	8	53 (c)
2206	6.1	19 (b) or (c)	2270	3	22 (b)	2327	8	53 (c)
2208	5.1	15 (c)	2271	3	31 (c)	2328	6.1	19 (c)
2209	8	63 (c)	2272	6.1	12 (c)	2329	3	31 (c)
2210	4.2	16 (c)	2273	6.1	12 (c)	2330	3	31 (c)
2211	9	4 (c)	2274	6.1	12 (c)	2331	8	11 (c)
2212	9	1 (b)	2275	3	31 (c)	2332	3	31 (c)
2213	4.1	6 (c)	2276	3	33 (c)	2333	3	17 (b)
2214	8	31 (c)	2277	3	3 (b)	2334	6.1	7 (a)2.
2215	8	31 (c)	2278	3	3 (b)	2335	3	17 (b)
2216	9	Exempt	2279	6.1	15 (c)	2336	3	17 (a)
2217	4.2	2 (c)	2280	8	52 (c)	2337	6.1	20 (a)
2218	8	32 (b)2.	2281	6.1	19 (b)	2338	3	3 (b)
2219	3	31 (c)	2282	3	31 (c)	2339	3	3 (b)
2222	3	31 (c)	2283	3	31 (c)	2340	3	3 (b)
2224	6.1	12 (b)	2284	3	11 (b)	2341	3	31 (c)
2225	8	35 (c)	2285	6.1	18 (b)	2342	3	3 (b)
2226	8	66 (b)	2286	3	31 (c)	2343	3	3 (b)
2227	3	31 (c)	2287	3	3 (b)	2344	3	3 (b)
2232	6.1	17 (a)	2288	3	3 (b)	2345	3	3 (b)
2233	6.1	17 (c)	2289	8	53 (c)	2346	3	3 (b)
2234	3	31 (c)	2290	6.1	19 (c)	2347	3	3 (b)
2235	6.1	17 (c)	2291	6.1	62 (c)	2348	3	31 (c)
2236	6.1	19 (b)	2293	3	31 (c)	2350	3	3 (b)
2237	6.1	17 (c)	2294	6.1	12 (c)	2351	3	3 (b) or 31 (c)
2238	3	31 (c)	2295	6.1	16 (a)	2352	3	3 (b)
2239	6.1	17 (c)	2296	3	3 (b)	2353	3	25 (b)
2240	8	1 (a)	2297	3	31 (c)	2354	3	16 (b)
2241	3	3 (b)	2298	3	3 (b)	2356	3	2 (a)
2242	3	3 (b)	2299	6.1	17 (c)	2357	8	54 (b)
2243	3	31 (c)	2300	6.1	12 (c)	2358	3	3 (b)
2244	3	31 (c)	2301	3	3 (b)	2359	3	27 (b)
2245	3	31 (c)	2302	3	31 (c)	2360	3	17 (b)
2246	3	2 (b)	2303	3	31 (c)	2361	3	33 (c)
2247	3	31 (c)	2304	4.1	5	2362	3	3 (b)
2248	8	54 (b)	2305	8	34 (b)	2363	3	2 (a)
2249	6.1	26 (a)	2306	6.1	12 (b)	2364	3	31 (c)
		Prohibited	2307	6.1	12 (b)	2366	3	31 (c)
2250	6.1	19 (b)	2308	8	1 (b)	2367	3	3 (b)
2251	3	3 (b)	2309	3	3 (b)	2368	3	31 (c)
2252	3	3 (b)	2310	3	32 (c)	2370	3	3 (b)
2253	6.1	12 (b)	2311	6.1	12 (c)	2371	3	1 (a)
2254	4.1	2 (c)	2312	6.1	24 (b)1.	2372	3	3 (b)

UN No.	Class	ADR item(s)	UN No.	Class	ADR item(s)	UN No.	Class	ADR item(s)
2373	3	3 (b)	2431	6.1	12 (c)	2495	5.1	5
2374	3	3 (b)	2432	6.1	12 (c)	2496	8	32 (c)
2375	3	3 (b)	2433	6.1	17 (c)	2498	3	31 (c)
2376	3	3 (b)	2434	8	36 (b)	2501	6.1	23 (b) or (c)
2377	3	3 (b)	2435	8	36 (b)	2502	8	35 (b)2.
2378	3	11 (b)	2436	3	3 (b)	2503	8	11 (c)
2379	3	22 (b)	2437	8	36 (b)	2504	6.1	15 (c)
2380	3	3 (b)	2438	6.1	10 (a)	2505	6.1	63 (c)
2381	3	3 (b)	2439	8	9 (b)	2506	8	13 (b)
2382	6.1	7 (a)2.	2440	8	11 (c)	2507	8	16 (c)
2383	3	22 (b)	2441	4.2	15 (a)	2508	8	11 (c)
2384	3	3 (b)	2442	8	35 (b)1.	2509	8	13 (b)
2385	3	3 (b)	2443	8	12 (b)	2511	8	32 (c)
2386	3	23 (b)	2444	8	12 (a)	2512	6.1	12 (c)
2387	3	3 (b)	2445	4.2	31 (a)	2513	8	35 (b)1.
2388	3	3 (b)	2446	6.1	12 (c)	2514	3	31 (c)
2389	3	1 (a)	2447	4.2	22	2515	6.1	15 (c)
2390	3	3 (b)	2448	4.1	15	2516	6.1	15 (c)
2391	3	3 (b)	2451	2	1TO	2517	2	2F
2392	3	31 (c)	2452	2	2F	2518	6.1	25 (c)
2393	3	3 (b)	2453	2	2F	2520	3	31 (c)
2394	3	3 (b)	2454	2	2F	2521	6.1	13 (a)
2395	3	25 (b)	2455	2	Prohibited	2522	6.1	12 (b)
2396	3	17 (b)	2456	3	1 (a)	2524	3	31 (c)
2397	3	3 (b)	2457	3	3 (b)	2525	6.1	14 (c)
2398	3	3 (b)	2458	3	3 (b)	2526	3	33 (c)
2399	3	23 (b)	2459	3	1 (a)	2527	3	31 (c)
2400	3	3 (b)	2460	3	2 (b)	2528	3	31 (c)
2401	3	23 (b)	2461	3	3 (b)	2529	8	33 (c)
2402	3	3 (b)	2463	4.3	16 (a)	2530	8	33 (c)
2403	3	3 (b)	2464	5.1	29 (b)	2531	8	32 (c)
2404	3	11 (b)	2465	5.1	26 (b)	2533	6.1	17 (c)
2405	3	31 (c)	2466	5.1	25 (a)	2534	2	2TFC
2406	3	3 (b)	2467	5.1	19 (c)	2535	3	23 (b)
2407	6.1	10 (a)	2468	5.1	26 (b)	2536	3	3 (b)
2409	3	3 (b)	2469	5.1	16 (c)	2538	4.1	6 (c)
2410	3	3 (b)	2470	6.1	12 (c)	2541	3	31 (c)
2411	3	11 (b)	2471	6.1	56 (a)	2542	6.1	12 (b)
2412	3	3 (b)	2473	6.1	34 (c)	2545	4.2	12 (a), (b)
2413	3	31 (c)	2474	6.1	21 (b)			or (c)
2414	3	3 (b)	2475	8	11 (c)	2546	4.2	12 (a), (b)
2416	3	3 (b)	2477	6.1	20 (a)			or (c)
2417	2	1TC	2478	3	14 (b) or 32 (c)	2547	5.1	25 (a)
2418	2	2TC	2480	6.1	5	2548	2	2TOC
2419	2	2F	2481	3	13	2552	6.1	17 (b)
2420	2	2TC	2482	6.1	6 (a)	2554	3	3 (b)
2421	2	Prohibited	2483	3	14 (a)	2555	4.1	24 (b)
2422	2	2A	2484	6.1	6 (a)	2556	4.1	24 (b)
2424	2	2A	2485	6.1	6 (a)	2557	4.1	24 (b)
2426	5.1	20	2486	3	14 (b)	2558	6.1	16 (a)
2427	5.1	11 (b) or (c)	2487	6.1	18 (a)	2560	3	31 (c)
2428	5.1	11 (b) or (c)	2488	6.1	18 (a)	2561	3	1 (a)
2429	5.1	11 (b) or (c)	2490	6.1	17 (b)	2564	8	32 (b)1. or (c)
2430	8	39 (a), (b)	2491	8	53 (c)	2565	8	53 (c)
		or (c)	2493	3	23 (b)	2567	6.1	17 (b)

Supplement No.2

UN No.	Class	ADR item(s)	UN No.	Class	ADR item(s)	UN No.	Class	ADR item(s)
2570	6.1	61 (a), (b) or (c)	2644	6.1	15 (a)	2719	5.1	29 (b)
2571	8	34 (b)	2645	6.1	17 (b)	2720	5.1	22 (c)
2572	6.1	12 (b)	2646	6.1	15 (a)	2721	5.1	11 (b)
2573	5.1	29 (b)	2647	6.1	12 (b)	2722	5.1	22 (c)
2574	6.1	23 (b)	2648	6.1	17 (b)	2723	5.1	11 (b)
2576	8	15	2649	6.1	17 (b)	2724	5.1	22 (c)
2577	8	36 (b)1.	2650	6.1	17 (b)	2725	5.1	22 (c)
2578	8	16 (c)	2651	6.1	12 (c)	2726	5.1	23 (c)
2579	8	52 (c)	2653	6.1	15 (b)	2727	6.1	68 (b)
2580	8	5 (c)	2655	6.1	64 (c)	2728	5.1	22 (c)
2581	8	5 (c)	2656	6.1	12 (c)	2729	6.1	15 (c)
2582	8	5 (c)	2657	6.1	55 (b)	2730	6.1	12 (c)
2583	8	1 (b)	2659	6.1	17 (c)	2732	6.1	12 (c)
2584	8	1 (b)	2660	6.1	12 (c)	2733	3	22 (a), (b) or 33 (c)
2585	8	34 (c)	2661	6.1	17 (c)			
2586	8	34 (c)	2662	6.1	14 (c)	2734	8	54 (a) or (b)
2587	6.1	14 (b)	2664	6.1	15 (c)	2735	8	53 (a), (b) or (c)
2588	6.1	73 (a), (b) or (c)	2666	6.1	12 (c)			
2589	6.1	16 (b)	2667	6.1	25 (c)	2738	6.1	12 (b)
2590	9	1 (c)	2668	6.1	11 (b)	2739	8	32 (c)
2591	2	3A	2669	6.1	14 (b)	2740	6.1	28 (a)
2599	2	2A	2670	8	39 (b)	2741	5	29 (b)
2600	2	1TF	2671	6.1	12 (b)	2742	6.1	28 (b)
2601	2	2F	2672	8	43 (c)	2743	6.1	28 (b)
2602	2	2A	2673	6.1	12 (b)	2744	6.1	28 (b)
2603	3	19 (b)	2674	6.1	64 (c)	2745	6.1	27 (b)
2604	8	33 (a)	2676	2	2TF	2746	6.1	27 (b)
2605	3	14 (a)	2677	8	42 (b) or (c)	2747	6.1	17 (c)
2606	6.1	8 (a)	2678	8	41 (b)	2748	6.1	27 (b)
2607	3	31 (c)	2679	8	42 (b) or (c)	2749	8	1 (a)
2608	3	31 (c)	2680	8	41 (b)	2750	6.1	17 (b)
2609	6.1	14 (c)	2681	8	42 (b) or (c)	2751	8	35 (b)1.
2610	3	33 (c)	2682	8	41 (b)	2752	3	31 (c)
2611	6.1	16 (b)	2683	8	45 (b)2.	2753	6.1	12 (c)
2612	3	2 (b)	2684	3	33 (c)	2754	6.1	12 (b)
2614	3	31 (c)	2685	8	54 (b)	2757	6.1	73 (a), (b) or (c)
2615	3	3 (b)	2686	8	54 (b)			
2616	3	3 (b) or 31 (c)	2687	4.1	11 (c)	2758	3	41 (a) or (b)
2617	3	31 (c)	2688	6.1	15 (c)	2759	6.1	73 (a), (b) or (c)
2618	3	31 (c)	2689	6.1	17 (c)			
2619	8	54 (b)	2690	6.1	12 (b)	2760	3	41 (a) or (b)
2620	3	31 (c)	2691	8	11 (b)	2761	6.1	73 (a), (b) or (c)
2621	3	31 (c)	2692	8	12 (a)			
2622	3	17 (b)	2693	8	17 (c)	2762	3	41 (a) or (b)
2623	4.1	2 (c)	2698	8	31 (c)	2763	6.1	73 (a), (b) or (c)
2624	4.3	12 (b)	2699	8	32 (a)			
2626	5.1	4 (b)	2705	8	66 (b)	2764	3	41 (a) or (b)
2627	5.1	23 (b)	2707	3	3 (b) or 31 (c)	2765	6.1	73 (a), (b) or (c)
2628	6.1	17 (a)	2709	3	31 (c)			
2629	6.1	17 (a)	2710	3	31 (c)	2766	3	41 (a) or (b)
2630	6.1	55 (a)	2713	6.1	12 (c)	2767	6.1	73 (a), (b) or (c)
2642	6.1	17 (a)	2714	4.1	12 (c)			
2643	6.1	17 (b)	2715	4.1	12 (c)	2768	3	41 (a) or (b)
			2716	6.1	14 (c)	2769	6.1	73 (a), (b) or (c)
			2717	4.1	6 (c)			

Supplement No.2

UN No.	Class	ADR item(s)	UN No.	Class	ADR item(s)	UN No.	Class	ADR item(s)
2770	3	41 (a) or (b)	2817	8	7 (b) or (c)	2903	6.1	72 (a), (b)
2771	6.1	73 (a), (b)	2818	8	45 (b)1. or (c)			or (c)
		or (c)	2819	8	38 (c)	2904	8	62 (c)
2772	3	41 (a) or (b)	2820	8	32 (c)	2905	8	62 (c)
2773	6.1	73 (a), (b)	2821	6.1	14 (b) or (c)	2907	4.1	23 (b)
		or (c)	2822	6.1	12 (b)	2910	7	Sch.1-4
2774	3	41 (a) or (b)	2823	8	31 (c)	2912	7	Sch.5-7, 13
2775	6.1	73 (a), (b)	2826	8	64 (b)	2913	7	Sch.8, 13
		or (c)	2829	8	32 (c)	2918	7	Sch.12,13
2776	3	41 (a) or (b)	2830	4.3	12 (b)	2920	8	68 (a) or (b)
2777	6.1	73 (a), (b)	2831	6.1	15 (c)	2921	8	67 (a) or (b)
		or (c)	2834	8	16 (c)	2922	8	76 (a), (b)
2778	3	41 (a) or (b)	2835	4.3	16 (b)			or (c)
2779	6.1	73 (a), (b)	2837	8	1 (b) or (c)	2923	8	75 (a), (b)
		or (c)	2838	3	3 (b)			or (c)
2780	3	41 (a) or (b)	2839	6.1	14 (c)	2924	3	26 (a), (b)
2781	6.1	73 (a), (b)	2840	3	31 (c)			or 33 (c)
		or (c)	2841	3	32 (c)	2925	4.1	8 (b) or (c)
2782	3	41 (a) or (b)	2842	3	31 (c)	2926	4.1	7 (b) or (c)
2783	6.1	73 (a), (b)	2844	4.3	12 (c)	2927	6.1	27 (a) or (b)
		or (c)	2845	4.2	6 (a)	2928	6.1	27 (a) or (b)
2784	3	41 (a) or (b)	2846	4.2	5 (a)	2929	6.1	26 (a)1. or (b)1.
2785	6.1	20 (c)	2849	6.1	17 (c)	2930	6.1	26 (a)2. or (b)2.
2786	6.1	73 (a), (b)	2850	3	31 (c)	2931	6.1	58 (b)
		or (c)	2851	8	10 (b)	2933	3	31 (c)
2787	3	41 (a) or (b)	2852	4.1	21 (a)2.	2934	3	31 (c)
2788	6.1	32 (a), (b)	2853	6.1	64 (c)	2935	3	31 (c)
		or (c)	2854	6.1	64 (c)	2936	6.1	21 (b)
2789	8	32 (b)2.	2855	6.1	64 (c)	2937	6.1	14 (c)
2790	8	32 (b)1. or (c)	2856	6.1	64 (c)	2940	4.2	5 (b)
2793	4.2	12 (c)	2857	2	6A	2941	6.1	12 (c)
2794	8	81 (c)	2858	4.1	13 (c)	2942	6.1	12 (c)
2795	8	81 (c)	2859	6.1	58 (b)	2943	3	31 (c)
2796	8	1 (b)	2861	6.1	58 (b)	2945	3	22 (b)
2797	8	42 (b)	2862	6.1	58 (b)	2946	6.1	12 (c)
2798	8	35 (b)1.	2863	6.1	58 (b)	2947	3	31 (c)
2799	8	35 (b)1.	2864	6.1	58 (b)	2948	6.1	17 (b)
2800	8	81 (c)	2865	8	16 (c)	2949	8	45 (b)1.
2801	8	66 (a), (b)	2869	8	11 (b) or (c)	2950	4.3	11 (c)
		or (c)	2870	4.2	17 (a)	2956	4.1	26 (c)
2802	8	11 (c)	2871	6.1	59 (c)	2965	4.3	2 (a)
2803	8	65 (c)	2872	6.1	15 (b) or (c)	2966	6.1	21 (b)
2805	4.3	16 (b)	2873	6.1	12 (c)	2967	8	16 (c)
2806	4.3	17 (a)	2874	6.1	14 (c)	2968	4.3	20 (c)
2807	9	Exempt	2875	6.1	15 (c)	2969	9	35 (b)
2809	8	66 (c)	2876	6.1	14 (c)	2974	7	Sch.9-11,13
2810	6.1	25 (a), (b)	2878	4.1	13 (c)	2975	7	Sch.9-11,13
		or (c)	2879	8	12 (a)	2976	7	Sch.5,6,9-11,13
2811	6.1	25 (a), (b)	2880	5.1	15 (b)	2977	7	Sch. 12,13
		or (c)	2881	4.2	12 (a), (b)	2978	7	Sch. 5,6,13
2812	8	Exempt			or (c)	2979	7	Sch. 9-11,13
2813	4.3	20 (a), (b)	2900	6.2	1, 2 or 3 (b)	2980	7	Sch. 5,6,9-11,13
		or (c)	2901	2	2TOC	2981	7	Sch.5,6,9-11,13
2814	6.2	1, 2 or 3 (b)	2902	6.1	71 (a), (b)	2982	7	Sch.9-11,13
2815	8	53 (c)			or (c)	2983	3	17 (a)

UN No.	Class	ADR item(s)	UN No.	Class	ADR item(s)	UN No.	Class	ADR item(s)
2984	5.1	1 (c)	3015	6.1	72 (a), (b)	3090	9	5
2985	3	21 (b)			or (c)	3091	9	5
2986	8	37 (b)	3016	6.1	71 (a), (b)	3092	3	31 (c)
2987	8	36 (b)			or (c)	3093	8	74 (a) or (b)
2988	4.3	1 (a)	3017	6.1	72 (a), (b)	3094	8	72 (a) or (b)
2989	4.1	11 (b) or (c)			or (c)	3095	8	69 (a) or (b)
2990	9	6	3018	6.1	71 (a), (b)	3096	8	71 (a) or (b)
2991	6.1	72 (a), (b)			or (c)	3097	4.1	Prohibited
		or (c)	3019	6.1	72 (a), (b)	3098	5.1	32 (a), (b)
2992	6.1	71 (a), (b)			or (c)			or (c)
		or (c)	3020	6.1	71 (a), (b)	3099	5.1	30 (a), (b)
2993	6.1	72 (a), (b)			or (c)			or (c)
		or (c)	3021	3	41 (a) or (b)	3100	5.1	Prohibited
2994	6.1	71 (a), (b)	3022	3	3 (b)	3101	5.2	1 (b)
		or (c)	3023	6.1	20 (a)	3102	5.2	2 (b)
2995	6.1	72 (a), (b)	3024	3	41 (a) or (b)	3103	5.2	3 (b)
		or (c)	3025	6.1	72 (a), (b)	3104	5.2	4 (b)
2996	6.1	71 (a), (b)			or (c)	3105	5.2	5 (b)
		or (c)	3026	6.1	71 (a), (b)	3106	5.2	6 (b)
2997	6.1	72 (a), (b)			or (c)	3107	5.2	7 (b)
		or (c)	3027	6.1	73 (a), (b)	3108	5.2	8 (b)
2998	6.1	71 (a), (b)			or (c)	3109	5.2	9 (b)
		or (c)	3028	8	81 (c)	3110	5.2	10 (b)
2999	6.1	72 (a), (b)	3048	6.1	43 (a)	3111	5.2	11 (b)
		or (c)	3049	4.2	32 (a)	3112	5.2	12 (b)
3000	6.1	71 (a), (b)	3050	4.2	32 (a)	3113	5.2	13 (b)
		or (c)	3051	4.2	31 (a)	3114	5.2	14 (b)
3001	6.1	72 (a), (b)	3052	4.2	32 (a)	3115	5.2	15 (b)
		or (c)	3053	4.2	31 (a)	3116	5.2	16 (b)
3002	6.1	71 (a), (b)	3054	3	31 (c)	3117	5.2	17 (b)
		or (c)	3055	8	53 (c)	3118	5.2	18 (b)
3003	6.1	72 (a), (b)	3056	3	31 (c)	3119	5.2	19 (b)
		or (c)	3057	2	2TC	3120	5.2	20 (b)
3004	6.1	71 (a), (b)	3064	3	6	3121	5.1	Prohibited
		or (c)	3065	3	3 (b) or 31 (c)	3122	6.1	68 (a) or (b)
3005	6.1	72 (a), (b)	3066	8	66 (b) or (c)	3123	6.1	44 (a) or (b)
		or (c)	3070	2	2A	3124	6.1	66 (a) or (b)
3006	6.1	71 (a), (b)	3071	6.1	20 (b)	3125	6.1	44 (a) or (b)
		or (c)	3072	9	7	3126	4.2	9 (b) or (c)
3007	6.1	72 (a), (b)	3073	6.1	11 (b)1.	3127	4.2	Prohibited
		or (c)	3076	4.2	32 (a)	3128	4.2	7 (b) or (c)
3008	6.1	71 (a), (b)	3077	9	12 (c)	3129	4.3	25 (a), (b)
		or (c)	3078	4.3	13 (b)			or (c)
3009	6.1	72 (a), (b)	3079	3	11 (a)	3130	4.3	23 (a), (b)
		or (c)	3080	6.1	18 (b)			or (c)
3010	6.1	71 (a), (b)	3082	9	11 (c)	3131	4.3	24 (a), (b)
		or (c)	3083	2	2TO			or (c)
3011	6.1	72 (a), (b)	3084	8	73 (a) or (b)	3132	4.3	Prohibited
		or (c)	3085	5.1	31 (a), (b)	3133	4.3	Prohibited
3012	6.1	71 (a), (b)			or (c)	3134	4.3	22 (a), (b)
		or (c)	3086	6.1	68 (a) or (b)			or (c)
3013	6.1	72 (a), (b)	3087	5.1	29 (a), (b)	3135	4.3	Prohibited
		or (c)			or (c)	3136	2	3A
3014	6.1	71 (a), (b)	3088	4.2	5 (b) or (c)	3137	5.1	Prohibited
		or (c)	3089	4.1	13 (b) or (c)	3138	2	3F

UN No.	Class	ADR item(s)	UN No.	Class	ADR item(s)	UN No.	Class	ADR item(s)
3139	5.1	28 (a),(b) or (c)	3187	4.2	19 (b) or (c)	3250	6.1	24 (b)2.
3140	6.1	90 (a), (b) or (c)	3188	4.2	21 (b) or (c)	3251	4.1	26 (c)
3141	6.1	59 (c)	3189	4.2	12 (b) or (c)	3252	2	2F
3142	6.1	25 (a), (b) or (c)	3190	4.2	16 (b) or (c)	3253	8	41 (c)
3143	6.1	25 (a), (b) or (c)	3191	4.2	18 (b) or (c)	3254	4.2	6 (a)
3144	6.1	90 (a), (b) or (c)	3192	4.2	20 (b) or (c)	3255	4.2	10 (a)
3145	8	40 (a), (b) or (c)	3194	4.2	17 (a)	3256	3	61 (c)
3146	6.1	32 (a), (b) or (c)	3200	4.2	16 (a)	3257	9	20 (c)
3147	8	65 (b) or (c)	3203	4.2	33 (a)	3258	9	21 (c)
3148	4.3	21 (a), (b) or (c)	3205	4.2	14 (b) or (c)	3259	8	52 (a), (b) or (c)
3149	5.1	1 (b)	3206	4.2	15 (b) or (c)	3260	8	16 (a), (b) or (c)
3150	2	6F	3207	4.3	3 (a), (b) or (c)	3261	8	39 (a), (b) or (c)
3151	9	2 (b)	3208	4.3	13 (a), (b) or (c)	3262	8	46 (a), (b) or (c)
3152	9	2 (b)	3209	4.3	14 (a), (b) or (c)	3263	8	55 (a), (b) or (c)
3153	2	2F	3210	5.1	11 (b) or (c)	3264	8	17 (a), (b) or (c)
3154	2	2F	3211	5.1	13 (b) or (c)	3265	8	40 (a), (b) or (c)
3155	6.1	17 (b)	3212	5.1	15 (b)	3266	8	47 (a), (b) or (c)
3156	2	1O	3213	5.1	16 (b) or (c)	3267	8	56 (a), (b) or (c)
3157	2	2O	3214	5.1	17 (b)	3268	9	8 (c)
3158	2	3A	3215	5.1	18 (c)	3269	3	5 (b), (c) or 31 (c)
3159	2	2A	3216	5.1	18 (c)	3270	4.1	3 (b)
3160	2	2TF	3218	5.1	22 (b) or (c)	3271	3	3 (b) or 31 (c)
3161	2	2F	3219	5.1	23 (b) or (c)	3272	3	3 (b) or 31 (c)
3162	2	2T	3220	2	2A	3273	3	11 (a) or (b)
3163	2	2A	3221	4.1	31 (b)	3274	3	24 (b)
3164	2	6A	3222	4.1	32 (b)	3275	6.1	11 (a) or (b)
3165	3	28	3223	4.1	33 (b)	3276	6.1	12 (a), (b) or (c)
3166	9	Exempt	3224	4.1	34 (b)	3277	6.1	27 (b)
3167	2	7F	3225	4.1	35 (b)	3278	6.1	23 (a), (b) or (c)
3168	2	7TF	3226	4.1	36 (b)	3279	6.1	22 (a) or (b)
3169	2	7T	3227	4.1	37 (b)	3280	6.1	34 (a), (b) or (c)
3170	4.3	13 (b) or (c)	3228	4.1	38 (b)	3281	6.1	36 (a), (b) or (c)
3171	9	Exempt	3229	4.1	39 (b)	3282	6.1	35 (a), (b) or (c)
3172	6.1	90 (a), (b) or (c)	3230	4.1	40 (b)	3283	6.1	55 (a), (b) or (c)
3174	4.2	13 (c)	3231	4.1	41 (b)	3284	6.1	57 (a), (b) or (c)
3175	4.1	4 (c)	3232	4.1	42 (b)	3285	6.1	58 (a), (b) or (c)
3176	4.1	5	3233	4.1	43 (b)	3286	3	27 (a) or (b)
3178	4.1	11 (b) or (c)	3234	4.1	44 (b)			
3179	4.1	16 (b) or (c)	3235	4.1	45 (b)			
3180	4.1	17 (b) or (c)	3236	4.1	46 (b)			
3181	4.1	12 (b) or (c)	3237	4.1	47 (b)			
3182	4.1	14 (b) or (c)	3238	4.1	48 (b)			
3183	4.2	6 (b) or (c)	3239	4.1	49 (b)			
3184	4.2	8 (b) or (c)	3240	4.1	50 (b)			
3185	4.2	10 (b) or (c)	3241	4.1	26 (c)			
3186	4.2	17 (b) or (c)	3242	4.1	26 (b)			
			3243	6.1	65 (b)			
			3244	8	65 (b)			
			3245	9	13 (b)			
			3246	6.1	27 (a)			
			3247	5.1	27 (b)			
			3248	3	19 (b) or 32 (c)			
			3249	6.1	90 (b) or (c)			

UN No.	Class	ADR item(s)	UN No.	Class	ADR item(s)	UN No.	Class	ADR item(s)
3287	6.1	65 (a), (b) or (c)	3299	2	2A	3310	2	2TOC
3288	6.1	65 (a), (b) or (c)	3300	2	2TF	3311	2	3O
			3301	8	70 (a) or (b)	3312	2	3F
			3302	6.1	12 (b)	3313	4.2	5 (b) or (c)
3289	6.1	67 (a) or (b)	3303	2	1TO	3314	9	4 (c)
3290	6.1	67 (a) or (b)	3304	2	1TC	3315	6.1	90 (a)
3291	6.2	4 (b)	3305	2	1TFC	3316	9	36 (b) or (c)
3292	4.3	31 (b)	3306	2	1TOC	3317	4.1	22 (a)1.
3293	6.1	65 (c)	3307	2	2TO	3318	2	4TC
3294	6.1	2	3308	2	2TC	3319	4.1	13 (b)
3295	3	1 (a), 2 (a), (b), 3 (b) or 31 (c)	3309	2	2TFC	3320	8	42 (b) or (c)
3296	2	2A						
3297	2	2A						
3298	2	2A						

SUPPLEMENT No.3

**Competent authorities for the purpose of the application of ADR
including in particular for the conclusion of bilateral and multilateral agreements
under marginals 2010 (Annex A) and 10 602 (Annex B) and for type approval
according to marginal 220 900 (Annex B)**

AUSTRIA

Bundesministerium für Wissenschaft, Verkehr und Kunst	Tel.:	(43) 1 71162 ext. 1500
Verwaltungsbereich Verkehr	Telex:	111 800
Sektion I/Abteilung A/5	Fax:	(43) 1 71162 1599
Radetzkystrasse 2		
A - 1030 VIENNA		

BELARUS

Ministry of Transport	Tel.:	(375) 172 687 407
Ul. Volodarskogo 8	Fax:	(375) 172 271 981
MINSK		

BELGIUM

Ministère des Communications	Tel.:	(32) 2 287 4493
Administration de la Réglementation de la Circulation		à 4499
et de l'Infrastructure	Telex:	TRANS B 23285
Service ADR	Fax:	(32) 2 287 4510
Résidence Palace, Bloc C, 5ème étage		
Rue de la Loi 155,		
B - 1000 BRUXELLES		
(Competent section as administrative section regarding		
marginal 220 900 for the types vehicules FL, OX and AT)		

Substances of Class 1
(including type approval for the vehicules types EX II
and EX III - Marginal 220 900):

Ministère des Affaires économiques	Tel.:	(32) 2 2336111
Service des explosifs de Belgique	Telex:	23509 energi b
Rue de Mot, 30		
B - 1040 BRUXELLES		

Substances of Class 7

Ministère de la Santé Publique	Tel.:	(32) 2 5648011
Administration de l'hygiène publique	Telex:	25768
Service des nuisances		
Cité administrative de l'Etat		
Quartier Vésale		
B - 1010 BRUXELLES		

BOSNIA AND HERZEGOVINA

Ministry of Transport of the Republic of Bosnia and Herzegovina	Tel.:	(41) 22 345 88 44
c/o Permanent Mission of the Republic of Bosnia and Herzegovina	Fax:	(41) 22 345 88 89
22 bis, rue Lamartine		
CH-1203 GENEVE		

BULGARIA

Ministry of Transport	Tel.:	(359)2 871 081
International Cooperation dept.	Fax:	(359)2 885 094
Dangerous Goods Section	Telex:	23 200 MT BG
9-11 Levsky Str.		
SOFIA - 1000		

Substances of Class 7

Committee of Nuclear Energy	Tel.:	(359) 2 720 217
Utilization for peace purposes	Fax:	(359) 2 702 143
69 Shipchensky Prohod Str.	Telex:	23 283 KAE BG
SOFIA 1574		

CROATIA

Minister of Transport	Tel.:	(385) 1 616 9111
Ministarstvo prometa	Fax:	(385) 1 518 113
Prisavije 14,		
41000 ZAGREB		

CZECH REPUBLIC

Ministry of Transport	Tel.:	(42) 230 31 111
nábř. Ludvíka Svobody 12		(Switchboard)
110 15 PRAHA 1 - Nové Mešto	Fax:	(42) 230 31 259

DENMARK

FAERDSELSSTYRELSEN	Tel.:	(45) 33 92 91 00
Road Safety and Transport Agency	Fax:	(45) 33 93 22 92
Mr Rasmussen		
Adelgade 13		
Postboks 9039		
DK - 1304 COPENHAGEN K		

Substances of Class 7

Statens Institut for Strålehygiejne	Tel.:	(45) 42 943773
Frederikssundsvej 378		
DK - 2700 BRØNSHØJ		

ESTONIA

Ministry of Transport and Communications   Fax: (70142) 44 92 06
9 Viru Str.
EE0 100 TALLINN

FINLAND

Ministry of Transport and Communications   Tel.:   (358) 0160 2563
Ms. S. Miettinen   Fax: (358) 0160 2597
Head of Section   Telex: 125472 LIMIN FIN
Box 235
FIN - 00131 HELSINKI 13

Type approval (marginal 220 900)
Administrative Department:

Vehicle administration   Tel.:   (358) 0 774 73446
Type Approval Division   Fax: (358) 0 774 73454
P.O.B. 24
FIN - 00231 HELSINKI

FRANCE

Ministère des Transports   Tel.:   (33) 1 40811728
Mission du Transport des matières dangereuses   Telex: 610835 F
Arche Sud   Fax: (33) 1 40811065
F - 92055 PARIS LA DEFENSE CEDEX

GERMANY

Federal Ministry of Transport   Tel.:   (49) 228 300-0
Division "Transport of Dangerous Goods" (A13)   Telex: 885 700 bmv d
Robert Schuman Platz 1   Fax: (49) 228 300-3428
Postfach 20 01 00   3429 - 2409
D - 53175 BONN

GREECE

Ministry of Transport   Tel.:   (30) 1 32.43.930
Xenofontos Str. 13   Fax.:   (30) 1 32.39.039
Syntagma Square   Telex: 21.63.69 YSYG GR
GR-10191 ATHENS

HUNGARY

Ministry of Transport, Communication and Water Management   Tel.:   (36) 1 3414-300
Dob u. 75-81   1 3423-722
P.O. Box 87   Fax: (36) 1 3226-891
H - 1400 BUDAPEST VII

HUNGARY (contd)

Type approval (marginal 220 900)
Administrative Department:

General Inspectorate of Transport	Tel.:	(36) 1 2101 770
P.O.B. 102	Fax:	(36) 1 2101 788
H-1389 BUDAPEST		

Substances of Class 7

L'institut Isotop de l'Académie des Sciences Hongroise
Kongoly Thege u. 23/29
H - BUDAPEST XII

ITALY

Ministero dei Trasporti e della Navigazione	Tel.:	(39) 6 41583150
Direzione Generale della Motorizzazione Civile	Fax:	(39) 6 41583209
e Trasporti in Concessione		
Divisione 49 (Mr. A. Roscetti)		
V. Caraci 36		
I - ROME		

Substances of Class 7

Agenzia Nazionale per la Protezione dell'Ambiente (ANPA)	Tel.:	(39) 6 50072013
Mr. C. Faloci and Mr. S. Benassai	Telex:	612167 ENEUR I
Via V. Brancati 48	Fax:	(39) 6 50072941
I - 00144 ROME		

LATVIA

Ministry of Transport of Latvia	Tel.:	(3712) 7 325 922
Ecological Division	Fax:	(3712) 7 217 180
58, Brivibas Street		
LV-1743 RIGA		

Type approval (marginal 220 900)
Administrative Department:

Road Traffic Safety Directorate	Tel./Fax:	(3712) 2 37 3914
25, Miera Street		
LV - 1104 RIGA		

LIECHTENSTEIN

Ministry of Transport and Telecommunications Regierungsgebäude	Tel.:	(75) 236 60 12
Städtle 49	Fax:	(75) 236 60 28
FL-9490 VADUZ		

LITHUANIA

Ms. Y. LILEYKENE   Tel.:   (370) 2 62 48 26
Chief Expert   Fax: (370) 2 22 43 35
Department of Environment
Protection and Transport of Dangerous Goods
Ministry of Transport
17, Gedimino Street
2679 VILNIUS

LUXEMBOURG

M. Paul Schmit   Tel.:   (352) 4794-1
Conseiller de gouvernement (1ère classe)   Telex: 1465 civair lu
Ministère des Transports du Grand-Duché de Luxembourg   Fax: (352) 46 43 15
BP 590
L - 2938 LUXEMBOURG

NETHERLANDS

The Director-General of Transport   Tel.:   (31) 70 351 6171
Ministry of Transport and Public Works   or direct   351 7014
Dangerous Goods Branch   Fax: (31) 70 3517051
Plesmanweg 1   direct: (31) 70 3516412
Postbus 20901
NL - 2500 EX's-GRAVENHAGE

Type Approval
Administrative Department:

Rijksdienst voor het Wegverkeer   Tel.:   (31) 79 3458324
P.O. Box 777   Fax.   (31) 79 3458034
NL-2700 AT ZOETERMEER

Radioactive materials

Ministry of Housing, Spatial Planning and the Environment   Tel.:   (31) 70 3394965
Directorate for Chemicals, External Safe and Radiation Protection/655   Fax: (31) 70 3391297
External Safety Division
Rynstraat 8
P.O. Box 30945
NL-2500 GX THE HAGUE

Applicants for permits or approvals should be addressed to:

Ministry of Social Affairs and Employment   Tel.:   (31) 70 3336529
Health Directorate   Fax: (31) 70 3334041
P.O. Box 90804
NL-2509 LV The Hague

NORWAY

Directorate for Fire and Explosion Prevention	Tel.:	(47) 333 98 800
POB 355	Fax:	(47) 333 10 660
N-3101 TØNSBERG		

Substances of Class 7

Norvegian Radiation Protection Authority	Tel.:	(47) 6714 4190
P.O. Box 55	Fax:	(47) 6714 7407
N - 1345 OSTERAS		

POLAND

Ministry of Transport and Maritime Economy	Tel.:	(48) 22 30.01.68
Road Traffic Department	Telex:	816651 pkp pl
4/6, Chalubinskiego Street	Fax:	(48) 22.24.41.10
PL-00-928 WARSAW		

For the provisions of Appendices A.5 et A.6

Centre de Recherche et du développement d'emballage (COBRO)	Tel.:	(48) 22 42 20 11
11 rue Konstancinska		
PL-02-942 WARSAW		

Substances of other classes except Class 7

Institute of Organic Industry	Tel.:	(48) 22 11 12 31
6 Annopol		
PL-03-236-WARSAW		

Type approval (marginal 220 900)
Administrative Department:

Road Traffic Department	Tel.:	(48) 22 30.01.68
4/6, Chalubinskiego Street	Telex:	816651 pkp pl
PL-00-928 WARSAW	Fax:	(48) 22.24.41.10

Technical Service

Motor Transport Institute	Tel.:	(48) 22 11 32 31
Ul. Jagiellonska 80	Fax:	(48) 22 11 09 06
PL-03-301 WARSAW		

PORTUGAL

Direcção-Geral de Transportes Terrestres	Tel.:	(351) 1 793 46 81
Avenida das Forcas Armadas, 40	Fax:	(351) 1 797 37 77
P - 1699 LISBOA Codex		

ROMANIA

Direction générale des transports terrestres   Tel.:   (40) 1.638.50.45
Ministère des Transports   Fax: (40) 1.638.45.97
Bd. Dinicu Golescu, 38
RO-77113 BUCAREST

RUSSIAN FEDERATION

Ministry of Transport   Tel.:   (7) 095 200.14.19
Office of International Relations   Fax: (7) 095 299 39 90
Sadovaja-Samotechnaja Street. 10
101433 MOSCOU, GSP-4

SLOVAKIA

M. Pavol REICH   Tel.:   (42) 7 54 32 449
Directeur de la Section du Transport routier et urbain   Tel./Fax: (42) 7 212 141
Ministère des Transports, de la Poste et des Télécommunications
Nám. Slobody 6
P.O. Box 100
810 05 BRATISLAVA

SLOVENIA

Ministry of the Interior   Tel.:   (386) 61.217 792
Stefanova 2   Fax: (386) 61 302 405
SL - 1501 LJUBLJANA

SPAIN

Mme M. FERNÁNDEZ BALBÍN   Tel.:   (34) 1-597 5936
Head of Division for the Transport of Dangerous Goods   (34) 1 597 6041
Comision Interministerial de Coordinación   Fax: (34) 1-597 6681
  del Transporte de mercancias peligrosas
Ministerio de Transportes, Turismo
y Comunicaciones
Piso 6° - Plaza de San Juan de la Cruz s/n
E - 28071 MADRID

Type Approval (marginal 220 900)
Administrative Department:

M. A. MUÑOZ MUÑOZ   Tel.:   (34) 1 3494000
Subdirector General de Calidad y Seguridad Industrial   Fax: (34) 1 3494300
Ministerio de Industria y Energia
Paseo de la Castellana, 160
E-28046 MADRID

SWEDEN

| Swedish Rescue Services Agency
Division for Dangerous Goods and Hazardous Materials
Karolinen
S - 65180 KARLSTAD | Tel.:

Telex:
Fax: | (46) 54 10 4000
(switchboard)
66197 SRVS
(46) 54 102889 |

Technical Body for approval tests and inspections of tanks

SAQ Kontroll AB
Design Review Department
Dangerous Goods
Gyllenkroksgatan 10 B
S-41261 GOTHENBURG

Type approval (marginal 220 900)
Administrative Department:

| Swedish Rescue Services Agency
Division for Dangerous Goods and Hazardous Materials
Karolinen
S - 65180 KARLSTAD | Tel.:

Fax.:
Telex: | (46) 54 10 4000
(switchboard)
(46) 54 102889
66197 SRVS |

Technical Service

Swedish Motor Vehicle Inspection Co.,
Box 508
S-16215 VÄLLINGBY

SWITZERLAND

| M. D.-M. GILABERT
Office fédéral de la Police
Division principale de la circulation routière
Section des transports spéciaux
Case postale
CH-3084 WABERN | Tel.:
Fax: | (41) 31 323 42 90
(41) 31 323 43 03 |

For the carriage of radioactive substances, the necessary certificates
of approval and authorizations are issued by:

| M. P. LAUG
Office fédéral de l'énergie
Division de l'économie énergétique
CH - 3003 BERN | Tel.:
Fax: | (41) 31 61 56 31
(41) 31 61 56 71 |

UNITED KINGDOM

Dangerous Goods Branch of the Department of Transport	Tel.:	(44) 1 71 271 4535
Great Minster House	Fax:	(44) 1 71 271 5241
76 Marsham Street	Telex:	22221 DOEMAR G
LONDON SW1P 4DR		
UNITED KINGDOM		

Type approval (marginal 220 900)
Administrative Department:

The Vehicle Inspectorate	Tel.:	(44) 1 792 45 42 68
Welcombe House	Fax:	(44) 1 792 45 42 11
91/92 The Strand		
SWANSEA SA1 2 DH		

YUGOSLAVIA

Federal Secretariat for Transport and Communications	Tel.:	(381) 11 602-643
Bulevar Avnoj-104	Fax:	(381) 11 196-441
11070 BEOGRAD		

Other useful addresses for non-contracting Parties to ADR

IRELAND

Road Haulage Division	Tel.:	(353) 1 67 89 522
Department of Transport, Energy and Communications	Fax:	(353) 1 67 11 886
Setanta Centre	Telex:	90870 PAD EI
DUBLIN 2 - IRELAND		

UKRAINE

Ukrainian Cargo Bureau	Tel./fax:	(0482) 65 71 11
15, Lanzheronovskaya		(0482) 65 70 73
ODESSA 270026	Fax:	(0482) 25 04 57

Reproduction in colour
of pages 360 and 363

(REPRODUCTION IN COLOUR OF PAGE 360)

250 001

Identification numbers shall be shown on the plate as indicated below:

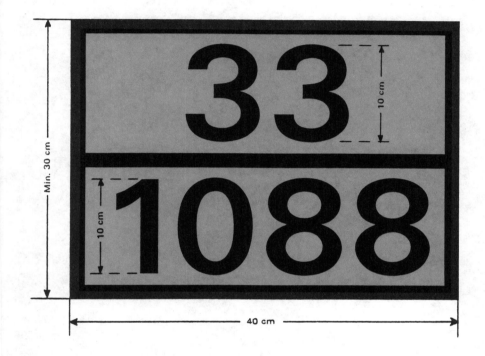

Identification number
of danger
(2 or 3 figures)

Identification number
of substance
(4 figures)

Background orange.
Border, horizontal line and figures black,
15 mm thickness.

**250 002-
259 999**

(REPRODUCTION IN COLOUR OF PAGE 363)

MARK FOR ELEVATED TEMPERATURE SUBSTANCES

270 000 The mark for elevated temperature substances required in marginals 91 500 (3), 211 960 and 212 960 is a triangular shaped mark with sides of at least 250 mm, to be shown in red, as reproduced below.